# SOLUTIONS MANUAL

*Merrill*
# Algebra 1
*Applications and Connections*

## GLENCOE
McGraw-Hill

New York, New York
Columbus, Ohio
Mission Hills, California
Peoria, Illinois

The copy in this text was word processed using ChiWriter Software from Horstmann
Software, P.O. Box 5039 San Jose, California  95192

1995 Impression
Copyright © 1992 by Glencoe/McGraw-Hill.

Send all inquires to:
Glencoe/McGraw-Hill
936 Eastwind Drive
Westerville, Oh  43081

ISBN 0-02-824187-8

3 4 5 6 7 8 9 10 POH 03 02 01 00 99 98 97 96 95

# Contents

# Chapter 1 An Introduction to Algebra

 Variables and Expressions

PAGE 11    CHECKING FOR UNDERSTANDING

1. $3,431,000 \div 575,000$

2. Algebraic expressions include variables.

3. $3 + a$; $3a$

4. Yes; multiply the measure of the side by itself 3 times.

5. $7x$    6. $\frac{r}{s}$    7. $a + 19$    8. $n - 4$    9. $b^3$

10. $25^2$    11. $5^3$    12. $7a^4$    13. $2m^3$    14. $5^3 x^2 y$

15. $2^4 = 2 \cdot 2 \cdot 2 \cdot 2 = 16$

16. $5^3 = 5 \cdot 5 \cdot 5 = 125$

17. $10^4 = 10 \cdot 10 \cdot 10 \cdot 10 = 10,000$

18. $3^6 = 3 \cdot 3 \cdot 3 \cdot 3 \cdot 3 \cdot 3 = 729$

PAGES 11-12    EXERCISES

19. $m$ minus 1    20. the product of $x$ and $y$

21. $n$ to the fourth power    22. 5 cubed

23. 8 times $y$ squared

24. $z$ to the seventh power plus 2    25. $x + 17$

26. $7x$    27. $2x^3$    28. $x^6$    29. $\frac{1}{2}x^2$ or $\frac{x^2}{2}$

30. $6x - 17$    31. $94 + 2x$    32. $\frac{3}{4}x^2$ or $\frac{3x^2}{4}$

33. $A = l \times w$    34. $V = l \cdot w \cdot h$
    $A = 5 \cdot 3$        $V = 12 \cdot 2 \cdot 12$
    $A = 15\ m^2$        $V = 288\ mm^3$

35. $6.2^6 = 6.2 \cdot 6.2 \cdot 6.2 \cdot 6.2 \cdot 6.2 \cdot 6.2 = 56,800.236$

36. $4.8^5 = 4.8 \cdot 4.8 \cdot 4.8 \cdot 4.8 \cdot 4.8 = 2548.040$

37. $5^5 + 6^6 + 7^7 = 5 \cdot 5 \cdot 5 \cdot 5 \cdot 5 +$
    $6 \cdot 6 \cdot 6 \cdot 6 \cdot 6 \cdot 6 +$
    $7 \cdot 7 \cdot 7 \cdot 7 \cdot 7 \cdot 7 \cdot 7$
    $= 3,125 + 46,656 + 823,543$
    $= 873,324$

38. $2^2 \cdot 3^3 \cdot 4^4 \cdot 5^5 = 2 \cdot 2 \cdot 3 \cdot 3 \cdot 3 \cdot$
    $4 \cdot 4 \cdot 4 \cdot 4 \cdot$
    $5 \cdot 5 \cdot 5 \cdot 5 \cdot 5$
    $= 4 \cdot 27 \cdot 256 \cdot 3125$
    $= 86,400,000$

39. $a + b - ab$    40. $a - b + \frac{a}{b}$

41. $4^2 = 4 \cdot 4 = 16$; $2^4 = 2 \cdot 2 \cdot 2 \cdot 2 = 16$
    They are equal; no; no.

42. $d^2 = 64^2$ C.M. $= 64 \cdot 64 = 4096$ C.M.

43. $A = l \times w$
    $= 168$ ft. $\cdot 85$ ft. $= 14,280$ square feet

44.

|  | 2,4 | 10,3 | -9,2 | 5.2,2 |
|---|---|---|---|---|
| $a+b$ | 2+4=6 | 10+3=13 | -9+2=-7 | 5.2+2=7.2 |
| $a-b$ | 2-4=-2 | 10-3=7 | -9-2=-11 | 5.2-2=3.2 |
| $a \times b$ | 2×4=8 | 10×3=30 | -9×2=-18 | 5.2×2=10.4 |
| $a \div b$ | 2÷4=0.5 | 10÷3=3.$\overline{3}$ | -9÷2=-4.5 | 5.2÷2=2.6 |
| $a^b$ | $2^4$=16 | $10^3$=1000 | $-9^2$=81 | $5.2^2$=27.04 |

## 1-2    Evaluating Expressions

PAGE 15    CHECKING FOR UNDERSTANDING

1. Multiply 5 by 3.

2. Parentheses, brackets, braces, fraction bar

3. Subtract 6 from 12.    Then multiply by 2.

4. Square 3.    Then subtract from 9.

5. Subtract 3 from 5.    Square the result.    Then multiply by 4.

6. Add 2 and 1.    Divide 6 by 3.    Then add 8.

7. $3 + 8 + 2 - 5 = 3 + 4 - 5$
    $= 7 - 5$
    $= 2$

8. $5(9 + 3) - 3 \cdot 4 = 5(12) - 3 \cdot 4$
    $= 60 - 12$
    $= 48$

9. $5^3 + 6^3 - 5^2 = 125 + 216 - 25$
    $= 341 - 25$
    $= 316$

10. $\frac{38 - 12}{2 \cdot 13} = (38 - 12) \div (2 \cdot 13)$
    $= 26 \div (2 \cdot 13)$
    $= 26 \div (26)$
    $= 1$

11. $a + b^2 + c^2 = 6 + 4^2 + 3^2$
    $= 6 + 16 + 9$
    $= 31$

12. $3ab - c^2 = 3 \cdot 6 \cdot 4 - 3^2$
    $= 3 \cdot 6 \cdot 4 - 9$
    $= 72 - 9$
    $= 63$

13. $8(a - c)^2 + 3 = 8(6 - 3)^2 + 3$

$\qquad\qquad = 8(3)^2 + 3$

$\qquad\qquad = 8(9) + 3$

$\qquad\qquad = 72 + 3$

$\qquad\qquad = 75$

14. $\dfrac{2ab - c^3}{7} = \dfrac{2 \cdot 6 \cdot 4 - 3^3}{7}$

$\qquad\qquad = (2 \cdot 6 \cdot 4 - 3^3) \div 7$

$\qquad\qquad = (2 \cdot 6 \cdot 4 - 27) \div 7$

$\qquad\qquad = (48 - 27) \div 7$

$\qquad\qquad = 21 \div 7$

$\qquad\qquad = 3$

**PAGES 15-17    EXERCISES**

15. $4 + 7 \cdot 2 + 8 = 4 + 14 + 8$

$\qquad\qquad = 26$

16. $12 \div 4 + 15 \cdot 3 = 3 + 15 \cdot 3$

$\qquad\qquad = 3 + 45$

$\qquad\qquad = 48$

17. $29 - 3(9 - 4) = 29 - 3(5)$

$\qquad\qquad = 29 - 15$

$\qquad\qquad = 14$

18. $4(11 + 7) - 9 \cdot 8 = 4(18) - 9 \cdot 8$

$\qquad\qquad = 72 - 9 \cdot 8$

$\qquad\qquad = 72 - 72$

$\qquad\qquad = 0$

19. $16 \div 2 \cdot 5 \cdot 3 \div 6 = 8 \cdot 5 \cdot 3 \div 6$

$\qquad\qquad = 40 \cdot 3 \div 6$

$\qquad\qquad = 120 \div 6$

$\qquad\qquad = 20$

20. $288 \div [3(9 + 3)] = 288 \div [3(12)]$

$\qquad\qquad = 288 \div 36$

$\qquad\qquad = 8$

21. $6(4^3 + 2^2) = 6(64 + 4)$

$\qquad\qquad = 6(68)$

$\qquad\qquad = 408$

22. $\dfrac{9 \cdot 4 + 2 \cdot 6}{7 \cdot 7} = (9 \cdot 4 + 2 \cdot 6) \div \quad (7 \cdot 7)$

$\qquad\qquad = (36 + 12) \div (49)$

$\qquad\qquad = 48 \div 49$

$\qquad\qquad = 0.980$

23. $\dfrac{2 \cdot 8^2 - 2^2 \cdot 8}{2 \cdot 8} = (2 \cdot 8^2 - 2^2 \cdot 8) \div (2 \cdot 8)$

$\qquad\qquad = (2 \cdot 64 - 4 \cdot 8) \div (2 \cdot 8)$

$\qquad\qquad = (128 - 32) \div (16)$

$\qquad\qquad = (96) \div (16)$

$\qquad\qquad = 6$

24. $\dfrac{3}{4}(6) + \dfrac{1}{3}(12) = \dfrac{9}{2} + 4$

$\qquad\qquad = \dfrac{17}{2} \text{ or } 8.5$

25. $25 - \dfrac{1}{3}(18 + 9) = 25 - \dfrac{1}{3}(27)$

$\qquad\qquad = 25 - 9$

$\qquad\qquad = 16$

26. $7(0.2 + 0.5) - 0.6 = 7(0.7) - 0.6$

$\qquad\qquad = 4.9 - 0.6$

$\qquad\qquad = 4.3$

27. $p = x + y + z = 3 + 4 + 5.5$

$\qquad\qquad = 12.5 \text{ mm}$

28. $p = 4z = 4 \cdot 5.5$

$\qquad\qquad = 22 \text{ yd}$

29. $p = 2(x + y) = 2(3 + 4)$

$\qquad\qquad = 2(7)$

$\qquad\qquad = 14 \text{ in.}$

30. $p = x + 2y + z = 3 + 2 \cdot 4 + 5.5$

$\qquad\qquad = 3 + 8 + 5.5$

$\qquad\qquad = 16.5 \text{ cm}$

31. $c = \pi y = 3.14 \cdot 4$

$\qquad\qquad = 12.56 \text{ ft}$

32. $p = \pi x + 2y = 3.14 \cdot 3 + 2 \cdot 4$

$\qquad\qquad = 9.42 + 8$

$\qquad\qquad = 17.42 \text{ m}$

33. $12d + bc = 12 \cdot \dfrac{1}{2} + 4 \cdot 3$

$\qquad\qquad = 6 + 12$

$\qquad\qquad = 18$

34. $a(8 - 3n) + 4d = 6\left(8 - 3 \cdot \dfrac{2}{3}\right) + 4 \cdot \dfrac{1}{2}$

$\qquad\qquad = 6(8 - 2) + 4 \cdot \dfrac{1}{2}$

$\qquad\qquad = 6(6) + 4 \cdot \dfrac{1}{2}$

$\qquad\qquad = 36 + 2$

$\qquad\qquad = 38$

35. $ax + bc = 6 \cdot 0.2 + 4 \cdot 3$

$\qquad\qquad = 1.2 + 12$

$\qquad\qquad = 13.2$

36. $x^2 + 6d = 0.2^2 + 6 \cdot \dfrac{1}{2}$

$\qquad\qquad = 0.04 + 6 \cdot \dfrac{1}{2}$

$\qquad\qquad = 0.04 + 3$

$\qquad\qquad = 3.04$

37. $(100x)^2 + 10y = (100 \cdot 0.2)^2 + 10 \cdot 1.3$

$\qquad\qquad = (20)^2 + 10 \cdot 1.3$

$\qquad\qquad = 400 + 10 \cdot 1.3$

$\qquad\qquad = 400 + 13$

$\qquad\qquad = 413$

38. $\dfrac{8b^2c}{x} = (8b^2c) \div x$

$\qquad\qquad = (8 \cdot 4^2 \cdot 3) \div 0.2$

$\qquad\qquad = (8 \cdot 16 \cdot 3) \div 0.2$

$\qquad\qquad = 384 \div 0.2$

$\qquad\qquad = 1920$

39. $\dfrac{a + b^2}{3bc} = (a + b^2) \div (3bc)$

$\qquad = (6 + 4^2) \div (3 \cdot 4 \cdot 3)$

$\qquad = (6 + 16) \div (3 \cdot 4 \cdot 3)$

$\qquad = (6 + 16) \div (36)$

$\qquad = (22) \div (36)$

$\qquad = \dfrac{11}{18}$ or $0.6\overline{1}$

40. $\dfrac{a^2 - b^2}{2 + d^3} = (a^2 - b^2) \div (2 + d^3)$

$\qquad = (6^2 - 4^2) \div \left(2 + \dfrac{1}{2}^3\right)$

$\qquad = (36 - 16) \div \left(2 + \dfrac{1}{8}\right)$

$\qquad = (20) \div \left(\dfrac{17}{8}\right)$

$\qquad = \dfrac{160}{17}$ or $9.412$

41. $2(a + b) = 2\left(3 + \dfrac{1}{2}\right)$

$\qquad = 2\left(\dfrac{7}{2}\right)$

$\qquad = 7$

42. $2(ab) = 2\left(3 \cdot \dfrac{1}{2}\right)$

$\qquad = 2\left(\dfrac{3}{2}\right)$

$\qquad = 3$

43. $b^2 + c = \dfrac{1}{2}^2 + 0$

$\qquad = \dfrac{1}{4} + 0$

$\qquad = \dfrac{1}{4}$ or $0.25$

44. $a^3 - b = 3^3 - \dfrac{1}{2}$

$\qquad = 27 - \dfrac{1}{2}$

$\qquad = 26\dfrac{1}{2}$ or $26.5$

45. As is, the expression equals 10. By changing the last minus sign to a plus sign the sum becomes 20.

$\qquad 61 - 13 - 12 - 8 - 7 - 6 - 5 = 10$

$\qquad 61 - 13 - 12 - 8 - 7 - 6 + 5 = 20$

46. $12 \cdot 12 \cdot 12 = 1728$ items

47. Answers may vary; for a 14-year old,

$\qquad 0.7(220 - a) = 0.7(220 - 14)$

$\qquad\qquad = 0.7(206)$

$\qquad\qquad = 144.2$

48. $p = 2(x + y)$

$\qquad = 2(12 + 16)$

$\qquad = 2(28)$

$\qquad = 56$ ft

49. $w - 7$

50. a number $y$ raised to the fifth power

51. $4 \cdot 4 \cdot 4 \cdot 4 = 4^4$

52. $2n - 25$

53. $A = l \cdot w$

$\qquad = 6 \cdot 4$

$\qquad = 24$ ft$^2$

## 1-3 Open Sentences

**PAGE 20    CHECKING FOR UNDERSTANDING**

1. statement

2. negation

3. open sentence or equation

4. replacement set

5. $\{3, 4, 5, 6\}$

6. $3 \in \{3, 4, 5, 6\}$

7. $3(11 - 5) = 3(6)$

$\qquad\qquad = 18$

Therefore, $18 > 18$ is false.

8. $0.01 + 0.01 = 0.02$

Therefore, $0.01 + 0.01 = 0.0002$ is false.

9. $\dfrac{3 + 15}{6} = \dfrac{18}{6}$

$\qquad\qquad = 3$

$\dfrac{1}{2}(6) = 3$

Therefore, $\dfrac{3 + 15}{6} = \dfrac{1}{2}(6)$ is true.

10. $\dfrac{1}{2} + \dfrac{3}{4} = \dfrac{5}{4}$

$\dfrac{3}{2} + \dfrac{1}{4} = \dfrac{7}{4}$

Therefore, $\dfrac{1}{2} + \dfrac{3}{4} = \dfrac{3}{2} + \dfrac{1}{4}$ is false.

11. $18 + 2 = 20$, $y = 2$

12. $3 \cdot 8 = 24$, $x = 8$

13. Foster, Winters, Gell, Rath, or Gordon

14. 50

15. $11 = 8 + 3$, $x = 11$

16. $11.97 = 12 - 0.03$, $y = 11.97$

17. $9 = \dfrac{3}{4} \cdot 12$, $a = 9$

18. $8.2 - 6.75 = 1.45$, $m = 1.45$

**PAGES 20-21    EXERCISES**

19. The capital of the U.S. is not Houston; true

20. George Bush is not the President of the United States; true or false

21. Birds do not have wings; false

22. Oranges are a citrus fruit; true

23. $\{1\}$, $\{2\}$, $\{1, 2\}$, $\emptyset$

24. $\{5\}$, $\{6\}$, $\{7\}$, $\{8\}$, $\{5, 6\}$, $\{5, 7\}$, $\{5, 8\}$, $\{6, 7\}$, $\{6, 8\}$, $\{7, 8\}$, $\{5, 6, 7\}$, $\{5, 6, 8\}$, $\{5, 7, 8\}$, $\{6, 7, 8\}$, $\{5, 6, 7, 8\}$, $\emptyset$

25. $a = \dfrac{12 + 8}{4}$

  $a = \dfrac{20}{4}$

  $a = 5$

26. $\dfrac{21 - 3}{12 - 3} = x$

  $\dfrac{18}{9} = x$

  $2 = x$

27. $14.8 - 3.75 = t$

  $11.05 = t$

28. $n = \dfrac{84 \div 7}{18 \div 9}$

  $n = \dfrac{12}{2}$

  $n = 6$

29. $\dfrac{2}{13} + \dfrac{5}{13} = p$

  $\dfrac{7}{13} = p$

30. $\dfrac{5}{8} + \dfrac{1}{4} = y$

  $\dfrac{7}{8} = y$

31. $d = 3\dfrac{1}{2} \div 2$

  $d = \dfrac{7}{2} \cdot \dfrac{1}{2}$

  $d = \dfrac{7}{4}$

32. $r = 5\dfrac{1}{2} + \dfrac{1}{3}$

  $r = 5\dfrac{3}{6} + \dfrac{2}{6}$

  $r = 5\dfrac{5}{6}$

33. $x + 2 > 7$

| $x + 2$ | 4 | 5 | 6 | 7 | 8 |
|---|---|---|---|---|---|
|  | 6 | 7 | 8 | 9 | 10 |

  $\{6, 7, 8\}$

34. $x - 3 > \dfrac{x + 1}{2}$

| | 4 | 5 | 6 | 7 | 8 |
|---|---|---|---|---|---|
| $x - 3$ | 1 | 2 | 3 | 4 | 5 |
| $\dfrac{x + 1}{2}$ | $\dfrac{5}{2}{=}2\dfrac{1}{2}$ | $\dfrac{6}{2}{=}3$ | $\dfrac{7}{2}{=}3\dfrac{1}{2}$ | $\dfrac{8}{2}{=}4$ | $\dfrac{9}{2}{=}4.5$ |

  $\{8\}$

35. $\dfrac{2(x - 2)}{3} = \dfrac{4}{7 - 5}$

  $\dfrac{4}{7 - 5} = \dfrac{4}{2} = 2$

| | 4 | 5 | 6 | 7 | 8 |
|---|---|---|---|---|---|
| $\dfrac{2(x - 2)}{3}$ | $\dfrac{4}{3}{=}1\dfrac{1}{3}$ | $\dfrac{6}{3}{=}2$ | $\dfrac{8}{2}{=}4$ | $\dfrac{10}{2}{=}5$ | $\dfrac{14}{3}{=}4\dfrac{2}{3}$ |

  $\{5\}$

36. $9x - 20 = x^2$

| | 4 | 5 | 6 | 7 | 8 |
|---|---|---|---|---|---|
| $9x - 20$ | 16 | 25 | 34 | 43 | 52 |
| $x^2$ | 16 | 25 | 36 | 42 | 64 |

  $\{4, 5\}$

37. $0.3(x + 4) \leq 0.4(2x + 3)$

| | 4 | 5 | 6 | 7 | 8 |
|---|---|---|---|---|---|
| $0.3(x + 4)$ | 2.4 | 2.7 | 3 | 3.3 | 3.6 |
| $0.4(2x + 3)$ | 4.4 | 5.2 | 6 | 6.8 | 7.6 |

  $\{4, 5, 6, 7, 8\}$

38. $1.3x - 12 < 0.9x + 4$

| | 4 | 5 | 6 | 7 | 8 |
|---|---|---|---|---|---|
| $1.3x - 12$ | $-6.8$ | $-5.5$ | $-4.2$ | $-2.9$ | $-1.6$ |
| $0.9x + 4$ | 7.6 | 8.5 | 9.4 | 10.3 | 11.2 |

  $\{4, 5, 6, 7, 8\}$

39. Answers will vary; some possible answers are $3x = 6$, $b + 5 = 7$, $y > 1$.

40. $V = 8 \cdot 4$

  $V = 32$ voices

41. $\$428.79 - \$1097.31 + 2 \cdot \$691.53 - \$100 = \$614.54$

42. $250{,}000{,}000 \cdot \dfrac{2}{3} = 166{,}666{,}666.7$

  so about $167{,}000{,}000$

43. $h^3$

44. $\dfrac{1}{2}a^2 b^3$

45. $3 \cdot 6 - 12 \div 4 = 18 - 12 \div 4$

  $= 18 - 3$

  $= 15$

46. $\dfrac{9 \cdot 3 - 4^2}{3^2 + 2^2} = (9 \cdot 3 - 4^2) \div (3^2 + 2^2)$

  $= (9 \cdot 3 - 16) \div (9 + 4)$

  $= (27 - 16) \div (9 + 4)$

  $= (11) \div (9 + 4)$

  $= (11) \div (13)$

  $= \dfrac{11}{13}$

47. $(15x)^3 - y = (15 \cdot 0.2)^3 - 1.3$

  $= (3)^3 - 1.3$

  $= 27 - 1.3$

  $= 25.7$

## 1-4  Identity and Equality Properties

PAGES 23-24   CHECKING FOR UNDERSTANDING

1. No; because properties are true for any number.

2. No; because $a + 1 \neq a$.

3. No; because $a \cdot 0 \neq a$.

4. Reflexive property of equality

5. Symmetric property of equality

6. Substitution property of equality

7. Substitution property of equality

8. Transitive property of equality

9. $1(8 - 2^3) = 1(8 - 8)$   Substitution property of equality

  $= 1(0)$   Substitution property of equality

  $= 0$   Multiplicative property of equality

**10.** $3 + 5(4 - 2^2) - 1$     Substitution property of

    $= 3 + 5(4 - 4) - 1$     equality

    $= 3 + 5(0) - 1$     Substitution property of

                            equality

    $= 3 + 0 - 1$     Multiplicative property of

                            zero

    $= 2$     Substitution property of

                            equality

**PAGES 24-25    EXERCISES**

**11.** $0 + 7 = 7$, $x = 7$

**12.** $5 \cdot 1 = 5$, $a = 5$

**13.** $7 \cdot 1 = 7$, $b = 1$

**14.** $0(18) = 0$, $n = 0$

**15.** Symmetric property of equality

**16.** Multiplicative property of zero

**17.** Multiplicative identity property

**18.** Substitution property of equality

**19.** Reflexive property of equality

**20.** Additive identity property

**21.** Substitution property of equality

**22.** Multiplicative identity

**23.** Multiplicative property of zero

**24.** Symmetric property of equality

**25.** Transitive property of equality

**26.** $5(9 + 3^2) = 5(9 + 9)$     Substitution property

                            of equality

           $= 5(1)$     Substitution property

                            of equality

           $= 5$     Multiplicative

                            identity property

**27.** $3 + 18(12 \div 6 - 2)$     Substitution property

    $= 3 + 18(2 - 2)$     of equality

    $= 3 + 18(0)$     Substitution property

                            of equality

    $= 3 + 0$     Multiplicative

                            property of zero

    $= 3$     Additive identity

                            property

**28.** $(19 - 12) \div 7 \cdot 23$     Substitution property

    $= 7 \div 7 \cdot 23$     of equality

    $= 1 \cdot 23$     Substitution property

                            of equality

    $= 23$     Multiplicative

                            identity property

**29.** $(2^5 - 5^2) + (4^2 - 2^4)$     Substitution property

    $= (32 - 25) + (16 - 16)$     of equality

    $= (7) + (0)$     Substitution property

                            of equality

    $= 7$     Additive identity

                            property

**30.** $(9 - 2 \cdot 3)^3 - 27 + 9 \cdot 2$     Substitution

    $= (9 - 6)^3 - 27 + 9 \cdot 2$     property of equality

    $= (3)^3 - 27 + 9 \cdot 2$     Substitution

                            property of equality

    $= 27 - 27 + 9 \cdot 2$     Substitution

                            property of equality

    $= 27 - 27 + 18$     Substitution

                            property of equality

    $= 0 + 18$     Substitution

                            property of equality

    $= 18$     Additive identity

                            property

**31.** $\left(13 + \dfrac{2}{5} \cdot 5\right)(3^2 - 2^3)$

    $= (13 + 2)(3^2 - 2^3)$     Substitution property

    $= (15)(3^2 - 2^3)$     Substitution property

    $= (15)(9 - 8)$     Substitution property

    $= (15)(1)$     Substitution property

    $= 15$     Multiplicative

                            identity property

**32.** a) No, if $a = a$, then $a$ is not greater than $a$.

    b) No, if $a > b$, then $b$ is not greater than $a$.

    c) Yes, if $a > b$, and $b > c$, then $a > c$.

**33.** A score is a group of 20 items.

    $4(20) + 7 = 87$ years

**34.** $92 \div 12 = 7.67 \approx 8$ years

**35.** $3.00 + 39(0.85) = \$36.15$

**36.** a number $x$ squared

**37.** $7(8 - 4) + 11 = 7(4) + 11$

                       $= 28 + 11$

                       $= 39$

**38.** true, $15 \div 3 + 7 = 5 + 7$

                       $= 12$

           $12 < 13$

**39.** $m = 20$, $\dfrac{1}{2}(20) = 10$

**PAGE 25    MID-CHAPTER REVIEW**

**1.** $n^3$

**2.** $n^2 + 7$

**3.** $8 \div 2 + 6 \cdot 2$, Divide 8 by 2. Multiply 2 by 6. Then add.

**4.** $3(3^2 - 3)$, Square 3. Subtract 3. Then multiply by 3.

**5.** $(8 + 6) \div 2 + 2$, Add 8 and 6. Divide by 2. Then add 2.

**6.** $\dfrac{2}{3}(16) - \dfrac{1}{3}(6) = \dfrac{32}{3} - \dfrac{6}{3}$

                               $= \dfrac{26}{3}$

7. $\frac{1}{2}(8 + 30) - 4 = \frac{1}{2}(38) - 4$

$\qquad\qquad\qquad = 19 - 4$

$\qquad\qquad\qquad = 15$

8. $d(a + b) - c = \frac{1}{2}(6 + 4) - 3$

$\qquad\qquad\qquad = \frac{1}{2}(10) - 3$

$\qquad\qquad\qquad = 5 - 3$

$\qquad\qquad\qquad = 2$

9. $x = 6 + 0.28$

$\quad x = 6.28$

10. $m = \dfrac{64 + 4}{17}$

$\quad m = \dfrac{68}{17} = 4$

11. $y = \dfrac{96 + 6}{8 + 2} = (96 + 6) \div (8 + 2)$

$\quad y = 16 + 4$

$\quad y = 4$

12.

| $10 - x$ | 4 | 5 | 6 | 7 | 8 |
|----------|---|---|---|---|---|
|          | 6 | 5 | 4 | 3 | 2 |

{4, 5, 6, 7, 8} is the solution set.

13.

| $\dfrac{x + 3}{2}$ | 4 | 5 | 6 | 7 | 8 |
|---|---|---|---|---|---|
| | $\frac{7}{2}=3\frac{1}{2}$ | $\frac{8}{2}=4$ | $\frac{9}{2}=4.5$ | $\frac{10}{2}=5$ | $\frac{11}{2}=5.5$ |

{4, 5, 6} is the solution set.

14.

| $\dfrac{2x + 1}{7}$ | 4 | 5 | 6 | 7 | 8 |
|---|---|---|---|---|---|
| | $\frac{9}{7}\frac{45}{35}$ | $\frac{11}{7}\frac{55}{35}$ | $\frac{13}{7}\frac{65}{35}$ | $\frac{15}{7}\frac{75}{35}$ | $\frac{17}{7}\frac{85}{35}$ |
| $\dfrac{x + 4}{5}$ | $\frac{8}{5}\frac{56}{35}$ | $\frac{9}{5}\frac{63}{35}$ | $\frac{10}{5}\frac{70}{35}$ | $\frac{11}{5}\frac{77}{35}$ | $\frac{12}{5}\frac{84}{35}$ |

{8} is the solution set.

15. Multiplicative property of zero

16. Symmetric property of equality

## 1-5 The Distributive Property

PAGE 29    CHECKING FOR UNDERSTANDING

1. $a(b + c) = ab + ac$; $(b + c)a = ba + ca$;

$a(b - c) = ab - ac$; $(b - c)a = ba - ca$

2. Answers may vary; The number outside the parentheses is multiplied by the numbers inside the parentheses.

3. 5    4. 1    5. $\frac{1}{3}$    6. 0.5    7. $6bc$, $bc$

8. $7a$, $29a$    9. $4xy$, $5xy$    10. $2rs^2$, $rs^2$    11. $5x$

12. $y^3$    13. in simplest form    14. 0

15. $3 \cdot 215$

$= 3 \cdot (200 + 15)$

$= 3 \cdot 200 + 3 \cdot 15$

$= 600 + 45$

$= 645$

16. $4 \cdot 98$

$= 4(100 - 2)$

$= 4 \cdot 100 - 4 \cdot 2$

$= 400 - 8$

$= 392$

17. $8(3x + 7)$

$= 8 \cdot 3x + 8 \cdot 7$

$= 24x + 56$

18. $4m - 4n$

$= 4(m - n)$

19. $13a + 5a$

$= (13 + 5)a$

$= 18a$

20. $21x - 10x$

$= (21 - 10)x$

$= 11x$

21. $3(5am - 4)$

$= 3 \cdot 5am - 3 \cdot 4$

$= 15am - 12$

22. $15x^2 + 7x^2$

$= (15 + 7)x^2$

$= 22x^2$

23. $9y^2 + 13y^2 + 3$

$= (9 + 13)y^2 + 3$

$= 22y^2 + 3$

24. $11a^2 - 11a^2 + 12a^2$

$= (11 - 11 + 12)a^2$

$= 12a^2$

25. $14a^2 + 13b^2 + 27$

in simplest form

26. $5a + 7a + 10b + 5b$

$= (5 + 7)a + (10 + 5)b$

$= 12a + 15b$

27. $3(x + 2y) - 2y$

$= 3 \cdot x + 3 \cdot 2y - 2y$

$= 3x + 6y - 2y$

$= 3x + (6 - 2)y$

$= 3x + 4y$

28. $5x + 3(x - y)$

$= 5x + 3x - 3y$

$= (5 + 3)x - 3y$

$= 8x - 3y$

29. $6(5a + 3b - 2b)$

$= 30a + 18b - 12b$

$= 30a + (18 - 12)b$

$= 30a + 6b$

30. $5ab^2 + 2a^2b + a^2b^2$

in simplest form

31. $4(3x + 2) + 2(x + 3)$

$= 4 \cdot 3x + 4 \cdot 2 + 2 \cdot x + 2 \cdot 3$

$= 12x + 8 + 2x + 6$

$= 8 + 12x + 2x + 6$

$= 8 + 14x + 6$

$= 14x + 8 + 6$

$= 14x + 14$

32. $x^2 + \frac{7}{8}x - \frac{x}{8}$

$= x^2 + \left(\frac{7}{8} - \frac{1}{8}\right)x$

$= x^2 + \frac{6}{8}x$

$= x^2 + \frac{3}{4}x$

33. $3.047xy^3 - 0.012y^3 + 5.78xy^3$

$= (3.047 + 5.78)xy^3 - 0.012y^3$

$= 8.827xy^3 - 0.012y^3$

34. $1.042a^2 + 8.0879a + 5.265a$

   $= 1.042a^2 + (8.0879 + 5.265)a$

   $= 1.042a^2 + 13.3529a$

35. $1436x^2 - 789x^2 + 5689x^2$

   $= (1436 - 789 + 5689)x^2$

   $= 6336x^2$

36. $5.8rs^3 - 4.06rs^3 + 0.92r^2s$

   $= (5.8 - 4.06)rs^3 + 0.92r^2s$

   $= 1.74rs^3 + 0.92r^2s$

37. No, counterexample $b = 1$, $c = 3$

   $2 + (b \cdot c) = (2 + b)(2 + c)$

   $2 + (1 \cdot 3) \quad (2 + 1)(2 + 3)$

   $2 + 3 \qquad\qquad 3 \cdot 5$

   $\quad 5 \qquad\qquad\quad \neq \quad 15$

38. $4.95(24 + 32)$

   $= 4.95(56)$

   $= \$277.20$

39. a.) $h = 61.412 + 2.317F$

   $h = 61.412 + 2.317 \cdot 47.9$

   $h = 61.412 + 110.984$

   $h = 172.396$ cm $= 172.4$ cm

   b.) $h = 73.570 + 2.970H$

   $h = 73.570 + 2.970 \cdot 35.7$

   $h = 73.570 + 106.029$

   $h = 179.599$ cm $= 179.6$ cm

40. a.) Yes, examples may vary; $a = 1$, $b = 2$, $c = 3$

   $\dfrac{a + b}{c} = \dfrac{a}{c} + \dfrac{b}{c}$

   $\dfrac{1 + 2}{3} = \dfrac{1}{3} + \dfrac{2}{3}$

   $\dfrac{3}{3} = \dfrac{3}{3}$

   b.) No, examples may vary; $a = 1$, $b = 2$, $c = 3$

   $(a + b)^2 = a^2 + b^2$

   $(1 + 2)^2 \quad 1^2 + 2^2$

   $3^2 \quad 1 + 4$

   $9 \neq 5$

41. $3^2a^3$ or $9a^3$

42. $196 \div [4(11 - 4)]$

   $= 196 \div [4(7)]$

   $= 196 \div 28$

   $= 7$

43. $9.6 + 4.53 = b$

   $14.13 = b$

44. Symmetric property of equality

45. $4 + 5 \cdot 0 = y$

   $4 + 0 = y$

   $4 = y$

## 1-6 Commutative and Associative Properties

**PAGE 33    CHECKING FOR UNDERSTANDING**

1. Associative property of addition
2. Commutative property of multiplication
3. Associative property of addition
4. Commutative property of addition
5. Distributive property
6. Substitution property of equality
7. Commutative property of multiplication
8. Associative property of addition
9. Associative property of multiplication
10. Distributive property
11. Commutative property of addition
12. Commutative property of multiplication
13. a. $6a + (8b + 2a) = 6a + (2a + 8b)$
      Commutative property of addition
    b. $\qquad\qquad = (6a + 2a) + 8b$
      Associative property of addition
    c. $\qquad\qquad = (6 + 2)a + 8b$
      Distributive property
    d. $\qquad\qquad = 8a + 8b$
      Substitution property of equality
14. a. $8a^2 + (8a + a^2) + 7a = 8a^2 + (a^2 + 8a) + 7a$
      Commutative property of addition
    b. $\qquad\qquad = (8a^2 + a^2) + (8a + 7a)$
      Associative property of addition
    c. $\qquad\qquad = (8a^2 + 1a^2) + (8a + 7a)$
      Multiplicative identity property
    d. $\qquad\qquad = (8 + 1)a^2 + (8 + 7)a$
      Distributive property
    e. $\qquad\qquad = 9a^2 + 15a$
      Substitution property of equality

**PAGES 33-35    EXERCISES**

15. Commutative property of addition
16. Multiplicative identity property
17. Associative property of addition
18. Commutative property of addition
19. Commutative property of multiplication
20. Associative property of multiplication
21. Addition identity property
22. Distributive property
23. Commutative property of addition
24. Associative property of addition
25. $(m + n) \cdot a = m \cdot a + n \cdot a$
    Distributive property
26. $0 + 7 = 7$   Additive identity property

27. $(1 \cdot a) + b = a + b$

Multiplicative identity property

28. $3m + nq = 3m + qn$

Commutative property of multiplication

29. $5a + 6b + 7a = 5a + 7a + 6b$

$\qquad = (5 + 7)a + 6b$

$\qquad = 12a + 6b$

30. $8x + 2y + x = 8x + x + 2y$

$\qquad = 8x + 1 \cdot x + 2y$

$\qquad = (8 + 1)x + 2y$

$\qquad = 9x + 2y$

31. $3x + 2y + 2x + 8y = 3x + 2x + 2y + 8y$

$\qquad = (3 + 2)x + (2 + 8)y$

$\qquad = 5x + 10y$

32. $\frac{2}{3}x^2 + 5x + x^2 = \frac{2}{3}x^2 + x^2 + 5x$

$\qquad = \frac{2}{3}x^2 + 1 \cdot x^2 + 5x$

$\qquad = \left(\frac{2}{3} + 1\right)x^2 + 5x$

$\qquad = \frac{5}{3}x^2 + 5x$

33. $3a + 5b + 2c + 8b = 3a + 5b + 8b + 2c$

$\qquad = 3a + (5 + 8)b + 2c$

$\qquad = 3a + 13b + 2c$

34. $5 + 7(ac + 2b) + 2ac$

$= 5 + 7ac + 7 \cdot 2b + 2ac$

$= 5 + 7ac + 14b + 2ac$

$= 5 + 7ac + 2ac + 14b$

$= 5 + (7 + 2)ac + 14b$

$= 5 + 9ac + 14b$

35. $3(4x + y) + 2x$

$= 3 \cdot 4x + 3y + 2x$

$= 12x + 3y + 2x$

$= 12x + 2x + 3y$

$= (12 + 2)x + 3y$

$= 14x + 3y$

36. $3(x + 2y) + 4(3x + y)$

$= 3x + 3 \cdot 2y + 4 \cdot 3x + 4y$

$= 3x + 6y + 12x + 4y$

$= 3x + 12x + 6y + 4y$

$= (3 + 12)x + (6 + 4)y$

$= 15x + 10y$

37. $\frac{3}{4} + \frac{2}{3}(x + 2y) + x$

$= \frac{3}{4} + \frac{2}{3}x + \frac{2}{3} \cdot 2y + x$

$= \frac{3}{4} + \frac{2}{3}x + \frac{4}{3}y + x$

$= \frac{3}{4} + \frac{2}{3}x + x + \frac{4}{3}y$

$= \frac{3}{4} + \left(\frac{2}{3} + 1\right)x + \frac{4}{3}y$

$= \frac{3}{4} + \frac{5}{3}x + \frac{4}{3}y$

38. $\frac{3}{5}\left(\frac{1}{2}x + 2y\right) + 2x$

$= \frac{3}{5} \cdot \frac{1}{2}x + \frac{3}{5} \cdot 2y + 2x$

$= \frac{3}{10}x + \frac{6}{5}y + 2x$

$= \frac{3}{10}x + 2x + \frac{6}{5}y$

$= \left(\frac{3}{10} + 2\right)x + \frac{6}{5}y$

$= \frac{23}{10}x + \frac{6}{5}y$

39. $0.2(3x + 0.2) + 0.5(5x + 3)$

$= 0.2 \cdot 3x + 0.2 \cdot 0.2 + 0.5 \cdot 5x + 0.5 \cdot 3$

$= 0.6x + 0.04 + 2.5x + 1.5$

$= 0.6x + 2.5x + 0.04 + 1.5$

$= (0.6 + 2.5)x + 0.04 + 1.5$

$= 3.1x + 1.54$

40. $3[4 + 5(2x + 3y)]$

$= 3[4 + 5 \cdot 2x + 5 \cdot 3y]$

$= 3[4 + 10x + 15y]$

$= 3 \cdot 4 + 3 \cdot 10x + 3 \cdot 15y$

$= 12 + 30x + 45y$

41. No, $24 + 6 = 4$

$\qquad 6 + 24 = 0.25;$

no, $36 + 9 = 4$

$\qquad 9 + 36 = 0.25;$

division is not commutative.

42. No, $12 - 8 = 4$

$\qquad 8 - 12 = -4;$

no, $27 - 10 = 17$

$\qquad 10 - 27 = -17;$

subtraction is not commutative.

43. a.

| | $8'' \times 11'' \times 2\frac{1}{2}''$ | $8\frac{1}{2}'' \times 10'' \times 2''$ | $7\frac{7}{8}'' \times 11'' \times 3''$ |
|---|---|---|---|
| $V = l \times h \times w$ | $=220$ | $=170$ | $=259.9$ |

$7\frac{7}{8}''$ by $11''$ by $3''$ is the size that has the

greatest volume.

b. Answers will vary, $l \times w \times h$, $w \times h \times l$,

$l \times h \times w$

c. 6 ways; $7\frac{7}{8} \times 11 \times 3$, $3 \times 7\frac{7}{8} \times 11$,

$\qquad 11 \times 3 \times 7\frac{7}{8}$, $3 \times 11 \times 7\frac{7}{8}$, $11 \times 7\frac{7}{8} \times 3$,

$\qquad 7\frac{7}{8} \times 3 \times 11$

44. $5a + 6b = 50$, Either $a = 10$ and $b = 0$ or $a = 4$

and $b = 5$, so $a = 4$ and $b = 5$.

45. 7 ft 11 in. $-$ 4 ft 8 in. $=$ 3 ft 3 in.

**46.** 9:00 PM;

distance of system ÷ speed of system

     (in miles)      (in miles per hour)

= travel time of system

      (in hours)

$150 \div 30 = 5$ hrs

4:00 PM + 5 hrs = 9:00 PM

**47.** $2x^2$

**48.** $c^2 + y^2 = 3^2 + 1.3^2$
$$= 9 + 1.69$$
$$= 10.69$$

**49.** $(15x)^3 - y = (15 \cdot 0.2)^3 - 1.3$
$$= (3)^3 - 1.3$$
$$= 27 - 1.3$$
$$= 25.7$$

**50.** $\frac{5}{6} \cdot 18 = m$
$$15 = m$$

**51.** $\frac{4}{5}$

**52.** $9a + 14(a + 3) = 9a + 14a + 14.3$
$$= 9a + 14a + 42$$
$$= (9 + 14)a + 42$$
$$= 23a + 42$$

**53.** Substitution property of equality

**54.** Distributive property

## 1-7    Formulas

### PAGES 37-38     CHECKING FOR UNDERSTANDING

**1.** A formula is a type of equation.

**2.** degrees Celsius and Fahrenheit

**3.** $A = s^2$

**4.** $P = 2(a + b)$

**5.** $P = 4s$

**6.** $C = 2\pi r$

**7.** $SA = 2(wh + lh + lw)$
$$= 2(8 \cdot 6 + 5 \cdot 6 + 5 \cdot 8)$$
$$= 2(48 + 30 + 40)$$
$$= 2(118)$$
$$= 236$$

**8.** $SA = 2(wh + lh + lw)$
$$= 2\left(12 \cdot 3\frac{1}{2} + 5\frac{1}{2} \cdot 3\frac{1}{2} + 5\frac{1}{2} \cdot 12\right)$$
$$= 2(42 + 19\frac{1}{4} + 66)$$
$$= 2\left(127\frac{1}{4}\right)$$
$$= 254\frac{1}{2}$$

**9.** $SA = 2(wh + lh + lw)$
$$= 2(10 \cdot 4 + 18 \cdot 4 + 18 \cdot 10)$$
$$= 2(40 + 72 + 180)$$
$$= 2(292)$$
$$= 584$$

**10.** $SA = 2(wh + lh + lw)$
$$= 2(11 \cdot 4.6 + 12.9 \cdot 4.6 + 12.9 \cdot 11)$$
$$= 2(50.6 + 59.34 + 141.9)$$
$$= 2(251.84)$$
$$= 503.68$$

**11.** $SA = 2(wh + lh + lw)$
$$= 2(3 \cdot 8 + 20\frac{1}{2} \cdot 8 + 20\frac{1}{2} \cdot 3)$$
$$= 2(24 + 164 + 61.5)$$
$$= 2(249.5)$$
$$= 499$$

**12.** $SA = 2(wh + lh + lw)$
$$= 2(6.5 \cdot 9.7 + 21.8 \cdot 9.7 + 21.8 \cdot 6.5)$$
$$= 2(63.05 + 211.46 + 141.7)$$
$$= 2(416.21)$$
$$= 832.42$$

### PAGES 38-39     EXERCISES

**13.** $2x + y^2 = z$

**14.** $a^2 - b^3 = c$

**15.** $(x + a)^2 = m$

**16.** $r = (a - b)^3$

**17.** $(abc)^2 = k$

**18.** $abc^2 = f$

**19.** $29 - xy = z$

For Problems 20-27, $A = \frac{1}{2}h(a + b)$.

**20.** $A = \frac{1}{2} \cdot 6(24 + 19)$
$$= \frac{1}{2} \cdot 6(43)$$
$$= 3(43)$$
$$= 129$$

**21.** $A = \frac{1}{2} \cdot 11(37 + 23)$
$$= \frac{1}{2} \cdot 11(60)$$
$$= \frac{11}{2}(60)$$
$$= 330$$

**22.** $A = \frac{1}{2} \cdot 12(24 + 40)$
$$= \frac{1}{2} \cdot 12(64)$$
$$= 6(64)$$
$$= 384$$

23. $A = \frac{1}{2} \cdot 3\frac{1}{3}\left(12 + 8\frac{1}{4}\right)$

$\quad = \frac{1}{2} \cdot 3\frac{1}{3}\left(20\frac{1}{4}\right)$

$\quad = \frac{10}{6}\left(20\frac{1}{4}\right)$

$\quad = \frac{810}{24} = 33\frac{3}{4}$

24. $A = \frac{1}{2} \cdot 10(19 + 54)$

$\quad = \frac{1}{2} \cdot 10(73)$

$\quad = 5(73)$

$\quad = 365$

25. $A = \frac{1}{2} \cdot 4(18.9 + 12.7)$

$\quad = \frac{1}{2} \cdot 4(31.6)$

$\quad = 2(31.6)$

$\quad = 63.2$

26. $A = \frac{1}{2} \cdot \frac{5}{8}\left(\frac{3}{4} + \frac{1}{2}\right)$

$\quad = \frac{1}{2} \cdot \frac{5}{8}\left(\frac{5}{4}\right)$

$\quad = \frac{5}{16}\left(\frac{5}{4}\right)$

$\quad = \frac{25}{64}$

27. $A = \frac{1}{2} \cdot 2.4(8.25 + 3.15)$

$\quad = \frac{1}{2} \cdot 2.4(11.4)$

$\quad = 1.2(11.4)$

$\quad = 13.68$

For Problems 28–35, $A = \frac{1}{2}\pi a^2 - a^2$.

28. $A = \frac{1}{2} \cdot 3.14 \cdot 6^2 - 6^2$

$\quad = \frac{1}{2} \cdot 3.14 \cdot 36 - 36$

$\quad = 56.52 - 36$

$\quad = 20.52 \approx 21$

29. $A = \frac{1}{2} \cdot 3.14 \cdot 4^2 - 4^2$

$\quad = \frac{1}{2} \cdot 3.14 \cdot 16 - 16$

$\quad = 25.12 - 16$

$\quad = 9.12 \approx 9$

30. $A = \frac{1}{2} \cdot 3.14 \cdot 81^2 - 81^2$

$\quad = \frac{1}{2} \cdot 3.14 \cdot 6561 - 6561$

$\quad = 10300.77 - 6561$

$\quad = 3739.77 \approx 3740$

31. $A = \frac{1}{2} \cdot 3.14 \cdot 64^2 - 64^2$

$\quad = \frac{1}{2} \cdot 3.14 \cdot 4096 - 4096$

$\quad = 6430.72 - 4096$

$\quad = 2334.72 \approx 2335$

32. $A = \frac{1}{2} \cdot 3.14 \cdot 3.8^2 - 3.8^2$

$\quad = \frac{1}{2} \cdot 3.14 \cdot 14.44 - 14.44$

$\quad = 22.67 - 14.44$

$\quad = 8.23 \approx 8$

33. $A = \frac{1}{2} \cdot 3.14 \cdot 5.6^2 - 5.6^2$

$\quad = \frac{1}{2} \cdot 3.14 \cdot 31.36 - 31.36$

$\quad = 49.24 - 31.36$

$\quad = 17.88 \approx 18$

34. $A = \frac{1}{2} \cdot 3.14 \cdot 18.3^2 - 18.3^2$

$\quad = \frac{1}{2} \cdot 3.14 \cdot 334.89 - 334.89$

$\quad = 525.78 - 334.89$

$\quad = 190.89 \approx 191$

35. $A = \frac{1}{2} \cdot 3.14 \cdot 27.4^2 - 27.4^2$

$\quad = \frac{1}{2} \cdot 3.14 \cdot 750.76 - 750.76$

$\quad = 1178.69 - 750.76$

$\quad = 427.93 \approx 428$

36.

$A$ = area of large square − area of shaded square

$A = a^2 - b^2$

37. Area of figure = area of rectangle +

$\qquad\qquad\qquad\quad$ area of semicircles

$\qquad = (l \times w) \quad + \quad 4\left(\frac{1}{2}\pi r^2\right)$

$\qquad = (s \times s) \quad + \quad 4\left(\frac{1}{2}\pi\left(\frac{1}{2}s\right)^2\right)$

$\qquad = s^2 \qquad\quad + \quad 2\pi\frac{1}{4}s^2$

$\qquad = s^2 \qquad\quad + \quad 2 \cdot \frac{1}{4} \cdot \pi s^2$

$\qquad = s^2 \qquad\quad + \quad \frac{1}{2}\pi s^2$

$\qquad A = s^2 + \frac{1}{2}\pi s^2$

Area of          +          Area of the
rectangle                  4 semicircles

38. $A = \frac{1}{2}$ the area of the circle below

$$= \frac{1}{2} \pi r^2$$

$$= \frac{1}{2} \pi a^2$$

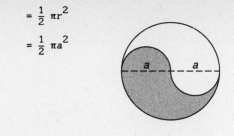

39. $A = \frac{1}{2} \cdot b \cdot h$

$420 = \frac{1}{2} \cdot 30 \cdot h$

$420 = 15 \cdot h$

$28 = h$

For problems 40–43, $d = r \cdot t$

40. $d = 50 \cdot 3$

$= 150$ miles

41. $d = 660 \cdot 30$

$= 19,800$ feet

42. $d = 330 \cdot 10$

$= 3,300$ meters

43. $93,000,000 = 186,000 \cdot t$

$t = 93,000,000 \div 186,000$

$= 500$ seconds

44. $12 \cdot 6 + 3 \cdot 2 + 8 = 72 + 3 \cdot 2 + 8$

$= 24 \cdot 2 \div 8$

$= 48 \div 8$

$= 6$

45. $m = 3\frac{1}{3} \div 3$

$= \frac{10}{3} \div 3$

$= \frac{10}{3} \cdot \frac{1}{3}$

$= \frac{10}{9} = 1\frac{1}{9}$

46. $b^3$, $4b^3$

47. $16a + 21a + 30b - 7b$

$= (16 + 21)a + (30 - 7)b$

$= 37a + 23b$

48. Commutative property of multiplication

# Technology: Formulas

**PAGE 40  EXERCISES**

1. Values for $L$ and $W$ may vary.

$L = 11, 2, 23, 4, 15$

$W = 3.6, 7, 8.1, 4.9, 100$

```
10    PRINT "L", "W", "P"
20    PRINT
30    READ L, W
40    IF L = 0 then 100
50    DATA 11, 3.6, 2, 7, 23, 8.1
60    DATA 4, 4.9, 15, 100, 0, 0
70    LET P = 2 * (L + W)
80    PRINT L, W, P
90    GOTO 30
100   END
```

2.

| | A | B | C | D | E | F |
|---|---|---|---|---|---|---|
| 1: | L | W | P | | | |
| 2: | | | | | | |
| 3: | 11 | 3.6 | 29.2 | | | |
| 4: | 2 | 7 | 18 | | | |
| 5: | 23 | 8.1 | 62.2 | | | |
| 6: | 4 | 4.9 | 17.8 | | | |
| 7: | 15 | 100 | 230 | | | |

3. Values for $H$, $A$, and $B$ may vary.

$H = 2, 9.1, 7, 20, 16$

$A = 15, 4, 13.4, 2, 51$

$B = 32, 12.2, 18, 9, 92$

```
10    PRINT "H", "A", "B", "AR"
20    PRINT
30    READ H, A, B
40    IF H = 0 then 110
50    DATA 2, 15, 32, 9.1, 4, 12.2
60    DATA 7, 13.4, 18, 20, 2, 9
70    DATA 16, 51, 92, 0, 0, 0
80    LET AR = 0.5 * H * (A + B)
90    PRINT H, A, B, AR
100   GOTO 30
110   END
```

4.

| | A | B | C | D | E | F |
|---|---|---|---|---|---|---|
| 1: | H | A | B | AR | | |
| 2: | | | | | | |
| 3: | 2 | 15 | 32 | 47 | | |
| 4: | 9.1 | 4 | 12.2 | 73.71 | | |
| 5: | 7 | 13.4 | 18 | 109.90 | | |
| 6: | 20 | 2 | 9 | 110 | | |
| 7: | 16 | 51 | 92 | 1144 | | |

# Problem-Solving:
## Explore Verbal Problems

1. learning to explore problems
2. You cannot solve the problem..
3. a. $1 bills
   b. 7
   c. $267
   d. none
   e. amount of money = $267 - 11($10)
                      = $267 - $110
                      = $157
   f. end of day
   g. $5n$ dollars
4. a. cookbooks
   b. 6
   c. yes
   d. 41
   e. $20 - n$
   f. crafts

5. a. does not say
   b. 7¢
   c. $2 \cdot \$3.59 = \$7.18$
   d. more
   e. $(n - 7)$¢ or $(359 - n)$¢
6. a. 1
   b. $59 - 18 = 41$¢
   c. $\$3 - 59$¢ $= \$2.41$
   d. cucumbers
   e. $n - 5$
7. a. no
   b. yes
   c. rock
   d. 13
   e. $n + 3$
8. a. 24
   b. 24 years
   c.   68   +   5   +   5   = 78 years
      sum of  Craig  Mother
       ages   5 yrs  5 yrs
              older  older
   d. $24 + 10 = 34$
   e. 24 years
9. a. $24 + 24 = 48$
   b. $24 + 24 + 24 = 72$
   c. No, $1\frac{1}{2} \div 2 = \frac{3}{4}$

10. a. Lorena
    b. $\frac{4}{5}$, if Lorena can paint 1 house in 25 hours then she can paint $\frac{1}{25}$ of a house in 1 hour.
    
    $$\frac{1}{25} \cdot 20 = \frac{20}{25} = \frac{4}{5} \text{ of a house}$$
    
    c. $\frac{x}{30}$
    
    d. $13\frac{7}{11}$, Let $\frac{a}{25}$ and $\frac{a}{30}$ represent the amount of house Lorena and Mia can paint respectively in $a$ hours.
    
    So $\frac{a}{25} + \frac{a}{30} = 1$
    $$\frac{11a}{50} = 1$$
    $$a = 13\frac{7}{11}$$

# Chapter 1   Summary and Review

1. $8y$   2. $2y^3$   3. $a^4$   4. $15x^3y^2$

5. $ab^2 = 5 \cdot 8^2$
   $= 5 \cdot 64$
   $= 320$

6. $3ac - bd$
   $= 3 \cdot 5 \cdot \frac{2}{3} - 8 \cdot \frac{1}{2}$
   $= 10 - 4$
   $= 6$

7. $a = 29 - 5^2$
   $= 29 - 25$
   $= 4$

8. $y = 5(6) - 3(5)$
   $= 30 - 15$
   $= 15$

9. $W = (0.2)(8 + 3)$
   $= (0.2)(11)$
   $= 2.2$

10. $m = \frac{2}{3}\left(3 - \frac{1}{2}\right)$
    $= \frac{2}{3}\left(2\frac{1}{2}\right)$
    $= \frac{10}{6} = \frac{5}{3}$

11. Additive identity property
12. Multiplicative identity property
13. Symmetric property of equality
14. $10x + x = (10 + 1)x$
    $= 11x$
15. $2(a + b) + b = 2a + 2b + b$
    $= 2a + 3b$
16. $2(3a + 2a + b) = 6a + 4a + 2b$
    $= 10a + 2b$
17. $9(r + s) - 2s = 9r + 9s - 2s$
    $= 9r + 7s$

18. Commutative property of addition
19. Associative property of multiplication
20. Associative property of addition
21. Commutative property of multiplication
22. $6a + 7b + 8a + 2b = 6a + 8a +\cdot 7b + 2b$
$$= 14a + 9b$$

23. $\dfrac{3a^2}{4} + \dfrac{2ab}{3} + ab = \dfrac{3a^2}{4} + \dfrac{5ab}{3}$

24. $18 - d^2 = f$

25. $c = (2x)^3$

### PAGE 46    APPLICATIONS AND CONNECTIONS

For Problems 26-28, $P$ = sum of the sides

26. $p = z + y + z + y + x$
$$= 1\tfrac{1}{2} + 3 + 1\tfrac{1}{2} + 3 + 7$$
$$= 16 \text{ ft}$$

27. $p = y + x + x + x + y + x + x + x$
$$= y + 3x + y + 3x$$
$$= y + y + 3x + 3x$$
$$= 2y + 6x$$
$$= 2 \cdot 3 + 6 \cdot 7$$
$$= 6 + 42 = 48 \text{ cm}$$

28. $p = z + z + z + z$
$$= 4z$$
$$= 4 \cdot 1\tfrac{1}{2}$$
$$= 6 \text{ in}$$

29. Ostriches can fly; false

30. Delaware is not the largest state in the U.S.;
true

31. less

32. $3.24, 3($1.08) = $3.24

33. $c + c + 10 = 108$

    1st    2nd
    can    can
    $2c + 10 = 108$
    $2(49) + 10 = 108$, so $c = 4$
    and the more expensive can costs 59 cents.

34. $60 \cdot 60 \cdot 24 = 86,400$ seconds

    sec    min    hrs in
    in a   in     a day
    min    an hr

35. $c = 3 \cdot 111$
$$= 333 \text{ calories}$$

36. ERA $= 9\left(\dfrac{a}{b}\right)$
$$= 9\left(\dfrac{23}{180}\right)$$
$$= \dfrac{23}{20} \text{ or } 1.15$$

37. Width:  $25 + 8 = 3$ bricks $+ 1$ in. mortar
    Height:  $7 + 2 = 3$ bricks $+ 1$ in. mortar
    So, there are $3 \times 3$ or 9 bricks.

# Chapter 1    Test

### PAGE 47

1. $x + 17$    2. $2x^2$    3. $x + x^3$    4. $2x - 23$

5. $(12 - 10)^4 = 2^4$
$$= 16$$

6. $13 + 4 \cdot 5^2 = 13 + 4 \cdot 25$
$$= 13 + 100$$
$$= 113$$

7. $0.7(1.4 + 0.6) = 0.7(2.0)$
$$= 1.4$$

8. $\dfrac{3}{4}(8 + 28) = \dfrac{3}{4}(36)$
$$= 27$$

9. $23 - 12(1.5) = 23 - 18$
$$= 5$$

10. $6 + 3(3.4) = 6 + 10.2$
$$= 16.2$$

11. $(mn)^2 = (8 \cdot 3)^2$
$$= 24^2$$
$$= 576$$

12. $pq^2 = \dfrac{3}{4} \cdot \dfrac{2}{3}^2$
$$= \dfrac{3}{4} \cdot \dfrac{4}{9}$$
$$= \dfrac{1}{3} \text{ or } 0.\overline{3}$$

13. $n + r^2 = 3 + 0.5^2$
$$= 3 + 0.25$$
$$= 3.25$$

14. $v = \dfrac{6^2 - 2^3}{7}$
$$= (6^2 - 2^3) \div 7$$
$$= (36 - 8) \div 7$$
$$= 28 \div 7$$
$$= 4$$

15. $y = 8(0.03) - 0.05$
$$= 0.24 - 0.05$$
$$= 0.19$$

16. $k = \dfrac{3}{4} - \left(\dfrac{1}{2}\right)^2$
$$= \dfrac{3}{4} - \dfrac{1}{4}$$
$$= \dfrac{2}{4} \text{ or } \dfrac{1}{2}$$

13

17. Additive identity property
18. Commutative property of addition
19. Multiplicative identity property
20. Distributive property
21. Symmetric property of equality
22. Commutative property of multiplication

23. $n + 5n = n(1 + 5)$
$\qquad = (1 + 5)n$
$\qquad = 6n$

24. $2.5x - x + y + 3.5y$
$\quad = 1.5x + 4.5y$

25. $3(a + 2) + 5a$
$\quad = 3a + 6 + 5a$
$\quad = 3a + 5a + 6$
$\quad = 8a + 6$

26. $4an + \frac{2}{3}am + 8an + \frac{1}{3}am$

$\quad = 4an + 8an + \frac{2}{3}am + \frac{1}{3}am$

$\quad = 12an + \frac{3}{3}am$

$\quad = 12an + 1am$

$\quad = 12an + am$

27. $\pi r^2 = A$

28. $a + b + c = P$

29. $d = r \cdot t$
$\quad = 60 \cdot 4$
$\quad = 240$ miles

30. 72 plants, Area of garden $A = 6 \times 12 = 72 \text{ ft}^2$

$\qquad\qquad$ Area of plant $A = 1 \text{ ft}^2$

31. $s = \quad 2 \quad \cdot \quad 4 \quad \cdot \quad 3$

$\qquad$ 2 socks $\quad$ # of $\qquad$ # of
$\qquad$ in a $\qquad$ pairs $\quad$ different
$\qquad$ pair $\qquad\qquad\qquad$ colors

$\quad = 24$ socks

**PAGE 47     BONUS**

$$x = \frac{4 + (2 + 6)^2 - \frac{2}{3} + 6 + 2 + 9^2}{\frac{3}{4} - \frac{2}{3} + 7^2 - 4^2 + 3^2}$$

$$= \frac{4 + 8^2 - \frac{2}{3} + 6 + 2 + 9^2}{\frac{3}{4} - \frac{2}{3} + 49 - 16 + 9}$$

$$= \frac{4 + 64 = \frac{2}{3} + 6 + 2 + 81}{\frac{505}{12}}$$

$$= \frac{4 + 64 - \frac{2}{3} + 3 + 81}{\frac{505}{12}}$$

$$= \frac{\frac{454}{3}}{\frac{505}{12}} = \frac{1816}{505} \text{ or } 3.596$$

14

# Chapter 2    Rational Numbers

## 2-1    Integers and the Number Line

PAGES 52-53    CHECKING FOR UNDERSTANDING

1. Answers may vary. Typical answers are sports, business, and weather.

2. The intersection has elements in both sets. The union has elements in either set or both sets.

3. Whole numbers are 0, 1, 2, 3, ... Integers include negative numbers ..., -3, -2, -1, 0, 1, 2, 3, ...

4. Draw an arrow starting at 0 and going to 4. Starting at 4 draw an arrow to the left 3 units long. The second arrow ends at the sum, 1.

5. -7    6. 8    7. -10    8. -2

9. 2    10. 6    11. -4    12. 3

13. {3,6,9,12}    14. {3,4,5,6}

15. {4,6,8,10,12}    16. {3,6}

17. {3,4,5,6,9,12}    18. {4,6}

19. {3,4,5,6,,8,10,12}    20. {3,4,5,6,8,9,10,12}

21. -3 + 5 = 2    22. 4 + (-5) = -1

23. -1 + (-4) = -5    24. -4 + 3 = -1

PAGES 53-54    EXERCISES

25. {-3,-2,-1,0}    26. {1,3,5}

27. {-1,0,1,2,3,4,...}    28. {-3,-2,-1,0,1,2,3}

29.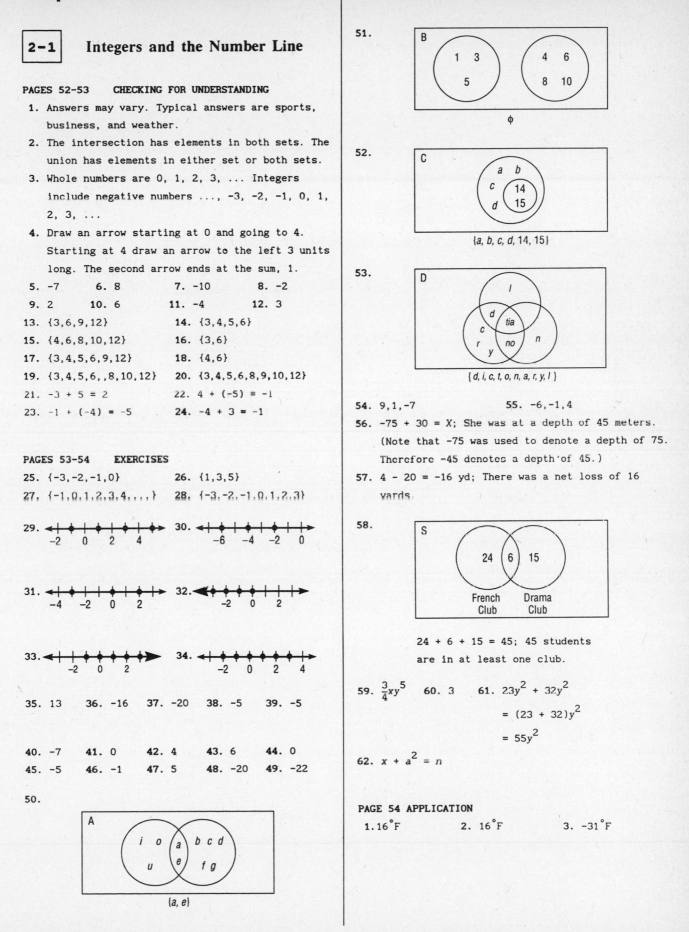
    -2  0  2  4

30.
    -6  -4  -2  0

31.
    -4  -2  0  2

32.
    -2  0  2

33.
    -2  0  2

34.
    -2  0  2  4

35. 13    36. -16    37. -20    38. -5    39. -5

40. -7    41. 0    42. 4    43. 6    44. 0

45. -5    46. -1    47. 5    48. -20    49. -22

50.

```
A
   i o  a  b c d
        e
   u       f g
```
{a, e}

51.
```
B
   1  3      4  6
      5      8  10
```
φ

52.
```
C
        a  b
      c    14
        d  15
```
{a, b, c, d, 14, 15}

53.
```
D
          l
        d   tia
       c
      r    no    n
        y
```
{d, i, c, t, o, n, a, r, y, l}

54. 9, 1, -7    55. -6, -1, 4

56. -75 + 30 = X; She was at a depth of 45 meters. (Note that -75 was used to denote a depth of 75. Therefore -45 denotes a depth of 45.)

57. 4 - 20 = -16 yd; There was a net loss of 16 yards.

58.
```
S
     24  6  15
   French  Drama
   Club    Club
```

24 + 6 + 15 = 45; 45 students are in at least one club.

59. $\frac{3}{4}xy^5$    60. 3    61. $23y^2 + 32y^2$
$$= (23 + 32)y^2$$
$$= 55y^2$$

62. $x + a^2 = n$

PAGE 54 APPLICATION

1. $16°F$    2. $16°F$    3. $-31°F$

15

## 2-2 Adding and Subtracting Integers

PAGES 57-58    CHECKING FOR UNDERSTANDING

1. $-713,000 + 425,000$,
   $713,000 - 425,000$
   $= 288,000$
   So $288,000 under
   budget or $-288,000$

2. $4 - (-1) = 4 + (+1)$
   $= 5$

3. Answer may vary; the absolute value is the number of units your number is from 0 on a number line.

4. Look at the addend with the greater absolute value.

5. $-8,8$   6. $24,24$   7. $0,0$   8. $-$   9. $+$

10. $+$   11. $5$   12. $-7$   13. $-4$   14. $-(13 + 8) = -21$

15. $-(10 - 4) = -6$   16. $-21 + 14 = -(12 - 14) = -7$

PAGES 58-59    EXERCISES

17. $+(18 + 22) = 40$   18. $-(6 + 13) = -19$

19. $+(16 - 3) = 13$   20. $+(27 - 19) = 8$

21. $-(13 - 8) = -5$   22. $+(17 + 23) = 40$

23. $+(14 - 9) = 5$   24. $+(31 - 5) = 26$

25. $-(18 + 11) = -29$   26. $-(21 - 0) = -21$

27. $(19 + 12)m = 31m$

28. $(8 + (-23))h = -(23 - 8)h = -15h$

29. $+(47 - 25) = 22$   30. $-(104 - 16) = -88$

31. $+(97 - 79) = 18$   32. $-(18 + 4)p = -22p$

33. $(24 + 9)b = 33b$   34. $(41 + 41)y = 82y$

35. $-(18 + 21) + 4 = -30 + 4 = -(30 - 4) = -26$

36. $(32 - 11) + 7 = 21 + 7 = 28$

37. $-5 + 13 = +(13 - 5) = 8$

38. $3 - 7 = -(7 - 3) = -4$

39. $15 + -6 = +(15 - 6) = 9$

40. $3 + (-18) = -(18 - 3) = -15$

41. $-6 + 6 = +(6 - 6) = 0$   42. $|-6| = 6$

43. $|7 + (-5)| = |2| = 2$

44. $|(-6) - 4| = |-10| = 10$

45. $|(-5) + 3| = |-2| = 2$

46. $|3| + |-6| = 3 + 6 = 9$

47. $-|-24 + -6| = -|-30| = -30$

48. $-|-5 + (-11)| = -|-16| = -16$

49. $|-(285 + 641)| = |-926| = 926$

50. $931 + 643 = 1574$

51. $-|-423 + 148| = -|-275| = -275$

52. $-|843 + 231| = -|1074| = -1074$

53. $n$   54. $-n$   55. $30 - 6 + 15 = s$; $39

56. $m = 4275 - 6324$; 2049 feet below sea level.

57a. $A1 = -1$        b. $A1 = -20$
     $S1 = -2$           $S1 = 5$
     $A2 = 3$            $A2 = 5$
     $S2 = -3$           $S2 = 5$
     Sums: 2,-3,-8, etc.   Sums: -15,-5,5, etc.

   c. $A1 = -12$
      $S1 = 1$
      $A2 = 7$
      $S2 = -3$
      Sums: -5,-7,-9, etc.

   d. The sums of the steps between the addends is equal to the step between the sums.

58. $0.12 + 1.2 = 1.32$   59. $\frac{42}{7} = 6$

60. $\frac{3}{4}y + x\left(\frac{1}{4} + 3\right) = 3\frac{1}{4}x + \frac{3}{4}y$

61. Associate property of addition

62.

63. $9$

PAGE 59    PUZZLE

| 3 | 4 | -1 |
|---|---|---|
| -2 | 2 | 6 |
| 5 | 0 | 1 |

Add 2

| -2 | -1 | -6 |
|---|---|---|
| -7 | -3 | 1 |
| 0 | -5 | -4 |

Add -3

| -6 | -5 | -10 |
|---|---|---|
| -11 | -7 | -3 |
| -4 | -9 | -8 |

Add -7

## 2-3 Inequalities and the Number Line

PAGE 63    CHECKING FOR UNDERSTANDING

1. is equal to   2. included   3. rational numbers

4. Because you cannot divide by 0.

5. False   6. True   7. False   8. True

9. False   10. False   11. $\{4,5,6,\ldots\}$

12. $\{0,1,2,3,4\}$        13. $\{0,1,2,3,4,5,7,\ldots\}$

14. yes   15. no   16. yes   17. yes

PAGES 63-64    EXERCISES

18. $x > 3$   19. $x \neq -3$   20. $x \geq 0$

21. $x < -3$   22. $x \neq 4$   23. $x \leq 2$

24.

25.

26. 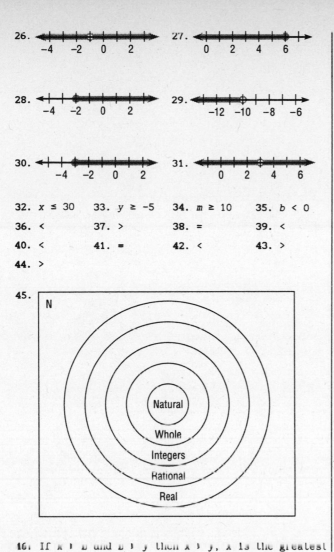 (number line −4 −2 0 2)  27. (number line 0 2 4 6)

28. (number line −4 −2 0 2)  29. (number line −12 −10 −8 −6)

30. (number line −4 −2 0 2)  31. (number line 0 2 4 6)

32. $x \leq 30$   33. $y \geq -5$   34. $m \geq 10$   35. $b < 0$

36. <   37. >   38. =   39. <

40. <   41. =   42. <   43. >

44. >

45.

N

Natural
Whole
Integers
Rational
Real

46. If $x > 0$ and $0 > y$ then $x > y$, $x$ is the greatest

47. none

48. $34 \div 2 = 17$, 16 boys is the greatest number.

49. $19,200 \div 4 = 4,800$ residents

50. $880 \div 4 \div 5 \div 4 = 11$   51. $1883 + 72 = 1955$

52. $5(1.3) + 3 = 9.5$   53. $\dfrac{m^2 n}{2}$, $5m^2 n$

54. 81,243,729   55. $4 + (-6) = -2$

56. 4   57. $-8 - 12 = -(8 + 12) = -20$

---

## 2-4 Comparing and Ordering Rational Numbers

### PAGE 67   CHECKING FOR UNDERSTANDING

1. a decimal that does not repeat and does not end

2. $\dfrac{1}{2}\left(\dfrac{1}{4} + \dfrac{1}{5}\right) = \dfrac{9}{40}$; $\dfrac{1}{2}\left(\dfrac{9}{40} + \dfrac{1}{5}\right) = \dfrac{17}{80}$; $\dfrac{1}{2}\left(\dfrac{17}{80} + \dfrac{1}{5}\right) = \dfrac{33}{160}$

3. $15 < 16$, $\dfrac{4}{5}$ is greater

4. $88 > 84$, $\dfrac{11}{12}$ is greater

5. $99 < 100$, $\dfrac{10}{11}$ is greater

6. $63 < 64$, $\dfrac{8}{9}$ is greater

7. $36 > 35$, $\dfrac{6}{5}$ is greater

8. $110 > 108$, $\dfrac{11}{9}$ is greater

9. $0.79 \div 21 \underline{\quad} 0.97 \div 28$

   $0.038 > 0.035$

   28 ounces for 97¢ is a better buy.

10. $4.27 \div 10 \underline{\quad} 3.64 \div 8$

   $0.427 < 0.455$

   10 ounce jar of coffee for
   $4.27 is a better buy.

### PAGES 67-68   EXERCISES

11. $\dfrac{6}{7} \underline{<} \dfrac{7}{8}$   12. $\dfrac{8}{7} \underline{>} \dfrac{9}{8}$   13. $\dfrac{7}{19} \underline{>} \dfrac{6}{17}$

   $48 < 49$     $64 > 63$     $119 > 114$

14. $\dfrac{8}{15} \underline{<} \dfrac{9}{16}$   15. $\dfrac{5}{14} \underline{=} \dfrac{25}{70}$   16. $\dfrac{0.4}{3} \underline{<} \dfrac{1.2}{8}$

   $128 < 135$     $350 = 350$     $3.2 < 3.6$

17. $\dfrac{17}{21} = 0.81$, $\dfrac{20}{27} = 0.74$, $\dfrac{19}{24} = 0.79$

   Therefore, $\dfrac{20}{27} < \dfrac{19}{24} < \dfrac{17}{21}$.

18. $\dfrac{17}{19} = 0.89$, $\dfrac{32}{35} = 0.91$, $\dfrac{45}{49} = 0.92$

   Therefore, $\dfrac{17}{19} < \dfrac{32}{35} < \dfrac{45}{49}$.

19. $\dfrac{3}{14} = 0.214$, $\dfrac{5}{23} = 0.217$, $\dfrac{9}{43} = 0.209$

   Therefore, $\dfrac{9}{43} < \dfrac{3}{14} < \dfrac{5}{23}$.

Problems 20-25, answers may vary.

20. $\dfrac{1}{2}\left(\dfrac{1}{2} + \dfrac{6}{7}\right) = \dfrac{19}{28}$; $0.679$

21. $\dfrac{1}{2}\left(\dfrac{4}{7} + \dfrac{9}{4}\right) = \dfrac{79}{56}$; $1.411$

22. $\dfrac{1}{2}\left(\dfrac{2}{9} + \dfrac{8}{11}\right) = \dfrac{47}{99}$; $0.475$

23. $\dfrac{1}{2}\left(\dfrac{19}{30} + \dfrac{31}{45}\right) = \dfrac{119}{180} = 0.661$

24. $\dfrac{7}{6} = \dfrac{21}{18}$, none       25. 0

26. $\dfrac{5}{12} - \dfrac{1}{24} = \dfrac{10}{24} - \dfrac{1}{24}$

   $= \dfrac{9}{24}$

   $\dfrac{9}{24} \div 3 = \dfrac{9}{24} \cdot \dfrac{1}{3} = \dfrac{3}{24} = \dfrac{1}{8}$

   $\dfrac{1}{24} + \dfrac{1}{8} = \dfrac{1}{24} + \dfrac{3}{24} = \dfrac{4}{24} = \dfrac{1}{6}$

   $\dfrac{5}{12} - \dfrac{1}{8} = \dfrac{10}{24} - \dfrac{3}{24} = \dfrac{7}{24}$

27. yes

28. $2.93 \div \frac{1}{2}$ ___ $4.19 \div \frac{3}{4}$

    $5.86$ $>$ $5.59$

The $\frac{3}{4}$ - pound bag is a better buy.

29. $2.25 \div 3$ ___ $1.69 \div 2$

    $0.75$ $<$ $0.85$

3 liters for \$2.25 is a better buy.

30. $0.93 \div 27$ ___ $0.79 \div 20$

    $0.03$ $<$ $0.04$

The 27-ounce loaf is a better buy.

31. $1.59 \div 12$ ___ $0.85 \div 6$

    $0.13$ $<$ $0.14$

A dozen oranges for \$1.59 is a better buy.

32. $3.50 \div 5$ ___ $1.38 \div 2$

    $0.70$ $>$ $0.69$

2 pounds for \$1.38 is a better buy.

33. $2.39 \div 48$ ___ $1.09 \div 22$

    $0.0497$ $>$ $0.0495$

The 22-ounce bottle is a better buy.

34. $r + 7$ or $7 + r$      35. Multiplicative identity

36. Commutative property of addition

37. $12$ ___ $15 - 27$    38. $(-7.502)(0.511)$ ___ $-3.115$

    $12$ $>$ $-12$                       $-3.834$ $<$ $-3.115$

## 2-5   Adding and Subtracting Rational Numbers

PAGE 71     CHECKING FOR UNDERSTANDING

1. Group the decimals together. $(1.6x + 0.4x) + [(-4y) + (-3y)]$. Then add. $2x + (-7y)$ or $2x - 7y$

2. Group the fractions with common denominators. $\left(-4\frac{1}{4} + -3\frac{3}{4}\right) + \left(6\frac{1}{3} + 2\frac{2}{3}\right)$. Then add. $-8 + 9$ or $1$

3. 4   4. 12   5. 18   6. 35   7. $\frac{17}{21} + \left(-\frac{13}{21}\right) = \frac{4}{21}$

8. $4.57 + (-3.69) = 0.88$

9. $-72.5 + -81.3 = -153.8$

10. $\frac{1}{6} + -\frac{2}{3} = \frac{1}{6} + -\frac{4}{6}$

    $= -\frac{3}{6} = -\frac{1}{2}$

11. $\left(-\frac{2}{7} + \frac{3}{7}\right) + \frac{3}{14} = \frac{1}{7} + \frac{3}{14}$

    $= \frac{2}{14} + \frac{3}{14} = \frac{5}{14}$

12. $(-3a + -14a) + 12a$

    $= -17a + 12a = -5a$

PAGES 71-73     EXERCISES

13. $\frac{-11}{9} + \left(-\frac{7}{9}\right) = -2$    14. $\frac{5}{11} + -\frac{6}{11} = -\frac{1}{11}$

15. $-\frac{7}{12} + \frac{5}{12} = -\frac{2}{12} = -\frac{1}{6}$    16. $-4.8 + 3.2 = -1.6$

17. $-38.9 + 24.2 = -14.7$      18. $-1.7 + -3.9 = -5.6$

19. $\frac{4}{14} - \frac{3}{14} = \frac{1}{14}$      20. $-\frac{1}{8} + \left(-\frac{20}{8}\right) = -\frac{21}{8}$

21. $\frac{6}{9} + \left(-\frac{2}{9}\right) = \frac{4}{9}$      22. $-0.007 + 0.06 = 0.053$

23. $-0.0005 + (-0.3) = -0.3005$

24. $-\frac{18}{30} + \frac{25}{30} = \frac{7}{30}$      25. $\frac{9}{24} + \left(-\frac{14}{24}\right) = -\frac{5}{24}$

26. $-\frac{28}{60} + \left(-\frac{25}{60}\right) = -\frac{53}{60}$    27. $-4.5 + -8.6 = -13.1$

28. $89.3 + 14.2 = 103.5$

29. $-5\frac{7}{8} - 2\frac{3}{4} = -5\frac{7}{8} + \left(-2\frac{6}{8}\right) = -8\frac{5}{8}$

30. $7\frac{3}{10} - \left(-4\frac{1}{5}\right) = 7\frac{3}{10} + 4\frac{2}{10} = 11\frac{5}{10} = 11\frac{1}{2}$

31. $-15m$   32. $-13c$ $=$ $-13c$   33.   $5.8k$   34. $-0.23x$

  $+\ 6m$      $-\ 28c$ $+\ -28c$     $+\ -3.6k$    $+\ -0.50x$

   $-9m$              $-41c$        $2.2k$      $-0.73x$

35. $1.9 - (-7) = 1.9 + 7 = 8.9$

36. $-18 - (-1.3) = -18 + 1.3 = -16.7$

37. $-1.8 - 3.7 = -1.8 + -3.7 = -5.5$

38. $\frac{11}{2} - \left(-\frac{5}{2}\right) = \frac{11}{2} + \frac{5}{2} = \frac{16}{2} = .8$

39. $\frac{11}{4} - \frac{27}{8} = \frac{22}{8} + -\frac{27}{8} = -\frac{5}{8}$

40. $-\frac{12}{7} - \frac{16}{21} = -\frac{36}{21} + -\frac{16}{21} = -\frac{52}{21}$

41. $5y + [(-12y) + (-21y)]$

    $= 5y + -33y = -28y$

42. $-3z + [(-17z) + (-18z)]$

    $= -3z + -35z = -38z$

43. $\frac{7}{3} + \left[\left(-\frac{5}{6}\right) + \left(-\frac{2}{3}\right)\right]$

    $= \frac{7}{3} + -\frac{9}{6} = \frac{14}{6} + -\frac{9}{6} = \frac{5}{6}$

44. $\left[-\frac{3}{5} + \left(-\frac{2}{35}\right)\right] + \frac{6}{7}$

    $= -\frac{23}{35} + \frac{6}{7} = -\frac{23}{35} + \frac{30}{35} = \frac{7}{35} = \frac{1}{5}$

45. $\left(\frac{3}{4} + \frac{3}{32}\right) + \left(-\frac{5}{8}\right) = \frac{27}{32} + \left(-\frac{5}{8}\right)$

    $= \frac{27}{32} + \left(-\frac{20}{32}\right) = \frac{7}{32}$

46. $6.7 + [(-8.1) + (-7.3)]$

    $= 6.7 + -15.4 = -8.7$

47. $[-4.13 + -5.18] + 9.63$

    $= -9.31 + 9.63 = 0.32$

48. $(-14a + -83a) + 36k + 12k)$

    $= -97a + 48k$

49. $-2.995$    50. $-1.785$    51. $5.18$    52. $4.2125$

53. $3\frac{1}{8} - \frac{3}{4} + \frac{1}{8}$             54. $-3 + 2 + -4 + -1$

    $= \left(3\frac{1}{8} + \frac{1}{8}\right) - \frac{3}{4}$        $= (-3 + -4 + -1) + 2$

    $= 3\frac{2}{8} - \frac{3}{4} = 3\frac{1}{4} - \frac{3}{4}$      $= -8 + 2 = -6$ or

    $= 3 - \frac{2}{4} = 2\frac{1}{2}$               6 under par

55. $+3 - 7 + 15 - 5 + 32 + 6 - 14$

$= (3 + 15 + 32 + 6) + (-7 -5 -14)$

$= 56 + -26 = +30$ yards

56. $-35.76 + -41.32 + 135.59 + -63.17$

$= (-35.76 + -41.32 + -63.17) + 135.59$

$= -140.25 + 135.59 = -\$4.66$

57. $\dfrac{4\left(\frac{1}{2}\right)^2}{4(3)\left(\frac{2}{3}\right)} = \dfrac{4\left(\frac{1}{4}\right)}{4(3)\left(\frac{2}{3}\right)} = \dfrac{1}{8}$

58. $+650$     59. $-25$     60. $f = 36 - 11$

$= 25^{\text{th}}$ floor

61.

62. $0.91 \div 184$ ___ $1.89 \div 340$

$0.005$ _<_ $0.006$

The 184-gram can for 91¢ is a
better buy.

### PAGE 73    MID-CHAPTER REVIEW

1.

2.

3.

4. $-(67 - 43) = -24$     5. $-(23 + 47) = -70$

6. $-(93 - 39) = -54$     7. $-(31 - 13) = -18$

8. $-23 + 12 = -11$     9. $-(47 + 35) = -82$

10. $-\left(\dfrac{8}{13} + \dfrac{11}{13}\right) = -\dfrac{19}{13}$     11. $-\dfrac{3}{8} + \dfrac{5}{24} =$

$\dfrac{9}{24} + \dfrac{5}{24} = -\dfrac{4}{24} = -\dfrac{1}{6}$

12. $-(3.948 + 4.826)$     13. $6$ ___ $4 + 2$

$= -8.774$     $6 = 6$

14. $10$ ___ $\dfrac{27}{3}$     15. $8\left(\dfrac{3}{4}\right)$ ___ $6\left(\dfrac{2}{3}\right)$

$10 > 9$     $6$ _>_ $4$

16. $\dfrac{2}{3}$ ___ $\dfrac{3}{5}$     17. $-\dfrac{7}{6}$ ___ $-\dfrac{21}{18}$

$\dfrac{10}{15}$ _>_ $\dfrac{9}{15}$     $-\dfrac{21}{18}$ _=_ $-\dfrac{21}{18}$

18. $\dfrac{1.1}{4}$ ___ $\dfrac{2.2}{5}$

$\dfrac{5.5}{20}$ _<_ $\dfrac{8.8}{20}$

19. $+5\dfrac{3}{8} + -6\dfrac{1}{4} + 11\dfrac{1}{8} + 3\dfrac{5}{8} + -7\dfrac{1}{2}$

$= \left(+5\dfrac{3}{8} + 11\dfrac{1}{8} + 3\dfrac{5}{8}\right) + -6\dfrac{1}{4} + -7\dfrac{1}{2}$

$= 19\dfrac{9}{8} + -6\dfrac{2}{8} + -7\dfrac{4}{8} = 6\dfrac{3}{8}$

20. Brand $x$: $3.92 \div 8 = 0.49$,

Brand $y$: $3.08 \div 6 = 0.51$,

Brand $z$: $1.09 \div 2 = 0.55$

Therefore Brand $x$ is the least expensive per
liter.

## 2-6    Multiplying Rational Numbers

1. Either $a$ and $b$ are both positive or they are
both negative.

2. Either $a$ or $b$ is negative, but not both.

3. Either $a$ or $b$ is zero or both are zero.

4. $-6$     5. $+16$     6. $+\dfrac{49}{9}$     7. $+24$     8. $-4$

9. $60$     10. $-66$     11. $30$     12. $-\dfrac{12}{35}$     13. $\dfrac{7}{24}$

14. $2$     15. $0.00879$     16. $72$     17. $-\dfrac{6}{5}$

18. $\dfrac{3}{8}$     19. $114.1482$     20. $0$     21. $-24$

22. $3$     23. $-6$     24. $a_n = a + (n - 1)d$

$a_{19} = 11 + (19 - 1)(-2)$

$= 11 + (18)(-2) = -25$

25. $a_n = a + (n - 1)d$

$a_{16} = 1.5 + (16 - 1)(0.5)$

$= 1.5 + (15)0.5 = 9$

26. $a_n = a + (n - 1)d$

$a_{43} = -19 + (43 - 1)(4)$

$= -19 + (42)4$

$= 149$

27. $a_n = a + (n - 1)d$

$a_{58} = 10 + (58 - 1)(-6)$

$= 10 + 57(-6) = -332$

28. $-30xy + -16xy = -46xy$     29. $-16 + 6 = -10$

30. $-10 - (-24) = 14$     31. $8xy - -90xy = 98xy$

32. $28 - 33 = -5$     33. $-5.776 - 62.64 = -68.416$

34. $\dfrac{1}{4} - 1 = -\dfrac{3}{4}$     35. $\dfrac{30}{42} - \left(-\dfrac{30}{42}\right) = \dfrac{60}{42} = \dfrac{10}{7}$

36. $5(3t - 2t) + 2(4t - 3t)$

$= 5t + 2t$

$= 7t$

37. $4[3x + (-2x)] - 5(3x + 2x)$

$= 4x - 25x$

$= -21x$

38. $\frac{5}{6}(-24a + 36b) + \left(-\frac{1}{3}\right)(60a - 42b)$

   $= -20a + 30b + -20a + 14b$

   $= -20a + -20a + 30b + 14b = -40a + 44b$

39. $1.2(4x - 5y) - 0.2(-1.5x + 8y)$

   $= 4.8x - 6y + 0.3x + -1.6y$

   $= 4.8x + 0.3x - 6y - 1.6y = 5.1x - 7.6y$

40. $9(2ab - 3c) - (4ab - 6c) = 18ab - 27c - 4ab + 6c$

   $= 18ab - 4ab - 27c + 6c = 14ab - 21c$

41. $a > 0$ or $a < 0$     42. $a > 0$

43. $a < 0$               44. It is positive.

45. It is negative.     46. $82 - 8\left(\frac{3}{4}\right) = 76$

47. $2(20) - 32.87 = \$7.13$     48. $-40$

49. $x^2 + 5x^2 + 3x + 2x = 6x^2 + 5x$     50. $3, 6, 9,$

51. $-197 + |-483| = -197 + 483 = 286$

52. $\{-4, -3, -2, \ldots\}$

53.    $\frac{1}{3} \underline{\quad} \frac{1}{4}$

   $4 \cdot 1 \geq 3 \cdot 1$    Therefore $\frac{1}{3}$ is greater.

54. $41y + 41y = 82y$

# Technology:   Adding Fractions

1. $\frac{10}{9}$     2. $\frac{17}{22}$     3. $\frac{11}{12}$     4. $\frac{107}{80}$     5. $\frac{29}{36}$

6. Make the following changes in the program
   written on page 79:
       50 LET N = A*D - B*C
       170 PRINT "THE DIFFERENCE IS";N;"/";X

## 2-7   Dividing Rational Numbers

1. Multiplication undoes division, and division
   undoes multiplication.

2. 5

3. To divide rational numbers, multiply the
   dividend by the multiplicative inverse or
   reciprocal of the divisor.

4. a. opposite    b. reciprocal    c. average

5. $\frac{1}{3}$     6. $-\frac{1}{5}$     7. none     8. $-1$     9. $\frac{3}{2}$

10. $-15$     11. $\frac{4}{13}$     12. $-\frac{7}{17}$     13. $-\frac{11}{71}$     14. $\frac{-30}{-5} = 6$

15. $\frac{-48}{8} = -6$     16. $\frac{-200x}{50} = -4x$     17. $\frac{45b}{9} = 5b$

18. $\frac{-\frac{5}{6}}{8} = -\frac{5}{6} \div 8$     19. $\frac{3a + 9}{3} = (3a + 9) \div 3$

   $= -\frac{5}{6}\left(\frac{1}{8}\right)$          $= (3a + 9)\left(\frac{1}{3}\right)$

   $= -\frac{5}{48}$               $= (3a)\frac{1}{3} + 9\left(\frac{1}{3}\right)$

                                  $= a + 3$

20. $\frac{30}{-6} = -5$     21. $\frac{-55}{11} = -5$     22. $\frac{-96}{-16} = 6$

23. $\frac{-450n}{10} = -45n$          24. $\frac{-36a}{-6} = 6a$

25. $\frac{63a}{-9} = -7a$          26. $-49 \div -7 = -49\left(-\frac{1}{7}\right) = 7$

27. $-16 \div 8 = -16\left(\frac{1}{8}\right) = -2$

28. $65 \div (-13) = 65\left(-\frac{1}{13}\right) = -5$

29. $-\frac{3}{4} \div 9 = -\frac{3}{4}\left(\frac{1}{9}\right) = -\frac{1}{12}$

30. $\frac{-1}{3} \div (-4) = \frac{-1}{3}\left(-\frac{1}{4}\right) = \frac{1}{12}$

31. $-9 \div \left(-\frac{10}{17}\right) = -9\left(-\frac{17}{10}\right) = \frac{153}{10}$

32. $\frac{\frac{7}{8}}{-10} = \frac{7}{8}\left(-\frac{1}{10}\right) = -\frac{7}{80}$

33. $\frac{7}{-\frac{2}{5}} = 7\left(-\frac{5}{2}\right) = -\frac{35}{2}$

34. $\frac{-5}{\frac{2}{7}} = -5\left(\frac{7}{2}\right) = -\frac{35}{2}$

35. $\frac{6a + 24}{6} = (6a + 24) \div 6$

   $= (6a + 24)\left(\frac{1}{6}\right)$

   $= 6a\left(\frac{1}{6}\right) + 24\left(\frac{1}{6}\right)$

   $= a + 4$

36. $\frac{20a + 30b}{-2} = (20a + 30b) \div -2$

   $= (20a + 30b)\left(-\frac{1}{2}\right)$

   $= 20a\left(-\frac{1}{2}\right) + 30b\left(-\frac{1}{2}\right)$

   $= -10a - 15b$

37. $\frac{-5x + (-10y)}{-5} = (-5x + (-10y)) \div -5$

   $= (-5x + (-10y))\left(-\frac{1}{5}\right)$

   $= -5x\left(-\frac{1}{5}\right) + (-10y)\left(-\frac{1}{5}\right)$

   $= x + 2y$

38. $\dfrac{70x - 30y}{-5} = (70x - 30y) \div -5$

$\qquad = (70x - 30y)\left(-\dfrac{1}{5}\right)$

$\qquad = 70x\left(-\dfrac{1}{5}\right) - 30y\left(-\dfrac{1}{5}\right)$

$\qquad = -14x + 6y$

39. $\dfrac{4 + 6 + 9 + 12 + 5}{5} = 36 \div 5$

$\qquad = 7\dfrac{1}{5}$ or 7.2

40. $\dfrac{10 + 3 + 8 + 15}{4} = 36 \div 4$

$\qquad = 9$

41. $\dfrac{10 + 4 + (-21) + 6 + (-3) + 8 + 5 + 5 + 2 + (-2)}{10}$

$\qquad = 14 \div 10 = 1\dfrac{2}{5}$ or 1.4

42. $\dfrac{2.5+6+18.5+29.5+32.5+28+24.5+20+16.5+5+(-2)+(-1)}{12}$

$\qquad = 180 \div 12 = 15°$

43. $-\dfrac{6}{5}$ ___ $-\dfrac{7}{6}$  44. $-\dfrac{9}{7}$ ___ $-\dfrac{7}{5}$  45. $-\dfrac{3}{4}$ ___ $-\dfrac{2}{3}$

$-36 < -35$ $\qquad$ $-45 > -49$ $\qquad$ $-9 < -8$

46. $-\dfrac{13}{11}$ ___ $-\dfrac{15}{13}$  47. $-\dfrac{1}{3}$ ___ $-\dfrac{2}{7}$  48. $-\dfrac{7}{6}$ ___ $-\dfrac{21}{18}$

$-169 < -165$ $\qquad$ $-7 < -6$ $\qquad$ $126 = 126$

49. ERROR; The reciprocal of 0 is $\dfrac{1}{0}$. Dividing by 0 is not defined.

50. The original number shows on the display. If $n$ is even, the original number is displayed. If $n$ is odd, the reciprocal of the number is displayed.

51. 1; A number times its reciprocal equals 1.

52. $\dfrac{15}{4}\left(\dfrac{2}{3}\right) = 2\dfrac{1}{2}$ yd

53. $(17 \cdot 60 \cdot 60) \div 39.66 \approx 1543$ airplanes

54. $1986 \cdot 3(76.3) = 2214$

55. $\left[(2132 \cdot 12) + 2\dfrac{1}{2}\right] \div \dfrac{1}{2}$

$\qquad = (25586.5)\left(\dfrac{2}{1}\right)$

$\qquad = 51,173$ slices

56. $b = x - m^3$ $\qquad$ 57. $|-8 + 3| = |-5| = 5$

58. $0.6 \le 1 - 0.4$ $\qquad$ 59. $1.98 \div 16$ ___ $1.80 \div 12$

$\quad 0.6 \le 0.6$; true $\qquad$ $0.12 < 0.14$

$\qquad\qquad\qquad\qquad$ The 1-pound package for

$\qquad\qquad\qquad\qquad$ \$1.98 is a better buy.

60. $9m + 43m + (-16m) = 36m$ $\quad$ 61. $4\left(-\dfrac{7}{8}\right) = -\dfrac{7}{2}$

---

## 2-8 Problem-Solving Strategy: Write an Equation

**PAGE 86 CHECK FOR UNDERSTANDING**

1. explore, plan, solve, and examine

2. The first time you read for overall sense; the second time you read for detail.

3. $2j = 16$  4. $947 + 117$  5. $49 - n$  6. $w + 4$

7. $n - 8$  8. $3000 \div 42$ or $\dfrac{3000}{42}$  9. \$5.65$n$

10. $2b + 8$

**PAGES 86-87 EXERCISES**

11. Let $k$ = Kimiko's age now; $k - 27 = 21$

12. Let $p$ = number of pounds lost each week;
$145 - 6p = 125$

13. Let $x$ = number of years for a tree to become $33\dfrac{1}{2}$ feet tall; $17 + 1\dfrac{1}{2}x = 33\dfrac{1}{2}$

14. Let $c$ = Cecile's age now; $3(c - 4) = 42$

15. Let $t$ = number of tapes; $t + \left(\dfrac{1}{2}t + 4\right) = 31$

16. Let $a$ = Sonia's age now;
$(a + 4) + (a - 3 + 4) = 59$

17. Let $q$ = number of quarters,
$q + (q + 4) + (q + 4 - 7) = 28$

18. Let $x$ = daughter's age now;
$(53 - x) + 8 = 2(x + 8)$

19. Twice Quincy's age 7 years ago was 50. How old is Quincy now?

20. Elena is 4 years older than Willie. In 10 years, the sum of their ages will be 54. How old is Willie now?

21. Ramon's car weighs 250 pounds more than Seth's car. The sum of the weights of both cars is 7140 pounds. How much does each car weigh?

22. Jason is 7 inches taller than Manuel. The sum of Jason's height and twice Manuel's height is 193 inches. How tall is Manuel?

23. Reggie is 31 cm shorter than Soto. The sum of Soto's height and twice Reggie's height is 502 cm. How tall is Soto?

**PAGE 87 COOPERATIVE GROUP ACTIVITY**

| | | |
|---|---|---|
| 3 boxes of chocolate: | $3(2.69) =$ | \$ 8.07 |
| 2 cartons of milk: | $2(0.69) =$ | \$ 1.38 |
| 1 pound of butter: | $1(1.09) =$ | \$ 1.09 |
| 12 boxes of sugar: | $12(0.75) =$ | \$ 9.00 |
| | total cost | \$19.54 |

1. Yes $\qquad$ 2. \$19.54 $\qquad$ 3. $4 \cdot 4.5 = 18$ lb

# Chapter 2    Summary and Review

1.

2.

3. $17 + -9 = 8$

4. $-9 + .-12 = -21$

5. $-12 + 8 = -4$

6. $-17 + -31 = -48$

7. $14 - 36 = -22$

8. $8 - -5 = 8 + 5 = 13$

9. $-7 - -11 = -7 + 11 = 4$

10. $-13x - -7x = -13x + 7x = -6x$

11. $|4 - -2| = |4 + 2| = 6$

12. $|-5| - 2.6 = 5 - 2.6 = 2.4$

13. $-|-3 + (-12)| = -|-15| = -15$

14.    15.

16. $-9 \underline{>} -11$

17. $-13 \underline{<} 13$

18. $-7 \underline{<} \dfrac{-3.6}{0.6}$

   because $-7 < -6$

19. $\dfrac{3}{8} \underline{>} \dfrac{4}{11}$

   because $33 > 32$

20. $-\dfrac{10}{11} \underline{<} \dfrac{11}{12}$

   because $-120 < 121$

21. $-\dfrac{9}{11} \underline{>} -\dfrac{7}{8}$

   because $-72 > -77$

For problems 22-24 answers may vary; sample answers are given.

22. $\dfrac{1}{2}\left(\dfrac{2}{9} + \dfrac{5}{8}\right)$

   $= \dfrac{1}{2}\left(\dfrac{16 + 45}{72}\right)$

   $= \dfrac{1}{2}\left(\dfrac{61}{72}\right)$

   $= \dfrac{61}{144}$

23. $\dfrac{1}{2}\left(\dfrac{3}{5} + \dfrac{7}{12}\right)$

   $= \dfrac{1}{2}\left(\dfrac{36}{60} + \dfrac{35}{60}\right)$

   $= \dfrac{1}{2}\left(\dfrac{71}{60}\right)$

   $= \dfrac{71}{120}$

24. 0; zero is a number between a positive number and a negative number.

25. $\dfrac{6}{7} + \left(-\dfrac{13}{7}\right) = -\dfrac{7}{7} = -1$

26. $-\dfrac{4}{3} + \dfrac{5}{6} + \left(-\dfrac{7}{3}\right) = -\dfrac{8}{6} + \dfrac{5}{6} + \left(-\dfrac{14}{6}\right) = -\dfrac{17}{6}$

27. $3.72 - (-8.65) = 3.72 + 8.65 = 12.37$

28. $-4.5y - 8.1y = -12.6y$

29. $(-11)(9) = -99$    30. $(-8)(-12) = 96$

31. $\dfrac{3}{5}\left(-\dfrac{5}{7}\right) = -\dfrac{15}{35} = -\dfrac{3}{7}$

32. $-3(7) + (-8)(-9) = -21 + 72 = 51$

33. $\dfrac{1}{2}(6a + 8b) - \dfrac{2}{3}(12a + 24b)$

   $= \dfrac{1}{2}(6a) + \dfrac{1}{2}(8b) - \dfrac{2}{3}(12a) - \dfrac{2}{3}(24b)$

   $= 3a + 4b - 8a - 16b$

   $= 3a - 8a + 4b - 16b$

   $= -5a - 12b$

34. $\dfrac{-54}{6} = -9$

35. $\dfrac{63b}{-7} = -9b$

36. $\dfrac{\frac{4}{5}}{-7} = \dfrac{4}{5}\left(-\dfrac{1}{7}\right) = -\dfrac{4}{35}$

37. $\dfrac{33a + 66}{11} = (33a + 66)\left(-\dfrac{1}{11}\right) = -3a - 6$

38.

   $\{a, e, i, o, u, q, r, s, t, v, w, x, y, z\}$

39.

   $\{1, 3, 5\}$

40. $432 - 189 = 243$ meters

41. $75 - 37 = \$38$

42. $3, 4.5, 6, 7.5, 9, 10.5, 12, 13.5$

43. $a_n = a + (n - 1)d$

   $a_{20} = 7 + (20 - 1)(-4)$

   $= 7 + (19)(-4)$

   $= 7 + -76$

   $= -69$

44. $a_n = a + (n - 1)d$

   $a_{24} = -6 + (24 - 1)(5)$

   $= -6 + (23)(5)$

   $= -6 + 115$

   $= 109$

45. $0.89 \div 0.75 \underline{\phantom{<}} 1.31 \div 1.25$

   $1.19 \underline{>} 1.05$

   1.25 liters of soda for $1.31 is a better buy.

46. $\dfrac{4 + 7.2 + 4 + 9 + 21 + 15 + 6 + 6.3 + 29 + 0}{10}$

   $= \dfrac{101.5}{10}$

   $= 10.15$

47. a. $\dfrac{10}{24} = \dfrac{5}{12}$ gold; $\dfrac{12}{12} - \dfrac{5}{12} = \dfrac{7}{12}$ not gold

   b. $\dfrac{a}{24} = \dfrac{2}{3}$, $a = 16$ karats

48. Let $w$ = Minal's weight; $w + (w + 8) = 182$

49. Let $n$ = the number; $3n - 21 = 57$

# Chapter 2    Test

1.    2.

3. $-11 + -13 = -24$    4. $12 - 19 = -7$

5. $1.654 + -2.367 = -0.713$

6. $-41 - (-52) = -41 + 52 = 11$

7. $6.32 - (-7.41) = 6.32 + 7.41 = 13.73$

8. $12x + -21x = -9x$     9. $\frac{3}{7} + -\frac{9}{7} = -\frac{6}{7}$

10. $-\frac{7}{16} - \frac{3}{8} = -\frac{7}{16} - \frac{6}{16} = -\frac{13}{16}$

11. $18b + 13xy - 46b$

$= 13xy + 18b - 46b$

$= 13xy - 28b$

12. $[4 + (-13)] - 12 = -9 - 12 = -21$

13. $\frac{5}{8} + -\frac{3}{16} + -\frac{3}{4} = \frac{10}{16} + -\frac{3}{16} + -\frac{12}{16} = -\frac{5}{16}$

14. $-(-2) - 38 = 2 - 38 = -36$

15. $\left|-\frac{1}{2} + \frac{1}{4}\right| = \left|-\frac{1}{4}\right| = \frac{1}{4}$

16. $-|6| + |-2| = -6 + 2 = -4$

17. $0 - -3.8 = 0 + 3.8 = 3.8$

18. $2 \underline{\;>\;} -7$   19. $-4 \underline{\;\leq\;} -3$   20. $\frac{5.4}{8} \underline{\;>\;} -4 + 1$

because $0.675 > -3$

21. $(4.1)(0.2) \underline{\;\leq\;} 8.2$   22. $\frac{7}{6} \underline{\;>\;} \frac{13}{12}$

because $0.82 < 8.2$     because $84 > 78$

23. $-\frac{12}{17} \underline{\;<\;} -\frac{9}{14}$   24. $\frac{1}{2}\left(\frac{5}{11} + \frac{13}{7}\right)$

because $-168 < -153$   $= \frac{1}{2}\left(\frac{35}{77} + \frac{144}{77}\right)$

$= \frac{1}{2}\left(\frac{178}{77}\right) = \frac{89}{77}$

25. $\frac{1}{2}\left(-\frac{2}{3} + -\frac{9}{14}\right)$   26. $0$   27. $\frac{8(-3)}{2} = -12$

$= \frac{1}{2}\left(-\frac{28}{42} + -\frac{27}{42}\right)$

$= \frac{1}{2}\left(-\frac{55}{42}\right) = -\frac{55}{84}$

28. $(-5)(-2)(-2) - (-6)(-3) = -20 - 18 = -38$

29. $\frac{2}{3}\left(\frac{1}{2}\right) - \left(-\frac{3}{2}\right)\left(-\frac{2}{3}\right)$

$= \frac{1}{3} - 1 = -\frac{2}{3}$

30. $\frac{70a - 42b}{-14} = (70a - 42b)\left(-\frac{1}{14}\right)$

$= \left(-\frac{1}{14}\right)70a - \left(-\frac{1}{14}\right)42b$

$= -5a + 3b$

31. $\frac{3}{4}(8x + 12y) - \frac{5}{7}(21x - 35y)$

$= 6x + 9y - 15x + 25y$

$= 6x - 15x + 9y + 25y$

$= -9x + 34y$

32. $\frac{\frac{11}{5}}{-6} = \frac{11}{5}\left(-\frac{1}{6}\right) = -\frac{11}{30}$

33. Let $w$ = number of weeks on sale;

$380.25 - 18.25w = 252.50$


PAGE 91     BONUS

$4|(-5 + 2)|^2 + (-72)$

$= 4|-3|^2 + (-72) = 4(9) - 72 = 36 - 72 = -36$

23

# Chapter 3 Equations

## 3-1 Solving Equations by Using Addition

PAGE 97   CHECKING FOR UNDERSTANDING

1. They will still be selling CDs for the same price.

2. Answers will vary; $x + 2 = 3$, $x + 2 + 4 = 3 + 4$, and $x + 2 - 17 = 3 - 17$

3. The $\boxed{+/-}$ key is the change sign key. It changes the sign of the number on display.

4. $-21$   5. $-13$   6. $5$   7. $9$   8. $10$   9. $13$

10.
$$m + 10 = 7$$
$$m + 10 - 10 = 7 - 10$$
$$m = -3$$

11.
$$a - 15 = -32$$
$$a - 15 + 15 = -32 + 15$$
$$a = -17$$

12.
$$5 + a = -14$$
$$5 + (-5) + a = -14 + (-5)$$
$$a = -19$$

13.
$$y + (-7) = -19$$
$$y + (-7) + 7 = -19 + 7$$
$$y = -12$$

14.
$$9 = x + 13$$
$$9 + (-13) = x + 13 + (-13)$$
$$-4 = x$$

15.
$$b + (-14) = 6$$
$$b + (-14) + 14 = 6 + 14$$
$$b = 20$$

PAGES 97-98   EXERCISES

16.
$$k + 11 = -21$$
$$k + 11 + (-11) = -21 + (-11)$$
$$k = -32$$

17.
$$0 = t + (-1.4)$$
$$0 + 1.4 = t + (-1.4) + 1.4$$
$$1.4 = t$$

18.
$$-11 = a + 8$$
$$-11 + (-8) = a + 8 + (-8)$$
$$-19 = a$$

19.
$$-12 + z = -36$$
$$-12 + 12 + z = -36 + 12$$
$$z = -24$$

20.
$$14 + c = -5$$
$$14 + (-14) + c = -5 + (-14)$$
$$c = -19$$

21.
$$x - 13 = 45$$
$$x - 13 + 13 = 45 + 13$$
$$x = 58$$

22.
$$p + 12 = -4$$
$$p + 12 + (-12) = -4 + (-12)$$
$$p = -16$$

23.
$$r + (-8) = 7$$
$$r + (-8) + 8 = 7 + 8$$
$$r = 15$$

24.
$$-12 + b = 12$$
$$-12 + 12 + b = 12 + 12$$
$$b = 24$$

25.
$$r + (-11) = -21$$
$$r + (-11) + 11 = -21 + 11$$
$$r = -10$$

26.
$$h + (-13) = -5$$
$$h + (-13) + 13 = -5 + 13$$
$$h = 8$$

27.
$$-11 = k + (-5)$$
$$-11 + 5 = k + (-5) + 5$$
$$-6 = k$$

28.
$$-7 = -16 - k$$
$$16 - 7 = 16 - 16 - k$$
$$9 = -k$$
$$-9 = k$$

29.
$$-27 = -6 - p$$
$$6 - 27 = 6 - 6 - p$$
$$-21 = -p$$
$$21 = p$$

30.
$$-14 - a = -21$$
$$-14 + 14 - a = -21 + 14$$
$$-a = -7$$
$$a = 7$$

31.
$$-23 = -19 + n$$
$$-23 + 19 = -19 + 19 + n$$
$$-4 = n$$

32.
$$-4.1 = m + (-0.5)$$
$$0.5 - 4.1 = m + (-0.5) + 0.5$$
$$-3.6 = m$$

33.
$$r - 6.5 = -9.3$$
$$r - 6.5 + 6.5 = -9.3 + 6.5$$
$$r = -2.8$$

34.
$$x + 4.2 = 1.5$$
$$x + 4.2 + (-4.2) = 1.5 + (-4.2)$$
$$x = -2.7$$

35.
$$-1.43 + w = 0.89$$
$$-1.43 + 1.43 + w = 0.89 + 1.43$$
$$w = 2.32$$

36. Let $x$ = the number.
$$x + 5 = 34$$
$$x + 5 + (-5) = 34 + (-5)$$
$$x = 29$$
The number is 29.

37. Let $x$ = the number.
$$x - 14 = -46$$
$$x - 14 + 14 = -46 + 14$$
$$x = -32$$
The number is -32.

38. Let $x$ = the number.
$$x - 13 = -5$$
$$x - 13 + 13 = -5 + 13$$
$$x = 8$$
The number is 8.

39. Let $x$ = the number.
$$x + (-45) = 77$$
$$x + (-45) + 45 = 77 + 45$$
$$x = 122$$
The number is 122.

40. Let $x$ = the number.
$$23 - x = 42$$
$$23 - 23 - x = 42 - 23$$
$$-x = 19$$
$$x = -19$$
The number is -19.

41. Let $x$ = the number.
$$9 + x = -23$$
$$9 + (-9) + x = -23 + (-9)$$
$$x = -32$$
The number is -32.

42. Let $x$ = the number.
$$x + x = x$$
$$x + (-x) + x = x + (-x)$$
$$x = 0$$
The number is 0.

43. Let $d$ = depth of the
cavern ceiling in meters.
$$d = -112 + 27$$
$$d = -85$$
The cavern ceiling was 85
meters below the cave entrance.

44. Let $g$ = area in square feet set
aside for gardens.
$$1520.2 = 132.7 + 253.6 + g$$
$$1133.9 = g$$
The area set aside for gardens
is 1133.9 square feet.

45. Let $s$ = sales one
year ago.
$$s - 36 = 27$$
$$s = 63$$
Jeff's sales a year
ago were 63.

46. Let $c$ = temperature
change.
$$12 - c = -7$$
$$c = -19$$
The temperature was 19°
lower.

47. $\dfrac{6ab^2}{x^3 + y^2} = 6ab^2 \div (x^3 + y^2)$

$$= 6(6)4^2 \div (0.2^3 + 1.3^2)$$
$$= 576 \div 1.698$$
$$= 339.2$$

48. $-21 + 52 = 31$

49. $-67.1 - (-38.2) = -67.1 + 38.2$
$$= -28.9$$

50. $\dfrac{7a + 35}{-7} = (7a + 35)\left(-\dfrac{1}{7}\right)$

$$= 7a\left(-\dfrac{1}{7}\right) + 35\left(-\dfrac{1}{7}\right)$$
$$= -a - 5$$

51. Let $d$ = the number of dimes Juan has.
$$15 + (8 + d) + d = 51$$
$$23 + 2d = 51$$
$$2d = 28$$
$$d = 14$$

$\boxed{3-2}$ **Solving Equations by Using Subtraction**

PAGE 101     CHECKING FOR UNDERSTANDING

1. Because subtraction is the inverse of addition.

2. $\qquad 190 + x = 225$
$$190 - 190 + x = 225 - 190$$
$$x = 35$$
Nolan needs to press 35 more pounds.

3. 16     **4.** 9     **5.** 5     **6.** 9     **7.** -3

8. -4     **9.** $m - 8$     **10.** $y + 11$     **11.** $z - 31$

12. $p + 47$     **13.** $\qquad y + 16 = 7$
$$y + 16 - 16 = 7 - 16$$
$$y = -9$$

14. $\qquad b + 15 = -32$
$$b + 15 - 15 = -32 - 15$$
$$b = -47$$

15. $\qquad x + (-8) = -31$
$$x - 8 + 8 = -31 + 8$$
$$x = -23$$

PAGES 101-102     EXERCISES

16. $\qquad d - (-27) = 13$
$$d + 27 = 13$$
$$d + 27 - 27 = 13 - 27$$
$$d = -14$$

17. $\qquad 18 + m = -57$
$$18 - 18 + m = -57 - 18$$
$$m = -75$$

18. $\qquad y + 3 = -15$
$$y + 3 - 3 = -15 - 3$$
$$y = -18$$

19. $\qquad y + 2.3 = 1.5$
$$y + 2.3 - 2.3 = 1.5 - 2.3$$
$$y = -0.8$$

20. $\qquad 2.4 = m + 3.7$
$$2.4 - 3.7 = m + 3.7 - 3.7$$
$$-1.3 = m$$

21. $\qquad h - 26 = -29$
$$h - 26 + 26 = -29 + 26$$
$$h = -3$$

22. $\qquad -15 + d = 13$
$$-15 + 15 + d = 13 + 15$$
$$d = 28$$

23. 

$$16 - y = 37$$
$$16 - 16 - y = 37 - 16$$
$$-y = 21$$
$$y = -21$$

24. 

$$41 = 32 - r$$
$$41 - 32 = 32 - 32 - r$$
$$9 = -r$$
$$-9 = r$$

25. 

$$k + (-13) = 21$$
$$k - 13 = 21$$
$$k - 13 + 13 = 21 + 13$$
$$k = 34$$

26. 

$$z + (-17) = 0$$
$$z - 17 = 0$$
$$z - 17 + 17 = 0 + 17$$
$$z = 17$$

27. 

$$m - (-13) = 37$$
$$m + 13 = 37$$
$$m + 13 - 13 = 37 - 13$$
$$m = 24$$

28. 

$$-27 - b = -7$$
$$-27 + 27 - b = -7 + 27$$
$$-b = 20$$
$$b = -20$$

29. 

$$t - (-16) = 9$$
$$t + 16 = 9$$
$$t + 16 - 16 = 9 - 16$$
$$t = -7$$

30. 

$$y + (-13) = -27$$
$$y - 13 = -27$$
$$y - 13 + 13 = -27 + 13$$
$$y = -14$$

31. 

$$-\frac{5}{8} + w = \frac{5}{8}$$
$$\frac{5}{8} - \frac{5}{8} + w = \frac{5}{8} + \frac{5}{8}$$
$$w = \frac{10}{8}; \frac{5}{4}; 1.25$$

32. 

$$x - \left(-\frac{5}{6}\right) = \frac{2}{3}$$
$$x + \frac{5}{6} = \frac{2}{3}$$
$$x + \frac{5}{6} - \frac{5}{6} = \frac{2}{3} - \frac{5}{6}$$
$$x = -\frac{1}{6}; -0.1\overline{6}$$

33. Let $i$ = the integer.

$$9 + i = -23$$
$$-9 + 9 + i = -9 - 23$$
$$i = -32$$

The solution is -32.

34. Let $x$ = the number.

$$82 + x = -34$$
$$-82 + 82 + x = -82 - 34$$
$$x = -116$$

The solution is -116.

35. Let $x$ = the number.

$$x + (-56) = -82$$
$$x + (-56) + 56 = -82 + 56$$
$$x = -26$$

The solution is -26.

36. Let $x$ = the number.

$$x - 45 = -78$$
$$x - 45 + 45 = -78 + 45$$
$$x = -33$$

The solution is -33.

37. Let $x$ = the number.

$$x - (-67) = -34$$
$$x + 67 = -34$$
$$x + 67 - 67 = -34 - 67$$
$$x = -101$$

The solution is -101.

38. Let $x$ = the number.

$$x - (-23) = 35$$
$$x + 23 = 35$$
$$x + 23 - 23 = 35 - 23$$
$$x = 12$$

The solution is 12.

39. Yes; $n^2 = 9$, $|n| = 15$, or $-7x = 0$.

40. Let $r$ = the number of runs.

$$41 - 17 = r$$
$$24 = r$$

They outscored them by 24 runs.

41. Let $t$ = Lisa's best time.

$$t + 13.7 = 139.8$$
$$t = 126.1$$

Lisa's best time was 126.1 seconds.

42. Let $n$ = new listing.

$$n = 37\frac{3}{4} - 2\frac{1}{8}$$
$$n = 35\frac{5}{8}$$

The new listing was $35\frac{5}{8}$ or 35.625 points.

43. Let $x$ = the number of cattle before the drought.

$$x - 47 = 396$$
$$x = 443$$

There were 443 cattle before the drought.

44. False

45.

46. Answer may vary; a typical answer is 0.

47. 

$$3(-4) + 2(-7) = -12 + -14$$
$$= -26$$

48. 

$$x + (-7) = 36$$
$$x + (-7) + 7 = 36 + 7$$
$$x = 43$$

49. 

$$r - 21 = -37$$
$$r - 21 + 21 = -37 + 21$$
$$r = -16$$

---

## 3-3 Solving Equations by Using Multiplication and Division

PAGES 105-106    CHECK FOR UNDERSTANDING

1. $p = \frac{r}{s}$    2. Yes, whenever it is more convenient.

3. Answer may vary; if each side of an equation is multiplied by the same nonzero number, the result is an equivalent equation.

4. Answer may vary; dividing each side of an equation by the same nonzero number results in an equivalent equation.

5. 3    6. 5    7. $\frac{4}{3}$    8. $-\frac{9}{5}$    9. $-\frac{1}{8}$    10. 9

11. 4    12. 4    13. 4    14. -5    15. -8    16. -6

17. $-4r = -28$

$$\frac{-4r}{-4} = \frac{-28}{-4}$$

$$r = 7$$

18. $-8t = 56$

$$\frac{-8t}{-8} = \frac{56}{-8}$$

$$t = -7$$

19. $5x = -45$

$$\frac{5x}{5} = \frac{-45}{5}$$

$$x = -9$$

20. $-5s = -85$

$$\frac{-5s}{-5} = \frac{-85}{-5}$$

$$s = 17$$

21. $9x = 40$

$$\frac{9x}{9} = \frac{40}{9}$$

$$x = \frac{40}{9} = 4.444$$

22. $-3y = 52$

$$\frac{-3y}{-3} = \frac{52}{-3}$$

$$y = -\frac{52}{3} = -17.\overline{3}$$

23. $3w = -11$

$$\frac{3w}{3} = \frac{-11}{3}$$

$$w = \frac{-11}{3} = -3.\overline{6}$$

24. $434 = -31y$

$$\frac{434}{-31} = \frac{-31y}{-31}$$

$$-14 = y$$

25. $42.51x = 8$

$$\frac{42.51x}{42.51} = \frac{8}{42.51}$$

$$x = 0.188$$

26. $5c = 8$

$$\frac{5c}{5} = \frac{8}{5}$$

$$c = \frac{8}{5}$$

27. $17b = -391$

$$\frac{17b}{17} = \frac{-391}{17}$$

$$b = -23$$

28. $0.49x = 6.277$

$$\frac{0.49x}{0.49} = \frac{6.277}{0.49}$$

$$x = 12.810$$

29. $\frac{k}{8} = 6$

$$8\left(\frac{k}{8}\right) = (8)(6)$$

$$k = 48$$

30. $11 = \frac{x}{5}$

$$(5)(11) = 5\left(\frac{x}{5}\right)$$

$$55 = x$$

31. $-10 = \frac{b}{-7}$

$$(-7)(-10) = -7\left(\frac{b}{-7}\right)$$

$$70 = b$$

32. $\frac{h}{11} = -25$

$$11\left(\frac{h}{11}\right) = (11)(-25)$$

$$h = -275$$

33. $-65 = \frac{f}{29}$

$$(29)(-65) = 29\left(\frac{f}{29}\right)$$

$$-1885 = f$$

34. $\frac{c}{-8} = -14$

$$-8\left(\frac{c}{-8}\right) = (-8)(-14)$$

$$c = 112$$

35. $\frac{2t}{5} = -10$

$$\frac{5}{2}\left(\frac{2t}{5}\right) = \left(\frac{5}{2}\right)(-10)$$

$$t = -25$$

36. $\frac{4t}{9} = 72$

$$\frac{9}{4}\left(\frac{4t}{9}\right) = a\left(\frac{9}{4}\right)(72)$$

$$t = 162$$

37. $-\frac{3y}{5} = -50$

$$-\frac{5}{3}\left(-\frac{3y}{5}\right) = \left(-\frac{5}{3}\right)(-50)$$

$$y = \frac{250}{3}; \ 83.\overline{3}$$

38. $-\frac{11x}{8} = 42$

$$-\frac{8}{11}\left(-\frac{11x}{8}\right) = \left(-\frac{8}{11}\right)(42)$$

$$x = -\frac{336}{11}; \ -30.\overline{54}$$

39. $-\frac{13y}{5} = -22$

$$-\frac{5}{13}\left(-\frac{13y}{5}\right) = \left(-\frac{5}{13}\right)(-22)$$

$$y = \frac{110}{13}; \ 8.462$$

40. $\frac{5x}{2} = -25$

$$\frac{2}{5}\left(\frac{5x}{2}\right) = \left(\frac{2}{5}\right)(-25)$$

$$x = -10$$

41. $3x = 4\frac{2}{3}$

$$3x = \frac{14}{3}$$

$$\frac{1}{3}(3x) = \left(\frac{1}{3}\right)\left(\frac{14}{3}\right)$$

$$x = \frac{14}{9}; \ 1.\overline{5}$$

42. $-5x = -3\frac{2}{3}$

$$-5x = -\frac{11}{3}$$

$$-\frac{1}{5}(-5x) = \left(-\frac{1}{5}\right)\left(-\frac{11}{3}\right)$$

$$x = \frac{11}{15}; \ 0.7\overline{3}$$

43. $-4\frac{1}{2}x = 36$

$$-\frac{9}{2}x = 36$$

$$-\frac{2}{9}\left(-\frac{9}{2}x\right) = \left(-\frac{2}{9}\right)(36)$$

$$x = -8$$

44. $8n = 216$

$$\frac{8n}{8} = \frac{216}{8}$$

$$n = 27$$

45. $-12n = -156$

$$\frac{-12n}{-12} = \frac{-156}{-12}$$

$$n = 13$$

46. $-7n = 1.476$

$$\frac{-7n}{-7} = \frac{1.476}{-7}$$

$$n = -0.211$$

47. $\frac{1}{4}n = -16.325$

$$4\left(\frac{1}{4}n\right) = (4)(-16.325)$$

$$n = -65.3$$

48. $\frac{4}{3}n = 4.82$

$$\frac{3}{4}\left(\frac{4}{3}n\right) = \left(\frac{3}{4}\right)(4.82)$$

$$n = 3.615$$

49. $A = \ell \cdot w$

$$= 3 \cdot 5$$

$$= 15 \text{ in}^2$$

50. Let $w$ = width of the figure.

$$A = \ell \cdot w$$

$$49 = 7 \cdot w$$

$$\left(\frac{1}{7}\right)(49) = \frac{1}{7}(7w)$$

$$7 = w$$

The width of the figure is 7 cm.

51. Let $\ell$ = length of the figure.

$$A = \ell \cdot w$$

$$32\frac{1}{2} = \ell \cdot 4\frac{1}{3}$$

$$\frac{65}{2} = \ell \cdot \frac{13}{3}$$

$$\left(\frac{3}{13}\right)\left(\frac{65}{2}\right) = \frac{3}{13}\left(\frac{13}{3}L\right)$$

$$\frac{15}{2} = \ell$$

The length of the figure is $\frac{15}{2}$ ft or 7.5 ft.

52. $3x = 15$

$$x = 5$$

$$9x = 45$$

53. $10y = 46$

$$y = \frac{46}{10}$$

$$5y = 23$$

54. $2a = -10$

$$a = -5$$

$$-6a = 30$$

55. $12b = -1$

$$b = \frac{-1}{12}$$

$$4b = -\frac{1}{3}; \ -0.\overline{3}$$

56. $7k - 5 = 4$

$$7k = 9$$

$$k = \frac{9}{7}$$

$$21k - 15 = 12$$

**57.** Let $x$ = the number.

$(2x)^2 = 0$

$x = 0$

The number is 0.

**58.** Let $c$ = the cost of each ticket.

$47.50 = 5(c)$

$47.50 \div 5 = c$

$9.50 = c$

The cost of each ticket is $9.50.

**59.** Let $x$ = the number of cans bought.

Since 6 cans cost $2.28, 1 can will cost $\frac{\$2.28}{6}$.

Mika receives $0.01 for 1 can.

Therefore, the expenditure for $x$ cans is:

$\frac{2.28}{2}x - 0.01x = 7.40$

$0.38x - 0.01x = 7.40$

$0.37x = 7.40$

$x = \frac{7.40}{0.37} = 20$

Mika bought 20 cans of ginger ale.

**60.** $4[1 + 4(5x + 2y)] = 4[1 + 20x + 8y]$

$= 4 + 80x + 32y$

**61.** $4, -7, -18$

**62.** $d + (-6) = -9$

$d - 6 = -9$

$d - 6 + 6 = -9 + 6$

$d = -3$

**63.** $x - (-33) = 14$

$x + 33 = 14$

$x + 33 - 33 = 14 - 33$

$x = -19$

**PAGE 107    MID-CHAPTER REVIEW**

**1.**    $4.4 = b + 6.3$

$4.4 - 6.3 = b + 6.3 - 6.3$

$-1.9 = b$

**2.**    $z + (-18) = 34$

$z - 18 = 34$

$z - 18 + 18 = 34 + 18$

$z = 52$

**3.**    $y - 7 = -32$

$y - 7 + 7 = -32 + 7$

$y = -25$

**4.**    $r - (-31) = 16$

$r + 31 = 16$

$r + 31 - 31 = 16 - 31$

$r = -15$

**5.**    $-19 - s = 41$

$19 - 19 - s = 19 + 41$

$-s = 60$

$s = -60$

**6.**    $6x = -42$

$\frac{1}{6}(6x) = \left(\frac{1}{6}\right)(-42)$

$x = -7$

**7.**    $-13 = \frac{b}{-8}$

$(-8)(-13) = (-8)\frac{b}{-8}$

$104 = b$

**8.**    $\frac{3x}{4} = -12$

$\frac{4}{3}\left(\frac{3x}{4}\right) = \left(\frac{4}{3}\right)(-12)$

$x = -16$

**9.** $5\frac{1}{2}x = 33$

$\frac{11}{2}x = 33$

$\frac{2}{11}\left(\frac{11}{2}x\right) = \left(\frac{2}{11}\right)(33)$

$x = 6$

**10.** Let $g$ = cost of Jon's gas bill.

$95.25 + g = 210.87$

$g = 115.62$

Jon's gas bill was $115.62.

**11.** Let $w$ = the weight of 1 meter of copper tubing.

$2w = 0.25$

$w = \frac{0.25}{2}$

50 meters of copper tubing will weigh:

$50w = 50\left(\frac{0.25}{2}\right) = 6.25$

So 50 meters of copper tubing weigh 6.25 kg.

**3-4**   **Problem-Solving Strategy: Work Backwards**

**PAGES 108-109    CHECKING FOR UNDERSTANDING**

1. Pick a total number of bags. Then work through the problem from beginning to end. If there are bags left, pick another number.

2. Start at the beginning with 30 bags and work through the problem from beginning to end.

3.

| Hour | Weight |
|------|--------|
| 8th | $\frac{5}{16}$ |
| $7^{th}$ | $2\left(\frac{5}{16}\right) = \frac{5}{8}$ |
| $6^{th}$ | $2\left(\frac{5}{8}\right) = \frac{5}{4}$ |
| $5^{th}$ | $2\left(\frac{5}{4}\right) = \frac{5}{2}$ |
| $4^{th}$ | $2\left(\frac{5}{2}\right) = 5$ |
| $3^{rd}$ | $2(5) = 10$ |
| $2^{nd}$ | $2(10) = 20$ |
| $1^{st}$ | $2(20) = 40$ |
| beginning | $2(40) = 80$ |

So the weight of the ice sculpture in the beginning was 80 pounds.

4. Working backwards, take the inverse of each operation.

$67 \cdot 3 = 201$    Multiply by 3.

$201 - 87 = 114$    Subtract 87.

$114 \div 6 = 19$    Divide by 6.

$19 + 35 = 54$    Add 35.

The original number was 54.

5. 

| Activity | Amount of Money After Activity | Amount of Money Spent on Activity | Amount of Money Before Activity |
|---|---|---|---|
| Amount Left | | | $13 |
| Lunch | $13 | $7 | $20 |
| Haircut | $20 | $20 | $40 |
| Gasoline | $40 | $40 + \frac{1}{5}x$ | $x$ |

Solve for $x$:  $40 + \frac{1}{5}x = x$

$$40 = \frac{4}{5}x$$

$$50 = x$$

So Kristin originally had $50.

## PAGES 109-110    EXERCISES

6. The numbers are in reverse alphabetical order; zero, two, three, six, seven, one, nine, four, five, eight.

7. Answers may vary;

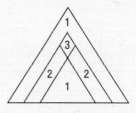

The sum of each side is 12.

8. 

| Day | Bacteria Population |
|---|---|
| 7 | 2,187,000 |
| 6 | 2,187,000 ÷ 3 = 729,000 |
| 5 | 729,000 ÷ 3 = 243,000 |
| 4 | 243,000 ÷ 3 = 81,000 |
| 3 | 81,000 ÷ 3 = 27,000 |
| 2 | 27,000 ÷ 3 = 9,000 |
| 1 | 9,000 ÷ 3 = 3,000 |

There were 3,000 bacteria on the first day.

9. Start with 990 since the sum of any 2 digits in any number above 990 will be greater than or equal to 10. 990 is not the greatest three-digit balanced number because it does not have <u>exactly</u> one digit that is the sum of the other digits. 981 is the greatest three-digit balanced number.

10. 

| Number of Packages Bought | Number of Plates in the Package | Total Number of Plates |
|---|---|---|
| | | 125 |
| 7 | 25 | 100 |
| 6 | 25 | 75 |
| 5 | 15 | 60 |
| 4 | 15 | 45 |
| 3 | 15 | 30 |
| 2 | 15 | 15 |
| 1 | 15 | 0 |

So Joe purchased 2 packages of 25 plates.

11. Top row:     3-letter word
    Middle row:  4-letter word
    Bottom row:  5-letter word
    All words are in alphabetical order.

12. Yes, answers may vary; if you will always get at least 1 pink flower and at least 1 yellow flower there can only be three flowers in Mary Ann's garden. The third flower must be yellow.

13. The sum of the numbers of each couple can be either 4, 9, 16, or 25.

| Sum of 4 | Sum of 9 | Sum of 16 | Sum of 25 |
|---|---|---|---|
| 1 + 3 | 1 + 8 | (1 + 15) | (7 + 18) |
| | 2 + 6 | (2 + 14) | (8 + 17) |
| | 3 + 5 | (3 + 13) | (9 + 16) |
| | | (4 + 12) | 10 + 15 |
| | | (5 + 11) | 11 + 14 |
| | | (6 + 10) | 12 + 13 |
| | | 7 + 9 | |
| | | 8 + 8 | |

The circled sums are dancing partners. The number of Patty Lee's partner is 15.

14. 3;

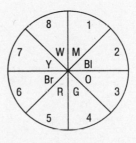

15. The possible combinations are:
    1. Kevin, Maria, Renee, Lori
    2. Kevin, Maria, Marquita, Kim, Paul
    3. Kevin, Maria, Marquita, John, Karlos
    So Mr. McCutcheon should choose Kevin, Maria, Marquita, Kim, Paul.

## PAGE 110    COOPERATIVE LEARNING ACTIVITY

# Solving Equations Using More Than One Operation

1. subtract, multiply    2. $2x + 3 = 11$

3. Subtract 2; $n - 2$.

4. Add 7 to both sides.

    Then divide both sides by 3.

    $$3x - 7 = 2$$
    $$3x - 7 + 7 = 2 + 7$$
    $$3x = 9$$
    $$\frac{3x}{3} = \frac{9}{3}$$
    $$x = 3$$

5. Subtract 8 from both sides.

    Then divide both sides by 3.

    $$8 + 3x = 5$$
    $$-8 + 8 + 3x = -8 + 5$$
    $$3x = -3$$
    $$\frac{3x}{3} = \frac{-3}{3}$$
    $$x = -1$$

6. Multiply both sides by 5.

    Then subtract 2 from both sides.

    $$\frac{a + 2}{5} = 10$$
    $$5\left(\frac{a + 2}{5}\right) = 5(10)$$
    $$a + 2 = 50$$
    $$a + 2 - 2 = 50 - 2$$
    $$a = 48$$

7. Add 7 to both sides.

    Then multiply both sides by $-\frac{13}{4}$.

    $$-\frac{4y}{13} - 7 = 6$$
    $$-\frac{4y}{13} - 7 + 7 = 6 + 7$$
    $$-\frac{4y}{13} = 13$$
    $$\left(-\frac{13}{4}\right)\left(-\frac{4y}{13}\right) = \left(-\frac{13}{4}\right)13$$
    $$y = -42\frac{1}{4}; \ -42.25$$

8. -2, -1, 0        9. 6, 8, 10        10. -7, -5, -3

11. Let $x$ = least integer.

    $x + (x + 1) = 17$

12. Let $x$ = least even integer.

    $x + (x + 2) + (x + 4) = 48$

13. Let $x$ = least odd integer.

    $x + (x + 2) = -36$

14. Let $x$ = a number.

    $17 - 2x = 5$

15.
$$4t - 7 = 5$$
$$4t - 7 + 7 = 5 + 7$$
$$4t = 12$$
$$\frac{4t}{4} = \frac{12}{4}$$
$$t = 3$$

16.
$$6 = 4n + 2$$
$$6 - 2 = 4n + 2 - 2$$
$$4 = 4n$$
$$\frac{4}{4} = \frac{4n}{4}$$
$$1 = n$$

17.
$$4 + 7x = 39$$
$$4 - 4 + 7x = 39 - 4$$
$$7x = 35$$
$$\frac{7x}{7} = \frac{35}{7}$$
$$x = 5$$

18.
$$34 = 8 - 2t$$
$$34 - 8 = 8 - 8 - 2t$$
$$26 = -2t$$
$$\frac{26}{-2} = \frac{-2t}{-2}$$
$$-13 = t$$

19.
$$-3x - 7 = 18$$
$$-3x - 7 + 7 = 18 + 7$$
$$-3x = 25$$
$$\frac{-3x}{-3} = \frac{25}{-3}$$
$$x = -\frac{25}{3}; \ -8.\overline{3}$$

20.
$$0.2n + 3 = 8.6$$
$$0.2n + 3 - 3 = 8.6 - 3$$
$$0.2n = 5.6$$
$$\frac{0.2n}{0.2} = \frac{5.6}{0.2}$$
$$n = 28$$

21.
$$\frac{3n}{4} - 3 = 9$$
$$\frac{3n}{4} - 3 + 3 = 9 + 3$$
$$\frac{3n}{4} = 12$$
$$\frac{4}{3}\left(\frac{3n}{4}\right) = \frac{4}{3}(12)$$
$$n = 16$$

22.
$$7 = 3 - \frac{n}{3}$$
$$7 - 3 = 3 - 3 - \frac{n}{3}$$
$$4 = -\frac{n}{3}$$
$$-3(4) = -3\left(-\frac{n}{3}\right)$$
$$-12 = n$$

23.
$$7 = \frac{x}{2} + 5$$
$$7 - 5 = \frac{x}{2} + 5 - 5$$
$$2 = \frac{x}{2}$$
$$2(2) = 2\left(\frac{x}{2}\right)$$
$$4 = x$$

24.
$$\frac{y}{3} + 6 = -45$$
$$\frac{y}{3} + 6 - 6 = -45 - 6$$
$$\frac{y}{3} = -51$$
$$3\left(\frac{y}{3}\right) = 3(-51)$$
$$y = -153$$

25.
$$\frac{c}{-4} - 8 = -42$$
$$\frac{c}{-4} - 8 + 8 = -42 + 8$$
$$\frac{c}{-4} = -34$$
$$-4\left(\frac{c}{-4}\right) = -4(-34)$$
$$c = 136$$

26.
$$\frac{d + 5}{3} = -9$$
$$3\left(\frac{d + 5}{3}\right) = 3(-9)$$
$$d + 5 = -27$$
$$d + 5 - 5 = -27 - 5$$
$$d = -32$$

27. $\dfrac{3 + n}{7} = -5$  

$7\left(\dfrac{3 + n}{7}\right) = 7(-5)$  

$3 + n = -35$  

$3 - 3 + n = -35 - 3$  

$n = -38$  

28. $5 = \dfrac{m - 5}{4}$  

$4(5) = 4\left(\dfrac{m - 5}{4}\right)$  

$20 = m - 5$  

$20 + 5 = m - 5 + 5$  

$25 = m$  

29. $16 = \dfrac{s - 8}{7}$  

$-7(16) = -7\left(\dfrac{s - 8}{7}\right)$  

$-112 = s - 8$  

$-112 + 8 = s - 8 + 8$  

$-104 = s$  

30. $\dfrac{4d + 5}{7} = 7$  

$7\left(\dfrac{4d + 5}{7}\right) = 7(7)$  

$4d + 5 = 49$  

$4d + 5 - 5 = 49 - 5$  

$4d = 44$  

$\dfrac{4d}{4} = \dfrac{44}{4}$  

$d = 11$  

31. $\dfrac{7n + (-1)}{8} = 8$  

$8\left(\dfrac{7n + (-1)}{8}\right) = 8(8)$  

$7n - 1 = 64$  

$7n - 1 + 1 = 64 + 1$  

$7n = 65$  

$\dfrac{7n}{7} = \dfrac{65}{7}$  

$n = \dfrac{65}{7};\ 9.286$  

32. $\dfrac{-3n - (-4)}{-6} = -9$  

$-6\left(\dfrac{-3n + 4}{-6}\right) = -6(-9)$  

$-3n + 4 = 54$  

$-3n + 4 - 4 = 54 - 4$  

$-3n = 50$  

$\dfrac{-3n}{-3} = \dfrac{50}{-3}$  

$n = -\dfrac{50}{3};\ -16.\overline{6}$  

33. Let $x$ = first integer;  
$x + 1$ = second integer;  
$x + 2$ = third integer.  

$x + (x + 1) + (x + 2) = 87$  

$3x + 3 = 87$  

$3x + 3 - 3 = 87 - 3$  

$3x = 84$  

$\dfrac{3x}{3} = \dfrac{84}{3}$  

$x = 28 \qquad x + 1 = 29$  

$\qquad\qquad\quad x + 2 = 30$  

The integers are 28, 29, 30.

34. Let $n$ = first integer;  
$n + 1$ = second integer;  
$n + 2$ = third integer;  
$n + 3$ = fourth integer.  

$n + (n + 1) + (n + 2) + (n + 3) = 130$  

$4n + 6 = 130$  

$4n + 6 - 6 = 130 - 6$  

$4n = 124$  

$\dfrac{4n}{4} = \dfrac{124}{4}$  

$n = 31$  

$n + 1 = 32,\ n + 2 = 33,\ n + 3 = 34$  

The integers are 31, 32, 33, 34.

35. Let $x$ = first integer;  
$x + 2$ = second integer.  

$x + x + 2 = 115$  

$2x + 2 = 115$  

$2x + 2 - 2 = 115 - 2$  

$2x = 113$  

$\dfrac{2x}{2} = \dfrac{113}{2}$  

$x = 56\dfrac{1}{2}$  

$56\dfrac{1}{2}$ is not an integer;  

There is no solution.

36. Let $s$ = length of first side;  
$s + 2$ = length of second side;  
$s + 4$ = length of third side.  

$s + (s + 2) + (s + 4) = 27$  

$3s + 6 = 27$  

$3s + 6 - 6 = 27 - 6$  

$3s = 21$  

$\dfrac{3s}{3} = \dfrac{21}{3}$  

$s = 7$  

$s + 2 = 9;\ s + 4 = 11$  

The lengths of the sides are 7m, 9m, and 11m.

37. $2x + (x + 6) = 96$  

$3x + 6 = 96$  

$3x = 90$  

$x = 30$  

$x + 2 = 32$  

$x + 4 = 34$  

$x + 6 = 36$  

38. $(2n - 1) + (2n + 1) + (2n + 3)$  

39. Let $x$ = the number of customers at start.  

$2x + 6 = 98$  

$2x + 6 - 6 = 98 - 6$  

$2x = 92$  

$\dfrac{2x}{2} = \dfrac{92}{2}$  

$x = 46$  

Karen started with 46 customers.

40. Let $b$ = the number of runs batted in.  

$2b + 9 = 117$  

$2b + 9 - 9 = 117 - 9$  

$2b = 108$  

$\dfrac{2b}{2} = \dfrac{108}{2}$  

$b = 54$  

He batted in 54 runs.

**41.** Let $T1$ = the first test score;

$T2$ = the second test score;

$T3$ = the third test score;

$T4$ = the fourth test score;

$T5$ = the final score.

$$\frac{T1 + T2 + T3 + T4}{4} = 76$$

$$4 \cdot \left(\frac{T1 + T2 + T3 + T4}{4}\right) = 4 \cdot 76$$

$$T1 + T2 + T3 + T4 = 304$$

After the final test, Namid would like an average of 80:

$$\frac{T1 + T2 + T3 + T4 + 2(T5)}{6} = 80$$

$$(T1 + T2 + T3 + T4) + 2(T5) = 480$$

$$304 + 2(T5) = 480$$

$$T5 = 88$$

Namid must get an 88 on his final test. After his final test, Namid would like an average of 85:

$$\frac{T1 + T2 + T3 + T4 + 2(T5)}{6} = 85$$

$$(T1 + T2 + T3 + T4) + 2(T5) = 510$$

$$304 + 2(T5) = 510$$

$$(T5) = 103$$

Namid would have to get 103 on his final test, so it is not possible for Namid to have an average of 85.

**42.** Let $p$ = place of next runner;

$p + 1$ = place of third runner;

$p + 2$ = place of fourth runner;

$p + 3$ = place of fifth runner.

$$2 + p + (p + 1) + (p + 2) + (p + 3) = 40$$

$$4p + 8 = 40$$

$$4p + 8 - 8 = 40 - 8$$

$$4p = 32$$

$$\frac{4p}{4} = \frac{32}{4}$$

$$p = 8$$

$$p + 1 = 9$$

$$p + 2 = 10$$

$$p + 3 = 11$$

The other runners placed 8th, 9th, 10th, and 11th.

**43.** a. They are multiples of 3 and odd.

b. They are multiples of 3 and even.

c. They are not divisible by 3.

**44.** Substitution property of equality

**45.** $m + 17 = -6 + 17 = 11$

**46.**
$$\frac{0.06}{0.4} \underline{<} \frac{0.9}{5}$$

$$(0.06)(5) \underline{\phantom{xx}} (0.4)(0.9)$$

$$0.30 \underline{<} 0.36$$

**47.**
$$d - 27 = -63$$
$$d - 27 + 27 = -63 + 27$$
$$d = -36$$

**48.**
$$-7w = -49$$
$$\frac{-7w}{-7} = \frac{-49}{-7}$$
$$w = 7$$

**49.** $2 \cdot 4 \cdot 4 = 32$ students

PAGE 115    PUZZLE

| | 3 | 5 | |
|---|---|---|---|
| 7 | 1 | 8 | 2 |
| | 4 | 6 | |

## 3-6  Solving Equations with the Variable on Both Sides

PAGE 118    CHECKING FOR UNDERSTANDING

**1.** 1,036,000; 987,000; yes

**2.** Rates of population change are not constant.

**3.** An identity is true for every value of the variable; an equation with no solution is never true.

**4.** Add 1 to each side. Subtract $3x$ from each side.

**5.** Add 10 to each side. Add $3y$ to each side. Divide each side by 11.

**6.** Multiply $3 + 5w$ by 4. Subtract 12 from each side. Divide each side by 20.

**7.** Multiply $x - 3$ by $-7$. Subtract 21 from each side. Divide each side by $-7$.

The check is left to the students.

**8.**
$$6x + 7 = 8x - 13$$
$$6x - 8x + 7 = 8x - 8x - 13$$
$$-2x + 7 = -13$$
$$-2x + 7 - 7 = -13 - 7$$
$$-2x = -20$$
$$\frac{-2x}{-2} = \frac{-20}{-2}$$
$$x = 10$$

**9.**
$$3(h + 2) = 12$$
$$3h + 6 = 12$$
$$3h + 6 - 6 = 12 - 6$$
$$3h = 6$$
$$\frac{3h}{3} = \frac{6}{3}$$
$$h = 2$$

**10.**
$$7 - 3x = x - 4(2 + x)$$
$$7 - 3x = x - 8 - 4x$$
$$7 - 3x = -3x - 8$$
$$7 - 3x + 3x = -3x - 8 + 3x$$
$$7 = -8$$
no solution

**11.**
$$-3(x + 5) = 3(x - 1)$$
$$-3x - 15 = 3x - 3$$
$$3x - 3x - 15 = 3x + 3x - 3$$
$$-15 = 6x - 3$$
$$-15 + 3 = 6x - 3 + 3$$
$$-12 = 6x$$
$$-2 = x$$

**PAGES 118-120   EXERCISES**

**12.**
$$2w + 2(w + 60) = 920$$
$$2w + 2w + 120 = 920$$
$$4w + 120 = 920$$
$$4w + 120 - 120 = 920 - 120$$
$$4w = 800$$
$$w = 200$$
$$w + 60 = 260$$
The dimensions of the rectangle are 200 m × 260 m.

**13.**
$$2w + 2(3w - 75) = 370$$
$$2w + 6w - 150 = 370$$
$$8w - 150 = 370$$
$$8w - 150 + 150 = 370 + 150$$
$$8w = 520$$
$$w = 65$$
$$3w - 75 = 120$$
The dimensions of the rectangle are 65 yd × 120 yd.

**14.**
$$2w + 2(2w - 40) = 220$$
$$2w + 4w - 80 = 220$$
$$6w - 80 = 220$$
$$6w - 80 + 80 = 220 + 80$$
$$6w = 300$$
$$w = 50$$
$$2w - 40 = 60$$
The dimensions of the rectangle are 50 ft × 60 ft.

**15.** The check is left to the students.
$$3 - 4x = 10x + 10$$
$$3 - 10 = 10x + 4x$$
$$-7 = 14x$$
$$-\frac{1}{2} = x$$
$$x = -\frac{1}{2};\ -0.5$$

**16.**
$$17 + 2n = 21 + 2n$$
$$17 + 2n - 2n = 21 + 2n - 2n$$
$$17 \neq 21$$
no solution

**17.**
$$14b - 6 = -2b + 8$$
$$14b + 2b - 6 = -2b + 2b + 8$$
$$16b - 6 = 8$$
$$16b - 6 + 6 = 8 + 6$$
$$16b = 14$$
$$b = \frac{14}{16};\ \frac{7}{8};\ 0.875$$

**18.**
$$\frac{2n}{3} + 8 = \frac{1n}{3} - 2$$
$$\frac{2n}{3} - \frac{1n}{3} + 8 = \frac{1n}{3} - \frac{1n}{3} - 2$$
$$\frac{n}{3} + 8 = -2$$
$$\frac{n}{3} + 8 - 8 = -2 - 8$$
$$\frac{n}{3} = -10$$
$$n = -30$$

**19.**
$$18 - 3.8x = 7.36 - 1.9x$$
$$18 - 3.8x + 3.8x = 7.36 - 1.9x + 3.8x$$
$$18 = 7.36 + 1.9x$$
$$18 - 7.36 = 7.36 - 7.36 + 1.9x$$
$$10.64 = 1.9x$$
$$5.6 = x$$

**20.**
$$\frac{3n}{4} + 16 = 2 - \frac{1n}{8}$$
$$\frac{1n}{8} + \frac{3n}{4} + 16 = 2 + \frac{1n}{8} - \frac{1n}{8}$$
$$\frac{7n}{8} + 16 = 2$$
$$\frac{7n}{8} + 16 - 16 = 2 - 16$$
$$\frac{7n}{8} = -14$$
$$\frac{8}{7}\left(\frac{7n}{8}\right) = \frac{8}{7}(-14)$$
$$n = -16$$

**21.**
$$6(y + 2) - 4 = -10$$
$$6y + 12 - 4 = -10$$
$$6y + 8 = -10$$
$$6y + 8 - 8 = -10 - 8$$
$$6y = -18$$
$$\frac{6y}{6} = \frac{-18}{6}$$
$$y = -3$$

**22.**
$$3x - 2(x + 3) = x$$
$$3x - 2x - 6 = x$$
$$x - 6 = x$$
$$x - x - 6 = x - x$$
$$-6 \neq 0$$
no solution

**23.**
$$7 + 2(x + 1) = 2x + 9$$
$$7 + 2x + 2 = 2x + 9$$
$$2x + 9 = 2x + 9$$
identity

24.
$$6 = 3 + 5(y - 2)$$
$$6 = 3 + 5y - 10$$
$$6 = 5y - 7$$
$$6 + 7 = 5y - 7 + 7$$
$$13 = 5y$$
$$\frac{13}{5} = \frac{5y}{5}$$
$$2.6; \frac{13}{5} = y$$

25.
$$4(x - 2) = 4x$$
$$4x - 8 = 4x$$
$$4x - 4x - 8 = 4x - 4x$$
$$-8 \neq 0$$
no solution

26. $5x - 7 = 5(x - 2) + 3$
$$5x - 7 = 5x - 10 + 3$$
$$5x - 7 = 5x - 7$$
identity

27. $5 - \frac{1}{2}(b - 6) = 4$
$$5 - \frac{b}{2} + 3 = 4$$
$$8 - \frac{b}{2} = 4$$
$$8 - 8 - \frac{b}{2} = 4 - 8$$
$$-\frac{b}{2} = -4$$
$$-2\left(\frac{b}{2}\right) = -2(-4)$$
$$b = 8$$

28.
$$5n + 4 = 7(n + 1) - 2n$$
$$5n + 4 = 7n + 7 - 2n$$
$$5n + 4 = 5n + 7$$
$$5n - 5n + 4 = 5n - 5n + 7$$
$$4 \neq 7$$
no solution

29.
$$4(2x - 1) = -10(x - 5)$$
$$8x - 4 = -10x + 50$$
$$10x + 8x - 4 = 10x - 10x + 50$$
$$18x - 4 = 50$$
$$18x - 4 + 4 = 50 + 4$$
$$18x = 54$$
$$\frac{18x}{18} = \frac{54}{18}$$
$$x = 3$$

30.
$$-8(4 + 9x) = 7(-2 - 11x)$$
$$-32 - 72x = -14 - 77x$$
$$14 - 32 - 72x = 14 - 14 - 77x$$
$$-18 - 72x = -77x$$
$$-18 - 72x + 72x = -77x + 72x$$
$$-18 = -5x$$
$$\frac{-18}{-5} = \frac{-5x}{-5}$$
$$3.6; \frac{18}{5} = x$$

31.
$$4(2a - 8) = \frac{1}{7}(49a + 70)$$
$$8a - 32 = 7a + 10$$
$$8a - 7a - 32 = 7a - 7a + 10$$
$$a - 32 = 10$$
$$a - 32 + 32 = 10 + 32$$
$$a = 42$$

32. $2(x - 3) + 5 = 3(x - 1)$
$$2x - 6 + 5 = 3x - 3$$
$$2x - 1 = 3x - 3$$
$$2x - 1 + 3 = 3x - 3 + 3$$
$$2x + 2 = 3x$$
$$2x - 2x + 2 = 3x - 2x$$
$$2 = x$$

33. $-3(2n - 5) = \frac{1}{2}(-12n + 30)$
$$-6n + 15 = -6n + 15$$
identity

34. $2[x + 3(x - 1)] = 18$
$$2[x + 3x - 3] = 18$$
$$2[4x - 3] = 18$$
$$8x - 6 = 18$$
$$8x - 6 + 6 = 18 + 6$$
$$8x = 24$$
$$\frac{8x}{8} = \frac{24}{8}$$
$$x = 3$$

35. Let $x$ = the number.
$$2x + 12 = 3x - 31$$
$$2x - 2x + 12 = 3x - 2x - 31$$
$$12 = x - 31$$
$$12 + 31 = x$$
$$43 = x$$
The number is 43.

36. Let $x$ = the first integer;
$x + 2$ = the second integer.
$$2(x + 2) = 3x - 13$$
$$2x + 4 = 3x - 13$$
$$2x - 2x + 4 = 3x - 2x - 13$$
$$4 = x - 13$$
$$4 + 13 = x - 13 + 13$$
$$17 = x$$
$$19 = x + 2$$
The integers are 17, 19.

37. Let $x$ = the first integer;

    $x + 2$ = the second integer;

    $x + 4$ = the third integer.

$$3(x + 4) = 2x + 38$$
$$3x + 12 = 2x + 38$$
$$3x - 2x + 12 = 2x - 2x + 38$$
$$x + 12 = 38$$
$$x + 12 - 12 = 38 - 12$$
$$x = 26$$
$$x + 2 = 28$$
$$x + 4 = 30$$

The integers are 26, 28, 30.

38. Sometimes true; when $x > 0$, $x > -x$; when $x = 0$,

    $x = -x$; when $x < 0$, $x < -x$.

39. Let $n$ = the number of vans Toshio sold.

$$2n + 7 = 83$$
$$2n + 7 - 7 = 83 - 7$$
$$2n = 76$$
$$\frac{2n}{2} = \frac{76}{2}$$
$$n = 38$$

Toshio sold 38 vans.

40. Let $p$ = place of second runner;

    $p + 1$ = place of third runner;

    $p + 2$ = place of fourth runner;

    $p + 3$ = place of fifth runner.

$$4 + p + (p + 1) + (p + 2) + (p + 3) = 70$$
$$4p + 10 = 70$$
$$4p + 10 - 10 = 70 - 10$$
$$4p = 60$$
$$\frac{4p}{4} = \frac{60}{4}$$
$$p = 15$$
$$p + 1 = 16$$
$$p + 2 = 17$$
$$p + 3 = 18$$

41. Let $w$ = width of field in yards.

    $3w - 75$ = length of field in yards

$$2w + 2(3w - 75) = 370$$
$$2w + 6w - 150 = 370$$
$$8w - 150 = 370$$
$$8w - 150 + 150 = 370 + 150$$
$$8w = 520$$
$$\frac{8w}{8} = \frac{520}{8}$$
$$w = 65$$
$$3w - 75 = 120$$

The field is 65 yards wide and 120 yards long.

42. distance = rate $\cdot$ time

    Let $t$ = time it takes Paloma to get to work.

$$\frac{40}{60} \cdot (t + 1) = \frac{45}{60} \cdot (t - 1)$$
$$\frac{40t}{60} + \frac{40}{60} = \frac{45t}{60} - \frac{45}{60}$$
$$\frac{40t}{60} - \frac{40t}{60} + \frac{40}{60} = \frac{45t}{60} - \frac{40t}{60} - \frac{45}{60}$$
$$\frac{40}{60} = \frac{5t}{60} - \frac{45}{60}$$
$$\frac{40}{60} + \frac{45}{60} = \frac{5t}{60} - \frac{45}{60} + \frac{45}{60}$$
$$\frac{85}{60} = \frac{5t}{60}$$
$$\frac{60}{5}\left(\frac{85}{60}\right) = \frac{60}{5}\left(\frac{5t}{60}\right)$$
$$17 = t;$$

it takes Paloma 17 minutes to get to work.

distance = $\frac{40}{60}(17 + 1) = 12$; Paloma drives 12 miles to work.

43. $A = m + n^2$

44. $\frac{3}{4} + -\frac{7}{12} = \frac{1}{6}$

45. $(-2.93)(-0.003) = 0.00879$

46. $y - 7.3 = 5.1$
$$y = 12.4$$

47. $w - (-37) = 28$
$$w = -9$$

48. $\frac{9x}{2} = -30$
$$\frac{2}{9}\left(\frac{9x}{2}\right) = \frac{2}{9}(-30)$$
$$x = -\frac{20}{3}; \; -6.\overline{6}$$

49. $7n - 4 = 17$
$$7n - 4 + 4 = 17 + 4$$
$$7n = 21$$
$$\frac{7n}{7} = \frac{21}{7}$$
$$n = 3$$

**PACE 120    PUZZLE**

Mercuria's formula = Mrs. Weatherby's approximation

$$\frac{9}{5}c + 32 = 2c + 30$$
$$\frac{9}{5}c - \frac{9}{5}c + 32 = 2c - \frac{9}{5}c + 30$$
$$32 = \frac{1}{5}c + 30$$
$$32 - 30 = \frac{1}{5}c + 30 - 30$$
$$2 = \frac{1}{5}c$$
$$5(2) = (5)\frac{1}{5}c$$
$$10^\circ = c$$
$$2c + 30 = 50^\circ$$

It was $10^\circ c$ or $50^\circ F$.

# Technology:  Solving Equations

1. $5x = x - 12$

   sub $x$     $5x - x = x - 12 - x$

   simp         $4x = -12$

   div 4       $\dfrac{4x}{4} = \dfrac{-12}{4}$

   simp          $x = -3$

2. $7 - x + 5 = -3 + 4x$

   add $x$     $7 - x + 5 + x = -3 + 4x + x$

   simp         $12 = -3 + 5x$

   add 3       $12 + 3 = -3 + 5x + 3$

   simp         $15 = 5x$

   div 5       $\dfrac{15}{5} = \dfrac{5x}{5}$

   simp         $3 = x$

3. $3(1 - 6x) = 2x + 1$

   simp         $3 - 18x = 2x + 1$

   add $18x$    $3 - 18x + 18x = 2x + 1 + 18x$

   simp         $3 = 20x + 1$

   sub 1       $3 - 1 = 20x + 1 - 1$

   simp         $2 = 20x$

   div 20      $\dfrac{2}{20} = \dfrac{20x}{20}$

   simp         $\dfrac{1}{10} = x$

4. $2 - (3x - 1) = 2(1 - 2x)$

   simp         $-3x + 3 = 2 - 4x$

   add $4x$    $-3x + 3 + 4x = 2 - 4x + 4x$

   simp         $x + 3 = 2$

   sub 3       $x + 3 - 3 = 2 - 3$

   simp         $x = -1$

5. $x = 4 - 5(x - 1) + 6x$

   simp         $x = x + 9$

       no solution

6. $3(x - 2) - 1 = x - (7 - 2x)$

   simp         $3x - 7 = 3x - 7$

       all numbers

## 3–7  More Equations

1. $16\left(\dfrac{a}{16} + \dfrac{1}{2}\right) = 16\left(\dfrac{1}{8}\right)$        2. yes

        $a + 8 = 2$

   The fractions are eliminated.

3. $29.99(2x) + 19.99x + 24.95x + 28.96x = 311.67$

4. 10; $12s + 81 = 35 - 20s$

5. 100; $817y = 420 - 370y$

6. 12; $9x - 84 = 96 + 8x$     7. 20; $8x = 140 - 15x$

8. $\begin{aligned} 0.2x + 1.7 &= 3.9 \\ 10(0.2x + 1.7) &= 10(3.9) \\ 2x + 17 &= 39 \\ 2x + 17 - 17 &= 39 - 17 \\ 2x &= 22 \\ x &= 11 \end{aligned}$

9. $\begin{aligned} 5.3 - 0.3x &= -9.4 \\ 10(5.3 - 0.3x) &= 10(-9.4) \\ 53 - 3x &= -94 \\ 53 - 53 - 3x &= -94 - 53 \\ -3x &= -147 \\ x &= 49 \end{aligned}$

10. $\begin{aligned} \dfrac{4 - x}{5} &= \dfrac{1x}{5} \\ 5\left(\dfrac{4 - x}{5}\right) &= 5\left(\dfrac{1x}{5}\right) \\ 4 - x &= 1x \\ 4 - x + x &= x + x \\ 4 &= 2x \\ x &= 2 \end{aligned}$

11. $\begin{aligned} \dfrac{5x}{8} + \dfrac{3}{5} &= x \\ 40\left(\dfrac{5x}{8} + \dfrac{3}{5}\right) &= 40(x) \\ 25x + 24 &= 40x \\ 25x - 25x + 24 &= 40x - 25x \\ 24 &= 15x \\ x &= \dfrac{8}{5};\ 1.6 \end{aligned}$

12. $\begin{aligned} \dfrac{y + 5}{3} &= 7 \\ 3\left(\dfrac{y + 5}{3}\right) &= 3(7) \\ y + 5 &= 21 \\ y &= 16 \end{aligned}$

13. $\begin{aligned} \dfrac{3n - 2}{5} &= \dfrac{7}{10} \\ 10\left(\dfrac{3n - 2}{5}\right) &= 10\left(\dfrac{7}{10}\right) \\ 6n - 4 &= 7 \\ 6n - 4 + 4 &= 7 + 4 \\ 6n &= 11 \\ n &= \dfrac{11}{6};\ 1.8\overline{3} \end{aligned}$

14. $\begin{aligned} 1.9s + 6 &= 3.1 - s \\ 10(1.9s + 6) &= 10(3.1 - s) \\ 19s + 60 &= 31 - 10s \\ 10s + 19s + 60 &= 31 - 10s + 10s \\ 29s + 60 &= 31 \\ 29s + 60 - 60 &= 31 - 60 \\ 29s &= -29 \\ s &= -1 \end{aligned}$

**15.**
$$28 - 2.2y = 11.6y + 262.6$$
$$10(28 - 2.2y) = 10(11.6y + 262.6)$$
$$280 - 22y = 116y + 2626$$
$$280 - 22y + 22y = 116y + 22y + 2626$$
$$280 = 138y + 2626$$
$$280 - 2626 = 138y + 2626 - 2626$$
$$-2346 = 138y$$
$$y = -17$$

**16.**
$$\frac{3}{4}x - 4 = 7 + \frac{1}{2}x$$
$$4\left(\frac{3}{4}x - 4\right) = 4\left(7 + \frac{1}{2}x\right)$$
$$3x - 16 = 28 + 2x$$
$$3x - 2x - 16 = 28 + 2x - 2x$$
$$x - 16 = 28$$
$$x - 16 + 16 = 28 + 16$$
$$x = 44$$

**17.**
$$\frac{3}{8} - \frac{1x}{4} = \frac{1x}{2} - \frac{3}{4}$$
$$8\left(\frac{3}{8} - \frac{1x}{4}\right) = 8\left(\frac{1x}{2} - \frac{3}{4}\right)$$
$$3 - 2x = 4x - 6$$
$$3 - 2x + 2x = 4x + 2x - 6$$
$$3 = 6x - 6$$
$$3 + 6 = 6x - 6 + 6$$
$$9 = 6x$$
$$x = \frac{3}{2};\ 1.5$$

**18.**
$$5.4y + 8.2 = 9.8y - 2.8$$
$$10(5.4y + 8.2) = 10(9.8y - 2.8)$$
$$54y + 82 = 98y - 28$$
$$54y + 82 + 28 = 98y - 28 + 28$$
$$54y + 110 = 98y$$
$$54y - 54y + 110 = 98y - 54y$$
$$110 = 44y$$
$$y = 2.5$$

**19.**
$$1.03x - 4 = -2.15x + 8.72$$
$$100(1.03x - 4) = 100(-2.15x + 8.72)$$
$$103x - 400 = -215x + 872$$
$$215x + 103x - 400 = 215x - 215x + 872$$
$$318x - 400 = 872$$
$$318x - 400 + 400 = 872 + 400$$
$$318x = 1272$$
$$x = 4$$

**20.**
$$3y - \frac{4}{5} = \frac{1y}{3}$$
$$15\left(3y - \frac{4}{5}\right) = 15\left(\frac{y}{3}\right)$$
$$45y - 12 = 5y$$
$$45y - 5y - 12 = 5y - 5y$$
$$40y - 12 = 0$$
$$40y - 12 + 12 = 0 + 12$$
$$40y = 12$$
$$y = \frac{3}{10};\ 0.3$$

**21.**
$$\frac{7 + 3t}{4} = -\frac{1t}{8}$$
$$8\left(\frac{7 + 3t}{4}\right) = 8\left(-\frac{1t}{8}\right)$$
$$14 + 6t = -t$$
$$14 + 6t + t = -t + t$$
$$14 + 7t = 0$$
$$14 - 14 + 7t = 0 - 14$$
$$7t = -14$$
$$t = -2$$

**22.**
$$\frac{3y}{2} - y = 4 + \frac{1y}{2}$$
$$4\left(\frac{3y}{2} - y\right) = 4\left(4 + \frac{1y}{2}\right)$$
$$6y - 4y = 16 + 2y$$
$$6y - 4y + 4y = 16 + 2y + 4y$$
$$6y = 16 + 6y$$
$$6y - 6y = 16$$
$$0 \neq 16$$
$$\text{no solution}$$

**23.**
$$\frac{x}{2} - \frac{1}{3} = \frac{x}{3} - \frac{1}{2}$$
$$6\left(\frac{x}{2} - \frac{1}{3}\right) = 6\left(\frac{x}{3} - \frac{1}{2}\right)$$
$$3x - 2 = 2x - 3$$
$$3x - 2x - 2 = 2x - 2x - 3$$
$$x - 2 = -3$$
$$x - 1 + 2 = -3 + 2$$
$$x = -1$$

**24.** $5x = y$
$$x = \frac{y}{5}$$

**25.**
$$\frac{x + a}{3} = c$$
$$3\left(\frac{x + a}{3}\right) = 3(c)$$
$$x + a = 3c$$
$$x + a - a = 3c - a$$
$$x = 3c - a$$

**26.**
$$ax + b = cx$$
$$ax + b - b = cx - b$$
$$ax = cx - b$$
$$ax - cx = cx - cx - b$$
$$ax - cx = -b$$
$$x(a - c) = -b$$
$$x = \frac{-b}{a - c}$$

**27.**
$$ex - 2y = 3z$$
$$ex - 2y + 2y = 3z + 2y$$
$$ex = 3z + 2y$$
$$x = \frac{3z + 2y}{e}$$

**28.**
$$ay - b = c$$
$$ay - b + b = c + b$$
$$ay = c + b$$
$$y = \frac{c + b}{a}$$

**29.**
$$ay + z = am - ny$$
$$ay + z - z = am - ny - z$$
$$ay = am - ny - z$$
$$ay + ny = am + ny - ny - z$$
$$ay + ny = am - z$$
$$y(a + n) = am - z$$
$$y = \frac{am - z}{a + n}$$

30. $a(y + 1) = b$

$$\frac{a(y + 1)}{a} = \frac{b}{a}$$

$$y + 1 = \frac{b}{a}$$

$$y + 1 - 1 = \frac{b}{a} - 1$$

$$y = \frac{b}{a} - 1$$

31. $\frac{3y}{5} + a = b$

$$\frac{3y}{5} + a - a = b - a$$

$$\frac{3y}{5} = b - a$$

$$\frac{5}{3}\left(\frac{3y}{5}\right) = \frac{5}{3}(b - a)$$

$$y = \frac{5}{3}(b - a)$$

32. Let $x$ = a number.

$$\frac{5x}{8} = 3 + \frac{1x}{2}$$

$$\frac{5x}{8} - \frac{1x}{2} = 3$$

$$\frac{1x}{8} = 3$$

$$x = 24$$

The number is 24.

33. Let $x$ = a number.

$$\frac{1}{2}x + 16 = \frac{2x}{3} - 4$$

$$6\left(\frac{1}{2}x + 16\right) = 6\left(\frac{2x}{3} - 4\right)$$

$$6\left(\frac{1}{2}x\right) + 6(16) = 6\left(\frac{2x}{3}\right) - 6(4)$$

$$3x + 96 = 4x - 24$$

$$3x - 3x + 96 = 4x - 3x - 24$$

$$96 = x - 24$$

$$96 + 24 = x - 24 + 24$$

$$120 = x$$

34. Let $x$ = a number.

$$\frac{2x}{3} + 5 = \frac{1x}{2} - 3$$

$$\frac{2x}{3} - \frac{1x}{2} + 5 = \frac{1x}{2} - \frac{1x}{2} - 3$$

$$\frac{x}{6} + 5 = -3$$

$$\frac{x}{6} + 5 - 5 = -3 - 5$$

$$\frac{x}{6} = -8$$

$$x = -48$$

The number is $-48$.

35. Let $x$ = a number.

$$\frac{x}{5} + 5x = 7x - 18$$

$$5\left(\frac{x}{5} + 5x\right) = 5(7x - 18)$$

$$x + 25x = 35x - 90$$

$$26x = 35x - 90$$

$$26x + 90 = 35x - 90 + 90$$

$$26x + 90 = 35x$$

$$26x - 26x + 90 = 35x - 26x$$

$$90 = 9x$$

$$x = 10$$

36. Let $x$ = the first number.

Let $y$ = the second number.

$x + y = 25$

Solve for $x$:
$$4x - 12 = 2y + 16$$
$$4x - 12 + 12 = 2y + 16 + 12$$
$$4x = 2y + 28$$
$$x = \frac{1y}{2} + 7$$

Solve for $y$: $\frac{1y}{2} + 7 + y = 25$

$$\frac{3y}{2} + 7 = 25$$

$$y = 12$$

$$x = \frac{12}{2} + 7 = 13$$

The numbers are 12 and 13.

37. Let $x$ = the first number.

Let $y$ = the second number.

$x - y = 12$

$$\frac{2x}{5} - 6 = \frac{1y}{3}$$

Solve for $y$: $\frac{2x}{5} - 6 = \frac{1y}{3}$.

$$y = 3\left(\frac{2x}{5} - 6\right)$$

$$x - 3\left(\frac{2x}{5} - 6\right) = 12$$

$$x - \frac{6x}{5} + 18 = 12$$

$$-\frac{x}{5} = -6$$

$$x = 30$$

$$30 - y = 12$$

$$y = 18$$

The numbers are 18 and 30 or 150 and 162.

38. Multiply each term by $x + 1$. Then use the distributive property to multiply 7 by $x + 1$ and solve the equation.

39. Let $w$ = the width of playground in meters.

$w + 60$ = length of playground in meters

$$2w + 2(w + 60) = 920$$

$$2w + 2w + 120 = 920$$

$$4w + 120 = 920$$

$$4w + 120 - 120 = 920 - 120$$

$$4w = 800$$

$$w = 200$$

$$w + 60 = 260$$

The length of the playground is 260 meters.

40. Let $c$ = the number of cans of tomato sauce.

$$2(0.69) + 1(2.49) + c(0.95) - 0.50 = 6.22$$

$$100[2(0.69) + 1(2.49) + c(0.95) - 0.50] = 100(6.22)$$

$$2(69) + 1(2.49) + c(95) - 50 = 622$$

$$95c = 285$$

$$c = 3$$

Luisa bought 3 cans of tomato sauce.

41. a. $4x + 6 = 4x + 6$; identity

b. $5x + (-7) = x + 3$; $\frac{5}{2}$; 2.5

c. $-3x + 6 = 3x + (-6)$; 2

d. $5.4x + 6.8 = 4.6x + 2.8$; $-5$

e. $2x + (-8) = 2x + (-6)$; no solution

42. $(-6.01)(-4.122) \underline{>} \dfrac{9.624}{2.2}$

43. $\dfrac{\frac{3}{11}}{-6} = \dfrac{3}{11}\left(-\dfrac{1}{6}\right) = -\dfrac{1}{22}$

44. Answers may vary; Yvette has 17 less pennies than nickels. If she has 63 coins total, how many pennies and nickels does Yvette have?

45.
$$2 - 7s = -19$$
$$2 - 7s + 7s = -19 + 7s$$
$$2 = -19 + 7s$$
$$19 + 2 = 19 - 19 + 7s$$
$$21 = 7s$$
$$s = 3$$

46.
$$3x - 5 = 7x + 7$$
$$3x - 3x - 5 = 7x - 3x + 7$$
$$-5 = 4x + 7$$
$$-5 - 7 = 4x + 7 - 7$$
$$-12 = 4x$$
$$x = -3$$

**PAGE 125    HISTORY CONNECTION**

Let $y$ = the number of years Diophantus lived.

$\dfrac{y}{6} + \dfrac{y}{12} + \dfrac{y}{7}$ is the number of years Diophantus lived before marriage.

$5 + \left(\dfrac{y}{2} + 4\right)$ is the number of years Diophantus lived after marriage.

$$y = \dfrac{y}{6} + \dfrac{y}{12} + \dfrac{y}{7} + 5 + \dfrac{y}{2} + 4$$
$$y = \dfrac{14y}{84} + \dfrac{7y}{84} + \dfrac{12y}{84} + 5 + \dfrac{42y}{84} + 4$$
$$y = \dfrac{75y}{84} + 9$$
$$y - \dfrac{75y}{84} = 9$$
$$\dfrac{9y}{84} = 9$$
$$y = 84$$

So Diophantus lived 84 years.

---

# Chapter 3    Summary and Review

**PAGES 126-128    SKILLS AND CONCEPTS**

The check is left for the students.

1.
$$x - 16 = 37$$
$$x - 16 + 16 = 37 + 16$$
$$x = 53$$

2.
$$k + 13 = 5$$
$$k + 13 - 13 = 5 - 13$$
$$k = -8$$

3.
$$15 - y = 9$$
$$15 - 9 - y = 9 - 9$$
$$6 - y = 0$$
$$6 - y + y = y$$
$$6 = y$$

4.
$$-13 = 6 - k$$
$$-13 + k = 6 - k + k$$
$$-13 + k = 6$$
$$13 - 13 + k = 13 + 6$$
$$k = 19$$

5.
$$19 = -8 + d$$
$$8 + 19 = 8 - 8 + d$$
$$27 = d$$

6.
$$m + (-5) = -17$$
$$m - 5 = -17$$
$$m - 5 + 5 = -17 + 5$$
$$m = -12$$

7. Let $x$ = the number.
$$x - 13 = 64$$
$$x - 13 + 13 = 64 + 13$$
$$x = 77$$
The number is 77.

8. Let $x$ = the number.
$$x + (-35) = 98$$
$$x - 35 = 98$$
$$x - 35 + 35 = 98 + 35$$
$$x = 133$$
The number is 133.

9.
$$z + 15 = -9$$
$$z + 15 - 15 = -9 - 15$$
$$z = -24$$

10.
$$19 = y + 7$$
$$19 - 7 = y + 7 - 7$$
$$12 = y$$

11.
$$p + (-7) = 31$$
$$p - 7 = 31$$
$$p - 7 + 7 = 31 + 7$$
$$p = 38$$

12.
$$r - (-5) = -8$$
$$r + 5 = -8$$
$$r + 5 - 5 = -8 - 5$$
$$r = -13$$

13.
$$y + (-9) = -35$$
$$y - 9 = -35$$
$$y - 9 + 9 = -35 + 9$$
$$y = -26$$

14.
$$m - (-4) = 21$$
$$m + 4 = 21$$
$$m + 4 - 4 = 21 - 4$$
$$m = 17$$

15. Let $x$ = the number.
$$x + (-16) = 39$$
$$x - 16 = 39$$
$$x - 16 + 16 = 39 + 16$$
$$x = 55$$
The number is 55.

16. Let $x$ = the number.
$$x - (-11) = -176$$
$$x + 11 = -176$$
$$x + 11 - 11 = -176 + 11$$
$$x = -187$$
The number is -187.

17.
$$-7x = -56$$
$$\dfrac{-7x}{-7} = \dfrac{-56}{-7}$$
$$x = 8$$

18.
$$23y = 1035$$
$$\dfrac{23y}{23} = \dfrac{1035}{23}$$
$$y = 45$$

19.
$$534 = -89r$$
$$\dfrac{534}{-89} = \dfrac{-89r}{-89}$$
$$-6 = r$$

20.
$$\dfrac{x}{5} = 7$$
$$5\left(\dfrac{x}{5}\right) = 5(7)$$
$$x = 35$$

21.
$$\dfrac{3x}{4} = -12$$
$$\dfrac{4}{3}\left(\dfrac{3x}{4}\right) = \dfrac{4}{3}(-12)$$
$$x = -16$$

**22.** $1\frac{2}{3}n = 1\frac{1}{2}$

$\frac{5n}{3} = \frac{3}{2}$

$\frac{3}{5}\left(\frac{5n}{3}\right) = \frac{3}{5}\left(\frac{3}{2}\right)$

$n = \frac{9}{10}$; $0.9$

**23.** Let $x$ = the number.

$6x = -96$

$\frac{6x}{6} = \frac{-96}{6}$

$x = -16$

The number is $-16$.

**24.** Let $x$ = the number.

$\frac{7n}{8} = 14$

$\frac{8}{7}\left(\frac{7n}{8}\right) = \frac{8}{7}(14)$

$n = 16$

The number is 16.

**25.** $3x - 8 = 22$

$3x - 8 + 8 = 22 + 8$

$3x = 30$

$\frac{3x}{3} = \frac{30}{3}$

$x = 10$

**26.** $-4y + 2 = 32$

$-4y + 2 - 2 = 32 - 2$

$-4y = 30$

$\frac{-4y}{-4} = \frac{30}{-4}$

$y = -\frac{15}{2}$; $-7.5$

**27.** $0.5n + 3 = -6$

$10(0.5n + 3) = 10(-6)$

$5n + 30 = -60$

$5n + 30 - 30 = -60 - 30$

$5n = -90$

$\frac{5n}{5} = \frac{-90}{5}$

$n = -18$

**28.** $-6 = 3.1t + 6.4$

$10(-6) = 10(3.1t + 6.4)$

$-60 = 31t + 64$

$-60 - 64 = 31t + 64 - 64$

$-124 = 31t$

$\frac{-124}{31} = \frac{31t}{31}$

$-4 = t$

**29.** $\frac{x}{-3} + 2 = -21$

$\frac{x}{-3} + 2 - 2 = -21 - 2$

$\frac{x}{-3} = -23$

$-3\left(\frac{x}{-3}\right) = -3(-23)$

$x = 69$

**30.** $\frac{r - 8}{-6} = 7$

$-6\left(\frac{r - 8}{-6}\right) = -6(7)$

$r - 8 = -42$

$r - 8 + 8 = -42 + 8$

$r = -34$

**31.** $5a - 5 = 7a - 19$

$5a - 5a - 5 = 7a - 5a - 19$

$-5 = 2a - 19$

$19 - 5 = 2a + 19 - 19$

$14 = 2a$

$a = 7$

**32.** $-3(x + 2) = -18$

$-3x - 6 = -18$

$-3x - 6 + 6 = -18 + 6$

$-3x = -12$

$x = 4$

**33.** $4(2y - 1) = -10(y - 5)$

$8y - 4 = -10y + 50$

$10y + 8y - 4 = 10y - 10y + 50$

$18y - 4 = 50$

$18y - 4 + 4 = 50 + 4$

$18y = 54$

$y = 3$

**34.** $11.2n + 6 = 5.2n$

$10(11.2n + 6) = 10(5.2n)$

$112n + 60 = 52n$

$112n + 60 - 60 = 52n - 60$

$112n = 52n - 60$

$112n - 52n = 52n - 52n - 60$

$60n = -60$

$n = -1$

**35.** Let $x$ = the number.

$2x + 12 = 3x - 31$

$2x - 2x + 12 = 3x - 2x - 31$

$12 = x - 31$

$12 + 31 = x - 31 + 31$

$43 = x$

The number is 43.

**36.** $\frac{2x}{3} + 5 = \frac{1x}{2} + 4$

$6\left(\frac{2x}{3} + 5\right) = 6\left(\frac{1x}{2} + 4\right)$

$4x + 30 = 3x + 24$

$4x - 3x + 30 = 3x - 3x + 24$

$x + 30 = 24$

$x + 30 - 30 = 24 - 30$

$x = -6$

**37.** $2.9m + 1.7 = 3.5 + 2.3m$

$10(2.9m + 1.7) = 10(3.5 + 2.3m)$

$29m + 17 = 35 + 23m$

$29m - 23m + 17 = 35 + 23m - 23m$

$6m + 17 = 35$

$6m + 17 - 17 = 35 - 17$

$6m = 18$

$m = 3$

**38.** $\frac{3t + 1}{4} = \frac{3t}{4} - 5$

$4\left(\frac{3t + 1}{4}\right) = 4\left(\frac{3t}{4} - 5\right)$

$3t + 1 = 3t - 5$

no solution

39. $$2.85y - 7 = 12.85y - 2$$
$$100(2.85y - 7) = 100(12.85y - 2)$$
$$285y - 700 = 1285y - 200$$
$$285y - 285y - 700 = 1285y - 285y - 200$$
$$-700 = 1000y - 200$$
$$-700 + 200 = 1000y - 200 + 200$$
$$-500 = 1000y$$
$$-0.5 = y$$

40. $$\frac{x + y}{c} = d$$
$$c\left(\frac{x + y}{c}\right) = c(d)$$
$$x + y = cd$$
$$x + y - y = cd - y$$
$$x = cd - y$$

41. $$5(2a + x) = 3b$$
$$10a + 5x = 3b$$
$$10a - 10a + 5x = 3b - 10a$$
$$5x = 3b - 10a$$
$$\frac{5x}{5} = \frac{3b - 10a}{5}$$
$$x = \frac{3b - 10a}{5}$$

42. $$\frac{2x - a}{3} = \frac{a + 3b}{4}$$
$$12\left(\frac{2x - a}{3}\right) = 12\left(\frac{a + 3b}{4}\right)$$
$$4(2x - a) = 3(a + 3b)$$
$$8x - 4a = 3a + 9b$$
$$8x - 4a + 4a = 3a + 9b + 4a$$
$$8x = 7a + 9b$$
$$\frac{8x}{8} = \frac{7a + 9b}{8}$$
$$x = \frac{7a + 9b}{8}$$

43. $$\frac{2x}{3} + a = a + b$$
$$3\left(\frac{2x}{3} + a\right) = 3(a + b)$$
$$2x + 3a = 3a + 3b$$
$$2x + 3a - 3a = 3a - 3a + 3b$$
$$2x = 3b$$
$$\frac{2x}{2} = \frac{3b}{2}$$
$$x = \frac{3b}{2}$$

**PAGE 128    APPLICATIONS AND CONNECTIONS**

44. Let $w$ = the width.
$$6\frac{1}{2} \cdot w = 42\frac{1}{4}$$
$$\frac{13w}{2} = \frac{169}{4}$$
$$\frac{2}{13}\left(\frac{13w}{2}\right) = \frac{2}{13}\left(\frac{169}{4}\right)$$
$$w = 6\frac{1}{2};\ 6.5$$

The width is $6\frac{1}{2}$; 6.5.

45. Let $w$ = the width.
$$3.5 \cdot w = 17.85$$
$$100(3.5w) = 100(17.85)$$
$$350w = 1785$$
$$\frac{350w}{350} = \frac{1785}{350}$$
$$w = 5.1$$
The width is 5.1 cm.

46. 3 days overdue cost 30¢.
24 days overdue cost $1.20.
So the books were 27 days overdue.

47. amount left + amount given to Kwon + amount used
= original amount
$$225 + 225 + 2(225) = 900$$
The original amount was 900 mL.

48. Let $x$ = the first even integer.
$x + 2$ = the next even integer.
$$x + x + 2 = 94$$
$$2x + 2 = 94$$
$$2x = 92$$
$$x = 46$$
$$x + 2 = 48$$
The two consecutive even integers are 46 and 48.

49. Let $x$ = the first odd integer;
$x + 2$ = the second odd integer;
$x + 4$ = the third odd integer.
$$x + x + 2 + x + 4 = 81$$
$$3x + 6 = 81$$
$$3x = 75$$
$$x = 25$$
$$x + 2 = 27$$
$$x + 4 = 29$$
The three consecutive odd
integers are 25, 27, 29.

50. $$2w + 2(w - 5) = 70$$
$$2w + 2w - 10 = 70$$
$$4w - 10 + 10 = 70 + 10$$
$$4w = 80$$
$$w = 20$$
$$w - 5 = 15$$
The dimensions are 15 in × 20 in.

51. $$2w + 2(5w + 1) = 188$$
$$2w + 10w + 2 = 188$$
$$12w + 2 = 188$$
$$12w = 186$$
$$w = 15.5$$
$$5w + 1 = 78.5$$
The dimensions are 15.5 m × 78.5 m.

52. $$19.2 - (-7.8) = 19.2 + 7.8$$
$$= 27\ points$$

53. Let $x$ = the first even integer;

 $x + 2$ = the second even integer;

 $x + 4$ = the third even integer;

 $x + 6$ = the fourth even integer.

$$x + x + 2 + x + 4 + x + 6 = 156$$
$$4x + 12 = 156$$
$$x = 36$$

The four consecutive even integers
are 36 ft, 38 ft, 40 ft, 42 ft.

# Chapter 3    Test

**PAGE 129**

The check is left for the student.

1. $m + 13 = -9$

 $m + 13 - 13 = -9 - 13$

 $m = -22$

2. $k + 16 = -4$

 $k + 16 - 16 = -4 - 16$

 $k = -20$

3. $y + (-3) = 14$

 $y - 3 = 14$

 $y - 3 + 3 = 14 + 3$

 $y = 17$

4. $x + (-6) = 13$

 $x - 6 = 13$

 $x - 6 + 6 = 13 + 6$

 $x = 19$

5. $k - (-3) = 28$

 $k + 3 = 28$

 $k + 3 - 3 = 28 - 3$

 $k = 25$

6. $-5 - k = 14$

 $-5 - k + k = 14 + k$

 $-5 = 14 + k$

 $-14 - 5 = -14 + 14 + k$

 $-19 = k$

7. $r - (-1.2) = -7.3$

 $r + 1.2 = -7.3$

 $r + 1.2 - 1.2 = -7.3 - 1.2$

 $r = -8.5$

8. $b - \frac{2}{3} = -\frac{5}{6}$

 $b - \frac{2}{3} + \frac{2}{3} = -\frac{5}{6} + \frac{2}{3}$

 $b = -\frac{1}{6};\ -0.16$

9. $-3y = 63$

 $\frac{-3y}{-3} = \frac{63}{-3}$

 $y = -21$

10. $\frac{3y}{4} = -27$

 $\frac{4}{3}\left(\frac{3y}{4}\right) = \frac{4}{3}(-27)$

 $y = -36$

11. $3x + 1 = 16$

 $3x + 1 - 1 = 16 - 1$

 $3x = 15$

 $x = 5$

12. $5.2n + 0.7 = 2.8 + 2.2n$

 $10(5.2n + 0.7) = 10(2.8 + 2.2n)$

 $52n + 7 = 28 + 22n$

 $30n = 21$

 $n = \frac{7}{10};\ 0.7$

13. $5(8 - 2n) = 4n - 2$

 $40 - 10n = 4n - 2$

 $42 = 14n$

 $n = 3$

14. $3(n + 5) - 6 = 3n + 9$

 $3n + 15 - 6 = 3n + 9$

 $3n + 9 = 3n + 9$

 all numbers

15. $7x + 9 = 3(x + 3)$

 $7x + 9 = 3x + 9$

 $10x = 0$

 $x = 0$

16. $-2(3n - 5) + 3n = 2 - n$

 $-6n + 10 + 3n = 2 - n$

 $-3n + 10 = 2 - n$

 $8 = 2n$

 $4 = n$

17. $\frac{3n}{4} - \frac{2n}{3} = 5$

 $\frac{n}{12} = 5$

 $n = 60$

18. $\frac{t - 7}{4} = 11$

 $t - 7 = 44$

 $t = 51$

19. $\frac{2r - 3}{-7} = 5$

 $2r - 3 = -35$

 $2r = -32$

 $r = -16$

20. $8r - \frac{r}{3} = 46$

 $3\left(8r - \frac{r}{3}\right) = 3(46)$

 $24r - r = 138$

 $23r = 138$

 $r = 6$

21. Let $x$ = an integer.

 $x + 8 = -11$

 $x = -19$

 The integer is -19.

22. Let $x$ = an integer.

 $x - (-11) = 26$

 $x + 11 = 26$

 $x = 15$

 The integer is 15.

23. Let $x$ = a number.

 $4x - 2x = 100$

 $2x = 100$

 $x = 50$

 The number is 50.

24. Let $x$ = an integer.

 $x + 1$ = the next integer

 $2x + x + 1 = 50$

 $3x + 1 = 50$

 $3x = 49$

 $x = \frac{49}{3};\ 16.\overline{3}$

 $x$ is not an integer;

 no solution

25. $x + r = q$

 $x + r - r = q - r$

 $x = q - r$

26. $\frac{x + y}{b} = c$

 $b\left(\frac{x + y}{b}\right) = b(c)$

 $x + y = bc$

 $x + y - y = bc - y$

 $x = bc - y$

27. $yx - a = cx$

 $yx - a + a = cx + a$

 $yx = cx + a$

 $yx - cx = cx - cx + a$

 $x(y - c) = a$

 $x = \frac{a}{y - c}$

28. $131.3 + 21.7 = 153$

 Jenny's time was 153 seconds.

29. $68 + 4 = 72$

 Maria's score was 72.

30. $d = r \cdot t$

 $d = 13.65 \cdot \frac{3}{4} = 10.238$

 Alma rides 10.238 miles.

Let $c$ = the cost of 5 T-shirts or 2 sweatshirts.

$$c + c = 115$$
$$2c = 115$$
$$c = 57.5$$

The cost of 5 T-shirts is $57.50; The cost of 1 T-shirt is $\frac{\$57.50}{5}$ or $11.50.

# Chapter 3    College Entrance Exam Preview

**PAGES 130-131**

**1. D**

Since $87 \div 3 = 29$, it is not a prime number.

**2. B**

$328 \div 4 = 72$

Since $400 - 328 = 72$ and $72 \div 4 = 18$, there are 18 numbers greater than 328 that are divisible by 4. Therefore there is a total of 19.

**3. B**

Since $201 - 99 = 102$ and $102 \div 2 = 51$, there are 51 numbers that are divisible by 2. 100 is divisible by 5; $200 - 100 = 100$ and $100 \div 5 = 20$, so there are $20 + 1$ or 21 numbers that are divisible by 5. Now subtract those that are divisible by both 2 and 5. 100 is divisible by 2 and 5 or 10; $200 - 100 = 100$ and $100 \div 10 = 10$, so there are $10 + 1$ or 11 numbers that are divisible by both 2 and 5.
So $51 + 21 - 11 = 61$ numbers between 99 and 201 are divisible by 2 or 5.

**4. B**

Between 5 and 12, there are $12 - 5 - 1$ or 6 integers: 6, 7, 8, 9, 10, 11. Between 5 and 1995, there are $1995 - 5 - 1$ or 1989 integers.

**5. B**

Draw a diagram.

| | | | | | | | | | | | | | | | | | | | | | | |
|1|2|3|4|5|6|7|8|9|10|11|12|13|14|15|16|17|18|19|20|21|22|23|
| | | | | | | | | | |11|10|9|8|7|6|5|4|3|2|1|

There are 23 people in line.

**6. C**

$$2 \quad 5 \quad 15 \quad 18 \quad 54 \quad 171 \quad 174 \quad 522$$
$$+3 \quad \times 3 \quad +3 \quad \times 3 \qquad +3 \quad \times 3$$

$54 + 3 = 57$
$57 \times 3 = 171$
57 is missing from the sequence.

**7. C**

a. $0.77$

b. $\frac{7}{9} = 0.7777\ldots$

c. $\frac{8}{11} = 0.7272\ldots$

d. $\frac{3}{4} = 0.75$

$\frac{8}{11}$ is the least.

**8. A**

$\frac{1}{4} = 0.25$ and $\frac{1}{3} = 0.333\ldots$

a. $\frac{4}{13} = 0.3077$

b. $\frac{1}{5} = 0.2$

c. $\frac{5}{12} = 0.4166\ldots$

d. $\frac{3}{4} = 0.75$

Since 0.3077 is greater than 0.25 and less than $0.\overline{3}$, $\frac{4}{13}$ is greater than $\frac{1}{4}$ and less than $\frac{1}{3}$.

**9. C**

$\frac{1}{5} = 0.2$

a. $\frac{3}{14} = 0.2143$

b. $\frac{21}{100} = 0.21$

c. $\frac{2}{11} = 0.1818\ldots$

d. $\frac{101}{501} = 0.2016$

Since $0.\overline{18}$ is less than 0.2, $\frac{2}{11}$ is less than $\frac{1}{5}$.

**10. D**

a. $\frac{1}{2} = 0.5$

b. $\frac{5}{11} = 0.4545\ldots$

c. $\frac{4}{9} = 0.4444\ldots$

d. $\frac{7}{18} = 0.5385$

Since 0.5385 is greater than the other decimals, $\frac{7}{13}$ is the greatest fraction.

**11. A**

$$\begin{array}{r} 80\triangle \\ -602 \\ \hline \square\,98 \end{array}$$

$$\begin{array}{r} 800 \\ -602 \\ \hline \square\,98 \end{array}$$

$\triangle$ must represent a 0.

Therefore, $\square$ must represent a 1.

**12. D**

$$42\tfrac{3}{8} = 42\tfrac{9}{24} = 41\tfrac{33}{24}$$
$$-41\tfrac{2}{3} = -41\tfrac{16}{24} = -41\tfrac{16}{24}$$
$$\overline{\qquad\qquad\qquad \tfrac{17}{24}}$$

$60 \times \frac{17}{24} = 42\frac{1}{2}$

13. C

Make a list.

Thursday 10 A.M.

3 P.M.

8 P.M.

Friday 1 A.M.

6 A.M.

11 A.M.

4 P.M.

9 P.M.

Saturday 2 A.M.

7 A.M.

12 Noon

14. C

Since −1 is less than −0.5, A cannot be the answer.

Since 3 is greater than −1, B cannot be the answer.

Since 3 is greater than −0.5, D cannot be the answer.

Therefore, the answer is C.

15. B

Find the LCM.

$4 = 2^2$

$6 = 2 \cdot 3$

$8 = 2^3$

LCM $= 2^3 \cdot 3$ or 24

Therefore 24 + 3 or 27 is the answer.

16. B

8(916) + 916 = 9(916)

5(916) + 4(916) = 9(916)

17. D

If Benito pays Carl $5, he will still owe Carl $7. If Benito pays Alan $3, Alan will owe Benito $7. Therefore, if Alan pays Carl $7, all the debts will have been paid.

18. A

100 ÷ 8 = 12.5

Therefore, only 12 jars can be filled.

19. B

Make a list of the prime numbers.

2    3    5    7    11    13    17    19    23    29

29 − 23 = 6

20. A

$(-9)(-9)(-9) = (-9)(-9)(-9)n$

$\dfrac{-729}{-729} = \dfrac{-729}{-729}n$

$1 = n$

21. C

1 + 2 + 3 + 4 + 5 = 15

7 + 8 + 9 + 10 + 11 = 45

23 + 24 + 25 + 26 + 27 = 125

15, 45, and 125 are

all divisible by 5.

22. C

$16 - 12 \div 2^2 \times 3 = 16 - 12 \div 4 \times 3$

$= 16 - 3 \times 3$

$= 16 - 9$

$= 7$

23. A

$\dfrac{5}{7} = 0.7143$

$\dfrac{7}{12} = 0.5833$

$\dfrac{6}{11} = 0.5454\ldots$

$\dfrac{3}{13} = 0.2308$

$\dfrac{5}{7}, \dfrac{7}{12}, \dfrac{6}{11}, \dfrac{3}{13}$

# Chapter 4 Applications of Rational Numbers

| 4-1 | Ratios and Proportions |
| --- | --- |

CHECKING FOR UNDERSTANDING

1. rate  2. extremes  3. ratio  4. means  5. $\frac{3}{11}$

6. $\frac{21}{16}$  7. $\frac{2}{1}$  8. $\frac{24}{7}$  9. $\frac{4}{1}$  10. $\frac{7}{24}$

11. $\frac{3}{4} = \frac{x}{8}$

$4x = 24$

$x = 6$

12. $\frac{2}{10} = \frac{1}{y}$

$2y = 10$

$y = 5$

13. $\frac{10}{a} = \frac{20}{28}$

$20a = 280$

$a = 14$

EXERCISES

14. $\frac{3}{15} = \frac{b}{45}$

$15b = 135$

$b = 9$

15. $\frac{6}{8} = \frac{7}{x}$

$6x = 56$

$x = \frac{56}{6} = \frac{28}{3};\ 9.\overline{3}$

16. $\frac{x}{9} = \frac{-7}{16}$

$16x = -63$

$x = \frac{-63}{16};\ -3.938$

17. $\frac{5}{2n} = \frac{-2}{1.6}$

$-4n = 8$

$n = -2$

18. $\frac{x+2}{5} = \frac{7}{5}$

$5(x + 2) = 35$

$5x + 10 = 35$

$5x = 25$

$x = 5$

19. $\frac{6}{14} = \frac{7}{x-3}$

$6(x - 3) = 98$

$6x - 18 = 98$

$6x = 116$

$x = \frac{116}{6} = \frac{58}{3};\ 19.\overline{3}$

20. $\frac{3}{5} = \frac{x+2}{6}$

$5(x + 2) = 18$

$5x + 10 = 18$

$5x = 8$

$x = \frac{8}{5};\ 1.6$

21. $\frac{14}{10} = \frac{5+x}{x-3}$

$14(x - 3) = 10(5 + x)$

$14x - 42 = 50 + 10x$

$4x = 92$

$x = 23$

22. $\frac{9}{x-8} = \frac{4}{5}$

$4(x - 8) = 45$

$4x - 32 = 45$

$4x = 77$

$x = \frac{77}{4};\ 19.25$

23. $\frac{4-x}{3+x} = \frac{16}{25}$

$16(3 + x) = 25(4 - x)$

$48 + 16x = 100 - 25x$

$41x = 52$

$x = \frac{52}{41};\ 1.268$

24. $\frac{x-12}{6} = \frac{x+7}{4}$

$6(x + 7) = -4(x - 12)$

$6x + 42 = -4x + 48$

$10x = 6$

$x = \frac{6}{10} = \frac{3}{5};\ 0.6$

25. $\frac{x+9}{5} = \frac{x-10}{11}$

$11(x + 9) = 5(x - 10)$

$11x + 99 = 5x - 50$

$6x = -149$

$x = \frac{-149}{6};\ -24.8\overline{3}$

26. $\frac{4.3}{25.8} = \frac{1}{2n}$

$8.6n = 25.8$

$n = 3$

27. $\frac{2}{0.19} = \frac{12}{0.5n}$

$n = 2.28$

28. $\frac{n}{8} = \frac{0.21}{2}$

$2n = 1.68$

$n = 0.84$

29. $\frac{x}{4.085} = \frac{5}{16.33}$

$16.33x = 20.425$

$x = 1.251$

30. $\frac{2.405}{3.67} = \frac{g}{1.88}$

$3.67g = 4.521$

$g = 1.232$

31. $\frac{3s}{9.65} = \frac{21}{1.066}$

$3.198s = 202.65$

$s = 63.368$

32. $10a = 25b$

$\frac{10a}{b} = \frac{25b}{b}$

$\frac{10a}{b} = 25$

$\frac{10a}{10b} = \frac{25}{10}$

$\frac{a}{b} = \frac{25}{10} = \frac{5}{2}$

33. $4a + 2b = 16a$

$-4a + 4a + 2b = 16a - 4a$

$2b = 12a$

$\frac{2b}{b} = \frac{12a}{b}$

$2 = \frac{12a}{b}$

$\frac{2}{12} = \frac{12a}{12b}$

$\frac{2}{12} = \frac{1}{6} = \frac{a}{b}$

34. $\frac{3a}{5} = \frac{12b}{7}$

$\frac{3a}{5b} = \frac{12b}{7b}$

$\frac{3a}{5b} = \frac{12}{7}$

$\frac{5}{3}\left(\frac{3a}{5b}\right) = \frac{5}{3}\left(\frac{12}{7}\right)$

$\frac{a}{b} = \frac{60}{21} = \frac{20}{7}$

35. Let $x$ = deer population in the preserve

$\frac{x}{239} = \frac{198}{42}$

$42x = 47322$

$x = 1126.7$

There are approximately 1127 deer in the preserve.

36. Let $x$ = the actual length

       $y$ = the actual width

$$\frac{1}{3} = \frac{5\frac{1}{2}}{x} \qquad \frac{1}{3} = \frac{7}{y}$$

$$x = 16\frac{1}{2} \qquad\qquad y = 21$$

The dimensions of the actual room are $16\frac{1}{2}$ ft by 21 ft.

37. Let $x$ = the actual distance

$$\frac{1}{57} = \frac{4.7}{x}$$

$$x = 267.9$$

Bismarck and Fargo are actually 267.9 kilometers apart.

38. a. $\frac{A}{30} = \frac{B}{15}$

    $15A = 30B$

    $\frac{15A}{B} = \frac{30B}{B}$

    $\frac{15A}{B} = 30$

    $\frac{15A}{15B} = \frac{30}{15}$

    $\frac{A}{B} = \frac{2}{1}$

    The ratio is 2:1.

  b. twice

39. $3^2 + 4(8 - 2) - 6(3) + 4 + 2 + (8 - 2)^2$

$= 3^2 + 4(6) - 6(3) + 4 \div 2 + (6)^2$

$= 9 + 4(6) - 6(3) + 4 + 2 + 36$

$= 9 + 24 - 18 + 2 + 36$

$= 53$

40. $6(2x + y) + 2(x + 4y) = 12x + 6y + 2x + 8y$

                          $= 14x + 14y$

41. $-17px + 22bq + 35px + (-37bq)$

$= -17px + 35px + 22bq - 37bq$

$= (-17 + 35)px + (22 - 37)bq$

$= 18px - 15bq$

42. Let $c$ = cup of butter

$$4 \cdot \frac{1c}{2} = 2c$$

There are 2 cups of butter in one pound.

43. $\qquad \frac{-7}{6} + k = \frac{5}{6}$

$+\frac{7}{6} - \frac{7}{6} + k = \frac{5}{6} + \frac{7}{6}$

$\qquad\qquad k = \frac{12}{6} = 2$

**PAGE 140**      **CHECKING FOR UNDERSTANDING**

1. $\frac{r}{100}$

2. Answers may vary; typical answers are sales, statistics, and test scores.

3. $\frac{31}{100} = 31\%$    4. $\frac{3}{10} = \frac{30}{100} = 30\%$    5. $\frac{1}{25} = \frac{4}{100} = 4\%$

6. $\frac{7}{20} = \frac{35}{100} = 35\%$

7. $\frac{3}{8} = \frac{x}{100}$

   $8x = 300$

    $x = 37.5$

   $\frac{3}{8} = 37.5\%$ or $37\frac{1}{2}\%$

8. $\frac{9}{5} = \frac{180}{100} = 180\%$

These problems can be solved by using a proportion or an equation. The proportions are given in [ ]. Notice step 2 is the same in either approach.

9. Let $x$ = the number

$$x = \frac{40}{100}(60) \qquad \left[\frac{x}{60} = \frac{40}{100}\right]$$

  $100x = 2400$

      $x = 24$

40% of 60 is 24.

10. Let $x$ = the percent

$$75 = \frac{x}{100}(250) \qquad \left[\frac{75}{250} = \frac{x}{100}\right]$$

  $7500 = 250x$

    $30 = x$

75 is 30% of 250.

11. Let $x$ = the number

$$21 = \frac{35}{100}(x) \qquad \left[\frac{21}{x} = \frac{35}{100}\right]$$

  $2100 = 35x$

    $60 = x$

21 is 35% of 60.

12. Let $x$ = percent

$$52 = \frac{x}{100}(80) \qquad \left[\frac{52}{80} = \frac{x}{100}\right]$$

  $5200 = 80x$

    $65 = x$

52 is 65% of 80.

**PAGES 140-141**      **EXERCISES**

13. Let $n$ = the percent

$$\frac{6}{15} = \frac{n}{100}$$

  $15n = 600$

    $n = 40$

6 is 40% of 15.

14. Let $x$ = the percent

$$\frac{35}{50} = \frac{x}{100}$$

$$50x = 3500$$

$$x = 70$$

35 is 70% of 50.

15. Let $x$ = the percent

$$\frac{5}{40} = \frac{x}{100}$$

$$40x = 500$$

$$x = 12\frac{1}{2}$$

5 is $12\frac{1}{2}$% of 40.

16. Let $x$ = the percent

$$\frac{225}{75} = \frac{x}{100}$$

$$75x = 22,500$$

$$x = 300$$

225 is 300% of 75.

17. Let $n$ = the number

$$x = \frac{40}{100}(80)$$

$$x = 32$$

32 is 40% of 80.

18. Let $x$ = the number

$$17.65 = \frac{25}{100}(x)$$

$$1765 = 25x$$

$$70.6 = x$$

17.65 is 25% of 70.6.

19. Let $p$ = the percent

$$14 = \frac{p}{100}(56)$$

$$1400 = 56p$$

$$25 = p$$

14 is 25% of 56.

20. Let $p$ = the percent

$$\frac{p}{100}(72) = 12$$

$$72p = 1200$$

$$p = 16\frac{2}{3}$$

$16\frac{2}{3}$% of 72 is 12.

21. Let $x$ = the number

$$36 = \frac{45}{100}(x) \qquad \left[\frac{36}{x} = \frac{45}{100}\right]$$

$$3600 = 45x$$

$$80 = x$$

36 is 45% of 80.

22. Let $x$ = the number

$$\frac{81}{100}(32) = x \qquad \left[\frac{81}{100} = \frac{x}{32}\right]$$

$$2592 = 100x$$

$$25.92 = x$$

81% of 32 is 25.92.

23. Let $x$ = the dollars

$$\frac{4}{100}(6070) = x \qquad \left[\frac{4}{100} = \frac{x}{6070}\right]$$

$$24280 = 100x$$

$$242.80 = x$$

4% of $6070 is $242.80.

24. Let $x$ = the percent

$$55 = \frac{x}{100}(88) \qquad \left[\frac{55}{88} = \frac{x}{100}\right]$$

$$5500 = 88x$$

$$62.5 = x$$

55 is $62\frac{1}{2}$% of 88.

25. Let $x$ = the dollars

$$54,000 = \frac{108}{100}(x) \qquad \left[\frac{54,000}{x} = \frac{108}{100}\right]$$

$$5,400,000 = 108x$$

$$50,000 = x$$

$54,000 is 108% of $50,000.

26. Let $x$ = the dollars

$$\frac{112}{100}(500) = x \qquad \left[\frac{112}{100} = \frac{x}{500}\right]$$

$$56,000 = 100x$$

$$560 = x$$

112% of $500 is $560.

27. Let $n$ = the dollars

$$n = \frac{0.12}{100}(5200.75) \qquad \left[\frac{0.12}{100} = \frac{n}{5200.75}\right]$$

$$100n = 624.09$$

$$n = 6.2409$$

$6.24 is 0.12% of $5200.75.

28. Let $n$ = the dollars

$$n = \frac{98.5}{100}(140.32) \qquad \left[\frac{98.5}{100} = \frac{n}{140.32}\right]$$

$$100n = 13821.52$$

$$n = 138.2152$$

$138.22 is 98.5% of $140.32.

29. $$a = \frac{2.25}{100}b$$

$$b = \frac{100}{2.25}a$$

$$b = 44.4a$$

$b$ is 44.4% of $a$.

30. Let $k$ = number of kilograms of metal in the sample

$$\frac{3.2}{100}(180) = k \qquad \left[\frac{3.2}{100} = \frac{k}{180}\right]$$

$$576 = 100k$$

$$5.76 = k$$

There were 5.76 kilograms of metal in the sample.

31. Let $x$ = the number of questions on the test

$$34 = \frac{85}{100}(x) \qquad \left[\frac{34}{x} = \frac{85}{100}\right]$$

$$3400 = 85x$$

$$40 = x$$

There were 40 questions on the test.

32. Let $x$ = rate of tax

$$\frac{x}{100}(20) = 0.90 \qquad \left[\frac{x}{100} = \frac{0.90}{20}\right]$$

$$20x = 90$$

$$x = 4.5$$

The tax rate was $4\frac{1}{2}$%.

33. Let $x$ = the number of people with an opinion.

94% of the people had an opinion.

$$\frac{94}{100}(8000) = x \qquad \left[\frac{94}{100} = \frac{x}{8000}\right]$$

$$752,000 = 100x$$

$$7520 = x$$

7520 people expressed an opinion.

34. a. visit family/friends

b. go to summer/winter resort

c. 100%

35. $2m + n^2 = y$

36. $18 - (-34) = 18 + 34 = 52$

37. $$y + \frac{7}{16} = -\frac{5}{8}$$

$$y + \frac{7}{16} - \frac{7}{16} = -\frac{5}{8} - \frac{7}{16}$$

$$y = -\frac{17}{16}$$

38. Let $x$ = the number of weeks to save $81

$$\frac{4}{18} = \frac{x}{81}$$

$$4(81) = 18x$$

$$324 = 18x$$

$$x = 18$$

It will take Isabel 18 weeks.

## 4-3  Application:  Simple Interest

PAGE 143    CHECKING FOR UNDERSTANDING

1. $I = prt$

   $= (1552.5)(0.07)(1)$

   $= 108.68$

   The interest will be $108.68.

2. The investment at 8% is probably less risky.

3. $I = prt$

   $I = (8000)(0.06)(1)$

   $I = 480$    $480

4. $I = prt$

   $I = (5000)(0.125)(5)$

   $I = 3125$    $3125

5. $I = prt$

   $1890 = (6000)(0.09)t$

   $1890 = 540t$

   $3.5 = t$    $3\frac{1}{2}$ years

6. $I = prt$

   $2160 = (6000)(0.08)t$

   $2160 = 480t$

   $4.5 = t$    $4\frac{1}{2}$ years

7. $I = prt$

   $2430 = (9000)r\left(2\frac{1}{4}\right)$

   $2430 = 20.250r$

   $0.12 = r$    12%

8. $I = prt$

   $780 = (6500)r(1)$

   $780 = 6500r$

   $0.12 = r$    12%

9. $I = prt$

   $756 = p(0.09)\left(3\frac{1}{2}\right)$

   $756 = 0.315p$

   $2400 = p$    $2400

10. $I = prt$

    $196 = p(0.10)(7)$

    $196 = 0.7p$

    $280 = p$    $280

11. Let $n$ = amount at 8%

$10,000 - n$ = amount at 12%

$$(0.08)n + (0.12)(10,000 - n) = 944$$

$$0.08n + 1200 - 0.12n = 944$$

$$-0.04n = -256$$

$$n = 6400$$

$$10,000 - n = 3600$$

She invested $6400 at 8% and $3600 at 12%.

12. Let $x$ = amount at 10%

$7200 - x$ = amount at 14%

$$0.10(x) + 0.14(7200 - x) = 960$$

$$0.10 + 1008 - 0.14x = 960$$

$$-0.04x = -48$$

$$x = 1200$$

$$7200 - x = 6000$$

He invested $1200 at 10% and $6000 at 14%

13. Let $n$ = amount at 9%

$5000 - n$ = amount at 12%

$$0.09n = 0.12(5000 - n) + 198$$

$$0.09n = 600 - 0.12n + 198$$

$$0.21n = 798$$

$$n = 3800$$

Fred invested $3800 at 9%.

14. Let $x$ = amount at 14%

$8500 - x$ = amount at 12%

$$0.14x = 0.12(8500 - x)$$

$$0.14x = 1020 - 0.12x$$

$$0.26x = 1020$$

$$x = 3923.08$$

Angela should invest $3923.08 at 14%.

15. Let $n$ = amount at 12%

$n + 1500$ = amount at 8%

$$0.12n = 0.08(n + 1500)$$

$$0.12n = 0.08n + 120$$

$$0.04n = 120$$

$$n = 3000$$

Charlotte invested $3000 at 12%.

16. Let $n$ = amount at 11%

$8000 - n$ = amount at 10%

$$(0.11)n + (0.10)(8000 - n) = 850$$

$$0.11n + 800 - 0.10n = 850$$

$$0.01n = 50$$

$$n = \frac{50}{0.01}$$

$$n = \$5000$$

John and Inger should invest $5000 at 11% and $3000 at 10%.

17. Let $r$ = rate at which to invest
$$2500(0.10) + 6000r = 940$$
$$250 + 6000r = 940$$
$$6000r = 690$$
$$r = 0.115$$
They should invest the $6000 at a rate of 11.5%.

18. Let $n$ = amount at 11%
$$7525 - n = \text{amount at 16%}$$
$$0.11(n) = 2[0.16(7525 - n)]$$
$$0.11n = 0.32(7525 - n)$$
$$0.11n = 2408 - 0.32n$$
$$0.43n = 2408$$
$$n = 5600 \qquad \text{Ken invested \$5600 at 11%.}$$

19. Let $P$ = amount invested
$$I = prt$$
$$45 = p(0.0025)(1)$$
$$45 = 0.0025p$$
$$18,000 = p$$
The investor invested $18,000.

20. a.

| Original Amount | Percent | After Increase | After Decrease |
|---|---|---|---|
| $100 | 10% | $110 | $99 |
| $40 | 20% | $48 | $38.40 |
| $500 | 15% | $575 | $488.75 |
| $6500 | 5% | $6825 | $6483.75 |

b. The final amount is less than the original amount.

21. Let $I$ = interest after the first 6 months.
$$I = prt$$
$$I = 1000(0.08)\left(\frac{1}{2}\right)$$
$$I = 40$$
New principal = $1000 + $40 = $1040
Let $I_2$ = interest after the second 6 months.
$$I_2 = prt$$
$$I_2 = 1040(0.08)\left(\frac{1}{2}\right)$$
$$I_2 = 41.60$$
New principal = $1040 + 41.60
$$= \$1081.60$$
Let $I_3$ = interest after the third 6 months.
$$I_3 = prt$$
$$I_3 = (1081.60)(0.08)\left(\frac{1}{2}\right)$$
$$I_3 = 43.264$$
New principal = $1081.60 + $43.26
$$= \$1124.86$$
The amount in the account was $1124.86.

22. $\frac{5}{6} \cdot 18 = m$

$15 = m$

23. $(-6.01)(-4.122) \underline{<} 25.005$
because $24.773 \underline{<} 25.005$

24. Answers may vary; typical answer is 0.

25.

| $x$: | | $y$: |
|---|---|---|
| 64 gal | | 64 gal |
| 96 gal | 32 gal → | 32 gal |
| 48 gal | ← 48 gal | 80 gal |
| 88 gal | 40 gal → | 40 gal |

At the beginning, $x$ contained 88 gallons and $y$ contained 40 gallons.

26. $28 = \frac{20}{100} \cdot x$

$x = 140$

PAGE 145    APPLICATION

Ana:                              Jim:
$$T = p(1 + r)^{+}$$               $$T = p(1 + r)^{+}$$
$$= 600\left(1 + \frac{0.12}{2}\right)^{4}$$      $$= 600\left(1 + \frac{0.12}{4}\right)^{8}$$
$$= 757.49$$                      $$= 760.06$$

Total amount in account after two years will be $757.49.

Total amount in account after two years will be $760.06.

Jim will have $2.57 more than Ana.

  Percent of Change

PAGE 148    CHECKING FOR UNDERSTANDING

1. Subtract old price from new price. Divide the result by old price. Move decimal point two places to right.
2. Multiply percent of discount by original price. Subtract result from original price.
3. Multiply tax rate by original price.
4. Divide retail price by 1 + percent of markup.
5. D, $6.00, 6.0%       6. I, $8.00, 8.0%
7. $172.00, $28.00      8. $358.95, $45.46
9. $47.89, 25.496%      10. $72.00, 50%

PAGE 149    EXERCISES

11. Let $n$ = the number.
$$n + 0.40n = 14$$
$$1.4n = 14$$
$$n = 10$$
The number is 10.

12. Let $n$ = the number.
$$n - 0.6\overline{6}n = 18$$
$$0.3\overline{3}n = 18$$
$$n = 54$$
The number is 54.

49

13. Let $n$ = the number.     14. Let $n$ = the number.

$14 = n - 0.50n$         $20 = n + 0.20n$

$14 = 0.50n$             $20 = 1.20n$

$28 = n$                 $16.\overline{6} = n$

The number is 28.       The number is $16.\overline{6}$.

15. Let $n$ = the number.     16. Let $n$ = the number.

$n = 30 + (0.30)(30)$    $n = 80 - (0.75)(80)$

$n = 30 + 9$             $n = 80 - 60$

$n = 39$                 $n = 20$

39 is 30% more than 30.   20 is 75% less than 80.

17. The amount of decrease is $10.00.

$\frac{10}{50} = \frac{r}{100}$

$50r = 1000$

$r = 20$

The percent of decrease was 20%.

18. The amount of increase is $10.00.

$\frac{10}{40} = \frac{r}{100}$

$1000 = 40r$

$25 = r$

The percent of increase was 25%.

19. Let $p$ = the price.

$p + 0.05p = 3.15$

$1.05p = 3.15$

$p = 3$

The price is $3.00.

20. Let $c$ = cost before the discount.

$c - 0.25c = 36$

$0.75c = 36$

$c = 48$

The cost before discount was $48.00.

21.  $345.00 - (0.12)(345.00)$

$= 345.00 - 41.40$

$= 303.60$

The price is $303.60.

22.  $74 + (0.065)(74)$

$= 74 + 4.81$

$= 78.81$

The total cost is $78.81.

23.  $44.00 - (0.10)(44.00)$

$= 44.00 - 4.40$

$= 39.60$ (discounted price)

$39.60 + (0.04)(39.60)$

$= 39.60 + 1.58$

$= 41.18$

The total cost is $41.18.

24.  $154.00 - (0.20)(154.00)$

$= 154.00 - 30.80$

$= 123.20$ (discounted price)

$123.00 + (0.05)(123.20)$

$= 123.20 + 6.16$

$= 129.36$

The total cost is $129.36.

25. $x + 10\% = x + 0.10x$

$= 1.1x$

$1.1x - 10\% = 1.1x - 0.10(1.1x)$

$= 1.1x - 0.11x$

$= 0.99x$

Since $x \neq 0.99x$, the answer is no.

26. Let $p$ = the percent

original price = $24.65 + 4.50 = 29.15$

$\frac{p}{100} = \frac{4.50}{29.15}$

$24.15p = 450$

$p = 0.15437$

The percent of discount is 15%.

27. Let $c$ = cost before taxes

$92.04 = c + 0.04c$

$92.04 = 1.04c$

$88.50 = c$

The cost before taxes was $88.50.

28. Let $p$ = new selling price

$550 + 0.2(550)$ = increased price

$550 + 110 = 660$

$p = 660 - (0.10)(660)$

$p = 660 - 66$

$p = 594$     The new selling price is $594.00.

29. $360 - (0.10)360 = 324$

Bob pays $324 after the 10% discount.

$324 - (0.05)324 = 307.80$

Bob pays $307.80 after the 5% discount.

30. $9a + 16b + 14a = 9a + 14a + 16b$

$= 23a + 16b$

31. $\frac{77b}{-11} = -7b$

32. $\quad -5 = 4 - 2(x - 5)$

$-5 = 4 - 2x + 10$

$-5 = -2x + 14$

$2x - 5 = 2x + -2x + 14$

$2x - 5 = 14$

$2x - 5 + 5 = 14 + 5$

$2x = 19$

$\frac{2x}{2} = \frac{19}{2}$

$x = \frac{19}{2}$

33. Let $p$ = the percent     34. $\quad I = prt$

$18 = \frac{p}{100} \cdot 60$        $3528 = 8400 \cdot 0.105 \cdot t$

$3528 = 882t$

$(100)18 = (100)\frac{p}{100} \cdot 60$     $\frac{3528}{882} = \frac{882t}{882}$

$1800 = p \cdot 60$            $4 = t$

$\frac{1800}{60} = \frac{p \cdot 60}{60}$         The time is 4 years.

$30 = p$

18 is 30% of 60.

# Technology: Successive Discounts

The program given on page 150 can be run to obtain the answers to exercises 1-5.

1. ] RUN
   ENTER ORIGINAL PRICE AND TWO DISCOUNTS AS DECIMALS.
   ? 49, .20, .10
   SUCCESSIVE DISCOUNTS                $35.28
   COMBINED DISCOUNTS                  $34.30
   A COMBINED DISCOUNT HAS A LOWER SALE PRICE.

2. ] RUN
   ENTER ORIGINAL PRICE AND TWO DISCOUNTS AS DECIMALS.
   ? 185, .25, .10
   SUCCESSIVE DISCOUNTS                $124.88
   COMBINED DISCOUNTS                  $120.55
   A COMBINED DISCOUNT HAS A LOWER SALE PRICE.

3. ] RUN
   ENTER ORIGINAL PRICE AND TWO DISCOUNTS AS DECIMALS.
   ? 12.50, .30, .125
   SUCCESSIVE DISCOUNTS                $7.66
   COMBINED DISCOUNTS                  $7.19
   A COMBINED DISCOUNT HAS A LOWER SALE PRICE.

4. ] RUN
   ENTER ORIGINAL PRICE AND TWO DISCOUNTS AS DECIMALS.
   ? 156.95, .30, .15
   SUCCESSIVE DISCOUNTS                $93.39
   COMBINED DISCOUNTS                  $86.32
   A COMBINED DISCOUNT HAS A LOWER SALE PRICE.

5. The sale price is lower if one combined discount is used.

## 4-5   Problem-Solving Strategy: Make a Table or Chart

**PAGE 152    CHECKING FOR UNDERSTANDING**

1. JOB A:  17,500 + 20,500 + 23,500 + 26,500 + 29,500 = 117,500
   JOB B:  20,000 + 22,000 + 24,000 + 26,000 + 28,000 = 120,000
   Job B would pay the most total money.

2. No; Adrienne and Darryl's favorite foods could not be determined.

3.

| Name | 1 hour | 2 hours | 3 hours | 4 hours |
|---|---|---|---|---|
| Ms. Agosto | $30 | $45 | $60 | $75 |
| Mr. Takamura | $45 | $55 | $65 | $75 |

They worked 4 hours.

4.

| Name | January | July | September | December |
|---|---|---|---|---|
| Amelia | N | N | Y | N |
| Brandon | N | Y | N | N |
| Lianna | Y | N | N | N |
| Jason | N | N | N | Y |

Amelia-September; Brandon-July; Lianna-January; Jason-December

5.

| Machine | A | B | Bolts Made |
|---|---|---|---|
| 3:30 | 24,000 | 9,000 | 33,000 |
| 2:30 | 21,000 | 7,200 | 28,200 |
| 1:30 | 18,000 | 5,400 | 23,400 |
| 12:30 | 15,000 | 3,600 | 18,600 |
| 11:30 | 12,000 | 1,800 | 13,800 |
| 10:30 | 9,000 | 0 | 9,000 |
| 9:30 | 6,000 | 0 | 6,000 |
| 8:30 | 3,000 | 0 | 3,000 |
| 7:30 | 0 | 0 | 0 |

The job is completed at 3:30 p.m.

6.

| Name | Butcher | Baker | Candlestick Maker |
|---|---|---|---|
| Mr. Smith | N | N | Y |
| Mr. Jones | Y | N | N |
| Mr. Chang | N | Y | N |

Mr. Smith-candlestick maker; Mr. Jones-butcher; Mr. Chang-baker

7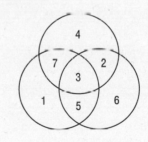

8. From the clues given, Lindsay must have brown hair.
   Paul must have blonde hair because if Paul is not a blonde, Kelly has red hair.
   So Lindsay has brown hair, Paul has blonde hair, and Kelly has red hair.

9. 4 squares

10. a.

| $n$ | Number of Dots |
|---|---|
| 1 | 1 |
| 2 | 3 |
| 3 | 6 |
| 4 | 10 |

The number of dots in each triangular number is the sum of all positive integers less than or equal to $n$.

b. 10th:  1 + 2 + 3 + 4 + 5 + 6 + 7 + 8 + 9 + 10 = 55
   The 10th triangular number is 55.

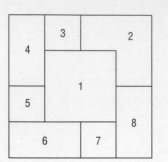

 **4-6**    **Application:   Mixtures**

**PAGES 155-156    CHECKING FOR UNDERSTANDING**

1. Let $c$ = the number of dozens of chocolate chip
cookies sold.

2. $0.25(40) + 0.80x = 0.30(40 + x)$

3.

| | Number | Total Value |
|---|---|---|
| Quarters | $x$ | $25x$ |
| Dimes | $x + 8$ | $10(x + 8)$ |

$25x + 10(x + 8) = 255$

4.

| | Pounds | Total Price |
|---|---|---|
| $3.00 peanuts | 12 | 36 |
| $6.00 cashews | $x$ | $6x$ |
| $4.20 mixture | $12 + x$ | $4.20(12 + x)$ |

$6x + 36 = 4.20(12 + x)$

5.

| | Quarts | Amount of Orange Juice |
|---|---|---|
| 10% Juice | 5 | $0.10(5)$ |
| Pure Juice | $x$ | $x$ |
| 40% Juice | $x + 5$ | $0.40(x + 5)$ |

$0.10(5) + x = 0.40(x + 5)$

6.

| | Amount | Yearly Interest |
|---|---|---|
| At 4.5% | $x$ | $0.045x$ |
| At 6% | $6000 - x$ | $0.06(6000 - x)$ |

$0.045x + 0.06(6000 - x) = 279$

**PAGES 156-157    EXERCISES**

7.

| | Number of Tickets | Total Value |
|---|---|---|
| Adults | $n$ | $5.50n$ |
| Children | $21 - n$ | $3.50(21 - n)$ |

$5.50n + 3.50(21 - n) = 83.50$

$5.50n + 73.5 - 3.50n = 83.50$

$2n = 10$

$n = 5$

$21 - n = 16$

16 children's tickets and 5 adult tickets

8. Let $x$ = amount of skim milk to be added.

$1(0.092) + 0.02x = (1 + x)(0.064)$

$0.092 + 0.02x = 0.064 + 0.064x$

$0.028 = 0.044x$

$x = 0.\overline{63} \approx 0.64$

0.64 liter should be added.

9. Let $n$ = number of pounds of the $7.28 coffee.

| | Number of Pounds | Total Price |
|---|---|---|
| $6.40/lb | 9 | $6.40(9)$ |
| $7.28/lb | $n$ | $7.28n$ |
| $6.95/lb | $9 + n$ | $6.95(9 + n)$ |

Total Cost      +      Total Cost     = Total Cost
of $6.40/lb Coffee  of $7.28/lb Coffee  of Mixture

$6.40(9)$       +       $7.28n$        $= 6.95(9 + n)$

$6.40(9) + 7.28n = 6.95(9 + n)$

$57.60 + 7.28n = 62.55 + 6.95n$

$7.28n - 6.95n = 62.55 - 57.60$

$0.33n = 4.95$

$n = 15$

10. Let $x$ = amount of peroxide added.

$150(0.25) + x = (150 + x)(0.40)$

$37.5 + x = 60 + 0.40x$

$0.60x = 22.5$

$x = 37.5$

37.5 dL of peroxide should be added.

11. Let $x$ = number of pounds of ground round.

$20(1.75) + 2.45x = 2.05(x + 20)$

$35 + 2.45x = 2.05x + 41$

$0.40x = 6$

$x = 15$

15 pounds of ground round must be added.

12. Let $x$ = the cost of a child's ticket.

Let $x + 6$ = the cost of an adult's ticket.

$2(x + 6) + 3x = 79.50$

$2x + 12 + 3x = 79.50$

$5x = 67.50$

$x = 13.50$

$x + 6 = 19.50$

The cost of a child's ticket is $13.50.

The cost of an adult's ticket is $19.50.

13. Let $x$ = amount drained off.

$16(0.25) - x(0.25) + x = 16(0.40)$

$4 + 0.75x = 6.4$

$0.75x = 2.4$

$x = 3.2$

3.2 quarts of the solution should be drained and
replaced with pure antifreeze.

14. Let $x$ = amount invested at 5% interest.

Let $33,600 - x$ = amount invested at 8% interest.

$$0.05x = 2(0.05)(33,600 - x)$$
$$0.05x = 2(2688 - 0.08x)$$
$$0.05x = 5376 - 0.16x$$
$$0.21x = 5376$$
$$x = 25,600$$
$$33,600 - x = 8000$$

Editon invested $25,600 at 5% interest and $8000 at 8% interest.

15. Let $x$ = amount of solution.

$$0.50(x - 10) + 10 = 0.75x$$
$$0.50x + 5 = 0.75x$$
$$5 = 0.25x$$
$$20 = x$$

There are 20 liters of the solution.

16. Answers may vary; Hal is doing a chemistry experiment that calls for a 40% solution of copper sulfate. Hal has 40 ml of 28% solution. How many milliliters of pure solution should Hal add to obtain the required 40% solution?

17. Let $x$ = yards gained in both games.

$$x = 134 + (134 - 17)$$
$$= 251$$

251 yards were gained in both games.

18. $$-7h = -91$$
$$\frac{-7h}{-7} = \frac{-91}{-7}$$
$$h = 13$$

19. Let $w$ = weight of the brain.

$$w = 160(0.02)$$
$$= 3.2$$

The weight of the brain is 3.2 pounds.

20. Let $c$ = the cost of the jeans.

$$45.10 = c + c(0.075)$$
$$45.10 = 1.075c$$
$$c = 41.95$$

The jeans cost $41.95.

PAGE 157    MID-CHAPTER REVIEW

1. $$\frac{6}{5} = \frac{18}{t}$$

$$6t = 5(18)$$
$$6t = 90$$
$$t = 15$$

2. $$\frac{21}{27} = \frac{x}{18}$$

$$21(18) = 27x$$
$$378 = 27x$$
$$14 = x$$

3. $$\frac{19.25}{a} = \frac{5.5}{2.94}$$

$$19.25(2.94) = 5.5a$$
$$56.595 = 5.5a$$
$$10.29 = a$$

4. $80(0.375) = 30$

5. $$.16 = x(0.40)$$
$$\frac{16}{0.40} = x$$
$$40 = x$$

6. Let $p$ = the percent.

$$37 = \frac{p}{100} \cdot 296$$
$$37(100) = 296p$$
$$3700 = 296p$$
$$12.5 = p$$

7. $$I = prt$$
$$14 = p(0.07)\left(\frac{3}{12}\right)$$
$$14 = 0.0175p$$
$$\frac{14}{0.0175} = \frac{0.0175p}{0.0175}$$
$$800 = p$$

Isaac deposited $800.

8. Let $f$ = the final price.

$$f = 148.00 - 148.00(0.18)$$
$$f = 148.00 - 26.64$$
$$f = 121.36$$

The final price is $121.36.

9. Let $f$ = the final price.

$$f = 38.50 + 38.50(0.06)$$
$$f = 38.50 + 2.31$$
$$f = 40.81$$

The final price is $40.81.

10. $5.12 for first 20 minutes

After 20 minutes, each minute costs

$$\frac{5.32 - 5.12}{2} = 0.10.$$

| Minutes | 20 Min + Extra Min | Total Cost |
|---|---|---|
| 20 | 20 | 5.12 |
| 22 | 20 + 2 | 5.12 + 2(0.10) |
| 60 | 20 + 40 | 5.12 + 40(0.10) |

$5.12 + 40(0.10) = $9.12$

60 minutes cost $9.12.

4-7    Application:   Uniform Motion

PAGE 159    CHECKING FOR UNDERSTANDING

1. distance, rate, and time respectively

2. to organize information and model the situation

3. a. $d = 40 \cdot 3$

$= 120$ mi

b. $d = 40 \cdot 4\frac{1}{2}$

$= 180$ mi

c. $d = 40 \cdot \frac{15}{60}$

$= 10$ mi

d. $d = 40 \cdot \frac{k}{60}$

$= \frac{2k}{3}$ mi

4. a. $270 = r \cdot 5$

$r = \frac{270}{5}$ or 54 km/h

b. $270 = r \cdot x$

$r = \frac{270}{x}$ km/h

53

5. a. $360 = 40 \cdot t$    b. $360 = 30 \cdot t$

    $9 = t$              $12 = t$

    9 hours         12 hours

  c. $360 = x \cdot t$

    $\dfrac{360}{x} = t$

    $\dfrac{360}{x}$ hours

**PAGES 160-161    EXERCISES**

6. Let $r$ = rate of second plane.

The first plane takes $\dfrac{2240}{280}$ or 8 hours.

If the second plane leaves 45 minutes later and arrives 15 minutes earlier, it travels 1 less hour (7 hours).

    $d = rt$

$2240 = r(7)$

 $320 = r$

The second plane travels 320 mph.

7. Let $t$ = time traveled.

   $40t + 30t = 245$

       $70t = 245$

         $t = 3\frac{1}{2}$

It takes $3\frac{1}{2}$ hours.

8. Let $r$ = Rosita's rate.

 $(16 - 2)r = 616$

     $14r = 616$

      $r = 44$

Rosita travels 44 mph.

9. Let $t$ = time each travels.

  $20t - 14t = 15$

      $6t = 15$

       $t = 2\frac{1}{2}$

They travel for $2\frac{1}{2}$ hours.

10. Let $r$ = rate Kris travels.

 $r + 5$ = rate Amy travels

$6r + 6(r + 5) = 510$

 $6r + 6r + 30 = 510$

       $12r = 480$

        $r = 40$

Kris travels 40 mph.

11. Let $t$ = time Boat A travels.

$t - \frac{1}{2}$ = time Boat B travels

$8t = 10\left(t - \frac{1}{2}\right)$

$8t = 10t - 5$

 $5 = 2t$

$2\frac{1}{2} = t$

The time is 9 AM + $2\frac{1}{2}$ hours or 11:30 AM.

12. Let $t$ = time Art travels.

$t - 1\frac{1}{2}$ = time Jennifer travels

$50t - 45\left(t - 1\frac{1}{2}\right) = 100$

$50t - 45t + 67\frac{1}{2} = 100$

       $5t = 32\frac{1}{2}$    $t = 6\frac{1}{2}$

The time is 10 AM + $6\frac{1}{2}$ hours or 4:30 PM.

13. Let $r$ = Jack's rate of travel.

  $5r = 30 + 40(5)$

  $5r = 30 + 200$

  $5r = 230$

   $r = 46$

Jack must travel 46 mph.

14. Let $r$ = rate of slower plane.

 $r + 80$ = rate of faster plane

$3r + 3(r + 80) = 2940$

 $3r + 3r + 240 = 2940$

        $6r = 2700$

        $r = 450$

    $r + 80 = 530$

The planes travel 450 mph and 530 mph.

15. Let $d$ = distance from Wheaton to Whitfield.

   $\dfrac{d}{80} = \dfrac{d}{48} - 2$

$240\left(\dfrac{d}{80}\right) = 240\left(\dfrac{d}{28}\right) - 240(2)$

    $3d = 5d - 480$

  $-2d = -480$

    $d = 240$

The distance is 240 km.

16. Let $y$ = yards headstart for Owen.

Jesse's rate = $\dfrac{440}{55}$

Owen's rate = $\dfrac{440}{88}$

$rt = d$ and both must cover 440 yards in 55 seconds

$\left(\dfrac{440}{55}\right)55 = \left(\dfrac{440}{88}\right)55 + y$

   $440 = 275 + y$

   $165 = y$

Owen gets a 165 yard headstart.

17. Let $t$ = time until trains pass.

 $45t + 35t = 240$

     $80t = 240$

      $t = 3$

The trains pass in 3 hours.

The bee flies for 3 hours at 75 mph or $3(75) = 225$ miles.

18.

| | Thursday | Friday |
|---|---|---|
| $d = rt$ | $d = 40t$ | $d = 45\left(t - \frac{2}{60}\right)$ |

Solve for $t$:  $40t = 45\left(t - \frac{2}{60}\right)$.

$$40t = 45t - 1.5$$
$$-5t = -1.5$$
$$t = 0.3 \text{ h}$$

Solve for $d$:  $d = 40(0.3) = 12$ miles.

Ms. Baylor drives 12 miles to work.

19. $w - 5$

20. Multiplicative property of zero

21. $-15 + 23 = 8$

22. money

| invested | interest rate |
|---|---|
| $25000 - x$ | 0.105 |
| $x$ | 0.1225 |

$$(25,000 - x)(0.105) + x(0.1225) = 2843.75$$
$$2625 - 0.105x + 0.1225x = 2843.75$$
$$2625 + 0.0175x = 2843.75$$
$$0.0175x = 218.75$$
$$x = 12,500$$
$$25000 - x = 12,500$$

$12,500 was invested at each rate.

## 4-8  Direct Variation

1. Divide each side of $y = kx$ by $x$.

2. False, because growth rates vary widely.

3. 3      4. -3      5. 7      6. $\frac{1}{3}$

7. $\frac{y}{12} = \frac{7}{3}$

$3y = 84$

$y = 28$

8. $\frac{y}{-8} = \frac{10}{2}$

$2y = -80$

$y = -40$

**PAGES 164-165     EXERCISES**

9. $\frac{y}{3} = \frac{-25}{15}$

$15y = -75$

$y = -5$

10. $\frac{y}{-7} = \frac{20}{-14}$

$-14y = -140$

$y = 10$

11. $\frac{x}{9} = \frac{-4}{-6}$

$-6x = -36$

$x = 6$

12. $\frac{x}{-3} = \frac{6}{-8}$

$-8x = -18$

$x = \frac{18}{8} = \frac{9}{4}$

$x = 2\frac{1}{4}$

13. $\frac{15}{12} = \frac{x}{21}$

$12x = 315$

$x = \frac{315}{12}$

$x = \frac{105}{4}$

$x = 26\frac{1}{4}$

14. $\frac{y}{2\frac{2}{3}} = \frac{1\frac{1}{8}}{\frac{1}{4}}$

$\frac{1}{4}y = \left(2\frac{2}{3}\right)\left(1\frac{1}{8}\right)$

$\frac{1}{4}y = \left(\frac{8}{3}\right)\left(\frac{9}{8}\right)$

$\frac{1}{4}y = 3$   $y = 12$

15. $k = \frac{y}{x}$

$k = \frac{-5}{-25}$

$y = \frac{1}{5}x$

16. $k = \frac{y}{x}$

$k = \frac{10}{20}$

$y = \frac{1}{2}x$

17. $k = \frac{y}{x}$

$k = \frac{-4}{6} = \frac{-2}{3}$

$y = \frac{-2}{3}x$

18. $k = \frac{y}{x}$

$k = \frac{24}{9} = \frac{8}{3}$

$y = \frac{8}{3}x$

19. $k = \frac{y}{x}$

$k = \frac{12}{15}$

$y = \frac{4}{5}x$

20. $k = \frac{y}{x}$

$k = \frac{2\frac{2}{3}}{\frac{1}{4}} = \frac{32}{3}$   $y = \frac{32}{3}x$

21. $\frac{y}{81} = \frac{14}{16}$

$16y = 1134$

$y = \frac{1134}{16} = \frac{567}{8}$

22. $\frac{x - 10}{7} = \frac{-13}{-12}$

$-12(x - 100) = -91$

$-12x + 120 = -91$

$-12x = -211$

$x = \frac{211}{12}$

23. No; there is no divisor or $x_2 y_1 = x_1 y_2$ that would produce this result.

24. $\frac{x}{75} = \frac{0.325}{2.5}$

$2.5x = (0.325)75 = 24.375$

$x = 9.75$

75 m of wire will weigh 9.75 kg.

25. $\frac{x}{40} = \frac{2}{6}$

$6x = 80$

$x = 13.3\overline{3}$

40 pounds of sugar will cost $13.33.

26. $\frac{x}{200} = \frac{5}{143}$

$143x = 1000$

$x = 6.993$

The car will use 6.993 gallons to go 200 miles.

27. $\frac{x}{200} = \frac{2.5}{150}$

$150x = 500$

$x = 3\frac{1}{3}$

The gas is $3\frac{1}{3}$ cubic feet in volume.

28. $5n + 3 = 9$

$5n + 3 - 3 = 9 - 3$

$5n = 6$

$n = \frac{6}{5}$

29. $11 + 11(0.06) = 11 + 0.66 = 11.66$

**30.**

| | Pieces of Paper |
|---|---|
| 17 | $2^{17}$ |
| 16 | $2^{16}$ |
| 15 | $2^{15}$ |
| 14 | $2^{14}$ |
| 13 | $2^{13}$ |
| 12 | $2^{12}$ |
| 11 | $2^{11}$ |
| 10 | $2^{10}$ |
| 9 | $2^9$ |
| 8 | $2^8$ |
| 7 | $2^7$ |
| 6 | $2^6$ |
| 5 | $2^5$ |
| 4 | $16 = 2^4$ |
| 3 | $8 = 2^3$ |
| 2 | $4 = 2^2$ |
| 1 | $2 = 2^1$ |

$2^{17}$ or 131,072 pieces of paper

**31.**

| | Pounds | Total Price |
|---|---|---|
| $3.00 coffee | $x$ | $3x$ |
| $3.50 coffee | 5 | 5(3.50) |
| $3.25 coffee | $5 + x$ | $3.25(5 + x)$ |

$3x + 5(3.50) = 3.25(5 + x)$

$3x + 17.50 = 16.25 + 3.25x$

$1.25 = 0.25x$

$x = 5$

5 pounds of coffee

**32.**

| | $r \cdot t = d$ | | |
|---|---|---|---|
| Brad | 12 | $t$ | $12t$ |
| Scott | 10 | $t$ | $10t$ |

$12t + 10t = 110$

$22t = 110$

$t = 5$

5 hours

**PAGE 165    HISTORY**

1. $\frac{1}{3} + \frac{1}{15}$    2. $\frac{1}{4} + \frac{1}{8}$    3. $\frac{1}{4} + \frac{1}{6}$    4. $\frac{1}{6} + \frac{1}{8}$

## 4-9    Inverse Variation

**PAGE 168    CHECKING FOR UNDERSTANDING**

1. inverse    2. direct    3. product rule

4. inverse variation, 6

5. direct variation, 3.14

6. inverse variation, 50

7. direct variation, $\frac{1}{5}$

8. direct variation, 3

9. inverse variation, 14

10. inverse variation, 1

11. inverse variation, 7

12. direct variation, 2

13. Emilio    14. Shawn

**PAGES 168-169    EXERCISES**

15. $x_1 y_1 = x_2 y_2$

$(8)(24) = 4y_2$

$48 = y_2$

$y = 48$

16. $x_1 y_1 = x_2 y_2$

$(-2)(-6) = 5y_2$

$\frac{12}{5} = y_2$

$y = \frac{12}{5}$

17. $x_1 y_1 = x_2 y_2$

$(11)(99) = x_2(11)$

$99 = x_2$

$x = 99$

18. $x_1 y_1 = x_2 y_2$

$\left(\frac{2}{3}\right)(7) = 7y_2$

$\frac{2}{3} = y_2$

$y = \frac{2}{3}$

19. $x_1 y_1 = x_2 y_2$

$(2.7)(8.1) = 3.6y_2$

$6.075 = y_2$

$y = 6.075$

20. $x_1 y_1 = x_2 y_2$

$(6.1)(4.4) = x_2(3.2)$

$8.3875 = x_2$

$x = 8.3875$

21. It is halved; It is divided by 3.

22. $P_1 V_1 = P_2 V_2$

$(1)(60) = (2)V_2$

$30 = V_2$

The volume is 30 m$^3$.

23. $P_1 V_1 = P_2 V_2$

$(1)(16) = (0.75)(V_2)$

$21.3\overline{3} = V_2$

The volume is $21\frac{1}{3}$ m$^3$.

24. Let $f$ = the frequency

$(10)(512) = (8)(f)$

$640 = f$

The frequency is 640 cycles per second.

25. Let $f$ = the frequency

$(36)(480) = (24)(f)$

$720 = f$

The frequency is 720 cycles per second.

26. Let $w$ = Mariel's weight

$(150)(8) = (w)(10)$

$120 = w$

Mariel weighs 120 pounds.

27. Let $d$ = the distance the 100 pound weight is from the fulcrum

$15 - d$ = the distance the 115 pound weight is from the fulcrum

$100d = 115(15 - d)$

$100d = 1725 - 115d$

$215d = 1725$

$d = 8.023$

The 100 pound weight is 8.023 feet from the fulcrum.

28. Let $d$ = the distance of Sue from the fulcrum

$5(108) + (5 + 2)(96) = d(101)$

$540 + 672 = 101d$

$1212 = 101d$

$12 = d$

Sue is 12 feet from the fulcrum.

29. $5 - 20 = -15$

30. $\dfrac{x - 7}{5} = 12$

$5\left(\dfrac{x - 7}{5}\right) = 5(12)$

$x - 7 = 60$

$x = 67$

31. $I = prt$

$3487.50 = 6000 \cdot r \cdot 3\frac{1}{2}$

$3487.50 = 21000r$

$0.16607 = r$

$r = 16.61\%$

32. Let $x$ = amount of water added

$2.5(0.70) = (2.5 + x)(0.50)$

$1.75 = 1.25 + 0.50x$

$0.50 = 0.50x$

$x = 1$

One liter of water should be added.

33. $\dfrac{x}{17} = \dfrac{110}{4}$

$4x = 1870$

$x = 467.50$

Hugo's wages for 17 days will be $467.50.

# Chapter 4    Summary and Review

PAGES 170-172    SKILLS AND CONCEPTS

1. $\dfrac{6}{15} = \dfrac{n}{45}$

$15n = 270$

$n = 18$

2. $\dfrac{4}{8} = \dfrac{11}{t}$

$4t = 88$

$t = 22$

3. $\dfrac{x}{11} = \dfrac{35}{55}$

$55x = 385$

$x = 7$

4. $\dfrac{5}{6} = \dfrac{a - 2}{4}$

$6(a - 2) = 20$

$6a - 12 = 20$

$6a = 32$

$a = \dfrac{32}{6}; \, 5.\overline{3}$

5. $\dfrac{y + 4}{y - 1} = \dfrac{4}{3}$

$3(y + 4) = 4(y - 1)$

$3y + 12 = 4y - 4$

$12 = y - 4$

$16 = y$

6. $\dfrac{z - 7}{6} = \dfrac{z + 3}{7}$

$7(z - 7) = 6(z + 3)$

$7z - 49 = 6z + 18$

$z - 49 = 18$

$z = 67$

7. $\dfrac{x}{80} = \dfrac{60}{100}$

$100x = 4800$

$x = 48$

8. $\dfrac{21}{x} = \dfrac{35}{100}$

$35x = 2100$

$x = 60$

9. $\dfrac{84}{96} = \dfrac{x}{100}$

$8400 = 96x$

$x = 87.5\%$

10. $\dfrac{34}{17} = \dfrac{x}{100}$

$17x = 3400$

$x = 200\%$

11. $\dfrac{x}{62.7} = \dfrac{0.3}{100}$

$100x = 18.81$

$x = 0.1881$

12.

| Amount Invested | Interest Earned |
|---|---|
| $8000 - x$ | $0.08(8000 - x)$ |
| $x$ | $0.12x$ |

$0.08(8000 - x) + 0.12x = 744$

$640 - 0.08x + 0.12x = 744$

$640 + 0.04x = 744$

$0.04x = 104$

$x = 2600$

$8000 - x = 5400$

$5400 at 8% and $2600 at 12%

13. $\dfrac{5}{40} = \dfrac{x}{100}$

$40x = 500$

$x = 12.5\%$

14. $\dfrac{2.1}{35} = \dfrac{x}{100}$

$35x = 210$

$x = 6\%$

15. 5.5% of $179.96 = 0.055(179.96)$

$= 9.90$

$179.96 + $9.90 = $189.86

16. 15% of $399 = 0.15(399)$

$= 59.85$

discounted price $= 399 - 59.85$

$= $339.15

6% of $339.15 = 0.06(339.15)$

$= 20.35$

final price $= 339.15 + 20.35$

$= $359.50

17.

|  | Gallons | Amount of Butterfat |
|---|---|---|
| 9% butterfat | $x$ | $0.09x$ |
| 4% butterfat | 1 | $0.4(1)$ |
| 6% butterfat | $x + 1$ | $0.06(x + 1)$ |

$0.09x + 0.04 = 0.06(x + 1)$

$0.09x + 0.04 = 0.06x + 0.06$

$0.03x + 0.04 = 0.06$

$0.03x = 0.02$

$x = 0.67$

18. a. $d = rt$

$d = 80 \cdot 2$

$= 160$ km

b. $d = rt$

$= 80 \cdot 6$

$= 480$ km

c. $d = rt$

$= 80 \cdot h$

$= 80h$ km

19. a. $d = rt$

$240 = r \cdot 6$

$r = 40$ mph

b. $d = rt$

$240 = rt$

$r = \dfrac{240}{t}$ mph

20. $\dfrac{15}{y} = \dfrac{5}{7}$

$5y = 105$

$y = 21$

21. $\dfrac{35}{y} = \dfrac{175}{75}$

$175y = 2625$

$y = 15$

22. $\dfrac{3}{y} = \dfrac{99.9}{522.81}$

$99.9y = 1568.43$

$y = 15.7$

23. $\dfrac{15}{y} = \dfrac{7}{5}$

$7y = 75$

$y = \dfrac{75}{7}; \, 10.714$

24. $\dfrac{35}{y} = \dfrac{75}{175}$

$75y = 6125$

$y = \dfrac{245}{3}; \, 81.\overline{6}$

25. $\dfrac{28}{y} = \dfrac{56}{42}$

$56y = 1176$

$y = 21$

26. $162 \cdot 0.77 = 124.74$ million

27. turkey - 12:30;

    potatoes - 3:45;

    yams - 3:30;

    green beans - 4:10;

    cranberry sauce - 4:55;

    gravy - 4:50;

    rolls - 4:45;

    jello - 12:45

28. $180f = 108(12 - f)$

    $180f = 1296 - 108f$

    $288f = 1296$

    $f = 4.5$

    4.5 feet from the end where Lee is seated

# Chapter 4    Test

PAGE 173

1. $\dfrac{7}{8} = \dfrac{5}{t}$

   $7t = 40$

   $t = \dfrac{40}{7}$; 5.714

2. $\dfrac{n}{4} = \dfrac{3.25}{52}$

   $52n = 13$

   $n = 0.25$

3. $\dfrac{y + 2}{8} = \dfrac{7}{5}$

   $5(y + 2) = 56$

   $5y + 10 = 56$

   $5y = 46$

   $= \dfrac{46}{5}$; 9.2

4. $\dfrac{2}{5} = \dfrac{x - 3}{-2}$

   $-4 = 5(x - 3)$

   $-4 = 5x - 15$

   $11 = 5x$

   $x = \dfrac{11}{5}$; 2.2

5. $\dfrac{9}{11} = \dfrac{x - 3}{x + 5}$

   $9(x + 5) = 11(x - 3)$

   $9x + 45 = 11x - 33$

   $78 = 2x$

   $x = 39$

6. $\dfrac{x + 1}{-3} = \dfrac{x - 4}{5}$

   $5(x + 1) = -3(x - 4)$

   $5x + 5 = -3x + 12$

   $8x = 7$

   $x = \dfrac{7}{8}$; 0.875

7. $80(0.065) = 5.2$

8. $\dfrac{42}{126} = \dfrac{x}{100}$

   $126x = 4200$

   $x = 33.\overline{3}\%$

9. $\dfrac{84}{x} = \dfrac{60}{100}$

   $60x = 8400$

   $x = 140$

10. $16 = x - x(0.20)$

    $16 = 0.80x$

    $x = 20$

11. $17(0.50) = 8.5$

12. $\dfrac{24}{8} = \dfrac{x}{100}$

    $2400 = 8x$

    $x = 300\%$

13. $52 = x + x\,(0.3\overline{3})$

    $52 = 1.\overline{3}x$

    $x = 39$

14. $54 = x + x(0.20)$

    $54 = 1.20x$

    $x = 45$

15. $\dfrac{15}{60} = \dfrac{x}{100}$

    $60x = 1500$

    $x = 25\%$

16. $3.40 = p - p(0.15)$

    $3.40 = 0.85p$

    $p = \$4.00$

17. $10.52 = p + p(0.0575)$

    $10.52 = 1.0575p$

    $p = \$9.95$

18. $21.96 = x - x(0.20)$

    $21.96 = 0.80x$

    $x = \$27.45$

19. $\dfrac{5}{12} = \dfrac{26}{x}$

    $5x = 312$

    $x = \$62.40$

20. Let $x$ = amount of 6% solution to be added

    $(0.10)12 + 0.06x = 0.07(x + 12)$

    $1.2 + 0.06x = 0.07x + 0.84$

    $-0.01x = -0.36$

    $x = 36$

    36 ounces of the 6% solution should be added.

21. $\dfrac{2}{5} = \dfrac{x}{15.75}$

    $5x = 2(15.75)$

    $5x = 31.5$

    $x = 6.3$

    They are 6.3 cm apart.

22. $d = rt$

    $d = 50(3.25)$

    Same distance at 45 mph:

    $50(3.25) = 45t$

    $162.5 = 45t$

    $t = 3.61$

    It will take 3.61 hours.

23. $w = 148 - 148(0.005)$

    $= 148 - 0.74$

    $= 147.26$ lb or

    147 lb and 4 oz

24. $I = prt$

    $7.80 = p(0.065)(0.5)$

    $7.80 = 0.0325p$

    $p = \$240$

25. $133(6) = w(7)$

    $798 = 7w$

    $w = 114$ pounds

PAGE 173    BONUS

|       | $d = r \cdot t$     |
|-------|---------------------|
| Ben   | $d = x \cdot t + 2$ |
| Rachel| $d = y \cdot t$     |

Rachel will overtake Ben when their distances are equal.

$xt + 2 = yt$

$2 = yt - xt$

$2 = t(y - x)$

$\dfrac{2}{y - x} = t$

Rachel will overtake Ben at $\dfrac{2}{y - x}$ hours.

# Chapter 5 Inequalities

## 5-1 Solving Inequalities Using Addition and Subtraction

**PAGE 178    CHECKING FOR UNDERSTANDING**

1. Subtraction is the inverse of addition.

2. Answers may vary; $x - 1 < 4$, $-2x > -10$, $x + 3 < 8$

3. Answers may vary; typical answers are $y + 2 > -2$ and $y + 4 > 0$.

4. $347 + t > 525$

   $t > 178$

   179 would be the lowest score.

5. 17  6. 8  7. 14.5  8. -4  9. 1  10. 11

11. -8  12. $8x$

13.     $r + 11 < 6$      14.     $y - 18 > -3$

$r + 11 - 11 < 6 - 11$    $y - 18 + 18 > -3 + 18$

       $r < -5$             $y > 15$

    $\{r \mid r < -5\}$        $\{y \mid y > 15\}$

15.    $10 \geq -3 + x$    16.    $4a - 3 \leq 5a$

$10 + 3 \geq -3 + 3 + x$   $4a - 4a - 3 \leq 5a - 4a$

    $13 > x$            $-3 \leq a$

   $\{x \mid x \leq 13\}$        $\{a \mid a \geq -3\}$

**PAGES 179-180    EXERCISES**

The check is left for the student.

17.     $a + 4 < 13$    18.    $x - 3 < -17$

$a + 4 - 4 < 13 - 4$    $x - 3 + 3 < -17 + 3$

      $a < 9$          $x < -14$

   $\{a \mid a < 9\}$      $\{x \mid x < -14\}$

19.    $r - 19 \geq 23$    20.    $y + 15 \geq -2$

$r - 19 + 19 \geq 23 + 19$   $y + 15 - 15 \geq -2 - 15$

    $r \geq 42$           $y \geq -17$

   $\{r \mid r \geq 42\}$      $\{y \mid y \geq -17\}$

21.    $9 + w \leq 9$    22.    $-9 + c > 9$

$9 - 9 + w \leq 9 - 9$    $9 - 9 + c > 9 + 9$

    $w \leq 0$           $c > 18$

   $\{w \mid w \leq 0\}$      $\{c \mid c > 18\}$

23.    $-11 > d - 4$

$-11 + 4 > d - 4 + 4$

   $-7 > d$

   $\{d \mid d < -7\}$

24.    $-11 \leq k - (-4)$

$-11 + (-4) \leq k - (-4) + (-4)$

    $-15 \leq k$

   $\{k \mid k \geq -15\}$

25.    $2x > x - 3$    26.    $5y + 4 < 6y$

$2x - x > x - x - 3$   $5y - 5y + 4 < 6y - 5y$

    $x > -3$          $4 < y$

   $\{x \mid x > -3\}$      $\{y \mid y > 4\}$

27.       $-7 < 16 - z$

    $-7 + z < 16 - z + z$

      $-7 + z < 16$

  $-7 + 7 + z < 16 + 7$

        $z < 23$

      $\{z \mid z < 23\}$

28.    $-p - 11 \geq 23$

$p - p - 11 \geq p + 23$

    $-11 \geq p + 23$

  $-11 - 23 \geq p + 23 - 23$

    $-34 \geq p$

   $\{p \mid p \leq -34\}$

29.    $2x - 3 \geq x$    30.    $7h - 1 \leq 6h$

$2x - 3 + 3 \geq x + 3$   $7h - 1 + 1 \leq 6h + 1$

   $2x \geq x + 3$        $7h \leq 6h + 1$

$2x - x \geq x - x + 3$   $7h - 6h \leq 6h - 6h + 1$

    $x \geq 3$          $h \leq 1$

   $\{x \mid x \geq 3\}$      $\{h \mid h \leq 1\}$

31.    $-5 + 14b \leq -4 + 15b$

$-5 + 14b - 14b \leq -4 + 15b - 14b$

    $-5 \leq -4 + b$

  $-5 + 4 \leq -4 + 4 + b$

    $-1 \leq b$

   $\{b \mid b \geq -1\}$

32.    $6r + 4 \geq 5r + 4$

$6r - 5r + 4 \geq 5r - 5r + 4$

   $r + 4 \geq 4$

$r + 4 - 4 \geq 4 - 4$

   $r \geq 0$

   $\{r \mid r \geq 0\}$

33.    $2s - 6.5 < -11.4 + s$

$2s - s - 6.5 < -11.4 + s - s$

   $s - 6.5 < -11.4$

$s - 6.5 + 6.5 < -11.4 + 6.5$

   $s < -4.9$

   $\{s \mid s < -4.9\}$

34.    $1.1v - 1 > 2.1v - 3$

$1.1v - 1.1v - 1 > 2.1v - 1.1v - 3$

    $-1 > v - 3$

  $-1 + 3 > v - 3 + 3$

    $2 > v$

   $\{v \mid v < 2\}$

**35.**
$$3x + \frac{4}{5} \le 4x + \frac{3}{5}$$
$$3x - 3x + \frac{4}{5} \le 4x - 3x + \frac{3}{5}$$
$$\frac{4}{5} \le x + \frac{3}{5}$$
$$\frac{4}{5} - \frac{3}{5} \le x + \frac{3}{5} - \frac{3}{5}$$
$$\frac{1}{5} \le x$$
$$\left\{ x \mid x \ge \frac{1}{5} \right\}$$

**36.**
$$\frac{1}{2}t + \frac{1}{4} \ge \frac{3}{2}t - \frac{2}{3}$$
$$\frac{1}{2}t - \frac{1}{2}t + \frac{1}{4} \ge \frac{3}{2}t - \frac{1}{2}t - \frac{2}{3}$$
$$\frac{1}{4} \ge t - \frac{2}{3}$$
$$\frac{1}{4} + \frac{2}{3} \ge t - \frac{2}{3} + \frac{2}{3}$$
$$\frac{11}{12} \ge t$$
$$\left\{ t \mid t \le \frac{11}{12} \right\}$$

**37.**
$$17.42 - 7.029z \ge 15.766 - 8.029z$$
$$17.42 - 7.029z + 8.029z \ge 15.766 - 8.029z + 8.029z$$
$$17.42 + z \ge 15.766$$
$$17.42 - 17.42 + z \ge 15.766 - 17.42$$
$$z \ge -1.654$$
$$\{ z \mid z \ge -1.654 \}$$

**38.**
$$x - 17 < -13$$
$$x - 17 + 17 < -13 + 17$$
$$x < 4$$
$$\{ x \mid x < 4 \}$$

**39.**
$$x + 4 \ge 3$$
$$x + 4 - 4 \ge 3 - 4$$
$$x \ge -1$$
$$\{ x \mid x \ge -1 \}$$

**40.**
$$21 - x \ge -2$$
$$21 - x + x \ge -2 + x$$
$$21 \ge -2 + x$$
$$21 + 2 \ge -2 + 2 + x$$
$$23 \ge x$$
$$\{ x \mid x \le 23 \}$$

**41.**
$$2x + 8 > 3x$$
$$2x - 2x + 8 > 3x - 2x$$
$$8 > x$$
$$\{ x \mid x < 8 \}$$

**42.**
$$6x + 4 \le 5x - 3$$
$$6x - 5x + 4 \le 5x - 5x - 3$$
$$x + 4 \le -3$$
$$x + 4 - 4 \le -3 - 4$$
$$x \le -7$$
$$\{ x \mid x \le -7 \}$$

**43.**
$$x + 18 < 25$$
$$x + 18 - 18 < 25 - 18$$
$$x < 7$$
The other number is less than 7.

**44.** 2  **45.** 12  **46.** 8  **47.** −5

**48.** Yes; examples are $x > x$ and $2x + 1 \le 2x$.

**49.** Let $s$ = biology test score.
$$453 + s \ge 630$$
$$453 - 453 + s \ge 630 - 453$$
$$s \ge 177$$
Eva can score a minimum of 177 points.

**50.** Let $x$ = amount in account before withdrawal.
$$x - 2000 - 1454 \ge 1200$$
$$x - 3454 \ge 1200$$
$$x - 3454 + 3454 \ge 1200 + 3454$$
$$x \ge 4654$$
At least $4654 was in the account before withdrawal.

**51.** Let $x$ = score of last event.
$$9.8 + 9.75 + 9.9 + x < 39.35$$
$$29.45 + x < 39.35$$
$$29.45 - 29.45 + x < 39.35 - 29.45$$
$$x < 9.9$$
Nyoko must score less than 9.9.

**52.** The program can be run to obtain the following answers.

a. ]RUN
ENTER THE FIRST NUMERATOR AND DENOMINATOR 9,11
ENTER THE SECOND NUMERATOR AND DENOMINATOR 15,19
9/11>15/19

b. ]RUN
ENTER THE FIRST NUMERATOR AND DENOMINATOR 7,8
ENTER THE SECOND NUMERATOR AND DENOMINATOR 13,15
7/8>13/15

c. ]RUN
ENTER THE FIRST NUMERATOR AND DENOMINATOR -7,8
ENTER THE SECOND NUMERATOR AND DENOMINATOR -13,15
-7/8<-13/15

d. ]RUN
ENTER THE FIRST NUMERATOR AND DENOMINATOR 16,17
ENTER THE SECOND NUMERATOR AND DENOMINATOR 17,18
16/17<17/18

e. ]RUN
ENTER THE FIRST NUMERATOR AND DENOMINATOR -7,6
ENTER THE SECOND NUMERATOR AND DENOMINATOR -21,18
-7/6=-21/18

**53.** $0.3(0.2 + 3y) + 0.21y = 0.06 + 0.9y + 0.21y$
$$= 0.06 + 1.11y$$

**54.**

**55.** $\frac{4}{9}x = -9$

$\frac{9}{4}\left(\frac{4}{9}x\right) = \frac{9}{4}(-9)$

$x = -\frac{81}{4}$

**56.** Let $x$ = cost of dress.

$x(1.06) = 32.86$

$x = 31$

The dress cost \$31.00 before tax.

**57.** $\frac{8}{y} = \frac{6}{24}$

$6y = 192$

$\frac{6y}{6} = \frac{192}{6}$

$y = 32$

## 5-2 Solving Inequalities Using Multiplication and Division

**PAGE 183   CHECKING FOR UNDERSTANDING**

**1.** Division is the inverse of multiplication.

**2.** negative   **3.** $-\frac{1}{6}$   **4.** acute   **5.** 4; no

**6.** $-\frac{7}{2}$; yes   **7.** $\frac{1}{10}$; no   **8.** -6; yes   **9.** -10; yes

**10.** 3.3; no   The check is left for the student.

**11.** $8x < -48$

$\frac{1}{8}(8x) < \frac{1}{8}(-48)$

$x < -6$

$\{x \mid x < -6\}$

**12.** $-10a < -30$

$-\frac{1}{10}(10a) > -\frac{1}{10}(-30)$

$a > 3$

$\{a \mid a > 3\}$

**13.** $-12d \le 30$

$-\frac{1}{12}(-12d) \ge -\frac{1}{12}(30)$

$d \ge -\frac{5}{2}$

$\left\{d \mid d \ge -\frac{5}{2}\right\}$

**14.** $0.1t \ge 3$

$\frac{1}{0.1}(0.1t) \ge \frac{1}{0.1}(3)$

$t \ge 30$

$\{t \mid t \ge 30\}$

**PAGES 184-185   EXERCISES**

**15.** $16x < 96$

$\frac{1}{16}(16x) < \frac{1}{16}(96)$

$x < 6$

$\{x \mid x < 6\}$

**16.** $-y \le 44$

$(-1) - y \ge (-1)44$

$y \ge -44$

$\{y \mid y \ge -44\}$

**17.** $-8z \ge -72$

$\left(-\frac{1}{8}\right)(-8z) \le \left(-\frac{1}{8}\right)(-72)$

$z \le 9$

$\{z \mid z \le 9\}$

**18.** $-102 > 17r$

$\frac{1}{17}(-102) > \frac{1}{17}(17r)$

$-6 > r$

$\{r \mid r < -6\}$

**19.** $396 > -11l$

$-\frac{1}{11}(396) < -\frac{1}{11}(-11t)$

$-36 < t$

$\{t \mid t > -36\}$

**20.** $-15a < -28$

$-\frac{1}{15}(-15a) > -\frac{1}{15}(-28)$

$a > \frac{28}{15}$

$\left\{a \mid a > \frac{28}{15}\right\}$

**21.** $4c \ge -6$

$\frac{1}{4}(4c) \ge \frac{1}{4}(-6)$

$c \ge -\frac{3}{2}$

$\left\{c \mid c \ge -\frac{3}{2}\right\}$

**22.** $6 \le 0.8n$

$\frac{1}{0.8}(6) \le \frac{1}{0.8}(0.8n)$

$7.5 \le n$

$\{n \mid n \ge 7.5\}$

**23.** $-4.3x < -2.58$

$-\frac{1}{4.3}(-4.3x) < -\frac{1}{4.3}(-2.58)$

$x < 0.6$

$\{x \mid x > 0.6\}$

**24.** $\frac{b}{-12} \le 3$

$-12\left(\frac{b}{-12}\right) \ge -12(3)$

$b \ge -36$

$\{b \mid b \ge -36\}$

**25.** $-25 > \frac{a}{-6}$

$-6(-25) < -6\left(\frac{a}{-6}\right)$

$150 < a$

$\{a \mid a > 150\}$

**26.** $13 \ge \frac{t}{13}$

$13(13) \ge 13\left(\frac{t}{13}\right)$

$169 \ge t$

$\{t \mid t \le 169\}$

**27.** $\frac{2}{3}m \ge -22$

$\frac{3}{2}\left(\frac{2}{3}m\right) \ge \frac{3}{2}(-22)$

$m \ge -33$

$\{m \mid m \ge -33\}$

**28.** $-\frac{7}{9}x < 42$

$-\frac{9}{7}\left(-\frac{7}{9}x\right) > -\frac{9}{7}(42)$

$x > -54$

$\{x \mid x > -54\}$

**29.** $\frac{3y}{8} \le 32$

$\frac{8}{3}\left(\frac{3y}{8}\right) \le \frac{8}{3}(32)$

$y \le \frac{256}{3}$

$\left\{y \mid y \le \frac{256}{3}\right\}$

**30.** $-\frac{5x}{6} < \frac{2}{9}$

$-\frac{6}{5}\left(-\frac{5x}{6}\right) > -\frac{6}{5}\left(\frac{2}{9}\right)$

$x > -\frac{4}{15}$

$\left\{x \mid x > -\frac{4}{15}\right\}$

**31.** $-\frac{2}{5} > \frac{4z}{7}$

$\frac{7}{4}\left(-\frac{2}{5}\right) > \frac{7}{4}\left(\frac{4z}{7}\right)$

$-\frac{7}{10} > z$

$\left\{z \mid z < -\frac{7}{10}\right\}$

**32.** $\frac{3b}{4} \le \frac{2}{3}$

$\frac{4}{3}\left(\frac{3b}{4}\right) \le \frac{4}{3}\left(\frac{2}{3}\right)$

$b \le \frac{8}{9}$

$\left\{b \mid b \le \frac{8}{9}\right\}$

**33.** $6d < 90$

$\frac{1}{6}(6d) < \frac{1}{6}(90)$

$d < 15$

**34.** $24d < 90$

$\frac{1}{24}(24d) < \frac{1}{24}(90)$

$d < 3.75$

**35.** $\frac{5d}{8} < 90$

$\frac{8}{5}\left(\frac{5d}{8}\right) < \frac{8}{5}(90)$

$d < 144$

**36.** $3.6d < 90$

$\frac{1}{3.6}(3.6d) < \frac{1}{3.6}(90)$

$d < 25$

The check is left for the students.

**37.** $6x < 216$

$\frac{1}{6}(6x) < \frac{1}{6}(216)$

$x < 36$

$\{x \mid x < 36\}$

**38.** $-8x \le 112$

$\frac{1}{-8}(-8x) \le \frac{1}{-8}(112)$

$x \ge -14$

$\{x \mid x \ge -14\}$

**39.** $\frac{x}{-4} \ge -2$

$-4\left(\frac{x}{-4}\right) \le -4(-2)$

$x \le 8$

$\{x \mid x \le 8\}$

**40.** $\frac{5x}{3} \le -15$

$\frac{3}{5}\left(\frac{5x}{3}\right) \le \frac{3}{5}(-15)$

$x \le -9$

$\{x \mid x \le -9\}$

**41.** $0.8x > 24$

$\frac{1}{0.8}(0.8x) > \frac{1}{0.8}(24)$

$x > 30$

$\{x \mid x > 30\}$

**42.** $-18x \ge 144$

$-\frac{1}{18}(-18x) \le \frac{1}{-18}(144)$

$x \le -8$

The number is −8 or less.

**43.** −48  **44.** 18k  **45.** <  **46.** ≥  **47.** $x > 0$

**48.** $x > 0$ and $x > |y|$

**49.** Let $g$ = pounds of glass.

$0.40g \le 15$

$\frac{1}{0.40}(0.40g) \le \frac{1}{0.40}(15)$

$g \le 37.5$

At least 37.5 pounds of glass

**50.** Let $g$ = gallons of gas.

$1.36g \le 17$

$\frac{1}{1.36}(1.36g) \le \frac{1}{1.36}(17)$

$g \le 12.5$

12.5 gallons or less

**51.** Let $n$ = number of shares.

$14n \le 0.60(885)$

$14n \le 531$

$\frac{1}{14}(14n) \le \frac{1}{14}(531)$

$n \le 37.9$

At most, 37 shares can be purchased.

**52.** a. ]RUN

ENTER THREE LENGTHS 11,14,26

NOT A TRIANGLE

b. ]RUN

ENTER THREE LENGTHS 5,12,13

THIS IS A TRIANGLE

c. ]RUN

ENTER THREE LENGTHS 75,87,110

THIS IS A TRIANGLE

d. ]RUN

ENTER THREE LENGTHS 1.5,2.0,2.5

THIS IS A TRIANGLE

**53.** $1.69 \div 12$ _____ $2.29 \div 16$

$.141 \underline{\quad < \quad} .143$

12 ounces at $1.69 is a better buy.

**54.** $5 - 3x = 32$

$5 - 5 - 3x = 32 - 5$

$-3x = 27$

$\frac{-3x}{-3} = \frac{27}{-3}$

$x = -9$

**55.** $6 - 9y < -10y$

$6 - 6 - 9y < -10y - 6$

$-9y < -10y - 6$

$10y - 9y < 10y - 10y - 6$

$y < -6$

$\{y \mid y < -6\}$

**56.** $\frac{4r + 8}{16} = 7$

$16\left(\frac{4r + 8}{16}\right) = 16(7)$

$4r + 8 = 112$

$4r + 8 - 8 = 112 - 8$

$4r = 104$

$r = 26$

**57.** $\frac{12 - x}{6} = \frac{x + 7}{4}$

$4(12 - x) = 6(x + 7)$

$48 - 4x = 6x + 42$

$48 - 4x + 4x = 6x + 4x + 42$

$48 = 10x + 42$

$48 - 42 = 10x + 42 - 42$

$6 = 10x$

$\frac{6}{10} = \frac{10x}{10}$

$\frac{3}{5} = x$

**58.**
$$3(4a - 9) = -7(2a - 3)$$
$$12a - 27 = -14a + 21$$
$$14a + 12a - 27 = 14a - 14a + 21$$
$$26a - 27 = 21$$
$$26a - 27 + 27 = 21 + 27$$
$$26a = 48$$
$$\frac{26a}{26} = \frac{48}{26}$$
$$a = \frac{24}{13}$$

**PAGE 185    READING ALGEBRA**

1. false    2. true    3. false    4. true

## 5-3  Inequalities with More Than One Operation

**PAGE 188    CHECKING FOR UNDERSTANDING**

1. Answers may vary; an example is $2x > 5x - 1$.

2. Add $5b$ to each side.  Subtract 29 from each side.  Divide each side by 5.

3.
$$70 + 0.16s > 90$$
$$70 - 70 + 0.16s > 90 - 70$$
$$0.16s > 20$$
$$\frac{0.16s}{0.16} > \frac{20}{0.16}$$
$$s > 125$$

more than \$125 worth of videotapes each week

4.
$$\frac{89 + 92 + 82 + s}{4} \geq 91$$
$$263 + s \geq 364$$
$$s \geq 101$$

No, since he would need to score at least a 101 on the fourth test.

5. Add 1 to each side.  Then divide each side by 3.
$$3x - 1 > 14$$
$$3x - 1 + 1 > 14 + 1$$
$$3x > 15$$
$$\frac{3x}{3} > \frac{15}{3}$$
$$x > 5$$
$$\{x \mid x > 5\}$$

6. Subtract 8 from each side.  Divide each side by 7.  Rewrite as $a \leq -4$.
$$-20 \geq 8 + 7a$$
$$-20 - 8 \geq 8 - 8 + 7a$$
$$-28 \geq 7a$$
$$\frac{-28}{7} \geq \frac{7a}{7}$$
$$-4 \geq a$$
$$\{a \mid a \leq -4\}$$

7. Multiply each side by $-2$ and reverse the inequality symbol.  Add 11 to each side.
$$\frac{n - 11}{-2} \leq -6$$
$$-2\left(\frac{n - 11}{-2}\right) \geq -2(-6)$$
$$n - 11 \geq 12$$
$$n - 11 + 11 \geq 12 + 11$$
$$n \geq 23$$
$$\{n \mid n \geq 23\}$$

8. Subtract 12 from each side.  Multiply each side by $-\frac{4}{5}$ and reverse the inequality symbol.
$$12 - \frac{5z}{4} < 37$$
$$12 - 12 - \frac{5z}{4} < 37 - 12$$
$$-\frac{5z}{4} < 25$$
$$\left(-\frac{4}{5}\right)\left(-\frac{5z}{4}\right) > \left(-\frac{4}{5}\right)(25)$$
$$z > -20$$
$$\{z \mid z > -20\}$$

9. Subtract $5y$ from each side.  Subtract 1 from each side.  Divide each side by $-4$ and reverse the inequality symbol.
$$y + 1 \geq 5y + 5$$
$$y - 5y + 1 \geq 5y - 5y + 5$$
$$-4y + 1 \geq 5$$
$$-4y + 1 - 1 \geq 5 - 1$$
$$-4y \geq 4$$
$$\frac{-4y}{-4} \leq \frac{4}{-4}$$
$$y \leq -1$$
$$\{y \mid y \leq -1\}$$

10. Add $k$ to each side.  Subtract 7 from each side.  Divide each side by 3.
$$2k + 7 > 11 - k$$
$$2k + k + 7 > 11 - k + k$$
$$3k + 7 > 11$$
$$3k + 7 - 7 > 11 - 7$$
$$3k > 4$$
$$\frac{3k}{3} > \frac{4}{3}$$
$$k > \frac{4}{3}$$
$$\left\{k \mid k > \frac{4}{3}\right\}$$

**PAGES 189-190    EXERCISES**

11.
$$9x + 2 > 20$$
$$9x + 2 - 2 > 20 - 2$$
$$9x > 18$$
$$\frac{9x}{9} > \frac{18}{9}$$
$$x > 2$$
$$\{x \mid x > 2\}$$

12.
$$4y - 7 < 21$$
$$4y - 7 + 7 < 21 + 7$$
$$4y < 28$$
$$\frac{4y}{4} < \frac{28}{4}$$
$$y < 7$$
$$\{y \mid y < 7\}$$

13. $-7a + 6 \le 48$

$-7a + 6 - 6 \le 48 - 6$

$-7a \le 42$

$\dfrac{-7a}{-7} \ge \dfrac{42}{-7}$

$a \ge -6$

$\{a \mid a \ge -6\}$

14. $-5 - 8b \ge 59$

$5 - 5 - 8b \ge 5 + 59$

$-8b \ge 64$

$\dfrac{-8b}{-8} \le \dfrac{64}{-8}$

$b \le -8$

$\{b \mid b \le -8\}$

15. $-12 + 11m \le 54$

$12 - 12 + 11m \le 12 + 54$

$11m \le 66$

$\dfrac{11m}{11} \le \dfrac{66}{11}$

$m \le 6$

$\{m \mid m \le 6\}$

16. $5 - 6n > -19$

$5 - 5 - 6n > -19 - 5$

$-6n > -24$

$\dfrac{-6n}{-6} < \dfrac{-24}{-6}$

$n < 4$

$\{n \mid n < 4\}$

17. $\dfrac{z}{4} + 7 \ge -5$

$\dfrac{z}{4} + 7 - 7 \ge -5 - 7$

$\dfrac{z}{4} \ge -12$

$4\left(\dfrac{z}{4}\right) \ge 4(-12)$

$z \ge -48$

$\{z \mid z \ge -48\}$

18. $\dfrac{2x}{3} - 3 \le 7$

$\dfrac{2x}{3} - 3 + 3 \le 7 + 3$

$\dfrac{2x}{3} \le 10$

$\left(\dfrac{3}{2}\right)\left(\dfrac{2x}{3}\right) \le \left(\dfrac{3}{2}\right)(10)$

$x \le 15$

$\{x \mid x \le 15\}$

19. $-2 - \dfrac{d}{5} < 23$

$2 - 2 - \dfrac{d}{5} < 2 + 23$

$-\dfrac{d}{5} < 25$

$-5\left(-\dfrac{d}{5}\right) > -5(25)$

$d > -125$

$\{d \mid d > -125\}$

20. $\dfrac{2t + 5}{3} < -9$

$3\left(\dfrac{2t + 5}{3}\right) < 3(-9)$

$2t + 5 < -27$

$2t + 5 - 5 < -27 - 5$

$2t < -32$

$\dfrac{2t}{2} < \dfrac{-32}{2}$

$t < -16$

$\{t \mid t < -16\}$

21. $\dfrac{11 - 6w}{5} > 10$

$5\left(\dfrac{11 - 6w}{5}\right) > 5(10)$

$11 - 6w > 50$

$11 - 11 - 6w > 50 - 11$

$-6w > 39$

$\dfrac{-6w}{-6} < \dfrac{39}{-6}$

$w < -\dfrac{13}{2}$

$\left\{w \mid w < -\dfrac{13}{2}\right\}$

22. $7y - 27 \ge 4y$

$7y - 27 + 27 \ge 4y + 27$

$7y \ge 4y + 27$

$7y - 4y \ge 4y - 4y + 27$

$3y \ge 27$

$\dfrac{3y}{3} \ge \dfrac{27}{3}$

$y \ge 9$

$\{y \mid y \ge 9\}$

23. $13r - 11 > 7r + 37$

$13r - 7r - 11 > 7r - 7r + 37$

$6r - 11 > 37$

$6r - 11 + 11 > 37 + 11$

$6r > 48$

$\dfrac{6r}{6} > \dfrac{48}{6}$

$r > 8$

$\{r \mid r > 8\}$

24. $6a + 9 < -4a + 29$

$6a + 4a + 9 < -4a + 4a + 29$

$10a + 9 < 29$

$10a + 9 - 9 < 29 - 9$

$10a < 20$

$\dfrac{10a}{10} < \dfrac{20}{10}$

$a < 2$

$\{a \mid a < 2\}$

25. $0.1y - 2 \le 0.3y - 5$

$0.1y - 0.1y - 2 \le 0.3y - 0.1y - 5$

$-2 \le 0.2y - 5$

$-2 + 5 \le 0.2y - 5 + 5$

$3 \le 0.2y$

$\dfrac{3}{0.2} \le \dfrac{0.2y}{0.2}$

$15 \le y$

$\{y \mid y \ge 15\}$

26. $1.3x + 6.7 \ge 3.1x - 1.4$

$1.3x - 1.3x + 6.7 \ge 3.1x - 1.3x - 1.4$

$6.7 \ge 1.8x - 1.4$

$6.7 + 1.4 \ge 1.8x - 1.4 + 1.4$

$8.1 \ge 1.8x$

$\dfrac{8.1}{1.8} \ge \dfrac{1.8x}{1.8}$

$4.5 \ge x$

$\{x \mid x \le 4.5\}$

27. $7(g + 8) < 3(g + 12)$

$7g + 56 < 3g + 36$

$7g + 56 - 56 < 3g + 36 - 56$

$7g < 3g - 20$

$7g - 3g < 3g - 3g - 20$

$4g < -20$

$\dfrac{4g}{4} < \dfrac{-20}{4}$

$g < -5$

$\{g \mid g < -5\}$

28. 
$$-5(k + 4) \geq 3(k - 4)$$
$$-5k - 20 \geq 3k - 12$$
$$-5k + 5k - 20 \geq 3k + 5k - 12$$
$$-20 \geq 8k - 12$$
$$-20 + 12 \geq 8k - 12 + 12$$
$$-8 \geq 8k$$
$$\frac{-8}{8} \geq \frac{8k}{8}$$
$$-1 \geq k$$
$$\{k \mid k \leq -1\}$$

29. 
$$8c - (c - 5) > c + 17$$
$$8c - c + 5 > c + 17$$
$$7c + 5 > c + 17$$
$$7c - c + 5 > c - c + 17$$
$$6c + 5 > 17$$
$$6c + 5 - 5 > 17 - 5$$
$$6c > 12$$
$$\frac{6c}{6} > \frac{12}{6}$$
$$c > 2$$
$$\{c \mid c > 2\}$$

30. 
$$3d - 2(8d - 9) < 3 - (2d + 7)$$
$$3d - 16d + 18 < 3 - 2d - 7$$
$$-13d + 18 < -2d - 4$$
$$-13d + 13d + 18 < -2d + 13d - 4$$
$$18 < 11d - 4$$
$$18 + 4 < 11d - 4 + 4$$
$$22 < 11d$$
$$\frac{22}{11} < \frac{11d}{11}$$
$$2 < d$$
$$\{d \mid d > 2\}$$

31. 
$$2x + 17 \leq 41$$
$$2x + 17 - 17 \leq 41 - 17$$
$$2x \leq 24$$
$$\frac{2x}{2} \leq \frac{24}{2}$$
$$x \leq 12$$
$$\{x \mid x \leq 12\}$$

32. 
$$\frac{2}{3}x - 27 \geq 9$$
$$\frac{2}{3}x - 27 + 27 \geq 9 + 27$$
$$\frac{2}{3}x \geq 36$$
$$\frac{3}{2}\left(\frac{2}{3}x\right) \geq \frac{3}{2}(36)$$
$$x \geq 54$$
$$\{x \mid x \geq 54\}$$

33. 
$$3(x + 7) > 5x - 13$$
$$3x + 21 > 5x - 13$$
$$3x - 3x + 21 > 5x - 3x - 13$$
$$21 > 2x - 13$$
$$21 + 13 > 2x - 13 + 13$$
$$34 > 2x$$
$$\frac{34}{2} > \frac{2x}{2}$$
$$17 > x$$
$$\{x \mid x < 17\}$$

34. 
$$2x + 32 \geq 2 - 3x$$
$$2x + 3x + 32 \geq 2 - 3x + 3x$$
$$5x + 32 \geq 2$$
$$5x + 32 - 32 \geq 2 - 32$$
$$5x \geq -30$$
$$\frac{5x}{5} \geq \frac{-30}{5}$$
$$x \geq -6$$
$$\{x \mid x \geq -6\}$$

35. Let $x$ = the first even integer;
$x + 2$ = the next even integer.
$$x + (x + 2) > 75$$
$$2x + 2 > 75$$
$$2x > 73$$
$$x > \frac{73}{2}$$

Since the sum must be the least, and $x > 36\frac{1}{2}$,
the integers are 38 and 40.

36. Let $x$ = the first odd integer;
$x + 2$ = the next odd integer.
$$x + x + 2 \leq 123$$
$$2x + 2 \leq 123$$
$$2x \leq 121$$
$$x \leq \frac{121}{2} \text{ or } 60\frac{1}{2}$$

Since the sum must be the greatest, and $x \leq 60\frac{1}{2}$,
the integers are 59 and 61.

37. Let $n$ = smaller odd integer;
$n + 2$ = larger odd integer.
$$n + n + 2 \leq 18$$
$$2n + 2 \leq 18$$
$$2n \leq 16$$
$$\frac{1}{2}(2n) \leq \frac{1}{2}(16)$$
$$n \leq 8$$

Since $n$ is odd, $n$ = 7, 5, 3, or 1 and the sets
are 7 and 9, 5 and 7, 3 and 5, or 1 and 3.

38. Let $x$ = the first even integer;
$x + 2$ = the second even integer;
$x + 4$ = the third even integer.
$$x + (x + 2) + (x + 4) < 30$$
$$3x + 6 < 30$$
$$3x < 24$$
$$x < 8$$

Since the integers must be positive, the sets
are 2, 4, and 6; 4, 6, and 8; 6, 8, and 10.

39. $$\dfrac{5y - 4}{3} > \dfrac{y + 5}{3}$$

$$3(5y - 4) > 3(y + 5)$$

$$15y - 12 > 3y + 15$$

$$12y > 27$$

$$\dfrac{1}{12}(12y) > \dfrac{1}{12}(27)$$

$$y > \dfrac{27}{12}$$

$$y > \dfrac{9}{4}$$

$$\left\{ y \mid y > \dfrac{9}{4} \right\}$$

40. $$\dfrac{2n + 1}{7} \geq \dfrac{n + 4}{5}$$

$$5(2n + 1) \geq 7(n + 4)$$

$$10n + 5 \geq 7n + 28$$

$$3n \geq 23$$

$$\dfrac{1}{3}(3n) \geq \dfrac{1}{3}(23)$$

$$n \geq \dfrac{23}{3}$$

$$\left\{ n \mid n \geq 7\dfrac{2}{3} \right\}$$

41. $$\dfrac{c + 8}{4} \leq \dfrac{5 - c}{9}$$

$$9(c + 8) \leq 4(5 - c)$$

$$9c + 72 \leq 20 - 4c$$

$$13c \leq -52$$

$$\dfrac{1}{13}(13c) \leq \dfrac{1}{13}(-52)$$

$$c \leq -4$$

$$\{c \mid c \leq -4\}$$

42. Answers may vary; an example is $x + 1 < x - 1$.

43. Let $s$ = the last test score.

$$\dfrac{85 + 89 + 90 + 81 + s}{5} \geq 87$$

$$\dfrac{345 + s}{5} \geq 87$$

$$5\left(\dfrac{345 + s}{5}\right) \geq 5(87)$$

$$345 + s \geq 435$$

$$s \geq 90$$

Abeytu must score at least 90 points on her last test.

44. Let $s$ = Don's sales.

$$24,000 + 0.08s \geq 30,000$$

$$0.08s \geq 6,000$$

$$s \geq 75,000$$

Don must have at least \$75,000 in sales per year.

45. Let $h$ = hours worked.

$$4.76h - 0.25(4.76h) - 25 \geq 100$$

$$4.76h - 1.19h - 25 \geq 100$$

$$3.57h \geq 125$$

$$h \geq 35$$

Maria must work at least 35 hours a week.

46. Let $x$ = number of points scored in both games.

$$12 + (12 + 4) = x$$

47. $$\dfrac{2}{5}x - 1 = \dfrac{1}{4}x + 2$$

$$\dfrac{2}{5}x - \dfrac{1}{4}x - 1 = \dfrac{1}{4}x - \dfrac{1}{4}x + 2$$

$$\dfrac{3}{20}x - 1 = 2$$

$$\dfrac{3}{20}x - 1 + 1 = 2 + 1$$

$$\dfrac{3}{20}x = 3$$

$$\dfrac{20}{3}\left(\dfrac{3}{20}x\right) = \dfrac{20}{3}(3)$$

$$x = 20$$

48. $$\dfrac{6}{20} = \dfrac{121}{x}$$

$$6x = 2420$$

$$\dfrac{6x}{6} = \dfrac{2420}{6}$$

$$x = \$403.33$$

49. $$-13z > -1.04$$

$$\dfrac{-13z}{-13} < \dfrac{-1.04}{-13}$$

$$z < 0.08$$

$$\{z \mid z < 0.08\}$$

PAGE 190    MID-CHAPTER REVIEW

1. $$a + 2 < 10$$

$$a + 2 - 2 < 10 - 2$$

$$a < 8$$

$$\{a \mid a < 8\}$$

2. $$-12 \leq s - (-3)$$

$$-12 - 3 \leq s + 3 - 3$$

$$-15 \leq s$$

$$\{s \mid s \geq -15\}$$

3. $$-3 + 13z > 14z$$

$$-3 + 13z - 13z > 14z - 13z$$

$$-3 > z$$

$$\{z \mid z < -3\}$$

4. $$23b \geq 276$$

$$\dfrac{23b}{23} \geq \dfrac{276}{23}$$

$$b \geq 12$$

$$\{b \mid b \geq 12\}$$

5. $$-\dfrac{1}{3}k > \dfrac{6}{7}$$

$$-3\left(-\dfrac{1}{3}k\right) < -3\left(\dfrac{6}{7}\right)$$

$$k < -\dfrac{18}{7}$$

$$\left\{ k \mid k < -\dfrac{18}{7} \right\}$$

6. $$\dfrac{4a}{5} \leq -\dfrac{13}{8}$$

$$\dfrac{5}{4}\left(\dfrac{4a}{5}\right) \leq \dfrac{5}{4}\left(-\dfrac{13}{8}\right)$$

$$a \leq -\dfrac{65}{32}$$

$$\left\{ a \mid a \leq -\dfrac{65}{32} \right\}$$

7. $$-6x + 9 < 4x + 29$$

$$-6x + 6x + 9 < 4x + 6x + 29$$

$$9 < 10x + 29$$

$$9 - 29 < 10x + 29 - 29$$

$$-20 < 10x$$

$$\dfrac{-20}{10} < \dfrac{10x}{10}$$

$$-2 < x$$

$$\{x \mid x > -2\}$$

8.  $9d - 5 \geq 8 - d$

$9d + d - 5 \geq 8 - d + d$

$10d - 5 \geq 8$

$10d - 5 + 5 \geq 8 + 5$

$10d \geq 13$

$\dfrac{10d}{10} \geq \dfrac{13}{10}$

$d \geq \dfrac{13}{10}$

$\left\{ d \mid d \geq \dfrac{13}{10} \right\}$

9.  $3(7 - 2n) < 2(3n + 13)$

$21 - 6n < 6n + 26$

$21 - 6n + 6n < 6n + 6n + 26$

$21 < 12n + 26$

$21 - 26 < 12n + 26 - 26$

$-5 < 12n$

$\dfrac{-5}{12} < \dfrac{12n}{12}$

$\dfrac{-5}{12} < n$

$\left\{ n \mid n > \dfrac{-5}{12} \right\}$

10.  $n + 11 \geq 23$

$n + 11 - 11 \geq 23 - 11$

$n \geq 12$

$\{ n \mid n \geq 12 \}$

11.  $\dfrac{3}{4}n < 90$

$\dfrac{4}{3}\left( \dfrac{3}{4}n \right) < \dfrac{4}{3}(90)$

$n < 120$

$\{ n \mid n < 120 \}$

12.  $2n - 9 \leq 75$

$2n - 9 + 9 \leq 75 + 9$

$2n \leq 84$

$\dfrac{2n}{2} \leq \dfrac{84}{2}$

$n \leq 42$

$\{ n \mid n \leq 42 \}$

13.  $10 - 3n \geq n + 6$

$10 - 3n + 3n \geq n + 3n + 6$

$10 \geq 4n + 6$

$10 - 6 \geq 4n + 6 - 6$

$4 \geq 4n$

$\dfrac{4}{4} \geq \dfrac{4n}{4}$

$1 \geq n$

$\{ n \mid n \leq 1 \}$

14.  $0.08p \geq 5.00$

$\dfrac{0.08p}{0.08} \geq \dfrac{5.00}{0.08}$

$p \geq 62.5$

63 papers or more must be delivered.

15.  $13 + 0.21c \leq 20$

$13 - 13 + 0.21c \leq 20 - 13$

$0.21c \leq 7$

$\dfrac{0.21c}{0.21} \leq \dfrac{7}{0.21}$

$c \leq 33.33$

Jay can make 33 or less calls.

# Technology:  Solving Inequalities

1.
| Enter | Result |
|---|---|
| $2x + 8 < 5x + 11$ | $2x + 8 < 5x + 11$ |
| sub $2x$ | $2x + 8 - 2x < 5x + 11 - 2x$ |
| simp | $8 < 3x + 11$ |
| sub 11 | $8 - 11 < 3x + 11 - 11$ |
| simp | $-3 < 3x$ |
| div 3 | $\dfrac{-3}{3} < \dfrac{3x}{3}$ |
| simp | $-1 < x$ |

2.
| Enter | Result |
|---|---|
| $5 - x > x - 7$ | $5 - x > x - 7$ |
| sub $x$ | $5 - x - x > -7$ |
| simp | $5 - 2x > -7$ |
| sub 5 | $5 - 2x - 5 > -7 - 5$ |
| simp | $-2x > -12$ |
| div $-2$ | $\dfrac{-2x}{-2} > \dfrac{-12}{-2}$ |
| simp | $x < 6$ |

3.  Enter

$6(x + 4) \geq 5x - 3 - 2x$

simp

sub $3x$

simp

sub 24

simp

div 3

simp

Result

$6(x + 4) \geq 5x - 3 - 2x$

$6x + 24 \geq 3x - 3$

$6x + 24 - 3x \geq 3x - 3 - 3x$

$3x + 24 \geq -3$

$3x + 24 - 24 \geq -3 - 24$

$3x \geq -27$

$\dfrac{3x}{3} \geq \dfrac{-27}{3}$

$x \geq -9$

4.  Enter

$8.6x - (6.4 + 4.2x) \leq 0.2$

simp

add 6.4

simp

div 4.4

simp

Result

$8.6x - 6.4 - 4.2x \leq 0.2$

$4.4x - 6.4 \leq 0.2$

$4.4x - 6.4 + 6.4 \leq 0.2 + 6.4$

$4.4x \leq 6.6$

$\dfrac{4.4x}{4.4} \leq \dfrac{6.6}{4.4}$

$x \leq 1.5$

**5.**

| Enter | Result |
|---|---|
| $(2x - 6)/5 > (3x + 2)/5$ | $\dfrac{2x - 6}{5} > \dfrac{3x + 2}{5}$ |
| mul 5 | $5\left(\dfrac{2x - 6}{5}\right) > 5\left(\dfrac{3x + 2}{5}\right)$ |
| simp | $2x - 6 > 3x + 2$ |
| sub $3x$ | $2x - 6 - 3x > 3x + 2 - 3x$ |
| simp | $-x - 6 > 2$ |
| add 6 | $-x - 6 + 6 > 2 + 6$ |
| simp | $-x > 8$ |
| div $-1$ | $\dfrac{-x}{-1} > \dfrac{8}{-1}$ |
| simp | $x < -8$ |

**6.**

| Enter | Result |
|---|---|
| $x/3 \{ (x + 1)/4$ | $\dfrac{x}{3} \le \dfrac{x + 1}{4}$ |
| mul 3 | $3\left(\dfrac{x}{3}\right) \le 3\left(\dfrac{x + 1}{4}\right)$ |
| simp | $x \le \dfrac{3x + 3}{4}$ |
| mul 4 | $4(x) \le 4\left(\dfrac{3x + 3}{4}\right)$ |
| simp | $4x \le 3x + 3$ |
| sub $3x$ | $4x - 3x \le 3x + 3 - 3x$ |
| simp | $x \le 3$ |

## 5-4 Problem-Solving Strategy: Make a Diagram

**PAGES 192-193    CHECKING FOR UNDERSTANDING**

1. Helps you plan the solution; provides the solution.

2. $11 + 10 + 9 + 8 + 7 + 6 + 5 + 4 + 3 + 2 + 1 = 66$ grams

3.

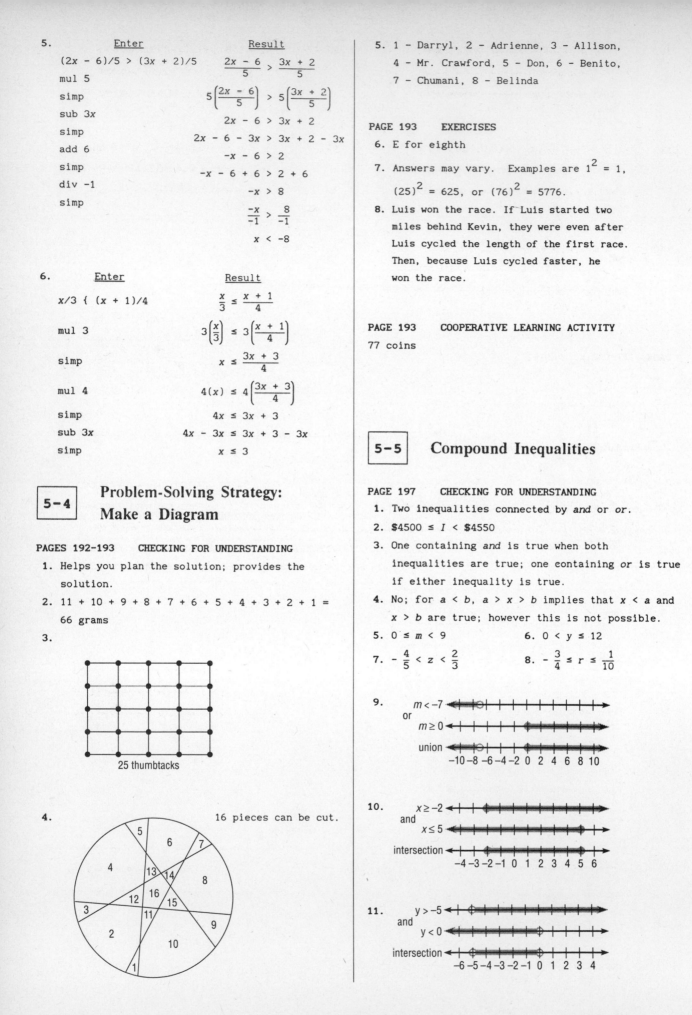

25 thumbtacks

4.                                       16 pieces can be cut.

**5.** 1 - Darryl, 2 - Adrienne, 3 - Allison,
4 - Mr. Crawford, 5 - Don, 6 - Benito,
7 - Chumani, 8 - Belinda

**PAGE 193    EXERCISES**

6. E for eighth

7. Answers may vary. Examples are $1^2 = 1$, $(25)^2 = 625$, or $(76)^2 = 5776$.

8. Luis won the race. If Luis started two miles behind Kevin, they were even after Luis cycled the length of the first race. Then, because Luis cycled faster, he won the race.

**PAGE 193    COOPERATIVE LEARNING ACTIVITY**

77 coins

## 5-5 Compound Inequalities

**PAGE 197    CHECKING FOR UNDERSTANDING**

1. Two inequalities connected by *and* or *or*.

2. $\$4500 \le I < \$4550$

3. One containing *and* is true when both inequalities are true; one containing *or* is true if either inequality is true.

4. No; for $a < b$, $a > x > b$ implies that $x < a$ and $x > b$ are true; however this is not possible.

5. $0 \le m < 9$          6. $0 < y \le 12$

7. $-\dfrac{4}{5} < z < \dfrac{2}{3}$          8. $-\dfrac{3}{4} \le r \le \dfrac{1}{10}$

**12.** $r >$
or
$r \le -2$
union
  −5 −4 −3 −2 −1 0 1 2 3 4 5

**13.** $w > -3$
or
$w < 1$
union
  −5 −4 −3 −2 −1 0 1 2 3 4 5

**14.** $n \le -5$
and
$n \ge -1$
intersection
  −7 −6 −5 −4 −3 −2 −1 0 1 2 3

PAGES 197–198    EXERCISES

**15.** $b > 5$
or
$b \le 0$
union
  −2 −1 0 1 2 3 4 5 6 7 8

**16.** $d > 0$
or
$d < 4$
union
  −2 −1 0 1 2 3 4 5 6 7 8

**17.** $d \ge -6$
and
$d \le -3$
intersection
  −7 −6 −5 −4 −3 −2 −1 0 1 2 3

**18.**
  −6 −4 −2 0 2

**19.** $s \ge 8$
or
$s < 5$
union
  −1 0 1 2 3 4 5 6 7 8 9

**20.**
  −2 0 2 4 6

**21.** $t < -3$
and
$t > 3$
intersection
  −5 −4 −3 −2 −1 0 1 2 3 4 5

**22.** $a \le 8$
or
$a \ge 3$
union
  −1 0 1 2 3 4 5 6 7 8 9

**23.** $r > -4$
or
$r \le 0$
union
  −6 −5 −4 −3 −2 −1 0 1 2 3 4

**24.** $3 + x < -4$ or $3 + x > 4$
    $x < -7$ or    $x > 1$
   $\{x \mid x < -7 \text{ or } x > 1\}$

$x < -7$
or
$x > 1$
union
  −10 −8 −6 −4 −2 0 2 4 6 8 10

**25.** $-1 + d > -4$ or $-1 + d < 3$
    $d > -3$ or    $d < 4$
      {all numbers}

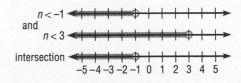

$d > -3$
or
$d < 4$
union
  −6 −5 −4 −3 −2 −1 0 1 2 3 4

**26.** $5n < 2n + 9$ and $9 - 2n > 11$
   $3n < 9$              $-2n > 2$
    $n < 3$      and      $n < -1$
        $\{n \mid n < -1\}$

$n < -1$
and
$n < 3$
intersection
  −5 −4 −3 −2 −1 0 1 2 3 4 5

**27.** $2 > 3z + 2$ and $3z + 2 > 14$
   $0 > 3z$              $3z > 12$
   $0 > z$      and      $z > 4$
    The solution is ∅.

$z < 0$
and
$z > 4$
intersection
  −2 −1 0 1 2 3 4 5 6 7 8

**28.** $-2 \leq x + 3$ and $x + 3 < 4$

$\qquad -5 \leq x \qquad$ and $\qquad x < 1$

$\qquad \{x \mid -5 \leq x < 1\}$

**29.** $8 + 3t < 2$ or $-12 < 11t - 1$

$\qquad 3t < -6 \qquad -11 < 11t$

$\qquad t < -2$ or $-1 < t$

$\qquad \{t \mid t < -2 \text{ or } t > -1\}$

**30.** $a \neq 6$ and $3a + 1 > 10$

$\qquad\qquad 3a > 9$

$\qquad\qquad a > 3$

$\qquad \{a \mid a \neq 6 \text{ and } a > 3\}$

**31.** $3x + 11 \leq 13$ or $2x \geq 5x - 12$

$\qquad 3x \leq 2 \qquad 12 \geq 3x$

$\qquad x \leq \frac{2}{3}$ or $\quad 4 \geq x$

$\qquad \{x \mid x \leq \frac{2}{3} \text{ or } x \leq 4\}$

**32.** $5(x - 3) + 2 < 7$ and $5x > 4(2x - 3)$

$\quad 5x - 15 + 2 < 7 \qquad 5x > 8x - 12$

$\quad 5x - 13 < 7 \qquad -3x > -12$

$\qquad 5x < 20$ and $x < 4$

$\qquad x < 4$

$\qquad \{x \mid x < 4\}$

**33.** $2 - 5(2x - 3) > 2$ or $3x < 2(x - 8)$

$\quad 2 - 10x + 15 > 2 \qquad 3x < 2x - 16$

$\quad -10x + 17 > 2 \qquad x < -16$

$\qquad -10x > -15$

$\qquad x < \frac{3}{2}$ or $x < -16$

$\qquad \left\{x \mid x < \frac{3}{2}\right\}$

**34.** $-2 < x \leq 3$

**35.** $x < -3$ or $x > 3$

**36.** $x \leq -4$ or $x \geq -1$

**37.** $-3 \leq x < 5$

**38.** $x + 2 \leq 6$ or $x + 2 \geq 10$

$\qquad x \leq 4$ or $\qquad x \geq 8$

**39.** $7 < 2n + 5 < 11$

$\qquad 2 < 2n < 6$

$\qquad 1 < n < 3$

**40.** $31 \leq 6n - 5 \leq 37$

$\qquad 36 \leq 6n \leq 42$

$\qquad 6 \leq n \leq 7$

**41.** Since $x \neq 0$, the following statement must be true for $\frac{5}{x} + 3 > 0$.

$\frac{5}{x} + 3 > 0$ and $x > 0$ or $\frac{5}{x} + 3 > 0$ and $x < 0$

$\qquad \frac{5}{x} > -3 \qquad\qquad\qquad \frac{5}{x} > -3$

$\qquad 5 > -3x \qquad\qquad\qquad 5 > -3x$

$\qquad -\frac{5}{3} < x$ and $x > 0$ or $-\frac{5}{3} > x$ and $x < 0$

$\left\{x \mid x > 0 \text{ or } x < -\frac{5}{3}\right\}$

**42.** $\qquad -3 - x < 2x \qquad$ and $\qquad 2x < 3 + x$

$\quad -3 - x + x < 2x + x \qquad 2x - x < 3 + x - x$

$\qquad -3 < 3x$

$\qquad \frac{-3}{3} < \frac{3x}{3}$

$\qquad -1 < x \qquad$ and $\qquad x < 3$

$\qquad\qquad -1 < x < 3$

**43.** $x - 5 < 2x - 1$ and $2x - 1 < x$

$\qquad -4 < x \qquad\qquad\qquad x < 1$

$\qquad\qquad -4 < x < 1$

44. When $a$ is negative or 0.

45. $0 \leq p \leq 1$; where $p$ is a possible probability.

46. Let $g$ = gallons of paint needed.

$14(9.75) < g < 18(9.75)$

$136.50 < g < 175.50$

between \$136.50 and \$175.50

47. Let $s$ = Wanita's sales.

$28,000 < 17,500 + 0.08s < 32,000$

$10,500 < \quad 0.08s \quad < 14,500$

$131,250 < s < 181,250$

between \$131,250 and \$181,250

48. Let $x$, $x + 1$, $x + 2$, $x + 3$ = team members finishing in consecutive order.

$35 < 1 + x + x + 1 + x + 2 + x + 3 < 45$

$35 < 4x + 5 < 45$

$30 < 4x < 40$

$7.5 < x < 10$

The other members finished 8th, 9th, 10th, 11th or 9th, 10th, 11th, 12th.

49. $4(1 - 2x) = 10(x + 13)$

$4 - 8x = 10x + 130$

$-126 = 18x$

$-7 = x$

50. $5.1n + 8.6 = 9.5n - 2.4$

$11 = 4.4n$

$2.5 = n$

51.

| | Number of Tickets | Cost |
|---|---|---|
| Children | $16 - x$ | $3.75(16 - x)$ |
| Adults | $x$ | $5.75x$ |

$3.75(16 - x) + 5.75x = 68$

$60 - 3.75x + 5.75x = 68$

$60 + 2x = 68$

$2x = 8$

$x = 4$

$16 - x = 12$

4 adult and 12 children's tickets were purchased.

52. $2r - 2.1 < -8.7 + r$

$r < -6.6$

$\{r \mid r < -6.6\}$

53. $10x - 2 \geq 4(x - 2)$

$10x - 2 \geq 4x - 8$

$6x \geq -6$

$x \geq -1$

$\{x \mid x \geq -1\}$

---

| 5-6 | Open Sentences Involving Absolute Value |

**PAGES 201-202    CHECKING FOR UNDERSTANDING**

1. c    2. a    3. d    4. b

5. a.

118 120 122 124 126

   b. $|w - 122| \leq 3$

   c. $119 \leq w \leq 125$

6. $|x| < 3$    7. two    8. no    9. and

10. The distance from 0 to $x$ is 4 units;

$x = 4$ or $x = -4$; $\{4, -4\}$

11. The distance from 0 to $y$ is more than 3 units;

$y > 3$ or $y < -3$; $\{y \mid y > 3$ or $y < -3\}$

12. The distance from 0 to $t - 1$ is at most 5 units;

$t - 1 \leq 5$ and $t - 1 \geq 5$; $\{t \mid -4 \leq t \leq 6\}$

13. The distance from 0 to $x - 12$ is less than 9 units;

$x - 12 < 9$ and $x - 12 > -9$; $\{x \mid 3 < x < 21\}$

14. The distance from 0 to $x + 2$ is at least 9 units;

$x + 2 \geq 9$ or $x + 2 \leq -9$; $\{x \mid x \geq 7$ or $x \leq -11\}$

15. The distance from 0 to $7 - r$ is 4 units;

$7 - r = 4$ or $7 - r = -4$; $\{3, 11\}$

**PAGES 202-203    EXERCISES**

16. $|T| > 5$         17. $|s - 90| < 6$

18. $|b - 1.5| \leq 0.005$

19. $|x - 1| < 4$

$x - 1 < 4$ and $x - 1 > -4$

$x < 5$ and $\quad x > -3$

$\{x \mid -3 < x < 5\}$

-6 -4 -2 0 2 4 6 8

20. $|y - 7| < 2$

$y - 7 < 2$ and $y - 7 > -2$

$y < 9$ and $\quad y > 5$

$\{y \mid 5 < y < 9\}$

3 4 5 6 7 8 9 10

21. $|a + 8| \geq 1$

$a + 8 \geq 1$ or $a + 8 \leq -1$

$a \geq -7$ or $\quad a \leq -9$

$\{a \mid -9 \geq a \geq -7\}$

-16 -14 -12 -10 -8 -6 -4 -2 0 2 4

**22.** $|2 - t| \leq 1$

$2 - t \leq 1$ and $2 - t \geq -1$

$-t \leq -1$      $-t \geq -3$

$t \geq 1$ and     $t \leq 3$

$\{t \mid 1 \leq t \leq 3\}$

**23.** $|9 - y| \geq 13$

$9 - y \geq 13$ or $9 - y \leq -13$

$-4 \geq y$ or    $22 \leq y$

$\{y \mid y \leq -4$ or $y \geq 22\}$

**24.** $|3 - 3x| = 0$

$3 - 3x = 0$

$-3x = -3$

$x = 1$     (1)

**25.** $|14 - 2z| = 16$

$14 - 2z = 16$ or $14 - 2z = -16$

$-2z = 2$        $-2z = -30$

$z = -1$ or      $z = 15$

**26.**      $|2b - 11| \geq 7$

$2b - 11 \geq 7$     $2b - 11 \leq -7$

$2b \geq 18$ or    $2b \leq 4$

$b \geq 9$ or      $b \leq 2$

**27.**      $|3x - 12| < 12$

$3x - 12 < 12$ and $3x - 12 > -12$

$3x < 24$        $3x > 0$

$x < 8$ and      $x > 0$

**28.** $|4k + 2| \leq 14$

$4k + 2 \leq 14$ and $4k + 2 \geq -14$

$4k \leq 12$       $4k \geq -16$

$k \leq 3$ and      $k \geq -4$

**29.** $|10w + 10| > 90$

$10w + 10 > 90$ or $10w + 10 < -90$

$10w > 80$        $10w < -100$

$w > 8$   or       $w < -10$

$\{w \mid w > 8$ or $w < -10\}$

**30.** $|x + 1| > -2$

$x + 1 > -2$ or $x + 1 < 2$

$x > -3$ or     $x < 1$

$\{$all numbers$\}$

**31.** $|2y - 7| \geq -6$

obviously true for all cases

$2y - 7 \geq -6$ or $2y - 7 \leq 6$

$2y \geq 1$        $2y \leq 13$

$y \geq \dfrac{1}{2}$   or     $y \leq \dfrac{13}{2}$

$\{$all numbers$\}$

**32.** $|a - 5| = -3$

There can be no expression whose absolute set is equal to a negative value. The solution is ø.

**33.** $|5b + 6| < 0$

There can be no expression whose absolute value is less than zero. The solution is ø.

**34.** $|13 - 5y| = 8$

$13 - 5y = 8$ or $13 - 5y = -8$

$-5y = -5$       $-5y = -21$

$y = 1$ or      $y = \dfrac{21}{5}$

$\left\{y \mid y = 1 \text{ or } y = \dfrac{21}{5}\right\}$

**35.** $\left|3t - \frac{1}{2}\right| \geq \frac{11}{2}$

$3t - \frac{1}{2} \geq \frac{11}{2}$ or $3t - \frac{1}{2} \leq -\frac{11}{2}$

$3t \geq 6$ $\qquad$ $3t \leq -5$

$t \geq 2$ or $\qquad$ $t \leq -\frac{5}{3}$

$\left\{t \mid t \geq 2 \text{ or } t \leq -\frac{5}{3}\right\}$

**36.** $\left|\frac{1}{2} - 3n\right| < \frac{7}{2}$

$\frac{1}{2} - 3n < \frac{7}{2}$ and $\frac{1}{2} - 3n > -\frac{7}{2}$

$-3n < 3$ $\qquad$ $-3n > -4$

$n > -1$ and $\qquad$ $n < \frac{4}{3}$

$\left\{n \mid -1 < n < \frac{4}{3}\right\}$

**37.** $|x| = 1$ **38.** $|x| < 3$ **39.** $|x| \geq 2$

**40.** $|x + 1| = 3$ **41.** $|x + 1| < 3$ **42.** $|x - 1| \geq 1$

**43.** $|x| \leq 2$ $\qquad\qquad$ **44.** $|x| < 4$

$x \leq 2$ and $x \geq -2$ $\qquad$ $x < 4$ and $x \geq -4$

$(-2, -1, 0, 1, 2)$ $\qquad$ $\{-3, -2, -1, 0, 1, 2, 3\}$

**45.** Using the answer to 43 as an example, we see that there are 5 or 2(2) + 1 solutions to 43. Thus, if $|x| \leq a$, there are $2a + 1$ solutions.

**46.** Using the answer to 44 as an example, we see that there are 7 or 4(2) - 1 solutions to 44. Thus, there are $2a - 1$ solutions.

**47.** $|x| = |y|$ $\qquad\qquad$ **48.** when $a \neq 0$; never

**49.** Let $T$ = temperature.

$|T + 2| < -257$

$T + 2 < -257$ $\qquad$ $T + 2 > 257$

$T < -259$ $\qquad\qquad$ $T > 255$

**50.** Let $d$ = distance.

$15(18) < d < 15(21)$

$270 < d < 315$

270 miles to 315 miles

**51.** Let $d$ = the diameter.

$2 - 0.04 \leq d \leq 2 + 0.04$

$1.96 \leq d \leq 2.04$

1.96 cm to 2.04 cm, inclusive

**52.** Let $n$ = number of books.

$40 < 0.8n + 6 < 50$

$34 < 0.8n < 44$

$42.5 < n < 55$

between 43 and 54 books

**53.** $3(2n - x) = 1 - n$

$2n - x = \frac{1 - n}{3}$

$-x = \frac{1 - n}{3} - 2n$

$x = \frac{-1 + n}{3} + \frac{6n}{3}$

$x = \frac{7n - 1}{3}$

**54.** $12 = x(0.15)$

$x = 80$

**55.** $8\%(x) + 10\%(10,000 - x) = 873$

$8(x) + 10(10,000 - x) = 87,300$

$8x + 100,000 - 10x = 87,300$

$-2x = -12,700$

$x = 6350$

\$6350 at 8%, \$3650 at 10%

**56.** $290 = \frac{x}{100} \cdot 87$

$100(290) = 100\left(\frac{x}{100} \cdot 87\right)$

$29,000 = 87x$

$x = 333\frac{1}{3}\%$

**57.**

6 + 5 + 4 + 3 + 2 + 1 = 21 line segments

**58.** Let $s$ = score on last test.

$88 \leq \frac{88 + 90 + 91 + s}{4} \leq 92$

$352 \leq 88 + 90 + 91 + s \leq 368$

$352 \leq 269 + s \leq 368$

$83 \leq s \leq 99$

between 83 and 99 inclusive

# Chapter 5 Summary and Review

PAGES 204-206 SKILLS AND CONCEPTS

**1.** $n - 4 < 9$ $\qquad$ **2.** $r + 8 \leq -3$

$n - 4 + 4 < 9 + 4$ $\qquad$ $r + 8 - 8 \leq -3 - 8$

$n < 13$ $\qquad\qquad$ $r \leq -11$

$\{n \mid n < 13\}$ $\qquad$ $\{r \mid r \leq -11\}$

**3.** $a - 2.3 \geq -7.8$

$a - 2.3 + 2.3 \geq -7.8 + 2.3$

$a \geq -5.5$

$\{a \mid a \geq -5.5\}$

**4.** $5z - 6 > 4z$

$5z - 6 + 6 > 4z - 6$

$5z > 4z - 6$

$5z - 4z > 4z - 4z - 6$

$z > 6$

$\{z \mid z > 6\}$

73

5. $2x + 7 < 3x$

$2x - 2x + 7 < 3x - 2x$

$7 < x$

$\{x \mid x > 7\}$

6. $y + \dfrac{5}{8} > \dfrac{11}{24}$

$y + \dfrac{5}{8} - \dfrac{5}{8} > \dfrac{11}{24} - \dfrac{5}{8}$

$y > -\dfrac{1}{6}$

$\left\{ y \mid y > -\dfrac{1}{6} \right\}$

7. $7 + n \geq 12$

$n \geq 5$

$\{n \mid n \geq 5\}$

8. $3n > 4n - 8$

$3n + 8 > 4n - 8 + 8$

$3n + 8 > 4n$

$3n - 3n + 8 > 4n - 3n$

$8 > n$

$\{n \mid n < 8\}$

9. $6x \leq -24$

$\dfrac{1}{6}(6x) \leq \dfrac{1}{6}(-24)$

$x \leq -4$

$\{x \mid x \leq -4\}$

10. $-7y \geq 91$

$-\dfrac{1}{7}(-7y) \geq -\dfrac{1}{7}(91)$

$y \leq -13$

$\{y \mid y \leq -13\}$

11. $0.8t > 0.96$

$\dfrac{1}{0.8}(0.8t) > \dfrac{1}{0.8}(0.96)$

$t > 1.2$

$\{t \mid t > 1.2\}$

12. $-\dfrac{4}{3}m < -16$

$-\dfrac{3}{4}\left(-\dfrac{4}{3}m\right) > -\dfrac{3}{4}(-16)$

$m > 12$

$\{m \mid m > 12\}$

13. $\dfrac{2}{3}k \geq \dfrac{2}{15}$

$\dfrac{3}{2}\left(\dfrac{2}{3}k\right) \geq \dfrac{3}{2}\left(\dfrac{2}{15}\right)$

$k \geq \dfrac{1}{5}$

$\left\{ k \mid k \geq \dfrac{1}{5} \right\}$

14. $\dfrac{4z}{7} \leq -\dfrac{2}{5}$

$\dfrac{7}{4}\left(\dfrac{4z}{7}\right) \leq \dfrac{7}{4}\left(-\dfrac{2}{5}\right)$

$z \leq -\dfrac{7}{10}$

$\left\{ z \mid z \leq -\dfrac{7}{10} \right\}$

15. $7n < -154$

$\dfrac{1}{7}(7n) < \dfrac{1}{7}(-154)$

$n < -22$

$\{n \mid n < -22\}$

16. $-\dfrac{3}{4}n \leq 30$

$-\dfrac{4}{3}\left(-\dfrac{3}{4}n\right) \geq -\dfrac{4}{3}(30)$

$n \geq -40$

$\{n \mid n \geq -40\}$

17. $7x - 12 < 30$

$7x - 12 + 12 < 30 + 12$

$7x < 42$

$\dfrac{1}{7}(7x) < \dfrac{1}{7}(42)$

$x < 6$

$\{x \mid x < 6\}$

18. $2r - 3.1 > 0.5$

$2r - 3.1 + 3.1 > 0.5 + 3.1$

$2r > 3.6$

$\dfrac{1}{2}(2r) > \dfrac{1}{2}(3.6)$

$r > 1.8$

$\{r \mid r > 1.8\}$

19. $4y - 11 \geq 8y + 7$

$4y - 4y - 11 \geq 8y - 4y + 7$

$-11 \geq 4y + 7$

$-11 - 7 \geq 4y + 7 - 7$

$-18 \geq 4y$

$\dfrac{1}{4}(-18) \geq \dfrac{1}{4}(4y)$

$-\dfrac{9}{2} \geq y$

$\left\{ y \mid y \leq -\dfrac{9}{2} \right\}$

20. $4(n - 1) < 7n + 8$

$4n - 4 < 7n + 8$

$4n - 4n - 4 < 7n - 4n + 8$

$-4 < 3n + 8$

$-4 - 8 < 3n$

$-12 < 3n$

$\dfrac{1}{3}(-12) < \dfrac{1}{3}(3n)$

$-4 < n$

$\{n \mid n > -4\}$

21. $0.3(z - 4) \leq 0.8(0.2z + 2)$

$0.3z - 1.2 \leq 0.16z + 1.6$

$0.3z - 0.16z - 1.2 \leq 0.16z - 0.16z + 1.6$

$0.14z - 1.2 \leq 1.6$

$0.14z - 1.2 + 1.2 \leq 1.6 + 1.2$

$0.14z \leq 2.8$

$\dfrac{1}{0.14}(0.14z) \leq \dfrac{1}{0.14}(2.8)$

$z \leq 20$

$\{z \mid z \leq 20\}$

22. $3n + 11 \leq 47$

$3n + 11 - 11 \leq 47 - 11$

$3n \leq 36$

$\dfrac{1}{3}(3n) \leq \dfrac{1}{3}(36)$

$n \leq 12$

$\{n \mid n \leq 12\}$

23. $12 - 2n \geq n + 27$

$12 - 2n + 2n \geq n + 2n + 27$

$12 \geq 3n + 27$

$12 - 27 \geq 3n + 27 - 27$

$-15 \geq 3n$

$\dfrac{1}{3}(-15) \geq \dfrac{1}{3}(3n)$

$-5 \geq n$

$\{n \mid n \leq -5\}$

24. $x > -1$ and $x \leq 3$

$\{x \mid -1 < x \leq 3\}$

25. $y \leq -3$ or $y > 0$

74

26. 
$$2a + 5 \leq 7 \qquad \text{or} \qquad 2a \geq a - 3$$
$$2a + 5 - 5 \leq 7 - 5 \qquad 2a - a \geq a - a - 3$$
$$2a \leq 2 \qquad\qquad a \geq -3$$
$$a \leq 1 \qquad \text{or} \qquad a \geq -3$$

-5 -4 -3 -2 -1  0  1  2  3

27. 
$$4r \geq 3r + 7 \qquad \text{and} \qquad 3r + 7 < r + 29$$
$$4r - 3r \geq 3r - 3r + 7 \qquad 3r - r + 7 < r - r + 29$$
$$r \geq 7 \qquad\qquad 2r + 7 < 29$$
$$2r + 7 - 7 < 29 - 7$$
$$2r < 22$$
$$r \geq 7 \qquad \text{and} \qquad r < 11$$
$$\{a \mid 7 \leq r < 11\}$$

6  8  10  12

28. $x \leq -3$ or $x \geq 1$ $\qquad$ 29. $-2 \leq x < 3$

30. 
$$|y - 2| > 0$$
$$y - 2 > 0 \text{ or } y - 2 < 0$$
$$y > 2 \text{ or } \qquad y < 2$$
$$\{y \mid y \neq 2\}$$

-2  0  2  4

31. 
$$|1 - n| \leq 5$$
$$1 - n \leq 5 \quad \text{and} \quad 1 - n \geq -5$$
$$n \geq -4 \qquad\qquad 6 \geq n$$
$$\{n \mid -4 \leq n \leq 6\}$$

-6 -4 -2  0  2  4  6  8

32. $|7x - 10| < 0$
There can be no expression whose absolute value is less than zero. The solution is ø.

33. 
$$\left| 2p - \frac{1}{2} \right| > \frac{9}{2}$$
$$2p - \frac{1}{2} > \frac{9}{2} \text{ or } 2p - \frac{1}{2} < -\frac{9}{2}$$
$$2p > 5 \qquad\qquad 2p < -4$$
$$p > \frac{5}{2} \text{ or } \qquad p < -2$$
$$\left\{ p \mid p > \frac{5}{2} \text{ or } p < -2 \right\}$$

-3  -2  -1  0  1  2  3

34. $0 < 3.6d < 90$
$0 < d < 25$

35. Let $x$ = the first integer;
$x + 1$ = the next integer;
$x + 2$ = the third integer.
$$x + x + 1 + x + 2 < 100$$
$$3x + 3 < 100$$
$$3x < 97$$
$$x < \frac{97}{3} = 32.\overline{3}$$
$x = 32$, $x + 1 = 33$, $x + 2 = 34$
The three integers are 32, 33, 34.

36. 

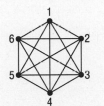

$5 + 4 + 3 + 2 + 1 = 15$
15 games are played.

37. 

| Day | Beginning Position (ft) | Position after Climbing (ft) |
|-----|------------------------|------------------------------|
| Mon | 0 | 4 |
| Tues | 3 | 7 |
| Wed | 6 | 10 |

The spider will reach the top on Wednesday.

38. Let $m$ = money spent on jeans.
$$2(15.30) + m \leq 85$$
$$30.60 + m \leq 85$$
$$m \leq 54.40$$
$54.40 or less

39. Let $e$ = amount Sung earns.
$$2e + e \leq 312$$
$$3e \leq 312$$
$$e \leq 104$$
Sung earns $104, Jill earns $208.

40. Let $c$ = number of checks.
$$3 < 1.75 + 0.08c < 4$$
$$1.25 < 0.08c < 2.25$$
$$15.625 < c < 28.125$$
Between 15 and 29 checks

41. Let $b$ = number of books.
$$55 < 30 + 1.5b < 60$$
$$25 < 1.5b < 30$$
$$16.\overline{6} < b < 20$$
17 to 19 books

75

**PAGE 207**

1.  $a - 2 > 11$
    $a - 2 + 2 > 11 + 2$
    $a > 13$
    $\{a \mid a > 13\}$

2.  $-12 \le d + 7$
    $-12 - 7 \le d + 7 - 7$
    $-19 \le d$
    $\{d \mid d \ge -19\}$

3.  $7x < 6x - 11$
    $7x - 6x < 6x - 6x - 11$
    $x < -11$
    $\{x \mid x < -11\}$

4.  $z - 1 \ge 2z - 3$
    $z - z - 1 \ge 2z - z - 3$
    $-1 \ge z - 3$
    $-1 + 3 \ge z - 3 + 3$
    $2 \ge z$
    $\{z \mid z \le 2\}$

5.  $3y > 63$
    $\frac{1}{3}(3y) > \frac{1}{3}(63)$
    $y > 21$
    $\{y \mid y > 21\}$

6.  $-\frac{2r}{3} \le \frac{7}{12}$
    $-\frac{3}{2}\left(-\frac{2r}{3}\right) \ge -\frac{3}{2}\left(\frac{7}{12}\right)$
    $r \ge -\frac{7}{8}$
    $\left\{r \mid r \ge -\frac{7}{8}\right\}$

7.  $3x + 1 \ge 16$
    $3x + 1 - 1 \ge 6 - 1$
    $3x \ge 15$
    $\frac{1}{3}(3x) \ge \frac{1}{3}(15)$
    $x \ge 5$
    $\{x \mid x \ge 5\}$

8.  $5 - 4b > -23$
    $5 - 5 - 4b > -23 - 5$
    $-4b > -28$
    $-\frac{1}{4}(-4b) < -\frac{1}{4}(-28)$
    $b < 7$
    $\{b \mid b < 7\}$

9.  $\frac{2n - 3}{-7} \le 5$
    $-7\left(\frac{2n - 3}{-7}\right) \ge -7(5)$
    $2n - 3 \ge -35$
    $2n - 3 + 3 \ge -35 + 3$
    $2n \ge -32$
    $\frac{1}{2}(2n) \ge \frac{1}{2}(-32)$
    $n \ge -16$
    $\{n \mid n \ge -16\}$

10. $8y + 3 < 13y - 9$
    $8y - 8y + 3 < 13y - 8y - 9$
    $3 < 5y - 9$
    $3 + 9 < 5y - 9 + 9$
    $12 < 5y$
    $\frac{12}{5} < y$
    $\left\{y \mid y > \frac{12}{5}\right\}$

11. $8(1 - 2z) \le 25 + z$
    $8 - 16z \le 25 + z$
    $8 - 16z + 16z \le 25 + z + 16z$
    $8 \le 25 + 17z$
    $8 - 25 \le 25 - 25 + 17z$
    $-17 \le 17z$
    $-1 \le z$
    $\{z \mid z \ge -1\}$

12. $0.3(m + 4) > 0.5(m - 4)$
    $0.3m + 1.2 > 0.5m - 2$
    $0.3m - 0.3m + 1.2 > 0.5m - 0.3m - 2$
    $1.2 > 0.2m - 2$
    $2 + 1.2 > 0.2m$
    $3.2 > 0.2m$
    $16 > m$
    $\{m \mid m < 16\}$

13. $x + 1 > -2$ and $3x < 6$
    $x > -3$ and $\;x < 2$
    $\{x \mid -3 < x < 2\}$

14. $2n + 1 \ge 15$ or $2n + 1 \le -1$
    $2n \ge 14 \qquad\qquad 2n \le -2$
    $n \ge 7$ or $\qquad n \le -1$
    $\{n \mid n \ge 7 \text{ or } n \le -1\}$

15. $8 + 3t > 2$ and $-12 > 11t - 1$
    $3t > -6 \qquad -11 > 11t$
    $t > -2$ and $\;-1 > t$
    $\{t \mid -2 < t < -1\}$

16. $|n| > 3$
    $n > 3$ or $n < -3$
    $\{n \mid n > 3 \text{ or } n < -3\}$

17. $|2x - 1| < 5$
    $2x - 1 < 5$ and $2x - 1 > -5$
    $2x < 6 \qquad\qquad 2x > -4$
    $x < 3$ and $\qquad x > -2$
    $\{x \mid -2 < x < 3\}$

18. $|5 - 3b| \ge 1$
    $5 - 3b \ge 1$ or $5 - 3b \le -1$
    $-3b \ge -4 \qquad\qquad -3b \le -6$
    $b \le \frac{4}{3}$ or $\qquad b \ge 2$
    $\left\{b \mid b \ge 2 \text{ or } b \le \frac{4}{3}\right\}$

19. $4n - 8 \geq 5n$

$-8 \geq n$

$\{n|n \leq -8\}$

20. $71 < 2n - 7 < 83$     21. $6x \geq 30$

$78 < 2n < 90$                    $x \geq 5$

$39 < n < 45$               5 or more

$\{n|39 < n < 45\}$

22. Let $x$ = the first integer;

$x + 2$ = the next integer;

$x + 4$ = the third consecutive odd integer;

$x + 6$ = the fourth consecutive odd integer.

$$\frac{x + (x + 2) + (x + 4) + (x + 6)}{4} < 20$$

$$\frac{4x + 12}{4} < 20$$

$$4x + 12 < 80$$

$$4x < 68$$

$$x < 17$$

$x = 15$, $x + 2 = 17$, $x + 4 = 19$, $x + 6 = 21$

The integers are 15, 17, 19, and 21.

23. Let $s$ = the last score.

$9.1 + 9.3 + 9.6 + 8.7 + s > 46.1$

$36.7 + s > 46.1$

$s > 9.4$

He must score more than 9.4 points.

24. Let $s$ = last score.

$$\frac{82 + 86 + 91 + s}{4} \geq 87$$

$$\frac{259 + s}{4} \geq 87$$

$$259 + s \geq 348$$

$$s \geq 89$$

She must score at least 89 points.

25. Let $s$ = Kathy's sales.

$37,000 < 18,000 + 0.05s < 40,000$

$19,000 < 0.05s < 22,000$

$380,000 < s < 440,000$

Her sales must be between $380,000 and $440,000.

PAGE 207     BONUS

26. $0 < 30 - \frac{1}{2}d < 90$

$-30 < \frac{1}{2}d < 60$

$60 > d > -120$

77

# Chapter 6  Polynomials

## 6-1   Problem-Solving Strategy: Look for a Pattern

PAGES 211-212   CHECKING FOR UNDERSTANDING

1.

| Square Size | Number of Squares |
|---|---|
| 1 × 1 | 100 |
| 2 × 2 | 81 |
| 3 × 3 | 64 |
| 4 × 4 | 49 |
| 5 × 5 | 36 |
| 6 × 6 | 25 |
| 7 × 7 | 16 |
| 8 × 8 | 9 |
| 9 × 9 | 4 |
| 10 × 10 | 1 |

The total number of squares on a 10 × 10 checkerboard is 100 + 81 + 64 + 49 + 36 + 25 + 16 + 9 + 4 + 1 or 385 squares.

2. $(9 - n)^2$

3. Every time 10 is added to each of the numbers being multiplied, $4n \times 6n$, $n \times 200$ is added to the previous answer.

| $4n \times 6n$ | $n \times 200$ | $n \times 200$ added to previous answer |
|---|---|---|
| 4 × 6 | – | 24 |
| 14 × 16 | 200 | 224 |
| 24 × 26 | 400 | 624 |
| 34 × 36 | 600 | 1224 |
| 44 × 46 | 800 | 2024 |
| 54 × 56 | 1000 | 3024 |
| 64 × 66 | 1200 | 4224 |
| 74 × 76 | 1400 | 5624 |
| 84 × 86 | 1600 | 7224 |
| 94 × 96 | 1800 | 9024 |
| 104 × 106 | 2000 | 11024 |
| 114 × 116 | 2200 | 13224 |
| 124 × 126 | 2400 | 15624 |

4. $12 - \dfrac{12}{12 + 1} = 12 - \dfrac{12}{13}$

5.
$$1^3 = 1^2 - 0^2$$
$$(1 + 1) \quad (1 + 2) \quad (0 + 1)$$
$$2^3 = 3^2 - 1^2$$
$$(2 + 1) \quad (3 + 3) \quad (1 + 2)$$
$$3^3 = 6^2 - 3^2$$
$$(3 + 1) \quad (6 + 4) \quad (3 + 3)$$
$$4^3 = 10^2 - 6^2$$
$$(4 + 1) \quad (10 + 5) \quad (6 + 4)$$
$$5^3 = 15^2 - 10^2$$
$$(5 + 1) \quad (15 + 6) \quad (10 + 5)$$
$$6^3 = 21^2 - 15^2$$

Each consecutive cube of $n^3 = x^2 - y^2$ is
$$(n + 1)^3 = (x + (n + 1))^2 - (y + n)^2.$$

6.

| Triangle Size | 1×1 | 2×2 | 3×3 | 4×4 | 5×5 | 6×6 | 7×7 | 8×8 |
|---|---|---|---|---|---|---|---|---|
| Number of Triangles | 36 | 28 | 21 | 15 | 10 | 6 | 3 | 1 |

Sum of all the triangles is 120, so there are 120 triangles.

7.

| Locker # | 1 | 2 | 3 | 4 | 5 | 6 | 7 | 8 | 9 | 10 |
|---|---|---|---|---|---|---|---|---|---|---|
| Shopper 1 | O | O | O | O | O | O | O | O | O | O |
| Shopper 2 | O | C | O | C | O | C | O | C | O | C |
| Shopper 3 | O | C | C | C | O | O | O | O | C | C |
| Shopper 4 | O | C | C | O | O | O | O | O | C | C |
| Shopper 5 | O | C | C | O | C | O | O | O | C | O |
| Shopper 6 | O | C | C | O | C | C | O | O | C | O |
| Shopper 7 | O | C | C | O | C | C | C | O | C | O |
| Shopper 8 | O | C | C | O | C | C | C | C | C | O |
| Shopper 9 | O | C | C | O | C | C | C | C | O | O |
| Shopper 10 | O | C | C | O | C | C | C | C | O | C |

The perfect squares remain open, 1, 4, 9, 16, 25.

8. a. 1, 1, 2, 3, 5, 8, 13, 21, 34, 55

   b. They approach 1.618.

## PAGE 212   EXERCISES

9. 29 days

10. 43 Little Bits

11. You could never say this for the first time. The first time you say it, you would be lying; therefore, only a Falsite could say it.

12.

| Number of Lines | 1 | 2 | 3 | 4 | 5 | 6 | 7 |
|---|---|---|---|---|---|---|---|
| Number of Parts | 4 | 7 | 10 | 13 | 16 | 19 | 22 |

| Number of Lines | 8 | 9 | 10 | ... | $n$ | ... | 100 |
|---|---|---|---|---|---|---|---|
| Number of Parts | 25 | 28 | 31 | | $3n + 1$ | | 301 |

301 parts

## PAGE 212   COOPERATIVE LEARNING ACTIVITY

| 0 | 1 | 2 | 3 | 4 | 5 | 6 | 7 | 8 | 9 |
|---|---|---|---|---|---|---|---|---|---|
| 6 | 2 | 1 | 0 | 0 | 0 | 1 | 0 | 0 | 0 |

**Multiplying Monomials**

1. $x^3$ and $y^7$ have different bases.

2. Answers may vary; When the bases are equivalent, the product is the equivalent base with an exponent equal to the sum of the exponents.

3. Answers may vary; When a power is raised to a power, the answer is the base with an exponent equal to the product of the exponents.

4. Answers may vary; When a product of powers is raised to a power, multiply each exponent by the outermost power and keep the bases the same.

5. $(4y)^2$ ____ $4y^2$
   $16y^2$ $\neq$ $4y^2$; no

6. $3xy^5$ ____ $3(xy)^5$
   $3xy^5$ $\neq$ $3x^5y^5$; no

7. $(2a)^3$ ____ $8a^3$
   $8a^3$ $=$ $8a^3$; yes

8. $(ab)^2$ ____ $a^2 \cdot b^2$
   $a^2b^2$ $=$ $a^2b^2$; yes

9. $xy^3$ $\neq$ $x^3y^3$; no

10. $4(x^3)^2$ ____ $16x^6$
    $4x^6$ $\neq$ $16x^6$; no

11. $A = p^7 \cdot p^7$
    $A = p^{7+7} = p^{14}$

12. $A = m^3 \cdot m$
    $A = m^{3+1} = m^4$

13. $A = x^5 \cdot x^3$
    $A = x^{5+3} = x^8$

14. $V = r^3 \cdot r^2 \cdot r^3$
    $V = r^{3+2+3} = r^8$

15. $V = (a^2)^3$
    $V = a^{2 \cdot 3} = a^6$

16. $V = (yz^4)^3$
    $V = y^3z^{4 \cdot 3} = y^3z^{12}$

17. $a^5(a)(a^7)$
    $= a^{5+1+7}$
    $= a^{13}$

18. $(a^2b)(ab^4)$
    $= (a^2 \cdot a)(b \cdot b^4)$
    $= (a^{2+1})(b^{1+4})$
    $= a^3b^5$

19. $(m^3n)(mn^2)$
    $= (m^3 \cdot m)(n \cdot n^2)$
    $= (m^{3+1})(n^{1+2})$
    $= m^4n^3$

20. $(10^2)^2 = 10^{2 \cdot 2}$
    $= 10^4$
    $= 10,000$

21. $[(-4)^2]^2 = (-4)^{2 \cdot 2}$
    $= (-4)^4$
    $= 256$

22. $[(3^2)^4]^2$
    $= (3^8)^2$
    $= 3^{16}$
    $= 43,046,721$

23. $(r^3t^4)(r^4t^4)$
    $= (r^3r^4)(t^4t^4)$
    $= (r^{3+4})(t^{4+4})$
    $= r^7t^8$

24. $(3a^2)(4a^3)$
    $= (3 \cdot 4)(a^2 \cdot a^3)$
    $= 12 \cdot a^{2+3}$
    $= 12a^5$

25. $(-10x^3y)(2x^2)$
    $= (-10 \cdot 2)(x^3x^2)(y)$
    $= -20(x^{3+2})y$
    $= -20x^5y$

26. $(m^2)^5 = m^{2 \cdot 5}$
    $= m^{10}$

27. $(-7z)^3 = (-7)^3z^3$
    $= -343z^3$

28. $\left(\frac{2}{5}d\right)^2 = \left(\frac{2}{5}\right)^2d^2$
    $= \frac{4}{25}d^2$

29. $(3y^3z)(7y^4)$
    $= (3 \cdot 7)(y^3 \cdot y^4)z$
    $= 21(y^{3+4})z$
    $= 21y^7z$

30. $m^4(m^3b^2)$
    $= (m^4 \cdot m^3)(b^2)$
    $= (m^{4+3})b^2$
    $= m^7b^2$

31. $(3x^2y^2z)(2x^2y^2z^3)$
    $= (3 \cdot 2)(x^2 \cdot x^2)(y^2 \cdot y^2)(z \cdot z^3)$
    $= 6(x^{2+2})(y^{2+2})(z^{1+3})$
    $= 6x^4y^4z^4$

32. $(0.6d)^3 = (0.6)^3d^3$
    $= 0.216d^3$

33. $(a^3x^2)^4$
    $= (a^3)^4(x^2)^4$
    $= (a^{3 \cdot 4})(x^{2 \cdot 4})$
    $= a^{12}x^8$

34. $(2a^2b)^2$
    $= 2^2(a^2)^2b^2$
    $= 4(a^{2 \cdot 2})b^2$
    $= 4a^4b^2$

35. $(ab)(ac)(bc)$
    $= (a \cdot a)(b \cdot b)(c \cdot c)$
    $= (a^{1+1})(b^{1+1})(c^{1+1})$
    $= a^2b^2c^2$

36. $-\frac{5}{6}c(12a^3)$
    $= -\frac{5}{6}(12)a^3c$
    $= 10a^3c$

37. $(-27ay^3)\left(-\frac{1}{3}ay^3\right)$
    $= (-27)\left(-\frac{1}{3}\right)(a \cdot a)(y^3 \cdot y^3)$
    $= 9(a^{1+1})(y^{3+3})$
    $= 9a^2y^6$

38. $-3(ax^3y)^2$
    $= -3a^2(x^3)^2y^2$
    $= -3a^2x^{3 \cdot 2}y^2$
    $= -3a^2x^6y^2$

39. $\left(\frac{1}{2}xy^2\right)^3$
    $= \left(\frac{1}{2}\right)^3x^3(y^2)^3$
    $= \frac{1}{8}x^3(y^{2 \cdot 3})$
    $= \frac{1}{8}x^3y^6$

**40.** $(0.3x^3y^2)^2$

$= (0.3)^2(x^3)^2(y^2)^2$

$= 0.09(x^{3 \cdot 2})(y^{2 \cdot 2})$

$= 0.09x^6y^4$

**41.** $(-3ab)^3(2b^2)$

$= (-3^3a^3b^3)(2b^2)$

$= (-27a^3b^3)(2b^2)$

$= (2 \cdot -27)a^3(b^3 \cdot b^2)$

$= -54a^3(b^{3+2})$

$= -54a^3b^5$

**42.** $(2x^2)^2\left(\frac{1}{2}y^2\right)^2$

$= 2^2(x^2)^2\left(\frac{1}{2}\right)^2(y^2)^2$

$= 4x^{2 \cdot 2}\left(\frac{1}{4}\right)y^{2 \cdot 2}$

$= x^4y^4$

**43.** $\left(\frac{3}{10}y^2\right)^2(10y^2)^3$

$= \left(\frac{9}{100}\right)y^{2 \cdot 2}(1000)y^{2 \cdot 3}$

$= 90y^4y^6$

$= 90y^{10}$

**44.** $\left(-\frac{1}{8}a\right)\left(-\frac{1}{6}\right)(b)(48c)$

$= \left(-\frac{1}{8}\right)\left(-\frac{1}{6}\right)(48)(abc)$

$= 1abc$

$= abc$

**45.** $\left(-\frac{1}{3}c^2b^3a\right)(18a^2b^2c^3)$

$= \left(-\frac{1}{3} \cdot 18\right)(a \cdot a^2)(b^3 \cdot b^2)(c^2 \cdot c^3)$

$= -6(a^{1+2})(b^{3+2})(c^{2+3})$

$= -6a^3b^5c^5$

**46.** $(3a^2)^3 + (5a^2)^3$

$= 3^3(a^2)^3 + 5^3(a^2)^3$

$= 27a^6 + 125a^6$

$= 152a^6$

**47.** $(-3x^3y)^3 - 3(x^2y)^2(x^5y)$

$= (-3)^3(x^3)^3y^3 - 3(x^2)^2y^2x^5y$

$= -27x^{3 \cdot 3}y^3 - 3x^{2 \cdot 2}x^5y^2y$

$= -27x^9y^3 - 3x^4x^5y^{2+1}$

$= -27x^9y^3 - 3x^{4+5}y^3$

$= -27x^9y^3 - 3x^9y^3$

$= -30x^9y^3$

**48.** no  **49.** no, $b \neq 0$  **50.** $T = p(1 + r)^t$

$T = 5000(1 + 0.07)^{10}$

$= 5000(1.07)^{10}$

$= \$9835.76$

**51.** $T = P\left[\dfrac{(1 + r)^t - 1}{r}\right]$

$T = 500\left[\dfrac{(1 + 0.07)^{10} - 1}{0.07}\right]$

$T = 500[13.81645]$

$T = \$6908.23$

No, you will not have more money.

**52.** Divide each number by 2.

$-1, -\frac{1}{2}, -\frac{1}{4}$

**53.** Let $d$ = daughters.

$d + 5d = 6$

$6d = 6$

$d = 1$

She has 1 daughter.

**54.** $2x + 4 \leq 6$ or $x \geq 2x - 4$

$2x \leq 2 \quad -x \geq -4$

$x \leq 1$ or $x \leq 4$

$\{x | x \leq 4\}$

**55.** $|6 - x| \leq x$

$6 - x \leq x$

$6 \leq 2x$

$3 \leq x$

$\{x | x \geq 3\}$

**56.** Let the letters A–L represent corners.

```
A     B     C     D     E     F
┌─────┬─────┬─────┬─────┬─────┐
│     │     │     │     │     │
└─────┴─────┴─────┴─────┴─────┘
G     H     I     J     K     L
```

| 1 large rectangle | AFGL | |
| 5 rectangles of 1 unit | | |
| 4 rectangles of 2 units | CEKI | DFLJ |
| | ACIG | BDJH |
| 3 rectangles of 3 units | ADJG | BEKH |
| | CFLI | |
| + 2 rectangles of 4 units | AEKG | BFLH |
| 15 rectangles | | |

$\boxed{6-3}$ **Dividing Monomials**

PAGE 219    CHECKING FOR UNDERSTANDING

**1.** Because division by 0 is undefined.

**2.** Look for a pattern: $16 \div 2 = 8$, $8 \div 2 = 4$,

$4 \div 2 = 2$, and $2 \div 2 = 1$

**3.** $0^0 = 0^{x-x} = \dfrac{0^x}{0^x}$ and division by 0 is undefined.

**4.** $5^0 = 1$            **5.** $(-8)^{-1} = -\frac{1}{8}$

**6.** $10^{-2} = \dfrac{1}{10^2} = \dfrac{1}{100}$      **7.** $(-2)^{-3} = \dfrac{1}{(-2)^3} = -\dfrac{1}{8}$

8. $(5^{-1})^2 = 5^{-2} = \dfrac{1}{5^2} = \dfrac{1}{25}$

9. $\dfrac{4^{-2}}{4} = 4^{-2-1} = 4^{-3} = \dfrac{1}{4^3} = \dfrac{1}{64}$

10. $\left(\dfrac{1}{3} \cdot \dfrac{1}{6}\right)^{-1} = \left(\dfrac{1}{18}\right)^{-1} = 18$

11. $(2^0 \cdot 3^{-2})^{-2} = (1 \cdot 3^{-2})^{-2} = 3^4 = 81$

12. $m^{-5}m^0 = \left(\dfrac{1}{m^5}\right)(1) = \dfrac{1}{m^5}$

13. $a^0 b^{-2} c^{-1} = 1b^{-2}c^{-1} = \dfrac{1}{b^2 c}$

14. $x^5 y^0 z^{-5} = x^5 \cdot 1 \cdot z^{-5} = \dfrac{x^5}{z^5}$

15. $\dfrac{5n^5}{n^8} = 5n^{5-8} = 5n^{-3} = \dfrac{5}{n^3}$

16. $\dfrac{b^9}{b^4 c^3} = \dfrac{b^{9-4}}{c^3} = \dfrac{b^5}{c^3}$   17. $\dfrac{1}{r^{-4}} = r^4$

18. $\dfrac{a^{-4}}{b^{-3}} = \dfrac{b^3}{a^4}$        19. $\dfrac{an^6}{n^5} = an^{6-5} = an$

PAGES 219-220     EXERCISES

20. $\dfrac{a^0}{a^{-2}} = a^{0-(-2)} = a^2$

21. $\dfrac{1}{r^{-3}} = r^3$

22. $\dfrac{k^{-2}}{k^4} = k^{-2-4} = k^{-6} = \dfrac{1}{k^6}$

23. $\dfrac{m^2}{m^{-4}} = m^{2-(-4)} = m^6$

24. $\dfrac{b^6 c^5}{b^3 c^2} = b^{6-3} c^{5-2} = b^3 c^3$

25. $\dfrac{(-a)^4 b^8}{a^4 b^7} = \dfrac{a^4 b^8}{a^4 b^7}$

$= a^{4-4} b^{8-7}$

$= a^0 b^1$

$= b$

26. $\dfrac{-x^3 y^3}{x^3 y^6} = -1x^{3-3} y^{3-6}$   27. $\dfrac{12b^5}{4b^4} = \dfrac{12}{4} b^{5-4}$

$= -1x^0 y^{-3}$                  $= 3b$

$= -\dfrac{1}{y^3}$

28. $\dfrac{10m^4}{30m} = \dfrac{10}{30} m^{4-1}$     29. $\dfrac{x^3 y^6}{x^3 y^3} = x^{3-3} y^{6-3}$

$= \dfrac{1}{3} m^3 = \dfrac{m^3}{3}$              $= x^0 y^3 = y^3$

30. $\dfrac{b^6 c^5}{b^{14} c^2} = b^{6-14} c^{5-2}$   31. $\dfrac{-r^5 s^8}{r^5 s^2} = -1r^{5-5} s^{8-2}$

$= b^{-8} c^3$                      $= -1r^0 s^6$

$= \dfrac{c^3}{b^8}$                       $= -s^6$

32. $\dfrac{30x^4 y^7}{-6x^{13} y^2} = \dfrac{30}{-6} x^{4-13} y^{7-2}$

$= -5x^{-9} y^5$

$= -\dfrac{5y^5}{x^9}$

33. $\dfrac{16b^4 c}{-4bc^3} = \dfrac{16}{-4} b^{4-1} c^{1-3}$

$= -4b^3 c^{-2}$

$= -\dfrac{4b^3}{c^2}$

34. $\dfrac{22a^2 b^5 c^7}{-11abc^2} = \dfrac{22}{-11} a^{2-1} b^{5-1} c^{7-2}$

$= -2ab^4 c^5$

35. $\dfrac{24x^2 y^7 z^3}{-6x^2 y^3 z^1} = \dfrac{24}{-6} x^{2-2} y^{7-3} z^{3-1}$

$= -4x^0 y^4 z^2$

$= -4y^4 z^2$

36. $\dfrac{7x^3 z^5}{4z^{15}} = \dfrac{7}{4} x^3 z^{5-15}$

$= \dfrac{7}{4} x^3 z^{-10}$

$= \dfrac{7x^3}{4z^{10}}$

37. $\dfrac{27a^4 b^6 c^9}{15a^3 c^{15}} = \dfrac{27}{15} a^{4-3} b^6 c^{9-15}$

$= \dfrac{9}{5} ab^6 c^{-6}$

$= \dfrac{9ab^6}{5c^6}$

38. $\dfrac{(a^7 b^2)^2}{(a^{-2} b)^{-2}} = \dfrac{a^{14} b^4}{a^4 b^{-2}}$

$= a^{14-4} b^{4-(-2)}$

$= a^{10} b^6$

39. $\dfrac{r^{-5} s^{-2}}{(r^2 s^5)^{-1}} = \dfrac{r^{-5} s^{-2}}{r^{-2} s^{-5}}$

$= r^{-5-(-2)} s^{-2-(-5)}$

$= r^{-3} s^3$

$= \dfrac{s^3}{r^3}$

**40.** $\dfrac{(r^{-4}k^2)^2}{(5k^2)^2} = \dfrac{r^{-8}k^4}{5^2k^4}$

$\qquad = \dfrac{k^{4-4}}{25r^8}$

$\qquad = \dfrac{1}{25r^8}$

**41.** $\left(\dfrac{3m^2n^2}{6m^{-1}k}\right) = 1$, any

Nonzero number raised to the zero power is one.

**42.** $\dfrac{(-b^{-1}c)^0}{4a^{-1}c^2} = \dfrac{1}{4a^{-1}c^2}$

$\qquad = \dfrac{a}{4c^2}$

**43.** $\left(\dfrac{7m^{-1}n^3}{n^2r^{-2}}\right)^{-1} = \dfrac{7^{-1}mn^{-3}}{n^{-2}r^2}$

$\qquad = \dfrac{mn^{-3-(-2)}}{7r^2}$

$\qquad = \dfrac{mn^{-1}}{7r^2}$

$\qquad = \dfrac{m}{7nr^2}$

**44.** $\left(\dfrac{2xy^{-2}z^4}{3xyz^{-1}}\right)^{-2} = \dfrac{2^{-2}x^{-2}y^4z^{-8}}{3^{-2}x^{-2}y^{-2}z^2}$

$\qquad = \dfrac{3^2x^{-2-(-2)}y^{4-(-2)}z^{-8}}{2^2}$

$\qquad = \dfrac{9x^0y^6z^{-10}}{4}$

$\qquad = \dfrac{9y^6}{4z^{10}}$

**45.** $y^2 \cdot y^b = y^{2+b}$

**46.** $x^{2a} \cdot x^{4a} = x^{2a+4a} = x^{6a}$

**47.** $(2^{7x+6})(2^{3x-4})$

$\qquad = 2^{7x+6+3x-4} = 2^{10x+2}$

**48.** $\dfrac{x^{y+2}}{x^{y-3}} = x^{(y+2)-(y-3)}$

$\qquad = x^{y+2-y+3}$

$\qquad = x^5$

**49.** $\dfrac{(a^{x+2})}{(a^{x-3})^2} = \dfrac{a^{2(x+2)}}{a^{2(x-3)}}$

$\qquad = \dfrac{a^{2x+4}}{a^{2x-6}}$

$\qquad = a^{(2x+4)-(2x-6)}$

$\qquad = a^{2x+4-2x+6}$

$\qquad = a^{10}$

**50.** $\dfrac{a}{a^{a-b}} = a^{b-(a-b)}$

$\qquad = a^{b-a+b}$

$\qquad = a^{2b-a}$

**51.** $B = P\left[\dfrac{1 - (1 + i)^{k-n}}{i}\right]$

$B = 213.87\left[\dfrac{1 - (1 + 0.009)^{24-48}}{0.009}\right]$

$B = 213.87[-21.4984]$

$B = \$4597.87$

**52.** $P = \left[\dfrac{i}{1 - (1 + i)^{-n}}\right]$

$A = 80,000 - 0.05(80,000)$

$\quad = 76,000$

$i = 12 \div 12 = 1\%$ or $0.01$

$n = 30 \times 12 = 360$

$P = 76,000\left[\dfrac{0.01}{1 - (1 + 0.01)^{-360}}\right]$

$P = 76,000|0.01|$

$P = \$781.75$

**53.** $\dfrac{12 \cdot 1.09}{27} \underline{\qquad} \dfrac{12 \cdot 0.99}{24}$

$\qquad 0.48 \quad < \quad 0.50$

So 12 eggs weighing 27 ounces for \$1.09 is a better buy.

**54.** $\quad -\dfrac{7}{6} + k = \dfrac{5}{6}$

$\qquad \dfrac{7}{6} - \dfrac{7}{6} + k = \dfrac{7}{6} + \dfrac{5}{6}$

$\qquad\qquad k = \dfrac{12}{6} = 2$

**55.** $\dfrac{1}{1.9} = \dfrac{3}{x}$

$\quad 1x = 3(1.9)$

$\quad\ x = 5.7$

Length would be 5.7 ft or 5 ft, $8\frac{2}{5}$ in.

**56.** Suzie is 4 feet from the top of the wall.

Sam is $9 - 7 = 2$ feet from the top of the wall.

Shirley is $9 - (7 - 3) = 5$ feet from the top.

So Sam is nearest to the top of the wall.

**57.** $a^2(a^5) = a^{2+5} = a^7$

**PAGE 220   READING ALGEBRA**

**1.** four squared   **2.** three cubed

**3.** $a$ to the fifth power   **4.** five times $b$ squared

**5.** twelve times $r$ the quantity to the fifth power

**6.** nine times $x$ cubed times $y$

**7.** $x$ plus two times $y$ the quantity squared

**8.** four times $m$ squared times $n$ to the fourth power

**9.** The quantity, $6a$ squared times $b$, raised to the fourth power

**10.** $a$ minus $b$ cubed

# 6-4 Scientific Notation

1. When the number is greater than or equal to 10.

2. When the number is less than 1.

3. decimal          4. scientific

5. $5.0 \times 10^3 = 5.0 \times 1000 = 5000$

   $57,900,000 = 5.79 \times 10^7$

6. $1.208 \times 10^4 = 1.208 \times 10,000 = 12,080$

   $108,230,000 = 1.0823 \times 10^8$

7. $1.276 \times 10^4 = 1.276 \times 10,000 = 12,760$

   $149,590,000 = 1.4959 \times 10^8$

8. $6.79 \times 10^3 = 6.79 \times 1000 = 6790$

   $227,920,000 = 2.2792 \times 10^8$

9. $1.432 \times 10^5 = 1.432 \times 100,000 = 143,200$

   $778,320,000 = 7.7832 \times 10^8$

10. $1.21 \times 10^5 = 1.21 \times 100,000 = 121,000$

    $1,427,000,000 = 1.427 \times 10^9$

11. $5.18 \times 10^4 = 5.18 \times 10,000 = 51,800$

    $2,870,000,000 = 2.87 \times 10^9$

12. $4.95 \times 10^4 = 4.95 \times 10,000 = 49,500$

    $4,497,000,000 = 4.497 \times 10^9$

13. $3 \times 10^3 = 3 \times 1000 = 3000$

    $5,900,000,000 = 5.9 \times 10^9$

14. 4293

    $= 4.293 \times 10^3$

15. 240,000

    $= 2.4 \times 10^5$

16. 0.000319

    $= 3.19 \times 10^{-4}$

17. 0.004296

    $= 4.296 \times 10^{-3}$

18. 0.000000092

    $= 9.2 \times 10^{-8}$

19. 0.00000000317

    $= 3.17 \times 10^{-9}$

20. $32 \times 10^5$

    $= 3.2 \times 10^6$

21. $284 \times 10^3$

    $= 2.84 \times 10^5$

22. $0.0031 \times 10^3$

    $= 3.1 \times 10^0$

23. $\dfrac{4.8 \times 10^3}{1.6 \times 10^1} = 3 \times 10^2$; 300

24. $\dfrac{5.2 \times 10^5}{1.3 \times 10^2} = 4 \times 10^3$; 4000

25. $\dfrac{7.8 \times 10^{-5}}{1.3 \times 10^{-7}} = 6 \times 10^2$; 600

26. $\dfrac{8.1 \times 10^2}{2.7 \times 10^{-3}} = 3 \times 10^5$; 300,000

27. $\dfrac{1.32 \times 10^{-6}}{2.4 \times 10^2} = 0.55 \times 10^{-8}$

    $= 5.5 \times 10^{-9}$; 0.0000000055

28. $\dfrac{2.31 \times 10^{-2}}{3.3 \times 10^{-3}} = 0.7 \times 10^1$

    $= 7 \times 10^0$; 7

29. $(2 \times 10^5)(3 \times 10^{-8}) = 6 \times 10^{-3}$; 0.006

30. $(4 \times 10^2)(1.5 \times 10^6) = 6 \times 10^8$; 600,000,000

31. $(3.1 \times 10^{-2})(2.1 \times 10^5)$

    $= 6.51 \times 10^3$; 6510

32. $(3.1 \times 10^4)(4.2 \times 10^{-3})$

    $= 13.02 \times 10^1 = 1.302 \times 10^2$; 130.2

33. $(78 \times 10^6)(0.01 \times 10^3)$

    $= 0.78 \times 10^9 = 7.8 \times 10^8$; 780,000,000

34. $(0.2 \times 10^5)(31 \times 10^{-6}) = 6.2 \times 10^{-1}$; 0.62

35. $(0.000003)(70,000) = (3 \times 10^{-6})(7 \times 10^4)$

    $= 21 \times 10^{-2} = 2.1 \times 10^{-1}$; 0.21

36. $(86,000,000)(0.005) = (8.6 \times 10^7)(5 \times 10^{-3})$

    $= 43 \times 10^4 = 4.3 \times 10^5$; 430,000

37. $24,000 \div 0.00006 = \dfrac{2.4 \times 10^4}{6 \times 10^{-5}}$

    $= 0.4 \times 10^9 = 4 \times 10^8$; 400,000,000

38. $0.0000039 \div 650,000 = \dfrac{3.9 \times 10^{-6}}{6.5 \times 10^5}$

    $= 0.6 \times 10^{-11} = 6 \times 10^{-12}$; 0.000000000006

39. $\dfrac{(35,987,000)(58 \times 10^3)}{42.5 \times 10^4}$

    $= \dfrac{208.7246 \times 10^{10}}{42.5 \times 10^4}$

    $= 4.91116706 \times 10^6$; 4,911,167.06

40. $\dfrac{(3 \times 10^8)(43 \times 10^{-4})}{23,000,000}$

    $= \dfrac{129 \times 10^4}{23 \times 10^6}$

    $= 5.608696 \times 10^{-2}$ ; 0.05608696

41. $\dfrac{8.9 \times 10^5}{(98,000)(14 \times 10^3)} = \dfrac{8.9 \times 10^5}{(9.8 \times 10^4)(14 \times 10^3)}$

    $= \dfrac{8.9 \times 10^5}{1.372 \times 10^9} = 6.48688 \times 10^{-4}$; 0.00064869

**42.** $\dfrac{57,800,000,000}{(2.3 \times 10^6)(38 \times 10^{-5})} = \dfrac{5.78 \times 10^{10}}{87.4 \times 10^1}$

$= 6.61327231 \times 10^7; \ 66,132,723.1$

**43.** $12,000,000 \div 4000 = (12 \times 10^6) \div (4 \times 10^3)$

$= \dfrac{12 \times 10^6}{4 \times 10^3} = 3 \times 10^3 = 3000$

**44.** $248,200,000 \div 3,540,000$

$= (2.482 \times 10^8) \div (3.54 \times 10^6)$

$= \dfrac{2.482 \times 10^8}{3.54 \times 10^6} = 0.70113 \times 10^2 = 70.113$

**45.** $220,000,000,000 \div 248,200,000$

$= \dfrac{2.2 \times 10^{11}}{2.482 \times 10^8} = 0.88638 \times 10^3 = \$886.38$

**46.** a. $(2.85 \times 10^8) \div (1.86 \times 10^5) = \dfrac{2.85 \times 10^9}{1.86 \times 10^5}$

$= 1.532 \times 10^4 = 15,320$ seconds

b. $4070 \times 24 = 97,680$ hours

$2.85 \times 10^9 \div 97,680 = 2.92 \times 10^4$ mph

**47.** a. 10 READ A,B

20 DATA 4,6,8

30 PRINT A↑2*B↑3*C↑4

40 END

RUN

1.416E + 7

b. 10 READ A,B

20 DATA 4,6

30 PRINT (-2A)↑2*(4B)↑3

40 END

RUN

884,736

c. 10 READ A,B

20 DATA 4,6

30 PRINT (4*A↑2*B↑4)↑3

40 END

RUN

5.706E + 14

d. 10 READ A,B,C

20 DATA 4,6,8

30 PRINT (A*C)↑3 + (3*B)↑2

40 END

RUN

33,092

**48.** $\dfrac{60a - 30b}{-6} = -10a + 5b$

**49.** Let $L$ = legs of a scorpion.

$(L + 2) + L = 18$

$2L + 2 = 18$

$2L = 16$

$L = 8$

A scorpion has 8 legs.

**50.** $35 = \dfrac{50}{100}x$

$3500 = 50x$

$70 = x$

**51.** $-16q > -128$

$\dfrac{-16q}{-16} < \dfrac{-128}{-16}$

$q < 8$

$\{q | q < 8\}$

**52.** $4(a^2b^3)^3 = 4(a^{2 \cdot 3}b^{3 \cdot 3})$

$= 4a^6b^9$

**53.** $\dfrac{48a^8}{12a} = 4a^{8-1} = 4a^7$

---

## 6-5 Polynomials

**PAGE 228    CHECKING FOR UNDERSTANDING**

1. It is not a product of a number and a variable.

2. Because $\dfrac{3}{b}$ involves division, not multiplication

3. Because $12 = 12x^0$

4. yes, trinomial      5. not a polynomial

6. yes, monomial       7. yes, monomial

8. yes, binomial       9. yes, trinomial

10. 1      11. 0      12. 3      13. 2

14. 4      15. none      16. 1      17. 4

18. 12      19. 29      20. 5      21. 7

**PAGES 228-229    EXERCISES**

22. 5      23. 4      24. 9      25. 4

26. 1      27. 3      28. 6      29. 3

30. 5            31. 7            32. $3 + 2x^2 + x^4$

33. $a^3 + 5ax + 2x^2$      34. $1 + x^2 + x^3 + x^5$

35. $3xy^3 - 2x^2y + x^3$      36. $11b^2x + 17bx^2 - x^3$

37. $5b + \dfrac{2}{3}bx + b^3x^2$      38. $x^5 + 4x^3 - 6x - 20$

39. $-3x^3 + 5x^2 + 2x + 7$

40. $4x^3y - x^2y^3 + 3xy^4 + y^4$

41. $7ax^3 + 11x^2 - 3x + 2a$

42. $\dfrac{3}{4}x^3y - x^2 + \dfrac{2}{3}x + 4$

43. $\dfrac{1}{5}x^5 - 8a^3x^3 + \dfrac{2}{3}x^2 + 7a^3x$

44. $3254 = 3(b)^3 + 2(b)^2 + 5(b) + 4$

45. yes

46. first year: $10,000 + 10,000(0.06) + 1,000$
$= 11,600$

second year: $11,600 + 11,600(0.06) + 1000$
$= 13,296$

third year: $13,296 + 13,296(0.06) + 1000$
$= 15,093.76$

fourth year: $15,093.76 + 15,093.76(0.06) + 1000$
$= 16,999.39$

fifth year: $16,999.39 + 16,999.39(0.06) + 1000$
$= 19,019.35;$

No; his money doubles the sixth year.

47. $14(3)^3 - 17(3)^2 - 16(3) + 34$
$= 14(27) - 17(9) - 16(3) + 34$
$= 378 - 153 - 48 + 34$
$= 211$ eggs

48.

49. $11y = -77$
$\dfrac{11y}{11} = \dfrac{-77}{11}$
$y = -7$

50. $(12,500 - x)(0.062) + x(0.086) = 967$
$775 - 0.062x + 0.086x = 967$
$775 + 0.024x = 967$
$0.024x = 192$

$8,000 at 8.6\%;$     $x = 8000$
$4,500 at 6.2\%$     $12,500 - x = 4500$

51. $10p - 14 < 8p - 17$
$2p < -3$
$p < -\dfrac{3}{2}$
$\left\{ p \mid p < -\dfrac{3}{2} \right\}$

52. $4.235 \times 10^4$       53. $6.28 \times 10^{-6}$

PAGE 229    MID-CHAPTER REVIEW

1.

| $3^n$ | $3^1$ | $3^2$ | $3^3$ | $3^4$ | $3^5$ | $3^6$ | $3^7$ | $3^8$ |
|---|---|---|---|---|---|---|---|---|
| | 3 | 9 | 27 | 81 | 243 | 729 | 2187 | 6561 |
| ones digit | 3 | 9 | 7 | 1 | 3 | 9 | 7 | 1 |

The ones digit repeats every fourth power. $999 \div 4 = 249\dfrac{3}{4}$ so the ones digit of $3^{999}$ is the third term in the repetition, 7.

2. $(b^4)(b^4)b = b^{4+4+1} = b^9$

3. $(x^3y)(xy^3) = (x^{3+1})(y^{1+3}) = x^4y^4$

4. $(-2n^4y^3)(3ny^4) = (-2 \cdot 3)(n^{4+1})(y^{3+4})$
$= -6n^5y^7$

5. $[(-5)^2]^3 = [25]^3 = 15,625$

6. $(4xy)^2(-3x) = (4^2x^2y^2)(-3x)$
$= (16 \cdot -3)(x^{2+1})y^2 = -48x^3y^2$

7. $(-3a^2b^5)^2 = (-3^2)(a^{2\cdot2})(b^{5\cdot2}) = 9a^4b^{10}$

8. $\dfrac{n^8}{n^5} = n^{8-5} = n^3$

9. $\dfrac{24a^3b^6}{-2a^2b^2} = \left(\dfrac{24}{-2}\right)(a^{3-2})(b^{6-2}) = -12ab^4$

10. $\dfrac{(5r^{-1}s)^3}{(s^2)^3} = \dfrac{5^3(r^{-1\cdot3})s^3}{s^{2\cdot3}} = \dfrac{5^3r^{-3}s^3}{s^6} = \dfrac{125}{r^3s^3}$

11. $28.5 \times 10^6 = 2.85 \times 10^7$

12. $0.005 \times 10^{-3} = 5 \times 10^{-6}$

13. $\dfrac{1}{4}x - \dfrac{2}{5}s^4x^2 + \dfrac{1}{3}s^2x^3 + 4x^4$

14. $21p^2x + 3px^3 + p^4$

6-6 ## Adding and Subtracting Polynomials

PAGE 232    CHECKING FOR UNDERSTANDING

1. Making sure that the terms are in the same order
2. by adding    3. $-3x - 2y$    4. $8m - 7n$
5. $-x^2 - 3x - 7$    6. $4h^2 + 5hk + k^2$
7. $3ab^2 - 5a^2b + b^3$    8. $-x^3 - 5x^2 + 3x + 11$
9. $5m, -3m; 4mn, -mn; 2n, 8n$
10. $5xy, 14xy, 12xy$
11. $8a^2b, 16a^2b; 11b^2, -2b^2$
12. $3p^3q, 10p^3q; -2p, -p$

PAGES 232-233    EXERCISES

13. $7ax^2 - 5a^2x - 7a^3 + 4$

14. $4a^3 + 2a^2b - b^2 + b^3$

15. $9a - 3b - 4c + 16d$    16. $8x^2 + x + 15$

17. $\begin{array}{l} 6x^2y^2 - 3xy - 7 \\ -(5x^2y^2 + 2xy + 3) \end{array} \Rightarrow \begin{array}{l} 6x^2y^2 - 3xy - 7 \\ \underline{-5x^2y^2 - 2xy - 3} \\ x^2y^2 - 5xy - 10 \end{array}$

18. $\begin{array}{l} 5x^2 \phantom{xxx} - 4 \\ -(3x^2 + 8x + 4) \end{array} \Rightarrow \begin{array}{l} 5x^2 \phantom{xxx} - 4 \\ \underline{-3x^2 - 8x - 4} \\ 2x^2 - 8x - 8 \end{array}$

19. $\begin{array}{l} 11m^2n^2 + 2mn - 11 \\ -(5m^2n^2 - 6mn + 17) \end{array} \Rightarrow \begin{array}{l} 11m^2n^2 + 2mn - 11 \\ \underline{-5m^2n^2 + 6mn - 17} \\ 6m^2n^2 + 8mn - 28 \end{array}$

85

20.
$$
\begin{array}{l}
\phantom{-}2a - 7 \qquad\qquad \phantom{-}+ 2a - 7 \\
\underline{-(5a^2 + 8a - 11)} \Rightarrow \underline{-5a^2 - 8a + 11} \\
\phantom{-(5a^2 + 8a} -5a^2 - 6a + 4
\end{array}
$$

21. $(5x + 6y) + (2x + 8y)$
$= (5x + 2x) + (6y + 8y)$
$= (5 + 2)x + (6 + 8)y$
$= 7x + 14y$

22. $(11m + 7n) - (4m + 2n)$
$= (11m + 7n) + [-4m + (-2n)]$
$= [11m + (-4m)] + [7n + (-2n)]$
$= [11 + (-4)]m + [7 + (-2)]n$
$= 7m + 5n$

23. $(3x - 7y) + (3y + 4x)$
$= (3x + 4x) + (-7y + 3y)$
$= (3 + 4)x + (-7 + 3)y$
$= 7x + -4y$
$= 7x - 4y$

24. $(5a - 6m) - (2a + 5m)$
$= (5a - 6m) + (-2a + -5m)$
$= [5a + (-2a)] + [-6m + (-5m)]$
$= [5 + (-2)]a + [-6 + (-5)]m$
$= 3a - 11m$

25. $(5m + 3n) + 8m$
$= (5m + 8m) + 3n$
$= (5 + 8)m + 3n$
$= 13m + 3n$

26. $(13x + 9y) - 11y$
$= (13x + 9y) + (-11y)$
$= 13x + [9y + (-11y)]$
$= 13x + [9 + (-11)]y$
$= 13x + (-2y)$
$= 13x - 2y$

27. $(3 + 2a + a^2) - (5 + 8a + a^2)$
$= (3 + 2a + a^2) + [-5 + (-8a) + (-a^2)]$
$= [3 + (-5)] + [2a + (-8a)] + [a^2 + (-a^2)]$
$= [3 + (-5)] + [2 + (-8)]a + [1 + (-1)]a^2$
$= -2 + -6a + 0a^2$
$= -2 - 6a$

28. $(n^2 + 5n + 3) + (2n^2 + 8n + 8)$
$= (n^2 + 2n^2) + (5n + 8n) + (3 + 8)$
$= (1 + 2)n^2 + (5 + 8)n + (3 + 8)$
$= 3n^2 + 13n + 11$

29. $(5ax^2 + 3a^2x - 5x) + (2ax^2 - 5ax + 7x)$
$= (5ax^2 + 2ax^2) + 3a^2x + (-5ax) + (-5x + 7x)$
$= 7ax^2 + 3a^2x - 5ax + 2x$

30. $(x^3 - 3x^2y + 4xy^2 + y^3)$
$\phantom{=} - (7x^3 + x^2y - 9xy^2 + y^3)$
$= (x^3 + (-3x^2y) + 4xy^2 + y^3)$
$\phantom{=} + [-7x^3 + (-1x^2y) + 9xy^2 + (-1y^3)]$
$= [x^3 + (-7x^3)] + [-3x^2y + (-1x^2y)]$
$\phantom{=} + (4xy^2 + 9xy^2) + [y^3 + (-1y^3)]$
$= -6x^3 - 4x^2y + 13xy^2$

31. $(x + y) + (x + y) = 2x + 2y$
$$
\begin{array}{l}
P = \phantom{-}3x + 3y \\
\phantom{P =} \underline{-(2x + 2y)} \\
\text{side} = \phantom{-}x + y
\end{array}
$$

32. $(2x + y) + (3x - 5y) = 5x - 4y$
$$
\begin{array}{l}
P = \phantom{-}7x + 2y \\
\phantom{P =} \underline{-(5x - 4y)} \\
\text{side} = \phantom{-}2x + 6y
\end{array}
$$

33. $(5x^2 - 13x + 24) + (x^2 + 7x + 9) = 6x^2 - 6x + 33$
$$
\begin{array}{l}
P = \phantom{-}11x^2 - 29x + 10 \\
\phantom{P =} \underline{-(6x^2 - 6x + 33)} \\
\text{side} = \phantom{-}5x^2 - 23x - 23
\end{array}
$$

34. $180 - (5 - 2x + 7 + 8x)$
$= 180 - (12 + 6x)$
$= 180 - 12 - 6x$
$= 168 - 6x$

35. $180 - (3x^2 - 5 + 4x^2 + 2x + 1)$
$= 180 - (7x^2 + 2x - 4)$
$= 180 - 7x^2 - 2x + 4$
$= -7x^2 - 2x + 184$

36. $180 - (4 - 2x + x^2 - 1) = 180 - (x^2 - 2x + 3)$
$\phantom{180 - (4 - 2x + x^2 - 1)} = 180 - x^2 + 2x - 3$
$\phantom{180 - (4 - 2x + x^2 - 1)} = -x^2 + 2x + 177$

37. $180 - (x^2 - 8x + 2 + x^2 - 3x - 1)$
$= 180 - (2x^2 - 11x + 1)$
$= 180 - 2x^2 + 11x - 1$
$= -2x^2 + 11x + 179$

38. $\dfrac{40}{t} = \dfrac{60}{1.5t}$ $\qquad \dfrac{60t + 40(1.5t)}{2.5t} = \dfrac{120t}{2.5t} = 48$ mph

39. Let $p$ = points scored by the Nuggets.
$p + (p + 2) = 370$
$\phantom{p +} 2p + 2 = 370$
$\phantom{p + 2p} 2p = 368$
$\phantom{p + 2p + } p = 184$
The Nuggets scored 184 points.

40. $x = 2.1$

**41.** Let $w$ = number of sports in Winter Olympics;

$\qquad$ $s$ = number of sports in Summer Olympics.

$\qquad$ $3w = s$ and $14 + w = s$

$\qquad\qquad$ $3w = 14 + w$

$\qquad\qquad$ $2w = 14$

$\qquad\qquad$ $w = 7$

$\qquad\qquad$ $s = 3w = 21$

$\qquad$ 21 sports in the Summer Olympics

**42.** $d = r \cdot t$ $\qquad\qquad$ **43.** $3m < 2m - 7$

$\quad$ **a.** $72 = 9 \cdot t$ $\qquad\qquad$ $m < -7$

$\qquad$ $t = 8$ hr $\qquad\qquad$ $\{m | m < -7\}$

$\quad$ **b.** $72 = 18 \cdot t$

$\qquad$ $t = 4$ hr

**44.** 3

## 6-7 Multiplying a Polynomial by a Monomial

**1.** Distributive $\qquad$ **2.** $\begin{array}{c} 5a + 6 \\ 3a \;\boxed{\phantom{xxxxxxxx}} \end{array}$

**3. a.** $3a(5a + 6)$ $\qquad$ **4.** $-60a^3$

$\quad$ **b.** $3a \cdot 5a + 3a \cdot 6$

$\qquad = 15a^2 + 18a$

**5.** $3m(8m + 7)$ $\qquad\qquad$ **6.** $-4m^3(5m^2 \cdot 2m)$

$\quad = 3m(8m) + 3m(7)$ $\qquad = -4m^3(5m^2) - 4m^3(2m)$

$\quad = 24m^2 + 21m$ $\qquad\quad = -20m^5 - 8m^4$

**7.** $\begin{array}{r} 5x - 3 \\ \times \quad\;\; 2 \\ \hline 10x - 6 \end{array}$ $\qquad\qquad$ **8.** $\begin{array}{r} m - 7 \\ \times \quad\;\; 2mn \\ \hline 2m^2n - 14mn \end{array}$

**9.** $\begin{array}{r} 5ab^2 + b^2 \\ \times \quad\quad 7ab \\ \hline 35a^2b^3 + 7ab^3 \end{array}$ $\qquad$ **10.** $b(4b - 1) + 10b$

$\qquad\qquad\qquad\qquad\qquad = 4b^2 - b + 10b$

$\qquad\qquad\qquad\qquad\qquad = 4b^2 + 9b$

**11.** $2a(a^3 - 2a^2 + 7) + 5(a^4 + 5a^3 - 3a + 5)$

$\quad = (2a^4 - 4a^3 + 14a) + (5a^4 + 25a^3 - 15a + 25)$

$\quad = (2a^4 + 5a^4) + (-4a^3 + 25a^3) + (14a - 15a) + 25$

$\quad = 7a^4 + 21a^3 - a + 25$

**12.** $11(a - 3) + 5 = 2a + 44$

$\qquad$ $11a - 33 + 5 = 2a + 44$

$\qquad\qquad$ $11a - 28 = 2a + 44$

$\qquad\qquad\qquad$ $9a - 28 = 44$

$\qquad\qquad\qquad\qquad$ $9a = 72$

$\qquad\qquad\qquad\qquad$ $a = 8$

**13.** $x(x + 2) + 3x = x(x - 3)$

$\qquad$ $x^2 + 2x + 3x = x^2 - 3x$

$\qquad\qquad$ $x^2 + 5x = x^2 - 3x$

$\qquad\qquad\qquad$ $5x = -3x$

$\qquad\qquad\qquad$ $8x = 0$

$\qquad\qquad\qquad$ $x = 0$

**14.** $5(3a + 7)$ $\qquad\qquad$ **15.** $-3(8x + 5)$

$\quad = 5(3a) + 5(7)$ $\qquad\qquad = -3(8x) - 3(5)$

$\quad = 15a + 35$ $\qquad\qquad\quad = -24x - 15$

**16.** $\frac{1}{2}x(8x + 6)$ $\qquad\qquad$ **17.** $3b(5b + 8)$

$\quad = \frac{1}{2}x(8x) + \frac{1}{2}x(6)$ $\qquad = 3b(5b) + 3b(8)$

$\quad = 4x^2 + 3x$ $\qquad\qquad\quad = 15b^2 + 24b$

**18.** $-2x(5x + 11)$ $\qquad\qquad$ **19.** $= 1.1a(2a) + 1.1a(7)$

$\quad = -2x(5x) - 2x(11)$ $\qquad\quad = 2.2a^2 + 7.7a$

$\quad = -10x^2 - 22x$

**20.** $7a(3a^2 - 2a)$ $\qquad\qquad$ **21.** $3st(5s^2 + 2st)$

$\quad = 7a(3a^2) + 7a(-2a)$ $\qquad = 3st(5s^2) + 3st(2st)$

$\quad = 21a^3 - 14a^2$ $\qquad\qquad = 15s^3t + 6s^2t^2$

**22.** $7xy(5x^2 - y^2)$

$\quad = 7xy(5x^2) + 7xy(-y^2)$

$\quad = 35x^3y - 7xy^3$

**23.** $2a(5a^3 - 7a^2 + 2)$

$\quad = 2a(5a^3) + 2a(-7a^2) + 2a(2)$

$\quad = 10a^4 - 14a^3 + 4a$

**24.** $7x^2y(5x^2 - 3xy + y)$

$\quad = 7x^2y(5x^2) + 7x^2y(-3xy) + 7x^2y(y)$

$\quad = 35x^4y - 21x^3y^2 + 7x^2y^2$

**25.** $5y(8y^3 + 7y^2 - 3y)$

$\quad = 5y(8y^3) + 5y(7y^2) + 5y(-3y)$

$\quad = 40y^4 + 35y^3 - 15y^2$

**26.** $-4x(7x^2 - 4x + 3)$

$\quad = -4x(7x^2) - 4x(-4x) - 4x(3)$

$\quad = -28x^3 + 16x^2 - 12x$

**27.** $5x^2y(3x^2 - 7xy + y^2)$

$\quad = 5x^2y(3x^2) + 5x^2y(-7xy) + 5x^2y(y^2)$

$\quad = 15x^4y - 35x^3y^2 + 5x^2y^3$

**28.** $4m^2(9m^2n + mn - 5n^2)$

$\quad = 4m^2(9m^2n) + 4m^2(mn) + 4m^2(-5n^2)$

$\quad = 36m^4n + 4m^3n - 20m^2n^2$

29. $-8xy(4xy + 7x - 14y^2)$

$= -8xy(4xy) - 8xy(7x) - 8xy(-14y^2)$

$= -32x^2y^2 - 56x^2y + 112xy^3$

30. $-\frac{1}{3}x(9x^2 + x - 5)$

$= -\frac{1}{3}x(9x^2) - \frac{1}{3}x(x) - \frac{1}{3}x(-5)$

$= -3x^3 - \frac{1}{3}x^2 + \frac{5}{3}x$

31. $-\frac{3}{4}ab^2\left(\frac{1}{3}b^2 - \frac{4}{9}b + 1\right)$

$= -\frac{3}{4}ab^2\left(\frac{1}{3}b^2\right) - \frac{3}{4}ab^2\left(-\frac{4}{9}b\right) - \frac{3}{4}ab^2(1)$

$= -\frac{1}{4}ab^4 + \frac{1}{3}ab^3 - \frac{3}{4}ab^2$

32. $-2mn(8m^2 - 3mn + n^2)$

$= -2mn(8m^2) - 2mn(-3mn) - 2mn(n^2)$

$= -16m^3n + 6m^2n^2 - 2mn^3$

33. $A = (4t \cdot 4t) - [t \cdot (t - 1)]$

$= 16t^2 - (t^2 - t)$

$= 15t^2 + t$

34. $A = [(2s + s) \cdot s] - (s \cdot 3)$

$= 2s^2 + s^2 - 3s$

$= 3s^2 - 3s$

35. $A = [3x \cdot (x + 2)] - (2x \cdot x)$

$= 3x^2 + 6x - 2x^2$

$= x^2 + 6x$

36. $6m(m^2 - 11m + 4) - 7(m^3 + 8m - 11)$

$= 6m^3 + (-66m^2) + 24m + (-7m^3) + (-56m) + 77$

$= [6m^3 + (-7m^3)] + (-66m^2) + [24m + (-56m)] + 77$

$= -m^3 - 66m^2 - 32m + 77$

37. $2.5t(8t - 12) + 5.1(6t^2 + 10t - 20)$

$= 20.0t^2 + (-30.0t) + 30.6t^2 + 51.0t + (-102.0)$

$= (20.0t^2 + 30.6t^2) + (-30.0t + 51.0t) + (-102)$

$= 50.6t^2 + 21t - 102$

38. $\frac{3}{4}m(8m^2 + 12m - 4) + \frac{3}{2}(8m^2 - 9m)$

$= 6m^3 + 9m^2 - 3m + 12m^2 - \frac{27}{2}m$

$= 6m^3 + (9m^2 + 12m^2) + \left(-3m - \frac{27}{2}m\right)$

$= 6m^3 + 21m^2 - \frac{33}{2}m$

39. $5m^2(m + 7) - 2m(5m^2 - 3m + 7) + 2(m^3 - 8)$

$= 5m^3 + 35m^2 - 10m^3 + 6m^2 - 14m + 2m^3 - 16$

$= (5m^3 - 10m^3 + 2m^3) + (35m^2 + 6m^2) - 14m - 16$

$= -3m^3 + 41m^2 - 14m - 16$

40. $6a^2(3a - 4) + 5a(7a^2 - 6a + 5) - 3(a^2 + 6a)$

$= 18a^3 - 24a^2 + 35a^3 - 30a^2 + 25a - 3a^2 - 18a$

$= (18a^3 + 35a^3) + (-24a^2 - 30a^2 - 3a^2)$

$+ (25a - 18a)$

$= 53a^3 - 57a^2 + 7a$

41. $3a^2(a - 4) + 6a(3a^2 + a - 7) - 4(a - 7)$

$= 3a^3 + (-12a^2) + 18a^3 + 6a^2 + (-42a) + (-4a)$

$+ 28$

$= (3a^3 + 18a^3) + (-12a^2 + 6a^2) + [-42a + (-4a)]$

$+ 28$

$= 21a^3 - 6a^2 - 46a + 28$

42. $8r^2(r + 8) - 3r(5r^2 - 11) - 9(3r^2 - 8r + 1)$

$= 8r^3 + 64r^2 + (-15r^3) + 33r + (-27r^2) + 72r$

$+ (-9)$

$= [8r^3 + (-15r^3)] + [64r^2 + (-27r^2)]$

$+ (33r + 72r) + (-9)$

$= -7r^3 + 37r^2 + 105r - 9$

43. $-3(2a - 12) + 48 = 3a - 3$

$-6a + 36 + 48 = 3a - 3$

$-6a + 84 = 3a - 3$

$-9a + 84 = -3$

$-9a = -87$

$a = \frac{87}{9} = \frac{29}{3}$

44. $2(5w - 12) = 6(-2w + 3) + 2$

$10w - 24 = -12w + 18 + 2$

$10w - 24 = -12w + 20$

$22w - 24 = 20$

$22w = 44$

$w = 2$

45. $-6(12 - 2w) = 7(-2 - 3w)$

$-72 + 12w = -14 - 21w$

$-72 + 33w = -14$

$33w = 58$

$w = \frac{58}{33}$

46. $7(x - 12) = 13 + 5(3x - 4)$

$7x - 84 = 13 + 15x - 20$

$7x - 84 = 15x - 7$

$-8x - 84 = -7$

$-8x = 77$

$x = -\frac{77}{8}$

47. $\frac{1}{2}(2x - 34) = \frac{2}{3}(6x - 27)$

$x - 17 = 4x - 18$

$-3x - 17 = -18$

$-3x = -1$

$x = \frac{1}{3}$

48. $w(w + 12) = w(w + 14) + 12$

$w^2 + 12w = w^2 + 14w + 12$

$12w = 14w + 12$

$-2w = 12$

$w = -6$

49. $a(a - 6) + 2a = 3 + a(a - 2)$

$a^2 - 6a + 2a = 3 + a^2 - 2a$

$a^2 - 4a = 3 + a^2 - 2a$

$-4a = 3 - 2a$

$-2a = 3$

$a = -\dfrac{3}{2}$

50. $q(2q + 3) + 20 = 2q(q - 3)$

$2q^2 + 3q + 20 = 2q^2 - 6q$

$3q + 20 = -6q$

$20 = -9q$

$-\dfrac{20}{9} = q$

51. $x(x + 8) - x(x + 3) - 23 = 3x + 11$

$x^2 + 8x - x^2 - 3x - 23 = 3x + 11$

$5x - 23 = 3x + 11$

$2x - 23 = 11$

$2x = 34$

$x = 17$

52. $y(y - 12) + y(y + 2) + 25 = 2y(y + 5) - 15$

$y^2 - 12y + y^2 + 2y + 25 = 2y^2 + 10y - 15$

$2y^2 - 10y + 25 = 2y^2 + 10y - 15$

$-10y + 25 - 10y = -15$

$-20y + 25 = -15$

$-20y = -40$

$y = 2$

53. Let $w$ = length of the upper base of the trapezoid.

$2w + 6$ = length of lower base.

$\dfrac{1}{2}(12)(w + 2w + 6) = 162$

$6(3w + 6) = 162$

$18w + 36 = 162$

$18w = 126$

$w = 7$

The length of the upper base is 7 m.

54. Let $w$ = width of rectangle;

$3w - 120$ = length.

$2w + 2(3w - 120) = 1040$

$2w + 6w - 240 = 1040$

$8w = 1280$

$w = 160$

$3(160) - 120 = 360$

The dimensions are 160 ft by 360 ft.

55. Work in yards. If bill was $902 at $22 per square yard, he bought 41 square yards.

Let $x$ = width of walk in yards;

$14 + 2x$ = length of yard + walk (in yards);

$9$ = width of yard + walk (in yards).

$9(14 + 2x) - 8(14) = 41$

$126 + 18x - 112 = 41$

$18x + 14 = 41$

$18x = 27$

$x = \dfrac{3}{2}$ or $1\dfrac{1}{2}$

The width of the walk is $1\dfrac{1}{2}$ yards or $4\dfrac{1}{2}$ ft.

56. $-7.9 + 3.5 + 2.4 = -2$

57. $\left(-\dfrac{1}{3}\right)\left(-\dfrac{3}{4}\right)\left(-\dfrac{4}{5}\right) = -\dfrac{1}{5}$

58. $x + \dfrac{4}{9} = -\dfrac{2}{27}$

$x = -\dfrac{2}{27} - \dfrac{4}{9}$

$x = -\dfrac{14}{27}$

59. Let $r$ = Patricia's interest rate.

$5000 + [5000(0.10)] - 125 = 5000 + 5000r$

$5375 = 5000 + 5000r$

$375 = 5000r$

$\dfrac{375}{5000} = r$

$0.075 = r$

The annual interest rate is 7.5%.

60. $|7 - x| \geq 4$

$7 - x \geq 4 \qquad 7 - x \leq -4$

$3 \geq x \qquad\qquad 11 \leq x$

$\{x \mid x \leq 3 \text{ or } x \geq 11\}$

61. $(4a + 6b) + (2a + 3b)$

$= 4a + 2a + 6b + 3b$

$= 6a + 9b$

## 6-8 Multiplying Polynomials

PAGES 240-241    CHECKING FOR UNDERSTANDING

1. first, outer, inner, last

2. $\left(4 + \dfrac{1}{2}\right)\left(6 + \dfrac{3}{4}\right)$

$= 4 \cdot 6 + 4 \cdot \dfrac{3}{4} + \dfrac{1}{2} \cdot 6 + \dfrac{1}{2} \cdot \dfrac{3}{4}$

$= 24 + 3 + 3 + \dfrac{3}{8}$

$= 30\dfrac{3}{8}$

3. $5x + 3x = 8x$  4. $a + 10a = 11a$

5. $25x - 3x = 22x$  6. $4x + 9x = 13x$

7. $-6b + 5b = -b$  8. $4m + 10m = 14m$

9. $(a + 3)(a + 7)$  10. $(m - 5)(m - 11)$

$= a^2 + 7a + 3a + 21$  $= m^2 - 11m - 5m + 55$

$= a^2 + 10a + 21$  $= m^2 - 16m + 55$

11. $(x + 11)(x - 4)$  12. $(2x + 1)(x + 8)$

$= x^2 - 4x + 11x - 44$  $= 2x^2 + 16x + x + 8$

$= x^2 + 7x - 44$  $= 2x^2 + 17x + 8$

PAGES 241-242  EXERCISES

13. $(c + 2)(c + 8)$  14. $(x - 4)(x - 8)$

$= c^2 + 8c + 2c + 16$  $= x^2 - 8x - 4x + 32$

$= c^2 + 10c + 16$  $= x^2 - 12x + 32$

15. $(y + 3)(y - 7)$  16. $(5y - 3)(y + 2)$

$= y^2 - 7y + 3y - 21$  $= 5y^2 + 10y - 3y - 6$

$= y^2 - 4y - 21$  $= 5y^2 + 7y - 6$

17. $(4a + 3)(2a - 1)$  18. $(7y - 1)(2y - 3)$

$= 8a^2 - 4a + 6a - 3$  $= 14y^2 - 21y - 2y + 3$

$= 8a^2 + 2a - 3$  $= 14y^2 - 23y + 3$

19. $(2x + 3y)(5x + 2y)$

$= 10x^2 + 4xy + 15xy + 6y^2$

$= 10x^2 + 19xy + 6y^2$

20. $(2a + 3b)(5a - 2b)$

$= 10a^2 - 4ab + 15ab - 6b^2$

$= 10a^2 + 11ab - 6b^2$

21. $(5q + 2r)(8q - 3r)$

$= 40q^2 - 15qr + 16qr - 6r^2$

$= 40q^2 + qr - 6r^2$

22. $(5r - 7s)(4r + 3s)$

$= 20r^2 + 15rs - 28rs - 21s^2$

$= 20r^2 - 13rs - 21s^2$

23. $(2r + 0.1)(5r - 0.3)$

$= 10r^2 - 0.6r + 0.5r - 0.03$

$= 10r^2 - 0.1r - 0.03$

24. $(0.7x + 2y)(0.9x + 3y)$

$= 0.63x^2 + 2.1xy + 1.8xy + 6y^2$

$= 0.63x^2 + 3.9xy + 6y^2$

25. $\left(3x + \dfrac{1}{4}\right)\left(6x - \dfrac{1}{2}\right)$

$= 18x^2 - \dfrac{3}{2}x + \dfrac{6}{4}x - \dfrac{1}{8}$

$= 18x^2 - \dfrac{1}{8}$

26. $(x - 2)(x^2 + 2x + 4)$

$= x(x^2 + 2x + 4) - 2(x^2 + 2x + 4)$

$= x \cdot x^2 + x \cdot 2x + x \cdot 4 - 2 \cdot x^2 - 2 \cdot 2x$
$\quad - 2 \cdot 4$

$= x^3 + 2x^2 + 4x - 2x^2 - 4x - 8$

$= x^3 - 8$

27.
$$
\begin{array}{r}
x^2 + 7x - 9 \\
\times \quad 2x + 1 \\
\hline
x^2 + 7x - 9 \\
2x^3 + 14x^2 - 18x \\
\hline
2x^3 + 15x^2 - 11x - 9
\end{array}
$$

28.
$$
\begin{array}{r}
a^2 - 3a + 11 \\
\times \quad 5a + 2 \\
\hline
2a^2 - 6a + 22 \\
5a^3 - 15a^2 + 55a \\
\hline
5a^3 - 13a^2 + 49a + 22
\end{array}
$$

29.
$$
\begin{array}{r}
3x^2 + 5xy + y^2 \\
\times \quad 4x - 3y \\
\hline
-9x^2y - 15xy^2 - 3y^3 \\
12x^3 + 20x^2y + 4xy^2 \\
\hline
12x^3 + 11x^2y - 11xy^2 - 3y^3
\end{array}
$$

30.
$$
\begin{array}{r}
6x^2 - 5xy + 9y^2 \\
\times \quad 5x - 2y \\
\hline
-12x^2y + 10xy^2 - 18y^3 \\
30x^3 - 25x^2y + 45xy^2 \\
\hline
30x^3 - 37x^2y + 55xy^2 - 18y^3
\end{array}
$$

31. $(3x + 5)(2x^2 - 5x + 11)$

$= (3x + 5)(2x^2) + (3x + 5)(-5x) + (3x + 5)(11)$

$= 6x^3 + 10x^2 - 15x^2 - 25x + 33x + 55$

$= 6x^3 - 5x^2 + 8x + 55$

32. $(4s + 5)(3s^2 + 8s - 9)$

$= (4s + 5)(3s^2) + (4s + 5)(8s) + (4s + 5)(-9)$

$= 12s^3 + 15s^2 + 32s^2 + 40s - 36s - 45$

$= 12s^3 + 47s^2 + 4s - 45$

90

33. $(2a - 8a^2 + 3)(3a + 5)$

Rearrange terms for multiplying.

$$-8a^2 + 2a + 3$$
$$3a + 5$$
$$\overline{\phantom{xxxxxxx}}$$
$$-40a^2 + 10a + 15$$
$$\underline{-24a^3 + 6a^2 + 9a}$$
$$-24a^3 - 34a^2 + 19a + 15$$

34. $(5x - 2)(7 - 5x^2 + 2x)$

Rearrange terms for multiplying.

$$-5x^2 + 2x + 7$$
$$5x - 2$$
$$\overline{\phantom{xxxxxxx}}$$
$$10x^2 - 4x - 14$$
$$\underline{-25x^3 + 10x^2 + 35x}$$
$$-25x^3 + 20x^2 + 31x - 14$$

35.
$$5x^2 - 6x + 9$$
$$4x^2 + 3x + 11$$
$$\overline{\phantom{xxxxxxx}}$$
$$55x^2 - 66x + 99$$
$$15x^3 - 18x^2 + 27x$$
$$\underline{20x^4 - 24x^3 + 36x^2}$$
$$20x^4 - 9x^3 + 73x^2 - 39x + 99$$

36.
$$5x^4 + 0x^3 - 2x^2 + 0x + 1$$
$$x^2 - 5x + 3$$
$$\overline{\phantom{xxxxxxx}}$$
$$15x^4 + 0x^3 - 6x^2 + 0x + 3$$
$$-25x^5 + 0x^4 + 10x^3 + 0x^2 - 5x$$
$$\underline{5x^6 + 0x^5 - 2x^4 + 0x^3 + x^2}$$
$$5x^6 - 25x^5 + 13x^4 + 10x^3 - 5x^2 - 5x + 3$$

37. $(x^2 - 7x + 4)(2x^2 - 3x - 6)$

$= (x^2 - 7x + 4)(2x^2) + (x^2 - 7x + 4)(-3x)$

$\quad + (x^2 - 7x + 4)(-6)$

$= 2x^4 - 14x^3 + 8x^2 - 3x^3 + 21x^2 - 12x - 6x^2$
$\quad + 42x - 24$

$= 2x^4 + (-14x^3 - 3x^3) + (8x^2 + 21x^2 - 6x^2)$
$\quad + (-12x + 42x) - 24$

$= 2x^4 - 17x^3 + 23x^2 + 30x - 24$

38. $(a^2 + 2a + 5)(a^2 - 3a - 7)$

$= (a^2 + 2a + 5)(a^2) + (a^2 + 2a + 5)(-3a)$

$\quad + (a^2 + 2a + 5)(-7)$

$= a^4 + 2a^3 + 5a^2 - 3a^3 - 6a^2 - 15a - 7a^2 - 14a$
$\quad - 35$

$= a^4 + (2a^3 - 3a^3) + (5a^2 - 6a^2 - 7a^2)$
$\quad + (-15a - 14a) - 35$

$= a^4 - a^3 - 8a^2 - 29a - 35$

39.
$$-2x^2 + 3x - 8$$
$$3x^2 + 7x - 5$$
$$\overline{\phantom{xxxxxxx}}$$
$$10x^2 - 15x + 40$$
$$-14x^3 + 21x^2 - 56x$$
$$\underline{-6x^4 + 9x^3 - 24x^2}$$
$$-6x^4 - 5x^3 + 7x^2 - 71x + 40$$

40.
$$-7b^3 + 0b^2 + 2b - 3$$
$$5b^2 - 2b + 4$$
$$\overline{\phantom{xxxxxxx}}$$
$$-28b^3 + 0b^2 + 8b - 12$$
$$14b^4 + 0b^3 - 4b^2 + 6b$$
$$\underline{-35b^5 + 0b^4 + 10b^3 - 15b^2}$$
$$-35b^5 + 14b^4 - 18b^3 - 19b^2 + 14b - 12$$

41. $(2x - 1)(3x + 2)$

$= 2x(3x + 2) - 1(3x + 2)$

$= 2x \cdot 3x + 2x \cdot 2 - 1 \cdot 3x - 1 \cdot 2$

$= 6x^2 + 4x - 3x - 2$

$= 6x^2 + x - 2$

42. $-3x^2(3x + 2) - (2x - 1)$

$= -3x^2 \cdot 3x + -3x^2 \cdot 2 - 2x + 1$

$= -9x^3 - 6x^2 - 2x + 1$

43. $(2x - 1)(3x + 2 + -3x^2)$

$= 2x \cdot 3x + 2x \cdot 2 + 2x \cdot (-3x^2) - 1(3x)$

$\quad + (-1) \cdot 2 + (-1) \cdot (-3x^2)$

$= 6x^2 + 4x - 6x^3 - 3x - 2 + 3x^2$

$= -6x^3 + 9x^2 + x - 2$

44. $3(2x - 1)[2(3x + 2) + 5(-3x^2)]$

$= (3 \cdot 2x - 3 \cdot 1)[2 \cdot 3x + 2 \cdot 2 + 5 \cdot (-3x^2)]$

$= (6x - 3)[6x + 4 - 15x^2]$

$= 6x \cdot 6x + 6x \cdot 4 - 6x \cdot 15x^2 - 3 \cdot 6x - 3 \cdot 4$

$\quad - 3(-15x^2)$

$= 36x^2 + 24x - 90x^3 - 18x - 12 + 45x^2$

$= -90x^3 + 81x^2 + 6x - 12$

45. Let $x$ = width in feet;

$2x + 5$ = length of garden.

$(x + 3)(2x + 5 + 3) - x(2x + 5) = 213$

$\quad (x + 3)(2x + 8) - x(2x + 5) = 213$

$\quad\quad 2x^2 + 14x + 24 - 2x^2 - 5x = 213$

$\quad\quad\quad\quad\quad\quad\quad\quad\quad\quad 9x = 189$

$\quad\quad\quad\quad\quad\quad\quad\quad\quad\quad x = 21$

$\quad\quad\quad\quad\quad\quad\quad\quad\quad 2x + 5 = 47$

The dimensions are 21 ft by 47 ft.

46. Let $w$ = original width;

$2w - 7$ = original length;

$w - 6$ = new width;

$2w - 7 + 11$ = new length.

$w(2w - 7) = (w - 6)(2w + 4) + 40$

$\quad 2w^2 - 7w = 2w^2 - 8w - 24 + 40$

$\quad\quad\quad\quad\quad w = 16$

$\quad\quad 2w - 7 = 25$

The original dimensions were 16 yd by 25 yd.

47.

|  | Jack | Jared | Jason |
|---|---|---|---|
|  | 40 | 40 | 40 |
| Jack Loses | 80 | 20 | 20 |
| Jared Loses | 40 | 70 | 10 |
| Jason Loses | 20 | 35 | 65 |

48. $11 + 11(0.06) + \$11.66$

49. $14 + 7x > 8x$

$\quad\quad 14 > x$

$\quad\quad\quad x < 14$

50. $a^{1-1} \cdot b^5 \cdot c^{1-1} = b^5$

51. $\frac{2}{3}a(6a + 15)$

$= \frac{2}{3}a \cdot 6a + \frac{2}{3}a \cdot 15$

$= 4a^2 + 10a$

---

6-9 **Some Special Products**

PAGE 245    CHECKING FOR UNDERSTANDING

1. The middle terms have different signs.

2. The square of difference is $(a - b)^2 = a^2 - 2ab + b^2$. The difference of two squares is $a^2 - b^2 = (a - b)(a + b)$.

3. $(a - b)^2 = a^2 - 2ab + b^2$

4. $(a + 2b)^2$

$= a^2 + 2(a)(2b) + (2b)^2$

$= a^2 + 4ab + 4b^2$

5. $(a - 3b)^2$

$= a^2 + 2(a)(-3b) + (-3b)^2$

$= a^2 - 6ab + 9b^2$

6. $(2x + y)^2$

$= (2x)^2 + 2(2x)(y) + y^2$

$= 4x^2 + 4xy + y^2$

7. $(3x - 2y)^2$

$= (3x)^2 + 2(3x)(-2y) + (-2y)^2$

$= 9x^2 - 12xy + 4y^2$

8. $(2a + 3)(2a - 3)$

$= (2a)^2 - 3^2$

$= 4a^2 - 9$

9. $(5a - 3b)(5a + 3b)$

$= (5a)^2 - (3b)^2$

$= 25a^2 - 9b^2$

PAGES 245-246    EXERCISES

10. $(4x + y)^2$

$= (4x)^2 + 2(4x)(y) + y^2$

$= 16x^2 + 8xy + y^2$

11. $(2a - b)^2$

$= (2a)^2 + 2(2a)(-b) + (-b)^2$

$= 4a^2 - 4ab + b^2$

12. $(6m + 2n)^2$

$= (6m)^2 + 2(6m)(2n) + (2n)^2$

$= 36m^2 + 24mn + 4n^2$

13. $(4x - 9y)^2$

$= (4x)^2 + 2(4x)(-9y) + (-9y)^2$

$= 16x^2 - 72xy + 81y^2$

14. $(5a - 12b)^2$

$= (5a)^2 + 2(5a)(-12b) + (-12b)^2$

$= 25a^2 - 120ab + 144b^2$

15. $(5x + 6y)^2$

$$= (5x)^2 + 2(5x)(6y) + (6y)^2$$

$$= 25x^2 + 60xy + 36y^2$$

16. $\left(\frac{1}{2}a + b\right)^2$

$$= \left(\frac{1}{2}a\right)^2 + 2\left(\frac{1}{2}a\right)(b) + b^2$$

$$= \frac{1}{4}a^2 + ab + b^2$$

17. $(5 - x)^2$

$$= (5)^2 + 2(5)(-x) + (-x)^2$$

$$= 25 - 10x + x^2$$

18. $(1 + x)^2$

$$= (1)^2 + 2(1)(x) + (x)^2$$

$$= 1 + 2x + x^2$$

19. $(1.1x + y)^2$

$$= (1.1x)^2 + 2(1.1x)(y) + y^2$$

$$= 1.21x^2 + 2.2xy + y^2$$

20. $(a^2 - 3b^2)^2$

$$= (a^2)^2 + 2(a^2)(-3b^2) + (-3b^3)^2$$

$$= a^4 - 6a^2b^2 + 9b^4$$

21. $(x^3 - 5y^2)^2$

$$= (x^3)^2 + 2(x^3)(-5y^2) + (-5y^2)^2$$

$$= x^6 - 10x^3y^2 + 25y^4$$

22. $(3x + 5)(3x - 5)$        23. $(8a + 2b)(8a - 2b)$

$\quad = (3x)^2 - 5^2$           $= (8a)^2 - (2b)^2$

$\quad = 9x^2 - 25$             $= 64a^2 - 4b^2$

24. $(7a^2 + b)(7a^2 - b)$     25. $(8x^2 - 3y)(8x^2 + 3y)$

$\quad = (7a^2)^2 - b^2$         $= (8x^2)^2 - (3y)^2$

$\quad = 49a^4 - b^2$           $= 64x^4 - 9y^2$

26. $\left(\frac{4}{3}x^2 - y\right)\left(\frac{4}{3}x^2 + y\right)$

$$= \left(\frac{4}{3}x^2\right)^2 - y^2$$

$$= \frac{16}{9}x^4 - y^2$$

27. $(x + 2)(x - 2)(2x + 5)$

$$= \left[(x)^2 + (2x) + (-2x) + (2)(-2)\right](2x + 5)$$

$$= (x^2 - 4)(2x + 5)$$

$$= (2x)(x^2) + (-4)(2x) + (5)(x^2) + (-4)(5)$$

$$= 2x^3 + 5x^2 - 8x - 20$$

28. $(4x - 1)(4x + 1)(x - 4)$

$$= \left[(4x)^2 + (-1)(4x) + (1)(4x) + (-1)(1)\right](x - 4)$$

$$= (16x^2 - 1)(x - 4)$$

$$= (16x^2)(x) + (-1)(x) + (-4)(16x^2) + (-1)(-4)$$

$$= 16x^3 - 64x^2 - x + 4$$

29. $(x - 3)(x + 4)(x + 3)(x - 4)$

$$= (x - 3)(x + 3)(x + 4)(x - 4)$$

$$= \left[(x)^2 + (-3x) + (3x) + (-3)(3)\right]\left[(x)^2 + (4x)\right.$$

$$\left. + (-4x) + (4)(-4)\right]$$

$$= (x^2 - 9)(x^2 - 16)$$

$$= (x^2)^2 + (-9x^2) + (-16x^2) + (-9)(-16)$$

$$= x^4 - 25x^2 + 144$$

30. $(x - 2y)^3$

$$= (x - 2y)(x - 2y)^2$$

$$= (x - 2y)(x^2 - 4xy + 4y^2)$$

$$= (x - 2y)(x^2) + (x - 2y)(-4xy) + (x - 2y)(4y^2)$$

$$= x^3 - 2x^2y - 4x^2y + 8xy^2 + 4xy^2 - 8y^3$$

$$= x^3 - 6x^2y + 12xy^2 - 8y^3$$

31. $(2x - 3y)^3$

$$= (2x - 3y)(2x - 3y)^2$$

$$= (2x - 3y)(4x^2 - 12xy + 9y^2)$$

$$= (4x^2 - 12xy + 9y^2)(2x)$$

$$\quad - (4x^2 - 12xy + 9y^2)(3y)$$

$$= 8x^3 - 24x^2y + 18xy^2$$

$$\quad - 12x^2y + 36xy^2 - 27y^3$$

$$= 8x^3 - 36x^2y + 54xy^2 - 27y^3$$

32. $(a + b)^4$

$$= (a + b)^2(a + b)^2$$

$$= (a^2 + 2ab + b^2)(a^2 + 2ab + b^2)$$

$$= (a^2 + 2ab + b^2)(a^2) + (a^2 + 2ab + b^2)(2ab)$$

$$\quad + (a^2 + 2ab + b^2)(b^2)$$

$$= a^4 + 2a^3b + a^2b^2 + 2a^3b + 4a^2b^2 + 2ab^3 + a^2b^2$$

$$\quad + 2ab^3 + b^4$$

$$= a^4 + (2a^3b + 2a^3b) + (a^2b^2 + 4a^2b^2 + a^2b^2)$$

$$\quad + (2ab^3 + 2ab^3) + b^4$$

$$= a^4 + 4a^3b + 6a^2b^2 + 4ab^3 + b^4$$

33. $(2x - y)^4$

$= (2x - y)^2(2x - y)^2$

$= (4x^2 - 4xy + y^2)(4x^2 - 4xy + y^2)$

$= (4x^2 - 4xy + y^2)(4x^2) + (4x^2 - 4xy + y^2)(-4xy)$

$\quad + (4x^2 - 4xy + y^2)(y^2)$

$= 16x^4 - 16x^3y + 4x^2y^2 - 16x^3y + 16x^2y^2 - 4xy^3$

$\quad + 4x^2y^2 - 4xy^3 + y^4$

$= 16x^4 + (-16x^3y - 16x^3y)$

$\quad + (4x^2y^2 + 16x^2y^2 + 4x^2y^2) + (-4xy^3 - 4xy^3)$

$\quad + y^4$

$= 16x^4 - 32x^3y + 24x^2y^2 - 8xy^3 + y^4$

34. $(3m + 2n)^4$

$= (3m + 2n)^2(3m + 2n)^2$

$= (9m^2 + 12mn + 4n^2)(9m^2 + 12mn + 4n^2)$

$= (9m^2 + 12mn + 4n^2)(9m^2)$

$\quad + (9m^2 + 12mn + 4n^2)(12mn)$

$\quad + (9m^2 + 12mn + 4n^2)(4n^2)$

$= 81m^4 + 108m^3n + 36m^2n^2 + 108m^3n + 144m^2n^2$

$\quad + 48mn^3 + 36m^2n^2 + 48mn^3 + 16n^4$

$= 81m^4 + (108m^3n + 108m^3n)$

$\quad + (36m^2n^2 + 144m^2n^2 + 36m^2n^2)$

$\quad + (48mn^3 + 48mn^3) + 16n^4$

$= 81m^4 + 216m^3n + 216m^2n^2 + 96mn^3 + 16n^4$

35. $(a - b)^5$

$= (a - b)(a - b)^2(a - b)^2$

$= (a - b)(a^2 - 2ab + b^2)(a^2 - 2ab + b^2)$

$= (a - b)(a^2 - 2ab + b^2)(a^2)$

$\quad + (a^2 - 2ab + b^2)(-2ab)$

$\quad + (a^2 - 2ab + b^2)(b^2)$

$= (a - b)(a^4 - 2a^3b + a^2b^2 - 2a^3b + 4a^2b^2 - 2ab^3$

$\quad + a^2b^2 - 2ab^3 + b^4)$

$= (a - b)(a^4 - 4a^3b + 6a^2b^2 - 4ab^3 + b^4)$

$= (a - b)(a^4) + (a - b)(-4a^3b) + (a - b)(6a^2b^2)$

$\quad + (a - b)(-4ab^3) + (a - b)(b^4)$

$= a^5 - a^4b - 4a^4b + 4a^3b^2 + 6a^3b^2 - 6a^2b^3$

$\quad - 4a^2b^3 + 4ab^4 + ab^4 - b^5$

$= a^5 - 5a^4b + 10a^3b^2 - 10a^2b^3 + 5ab^4 - b^5$

36. $(a + b + c)^2 = a^2 + b^2 + c^2 + 2ab + 2ac + 2bc$

37. Let $w$ = length of the lower base of the trapezoid;

$3w - 14$ = length of the upper base.

$\frac{1}{2}(9)(w + 3w - 14) = 81$

$\frac{1}{2}(4w - 14) = 9$

$2w - 7 = 9$

$2w = 16$

$w = 8$

The length of the lower base is 8 miles.

38. Let $x$ = original dimensions.

$x^2 - (x - 2)^2 = 40$

$x^2 - (x^2 - 4x + 4) = 40$

$x^2 - x^2 + 4x - 4 = 40$

$4x = 44$

$x = 11$

The photo was 11 in. by 11 in.

39. $\frac{4y + 3}{7} = \frac{9}{14}$

$14(4y + 3) = 7(9)$

$56y + 42 = 63$

$56y = 21$

$y = \frac{3}{8}$

40. Let $n$ = notebooks sold for \$1.25.

$(264 - x)(0.95) + x(1.25) = 297$

$250.8 - 0.95x + 1.25x = 297$

$250.8 + 0.3x = 297$

$0.3x = 46.2$

$x = 154$

$264 - x = 110$

110 at 95 cents, 154 at \$1.25

41. $3 - 1\frac{1}{2} = \frac{3}{2}$

$\frac{3}{2} \neq \frac{1}{2}$

The statement is false.

PAGE 246  APPLICATION

The area of the Punnett square can be thought of as a square of a polynomial.

$(T + t)^2 = T^2 + 2Tt + t^2$

# Technology:  Volume and Surface Area

PAGE 247    EXERCISES

1. Find the sum of twice the products of the values in cells B1 and B2, B1 and B3, and B2 and B3.

2. Volume = $B5 * B5 * B5$ or $B5\uparrow3$
   Surface Area: $6 * B5 * B5$ or $6*B\uparrow2$
3. cell

| A3 | "AREA" |
|---|---|
| B3 | B1*B2 |
| A4 | "PERIMETER" |
| B4 | 2*B1 + 2*B2 |

# Chapter 6    Summary and Review

**PAGES 248-250    SKILLS AND CONCEPTS**

1. $y^3 \cdot y^3 \cdot y$
   $= y^{3+3+1}$
   $= y^7$

2. $(3ab)(-4a^2b^3)$
   $= (3 \cdot -4)(aa^2)(bb^3)$
   $= -12(a^{1+2})(b^{1+3})$
   $= -12a^3b^4$

3. $(-4a^2x)(-5a^3x^4)$
   $= (-4 \cdot -5)(a^2a^3)(xx^4)$
   $= 20(a^{2+3})(x^{1+4})$
   $= 20a^5x^5$

4. $(4a^2b)^3$
   $= 4^3(a^2)^3b^3$
   $= 64(a^{2\cdot3})b^3$
   $= 64a^6b^3$

5. $(-3xy)^2(4x)^3$
   $= 9x^2y^2(64x^3)$
   $= 576(x^{2+3})y^2$
   $= 576x^5y^2$

6. $(2c^2d)^4(3c^2)^3$
   $= 16c^8d^4(-27c^6)$
   $= -432(c^{8+6})d^4$
   $= -432c^{14}d^4$

7. $\frac{1}{2}(m^2n^4)^2$
   $= -\frac{1}{2}m^4n^8$

8. $(5a^2)^3 + 7a^6$
   $= (125a^{2\cdot3}) + 7a^6$
   $= 125a^6 + 7a^6$
   $= 132a^6$

9. $\frac{y}{y^6} = y^{10-6} = y^4$

10. $\frac{(3y)^0}{6a} = \frac{1}{6a}$

11. $\frac{42b}{14b^4} = \frac{42}{14} \cdot \frac{b}{b^4}$
    $= 3b^{7-4}$
    $= 3b^3$

12. $\frac{27b^{-2}}{14b^{-3}} = \frac{27}{14} \cdot \frac{b^{-2}}{b^{-3}}$
    $= \frac{27}{14}b^{-2-(-3)}$
    $= \frac{27}{14}b$

13. $\frac{(3a^3bc^2)^2}{18a^2b^3c^4}$
    $= \frac{9a^6b^2c^4}{18a^2b^3c^4}$
    $= \frac{1}{2}a^{6-2}b^{2-3}c^{4-4}$
    $= \frac{a^4b^{-1}c^0}{2} = \frac{a^4}{2b}$

14. $\frac{-16a^3b^2x^4y}{-48a^4bxy^3}$
    $= \frac{1}{3}a^{3-4}b^{2-1}x^{4-1}y^{1-3}$
    $= \frac{bx^3}{3ay^2}$

15. $2.4 \times 10^5$

16. $4.88 \times 10^9$

17. $3.14 \times 10^{-4}$

18. $1.87 \times 10^{-6}$

19. $(2 \times 10^5)(3 \times 10^6) = 6 \times 10^{11}$

20. $(3 \times 10^3)(1.5 \times 10^6) = 4.5 \times 10^9$

21. $\frac{5.4 \times 10^3}{0.9 \times 10^4} = 6 \times 10^{-1}$

22. $\frac{8.4 \times 10^{-6}}{1.4 \times 10^{-9}} = 6 \times 10^3$

23. 2     24. 4     25. 4     26. 4

27. $3x^4 + x^2 - x - 5$     28. $-5x^3 + ax^2 + a^2x - a^3$

29. $(2x^2 - 5x + 7) - (3x^3 + x^2 + 2)$
    $= 2x^2 - 5x + 7 - 3x^3 - x^2 - 2$
    $= -3x^3 + (2x^2 - x^2) - 5x + (7 - 2)$
    $= -3x^3 + x^2 - 5x + 5$

30. $(x^2 - 6xy + 7y^2) + (3x^2 + xy - y^2)$
    $= x^2 - 6xy + 7y^2 + 3x^2 + xy - y^2$
    $= (x^2 + 3x^2) + (-6xy + xy) + (7y^2 - y^2)$
    $= 4x^2 - 5xy + 6y^2$

31. $11m^2n^2 + 4mn - 6$
    $+ 5m^2n^2 - 6mn + 17$
    _____
    $16m^2n^2 - 2mn + 11$

32. $7z^2 \qquad + 4$
    $- (3z^2 + 2z - 6)$
    _____
    $4z^2 - 2z + 10$

33. $4ab(3a^2 - 7b^2)$
    $= 4ab \cdot 3a^2 - 4ab \cdot 7b^2$
    $= 12(a^{1+2})b - 28a(b^{1+2})$
    $= 12a^3b - 28ab^3$

34. $7xy(x^2 + 4xy - 8y^2)$
    $= 7xy(x^2) + 7xy(4xy) + 7xy(-8y^2)$
    $= 7x^3y + 28x^2y^2 - 56xy^3$

35. $x(3x - 5) + 7(x^2 - 2x + 9)$
    $= 3x^2 - 5x + 7x^2 - 14x + 63$
    $= (3x^2 + 7x^2) + (-5x - 14x) + 63$
    $= 10x^2 - 19x + 63$

36. $4x^2(x + 8) - 3x(2x^2 - 8x + 3)$

$= 4x^3 + 32x^2 - 6x^3 + 24x^2 - 9x$

$= -2x^3 + 56x^2 - 9x$

37. $(r - 3)(r + 7)$

$= r^2 + 7r - 3r - 21$

$= r^2 + 4r - 21$

38. $(x + 5)(3x - 2)$

$= x^2 - 2x + 15x - 10$

$= 3x^2 + 13x - 10$

39. $(4x - 3)(x + 4)$

$= 4x^2 + 16x - 3x - 12$

$= 4x^2 + 13x - 12$

40. $(2x + 5y)(3x - y)$

$= 6x^2 - 2xy + 15xy - 5y^2$

$= 6x^2 + 13xy - 5y^2$

41. $(x - 4)(x^2 + 5x - 7)$

$= (x - 4)x^2 + (x - 4)(5x) + (x - 4)(-7)$

$= x^3 - 4x^2 + 5x^2 - 20x - 7x + 28$

$= x^3 + x^2 - 27x + 28$

42. $(2a + b)(a^2 - 17ab - 3b^2)$

$= (2a + b)a^2 + (2a + b)(-17ab) + (2a + b)(-3b^2)$

$= 2a^3 + ba^2 - 34a^2b - 17ab^2 - 6ab^2 - 3b^3$

$= 2a^3 - 33a^2b - 23ab^2 - 3b^3$

43. $(x - 6)(x + 6)$

$= x^2 + 6x - 6x - 36$

$= x^2 - 36$

44. $(5x - 3y)(5x + 3y)$

$= 25x^2 + 15xy - 15xy - 9y^2$

$= 25x^2 - 9y^2$

45. $(4x + 7)^2$

$= (4x)^2 + 2(4x)(7) + 7^2$

$= 16x^2 + 56x + 49$

46. $(a^2 + b)^2$

$= (a^2)^2 + 2(a^2)(b) + b^2$

$= a^4 + 2a^2b + b^2$

47. $(8x - 5)^2$

$= (8x)^2 - 2(8x)(5) + 5^2$

$= 64x^2 - 80x + 25$

48. $(6a - 5b)^2$

$= (6a)^2 - 2(6a)(5b) + (5b)^2$

$= 36a^2 - 60ab + 25b^2$

**PAGE 250    APPLICATIONS AND CONNECTIONS**

49. 2 grandparents; 3 great-grandparents; The pattern of the bee's ancestry is a Fibonacci sequence.

50.

| Number of Rings | Number of Guests |
|---|---|
| 1 | 1 |
| 2 | 3 |
| 3 | 5 |
| 4 | 7 |
| 5 | 9 |
| 6 | 11 |
| 7 | 13 |
| 8 | 15 |
| 9 | 17 |
| 10 | 19 |
| Total | 100 |

51. Let $s$ = the third side.

$3x^2 - 12 = x^2 - 4 + x^2 - 4 + s$

$3x^2 - 12 = 2x^2 - 8 + s$

$x^2 - 4 = s$

52. $A = 2x(x + 3) - x(x + 2)$

$= 2x^2 + 6x - x^2 + 2x$

$= x^2 + 4x$

# Chapter 6    Test

**PAGE 251**

1. $a^2 \cdot a^3 \cdot b^4 \cdot b^5$

$= a^{2+3} \cdot b^{4+5}$

$= a^5b^9$

2. $(-12abc)(4a^2b^3)$

$= (-12)(4)(aa^2)(bb^3)c$

$= -48a^{1+2}b^{1+3}c$

$= -48a^3b^4c$

3. $(9a)^2 = 9^2a^2$

$= 81a^2$

4. $(-3a)^4(a^5b)$

$= (-3)^4a^4a^5b$

$= 81a^9b$

5. $(-5a^2)(-6b)^2$

$= -5a^2(-6)^2b^2$

$= -5a^2(36)b^2$

$= -180a^2b^2$

6. $(5a)^2b + 7a^2b$

$= 5^2a^2b + 7a^2b$

$= 25a^2b + 7a^2b$

$= 32a^2b$

7. $\dfrac{y^{11}}{y^6} = y^{11-6} = y^5$

8. $\dfrac{y^3x}{yx} = y^{3-1}x^{1-1}$

$= y^2$

9. $\dfrac{63a^2bc}{9abc} = 7a^{2-1}b^{1-1}c^{1-1} = 7a$

10. $\dfrac{48a^2bc^5}{(3ab^3c^2)^2} = \dfrac{48a^2bc^5}{9a^2b^6c^4} = \dfrac{48}{9}a^{(2-2)}b^{(1-6)}c^{(5-4)}$

$= \dfrac{16}{3}b^{-5}c = \dfrac{16c}{3b^5}$

11. $\dfrac{14ab^{-3}}{21a^2b^{-5}} = \dfrac{2}{3}a^{1-2}b^{-3-(-5)} = \dfrac{2b^2}{3a}$

12. $\dfrac{10a^2bc}{20a^{-1}b^{-1}c} = \dfrac{1}{2}a^{2-(-1)}b^{1-(-1)}c^{1-1} = \dfrac{1}{2}a^3b^2$

13. $52,800 = 5.28 \times 10^4$

14. $0.00378 = 3.78 \times 10^{-3}$

15. $(3 \times 10^3)(2 \times 10^4)$

$= 3(2)(10^3)(10^4)$

$= 6(10^{3+4}) = 6 \times 10^7$

16. $(4 \times 10^{-3})(3 \times 10^{16})$

$= 4(3)(10^{-3})(10^{16})$

$= 12(10^{16-3}) = 12 \times 10^{13} = 1.2 \times 10^{14}$

17. $\dfrac{2.5 \times 10^3}{5 \times 10^{-3}} = 5 \times 10^5$

18. $\dfrac{91 \times 10^{18}}{13 \times 10^{14}} = 7 \times 10^{18-14} = 7 \times 10^4$

19. $x^3 + 5x^2 + 5x - 3$    20. $x^3y^2 - x^2 - xy^3 + 5$

21. $(a + 5)^2$         22. $(2x - 5)(7x + 3)$

$- a^2 + 2 \cdot a \cdot 5 + 5^2$    $= 14x^2 + 6x - 35x - 15$

$= a^2 + 10a + 25$      $= 14x^2 - 29x - 15$

23. $(3a^2 + 3)[2a - (-6)]$

$= (3a^2 + 3)(2a + 6)$

$= 6a^3 + 18a^2 + 6a + 18$

$= 6a^3 + 18a^2 + 6a + 18$

24. $3x^2y^3(2x \quad xy^2)$

$= 6x^3y^3 - 3x^3y^5$

25. $-4xy(5x^2 - 6xy^3 + 2y^2)$

$= -20x^3y + 24x^2y^4 - 8xy^3$

26. $(4x^2 - y^2)(4x^2 + y^2)$

$= 16x^4 + 4x^2y^2 - 4x^2y^2 - y^4$

$= 16x^4 - y^4$

27. $0.3b(0.4b^2 - 0.7b + 4)$

$= 0.12b^3 - 0.21b^2 + 1.2b$

28. $(2a^2b + b^2)^2$

$= (2a^2b)^2 + 2(a^2b)(b^2) + (b^2)^2$

$= 4a^4b^2 + 4a^2b^3 + b^4$

29. $x^2(x - 8) - 3x(x^2 - 7x + 3) + 5(x^3 - 6x^2)$

$= x^3 - 8x^2 - 3x^3 + 21x^2 - 9x + 5x^3 - 30x^2$

$= (x^3 - 3x^3 + 5x^3) + (-8x^2 + 21x^2 - 30x^2) - 9x$

$= 3x^3 - 17x^2 - 9x$

30. $a^2(a + 5) + 7a(a^2 + 8) - 7(a^3 - a + 2)$

$= a^3 + 5a^2 + 7a^3 + 56a - 7a^3 + 7a - 14$

$= (a^3 + 7a^3 - 7a^3) + 5a^2 + (56a + 7a) - 14$

$= a^3 + 5a^2 + 63a - 14$

31. $5y - 8 - 13y = 12y + 6$

$-8y - 8 = 12y + 6$

$-20y - 8 = 6$

$-20y = 14$

$y = -\dfrac{14}{20} = -\dfrac{7}{10}$

32. $2(a + 2) + 3a = 13 - (2a + 2)$

$2a + 4 + 3a = 13 - 2a - 2$

$5a + 4 = 11 - 2a$

$7a = 7$

$a = 1$

33. Let $w$ = the width;

$8w$ = the length.

$(8w - 10)(w - 2) = 8w(w) - 162$

$8w^2 - 26w + 20 = 8w^2 - 162$

$-26w + 20 = -162$

$-26w = -182$

$w = 7$

The original dimensions were 7 meters by 56 meters.

## PAGE 251    BONUS

$2^{n+3} \cdot 2^{3n-2} \cdot 2^{5n+1} = 2^5$

$2^{n+3+3n-2+5n+1} = 2^5$

$2^{9n+2} = 2^5$

so $9n + 2 = 5$

$9n = 3, \; n = \dfrac{1}{3}$

# Chapter 6    College Entrance Exam Preview

PAGES 252-253

1. B

Since six are honor students, $27 - 6$ or 21 students are not.

$\dfrac{21}{27} = \dfrac{7}{9}$

2. B

April, May, June, July, August, September,

   1     2     3     4     5        6

October, November, December

   7       8       9

$\dfrac{9}{12} = \dfrac{3}{4}$

3. A

$\frac{1}{6}$ of a day = $\frac{1}{6}$(24 hours) = 4 hours

24 × 7 = 168 hours in a week

$\frac{4}{168} = \frac{1}{42}$

4. D

$\frac{7}{x} = 0.7\%$

$\frac{7}{x} = 0.007$

$\frac{7}{0.007} = \frac{0.007}{0.007}x$

1000 = x

5. B

37.5% - 0.375 = $\frac{3}{8}$

6. C

$\frac{5}{6} = \frac{x}{7}$

35 = 6x

$5\frac{5}{6} = x$

7. A

$\frac{x}{11} = 75\%$

$\frac{x}{11} = 0.75$

$x = 8\frac{1}{4}$

8. D

90%(270) = 2.7%x

0.9(270) = 0.027x

9000 = x

9. B

$\frac{9}{60} = 15\%$

100% - 15% - 35% = 50% are green

10. C

Let r = rate, t = time, p = percent of increase of speed.

$r \cdot t = (1 + p)r \cdot 0.8t$

1 = (1 + p)0.8

1.25 = 1 + p

0.25 = p

11. B

1.50(5c) = b

7.5c = b

(x)(2b) = c

(x)(2 · 7.5c) = c

x(15c) = c

15x = 1

$x = \frac{1}{15}$ or $6\frac{2}{3}\%$

12. A

$\frac{2}{5}\left(\frac{5}{7}\right) = x\left(\frac{6}{11}\right)$

$\frac{2}{7} = \frac{6}{11}x$

$\frac{11}{21} = x$    A

13. C

$\frac{1}{2}\left(\frac{3}{4}\right)x = 30,000$

$\frac{3}{8}x = 30,000$

x = 80,000

14. B

$\frac{1.75}{21} = \frac{0.6}{x}$

1.75x = 12.6

x = 7.2

15. D

$\frac{6}{2} = \frac{4}{x}$

6x = 8

$x = 1\frac{1}{3}$

16. B

x - 0.10x = 0.9x

0.9x - 0.2(0.9x) = 0.9x - 0.18x = 0.72x

x - 0.72x = 0.28x

17. D

50 - 40 = 10 → $\frac{10}{50}$ ⇒ 20% off

160 - (1.5)(0.2)160 = 112

18. B

x + x + x + x + x + x + 2x + x + x + x + x + x = 13x

$\frac{2x}{13x} = \frac{2}{13}$

19. B

$\frac{68 + 68 + 68 + 68}{4} = \frac{272}{4} = 68$

20. B

4965 + 12(16) = 5157

21. A

$\frac{10 + 7 + 13 + 2 + x}{5} = \frac{32 + x}{5}$

If x = 3, $\frac{32 + 3}{5} = 7$. But x > 4.

22. D

127.6 × 8 = 1020.8 which is not the sum of 8 integers.

130.8 × 8 = 1046.4 which is not the sum of 8 integers.

131.3 × 8 = 1050.4 which is not the sum of 8 integers.

135.5 × 8 = 1084

23. A

nb + y = t

nb = t - y

$n = \frac{t - y}{b}$

24. C

69 wpm = 60 · 60 or 3600 words per hour

r · t = w

$t = \frac{w}{r}$

$t = \frac{360k}{3600}$

$t = \frac{k}{10}$

25. B

Make a diagram.

# Chapter 7 Factoring

## 7-1 Factors and Greatest Common Factors

PAGE 258 CHECKING FOR UNDERSTANDING

1.

2. 2, 3, 5, 7, 11, 13, 17, 19, 23, 29

3. No; 4 is not prime.

4. A common factor is any number that is a factor of both numbers. The greatest common factor is the largest of all the common factors.

5. prime    6. composite    7. composite

$$39 = 3 \cdot 13$$

$$\begin{aligned} 24 &= 2 \cdot 12 \\ &= 2 \cdot 2 \cdot 6 \\ &= 2 \cdot 2 \cdot 2 \cdot 3 \\ &= 2^3 \cdot 3 \end{aligned}$$

8. composite

$$91 = 7 \cdot 13$$

9. $4 = ②\cdot②$

$12 = ②\cdot②\cdot 3$

The GCF of 4 and 12 is $2 \cdot 2$ or 4.

10. $9 = ③\cdot③$

$36 = 2 \cdot 2 \cdot ③\cdot③$

The GCF of 9 and 36 is $3 \cdot 3$ or 9.

11. $15 = 3 \cdot ⑤$

$5 = ⑤$

The GCF of 15 and 5 is 5.

12. $11 = ⑪$

$22 = 2 \cdot ⑪$

The GCF of 11 and 22 is 11.

13. $10 = 2 \cdot ⑤$

$15 = 3 \cdot ⑤$

The GCF of 10 and 15 is 5.

14. $20 = ②\cdot 2 \cdot ⑤$

$30 = ②\cdot 3 \cdot ⑤$

The GCF of 20 and 30 is $2 \cdot 5$ or 10.

15. $18 = 2 \cdot 3 \cdot 3$

$35 = 5 \cdot 7$

The GCF of 18 and 35 is 1.

16. $16 = ②\cdot 2 \cdot 2 \cdot 2$

$18 = ②\cdot 3 \cdot 3$

The GCF of 16 and 18 is 2.

17. $21 = 3 \cdot 7$

18. $\begin{aligned} 28 &= 2 \cdot 14 \\ &= 2 \cdot 2 \cdot 7 \\ &= 2^2 \cdot 7 \end{aligned}$

19. $\begin{aligned} 60 &= 2 \cdot 30 \\ &= 2 \cdot 2 \cdot 15 \\ &= 2 \cdot 2 \cdot 3 \cdot 5 \\ &= 2^2 \cdot 3 \cdot 5 \end{aligned}$

20. $51 = 3 \cdot 17$

21. $\begin{aligned} 63 &= 3 \cdot 21 \\ &= 3 \cdot 3 \cdot 7 \\ &= 3^2 \cdot 7 \end{aligned}$

22. $\begin{aligned} 72 &= 2 \cdot 36 \\ &= 2 \cdot 2 \cdot 18 \\ &= 2 \cdot 2 \cdot 2 \cdot 9 \\ &= 2 \cdot 2 \cdot 2 \cdot 3 \cdot 3 \\ &= 2^3 \cdot 3^2 \end{aligned}$

23. $\begin{aligned} 112 &= 2 \cdot 56 \\ &= 2 \cdot 2 \cdot 28 \\ &= 2 \cdot 2 \cdot 2 \cdot 14 \\ &= 2 \cdot 2 \cdot 2 \cdot 2 \cdot 7 \\ &= 2^4 \cdot 7 \end{aligned}$

24. $\begin{aligned} 150 &= 2 \cdot 75 \\ &= 2 \cdot 3 \cdot 25 \\ &= 2 \cdot 3 \cdot 5 \cdot 5 \\ &= 2 \cdot 3 \cdot 5^2 \end{aligned}$

25. $\begin{aligned} 304 &= 2 \cdot 152 \\ &= 2 \cdot 2 \cdot 76 \\ &= 2 \cdot 2 \cdot 2 \cdot 38 \\ &= 2 \cdot 2 \cdot 2 \cdot 2 \cdot 19 \\ &= 2^4 \cdot 19 \end{aligned}$

26. $\begin{aligned} 216 &= 2 \cdot 108 \\ &= 2 \cdot 2 \cdot 54 \\ &= 2 \cdot 2 \cdot 2 \cdot 27 \\ &= 2 \cdot 2 \cdot 2 \cdot 3 \cdot 9 \\ &= 2 \cdot 2 \cdot 2 \cdot 3 \cdot 3 \cdot 3 \\ &= 2^3 \cdot 3^3 \end{aligned}$

27. $\begin{aligned} 300 &= 2 \cdot 150 \\ &= 2 \cdot 2 \cdot 75 \\ &= 2 \cdot 2 \cdot 3 \cdot 25 \\ &= 2 \cdot 2 \cdot 3 \cdot 5 \cdot 5 \\ &= 2^2 \cdot 3 \cdot 5^2 \end{aligned}$

28. $\begin{aligned} 1540 &= 2 \cdot 770 \\ &= 2 \cdot 2 \cdot 385 \\ &= 2 \cdot 2 \cdot 5 \cdot 77 \\ &= 2 \cdot 2 \cdot 5 \cdot 7 \cdot 11 \\ &= 2^2 \cdot 5 \cdot 7 \cdot 11 \end{aligned}$

29. $\begin{aligned} -64 &= -1 \cdot 64 \\ &= -1 \cdot 2 \cdot 32 \\ &= -1 \cdot 2 \cdot 2 \cdot 16 \\ &= -1 \cdot 2 \cdot 2 \cdot 2 \cdot 8 \\ &= -1 \cdot 2 \cdot 2 \cdot 2 \cdot 2 \cdot 4 \\ &= -1 \cdot 2 \cdot 2 \cdot 2 \cdot 2 \cdot 2 \cdot 2 \end{aligned}$

30. $\begin{aligned} -26 &= -1 \cdot 26 \\ &= -1 \cdot 2 \cdot 13 \end{aligned}$

**31.** $-240 = -1 \cdot 240$
$= -1 \cdot 2 \cdot 120$
$= -1 \cdot 2 \cdot 2 \cdot 60$
$= -1 \cdot 2 \cdot 2 \cdot 2 \cdot 30$
$= -1 \cdot 2 \cdot 2 \cdot 2 \cdot 2 \cdot 15$
$= -1 \cdot 2 \cdot 2 \cdot 2 \cdot 2 \cdot 3 \cdot 5$

**32.** $-231 = -1 \cdot 231$
$= -1 \cdot 3 \cdot 77$
$= -1 \cdot 3 \cdot 7 \cdot 11$

**33.** $98a^2b = 98 \cdot a \cdot a \cdot b$
$= 2 \cdot 49 \cdot a \cdot a \cdot b$
$= 2 \cdot 7 \cdot 7 \cdot a \cdot a \cdot b$

**34.** $44rs^2t^3 = 44 \cdot r \cdot s \cdot s \cdot t \cdot t \cdot t$
$= 2 \cdot 22 \cdot r \cdot s \cdot s \cdot t \cdot t \cdot t$
$= 2 \cdot 2 \cdot 11 \cdot r \cdot s \cdot s \cdot t \cdot t \cdot t$

**35.** $756(mn)^3 = 756 \cdot m \cdot m \cdot m \cdot n \cdot n \cdot n$
$= 2 \cdot 378 \cdot m \cdot m \cdot m \cdot n \cdot n \cdot n$
$= 2 \cdot 2 \cdot 189 \cdot m \cdot m \cdot m \cdot n \cdot n \cdot n$
$= 2 \cdot 2 \cdot 3 \cdot 63 \cdot m \cdot m \cdot m \cdot n \cdot n \cdot n$
$= 2 \cdot 2 \cdot 3 \cdot 3 \cdot 21 \cdot m \cdot m \cdot m \cdot n \cdot n \cdot n$
$= 2 \cdot 2 \cdot 3 \cdot 3 \cdot 3 \cdot 7 \cdot m \cdot m \cdot m \cdot n \cdot n \cdot n$

**36.** $-102x^3y = -102 \cdot x \cdot x \cdot x \cdot y$
$= -1 \cdot 102 \cdot x \cdot x \cdot x \cdot y$
$= -1 \cdot 2 \cdot 51 \cdot x \cdot x \cdot x \cdot y$
$= -1 \cdot 2 \cdot 3 \cdot 17 \cdot x \cdot x \cdot x \cdot y$

**37.** $16 = 2 \cdot 2 \cdot 2 \cdot 2$
$60 = 2 \cdot 2 \cdot 3 \cdot 5$
The GCF of 16 and 60 is $2 \cdot 2$ or 4.

**38.** $15 = 3 \cdot 5$
$50 = 2 \cdot 5 \cdot 5$
The GCF of 15 and 50 is 5.

**39.** $-80 = -1 \cdot 2 \cdot 2 \cdot 2 \cdot 2 \cdot 5$
$45 = 3 \cdot 3 \cdot 5$
The GCF of -80 and 45 is 5.

**40.** $29 = 29$
$-58 = -1 \cdot 2 \cdot 29$
The GCF of 29 and -58 is 29.

**41.** $305 = 5 \cdot 61$
$55 = 5 \cdot 11$
The GCF of 305 and 55 is 5.

**42.** $252 = 2 \cdot 2 \cdot 3 \cdot 3 \cdot 7$
$126 = 2 \cdot 3 \cdot 3 \cdot 7$
The GCF of 252 and 126 is $2 \cdot 3 \cdot 3 \cdot 7$ or 126.

**43.** $128 = 2 \cdot 2 \cdot 2 \cdot 2 \cdot 2 \cdot 2 \cdot 2$
$245 = 5 \cdot 7 \cdot 7$
The GCF of 128 and 245 is 1.

**44.** $95 = 5 \cdot 19$
$304 = 2 \cdot 2 \cdot 2 \cdot 2 \cdot 19$
The GCF of 95 and 304 is 19.

**45.** $7y^2 = 7 \cdot y \cdot y$
$14y^2 = 2 \cdot 7 \cdot y \cdot y$
The GCF of $7y^2$ and $14y^2$ is $7 \cdot y \cdot y$ or $7y^2$.

**46.** $17a = 17 \cdot a$
$34a^2 = 2 \cdot 17 \cdot a \cdot a$
The GCF of $17a$ and $34a^2$ is $17 \cdot a$ or $17a$.

**47.** $-12ab = -1 \cdot 2 \cdot 2 \cdot 3 \cdot a \cdot b$
$4a^2b^2 = 2 \cdot 2 \cdot a \cdot a \cdot b \cdot b$
The GCF of $-12ab$ and $4a^2b^2$ is $2 \cdot 2 \cdot a \cdot b$ or $4ab$.

**48.** $4xy = 2 \cdot 2 \cdot x \cdot y$
$-6x = -1 \cdot 2 \cdot 3 \cdot x$
The GCF of $4xy$ and $-6x$ is $2 \cdot x$ or $2x$.

**49.** $50n^4 = 2 \cdot 5 \cdot 5 \cdot n \cdot n \cdot n \cdot n$
$40n^2p^2 = 2 \cdot 2 \cdot 2 \cdot 5 \cdot n \cdot n \cdot p \cdot p$
The GCF of $50n^4$ and $40n^2p^2$ is
$2 \cdot 5 \cdot n \cdot n$ or $10n^2$.

**50.** $60x^2y^2 = 2 \cdot 2 \cdot 3 \cdot 5 \cdot x \cdot x \cdot y \cdot y$
$35xz^3 = 5 \cdot 7 \cdot x \cdot z \cdot z \cdot z$
The GCF of $60x^2y^2$ and $35xz^3$ is $5 \cdot x$ or $5x$.

**51.** $12an^2 = 2 \cdot 2 \cdot 3 \cdot a \cdot n \cdot n$
$40a^2 = 2 \cdot 2 \cdot 2 \cdot 5 \cdot a \cdot a$
The GCF of $12an^2$ and $40a^2$ is $2 \cdot 2 \cdot a$ or $4a$.

**52.** $56x^3y = 2 \cdot 2 \cdot 2 \cdot 7 \cdot x \cdot x \cdot x \cdot y$
$49ax^2 = 7 \cdot 7 \cdot a \cdot x \cdot x$
The GCF of $56x^3y$ and $49ax^2$ is $7 \cdot x \cdot x$
or $7x^2$.

**53.** $5 = 5$
$15 = 3 \cdot 5$
$10 = 2 \cdot 5$
The GCF of 5, 15, and 10 is 5.

**54.** $16 = 2 \cdot 2 \cdot 2 \cdot 2$
$24 = 2 \cdot 2 \cdot 2 \cdot 3$
$28 = 2 \cdot 2 \cdot 7$
The GCF of 16, 24, and 28 is $2 \cdot 2$ or 4.

**55.** $18 = 2 \cdot 3 \cdot 3$
$30 = 2 \cdot 3 \cdot 5$
$54 = 2 \cdot 3 \cdot 3 \cdot 3$
The GCF of 18, 30, and 54 is $2 \cdot 3$ or 6.

**56.** $24 = 2 \cdot 2 \cdot 2 \cdot 3$
$84 = 2 \cdot 2 \cdot 3 \cdot 7$
$168 = 2 \cdot 2 \cdot 2 \cdot 3 \cdot 7$
The GCF of 24, 84, and 168 is $2 \cdot 2 \cdot 3$ or 12.

**57.** $16 = 2 \cdot 2 \cdot 2 \cdot 2$
$24 = 2 \cdot 2 \cdot 2 \cdot 3$
$30 = 2 \cdot 3 \cdot 5$
The GCF of 16, 24, and 30 is 2.

**58.** $12mn = 2 \cdot 2 \cdot 3 \cdot m \cdot n$
$10mn = 2 \cdot 5 \cdot m \cdot n$
$15mn = 3 \cdot 5 \cdot m \cdot n$
The GCF of $12mn$, $10mn$, and $15mn$ is $m \cdot n$ or $mn$.

**59.** $6a^2 = 2 \cdot 3 \cdot a \cdot a$
$18b^2 = 2 \cdot 3 \cdot 3 \cdot b \cdot b$
$9b^3 = 3 \cdot 3 \cdot b \cdot b \cdot b$
The GCF of $6a^2$, $18b^2$, $9b^3$ is 3.

**60.** $8b^4 = 2 \cdot 2 \cdot 2 \cdot b \cdot b \cdot b \cdot b$

$5c = 5 \cdot c$

$3a^2b = 3 \cdot a \cdot a \cdot b$

The GCF of $8b^4$, $5c$, and $3a^2b$ is 1.

**61.** $15abc = 3 \cdot 5 \cdot a \cdot b \cdot c$

$35a^2c = 5 \cdot 7 \cdot a \cdot a \cdot c$

$105a = 3 \cdot 5 \cdot 7 \cdot a$

The GCF of $15abc$, $35a^2c$, and $105a$ is $5 \cdot a$ or $5a$.

**62.** $14a^2b^2 = 2 \cdot 7 \cdot a \cdot a \cdot b \cdot b$

$18ab = 2 \cdot 3 \cdot 3 \cdot a \cdot b$

$2a^3b^3 = 2 \cdot a \cdot a \cdot a \cdot b \cdot b \cdot b$

The GCF of $14a^2b^2$, $18ab$, and $2a^3b^3$ is $2 \cdot a \cdot b$ or $2ab$.

**63.** $18x^2y^2 = 2 \cdot 3 \cdot 3 \cdot x \cdot x \cdot y \cdot y$

$6y^2 = 2 \cdot 3 \cdot y \cdot y$

$42x^2y^3 = 2 \cdot 3 \cdot 7 \cdot x \cdot x \cdot y \cdot y \cdot y$

The GCF of $18x^2y^2$, $6y^2$, and $42x^2y^3$ is $2 \cdot 3 \cdot y \cdot y$ or $6y^2$.

**64.** $16a^2b^2$  **65.** $-4x^2y^3$  **66.** $3m^2n$  **67.** $6a^3b^2$

**68.** $1363 = 29 \cdot 47$

Its dimensions are 29 in. by 47 in.

**69.**

**70.** 8 pairs

3, 5; 5, 7; 11, 13; 17, 19; 29, 31; 41, 43;

59, 61; 71, 73

**71.**  5 rows of 20

10 rows of 10

20 rows of 5

25 rows of 4

50 rows of 2

**72.** Let $r$ = Jaime's rate.

Let $r + 10$ = Jackie's rate.

|  | $d$ | $r$ | $t$ |
|---|---|---|---|
| Jaime | 300 | $r$ | $\dfrac{300}{r}$ |
| Jackie | 300 | $r + 10$ | $\dfrac{300}{r + 10}$ |

$$\frac{300}{r} - 1 = \frac{300}{r + 10}$$

$$\frac{300}{r} = \frac{300}{r + 10} + 1$$

$$\frac{300}{r} - \frac{300}{r + 10} = 1$$

$$300(r + 10) - 300r = r(r + 10)$$

$$300r + 3000 - 300r = r^2 + 10r$$

$$r^2 + 10r - 3000 = 0$$

$$(r - 50)(r + 60) = 0$$

$$r = 50$$

Jaime's average speed was 50 mph.

**73.** Each square of sod is $2 \times 2$ yd or 4 yd$^2$.

Therefore $\dfrac{6000 \text{ yd}^2}{4 \text{ yd}^2}$

= 1500 squares of sod.

**74. a.** 6  **b.** 27  **c.** 19  **d.** 1

**75.**  10 PRINT "ENTER THREE NUMBERS."

20 INPUT A, B, C

30 FOR F = A TO 1 STEP -1

40 IF INT (A/F) = A/F THEN 60

50 NEXT F

60 IF INT (B/F) = B/F THEN 80

70 NEXT F

80 IF INT (C/F) = C/F THEN 100

90 NEXT F

100 PRINT "THE GCF OF"; A;

110 PRINT ", "; B; " AND ";C;

120 PRINT "IS "; F "."

130 END

**a.** 16  **b.** 1  **c.** 12

**76.** $6(x - 2) = 5(x - 11) - 21$

$6x - 12 = 5x - 55 - 21$

$6x - 12 = 5x - 76$

$x - 12 = -76$

$x = -64$

**77.**  $x + r = 2d$

$x + r - r = 2d - r$

$x = 2d - r$

**78.**

|  | Pounds | Amount of Aluminum |
|---|---|---|
| 30% alloy | 24 | .30(24) |
| 60% alloy | $n$ | .60$n$ |
| 48% alloy | 24 + $n$ | .48(24 + $n$) |

$$0.30(24) + 0.60n = 0.48(24 + n)$$
$$7.2 + 0.60n = 11.52 + 0.48n$$
$$0.12n = 4.32$$
$$n = 36$$

36 pounds of the 60% alloy should be added.

**79.**  $5x \le 10(3x + 4)$
$$5x \le 30x + 40$$
$$-25x \le 40$$
$$x \ge \frac{40}{-25}$$
$$x \ge \frac{-8}{5}$$
$$\left\{x \mid x \ge \frac{-8}{5}\right\}$$

**80.**  $|2y - 5| \ge 4$

$$2y - 5 \le -4 \qquad\qquad 2y - 5 \ge 4$$
$$2y \le 1 \qquad\qquad 2y \ge 9$$
$$y \le \frac{1}{2} \qquad\qquad y \ge \frac{9}{2}$$
$$\left\{y \mid y \ge \frac{9}{2} \text{ or } y \le \frac{1}{2}\right\}$$

**81.**  $-8a(5a^2 + 8a - 3)$
$$= -40a^3 - 64a^2 + 24a$$

**82.**  $(5r - 7s)^2$
$$= 25r^2 - 70rs + 49s^2$$

**PAGE 260  HISTORY CONNECTION**

2̶  3  4̸  5̲  6̸  7̲  8̸  9̸  1̶0̶  1̲1̲  1̶2̶  1̲3̲  1̸4̸  1̸5̸  1̸6̸
1̲7̲  1̸8̸  1̲9̲  2̸0̸  2̸1̸  2̸2̸  2̲3̲  2̸4̸  2̸5̸  2̶6̶  2̸7̸  2̸8̸  2̲9̲  3̸0̸  3̲1̲
3̸2̸  3̸3̸  3̶4̶  3̸5̸  3̶6̶  3̲7̲  3̸8̸  3̸9̸  4̶0̶  4̲1̲  4̸2̸  4̲3̲  4̸4̸  4̸5̸  4̸6̸
4̲7̲  4̸8̸  4̸9̸  5̸0̸  5̸1̸  5̸2̸  5̲3̲  5̸4̸  5̸5̸  5̸6̸  5̸7̸  5̸8̸  5̲9̲  6̸0̸  6̲1̲
6̸2̸  6̸3̸  6̸4̸  6̸5̸  6̸6̸  6̲7̲  6̸8̸  6̸9̸  7̸0̸  7̲1̲  7̸2̸  7̲3̲  7̸4̸  7̸5̸  7̸6̸
7̲7̲  7̸8̸  7̲9̲  8̸0̸  8̸1̸  8̸2̸  8̲3̲  8̸4̸  8̸5̸  8̸6̸  8̸7̸  8̸8̸  8̲9̲  9̸0̸  9̸1̸
9̸2̸  9̸3̸  9̸4̸  9̸5̸  9̸6̸  9̲7̲  9̸8̸  9̸9̸  1̸0̸0̸

Underlined numbers are prime.

---

## 7-2  Factoring Using the Distributive Property

**PAGES 262-263   CHECKING FOR UNDERSTANDING**

**1.** distributive

**2.** $3(5a + 4a^2)$, $a(15 + 12a)$, $3a(5 + 4a)$

**3.** $3a(5 + 4a)$

$3a$ is the GCF of $15a$ and $12a^2$.

**4.**  $3y^2 = \boxed{3} \cdot y \cdot y$
     $12 = 2 \cdot 2 \cdot \boxed{3}$
   The GCF is 3.

**5.**  $4a = \boxed{2} \cdot 2 \cdot a$
     $2b = \boxed{2} \cdot b$
   The GCF is 2.

**6.**  $5y = 5 \cdot \boxed{y}$
     $9y^2 = 3 \cdot 3 \cdot \boxed{y} \cdot y$
   The GCF is $y$.

**7.**  $9b = 3 \cdot 3 \cdot b$
     $5c = 5 \cdot c$
   The GCF is 1.

**8.**  $9a^2 = \boxed{3} \cdot 3 \cdot \boxed{a} \cdot a$
     $3a = \boxed{3} \cdot \boxed{a}$
   The GCF is $3a$.

**9.**  $7mn = \boxed{7} \cdot \boxed{m} \cdot n$
     $21m^3 = 3 \cdot \boxed{7} \cdot \boxed{m} \cdot m \cdot m$
   The GCF is $7m$.

**10.** $2x$  **11.** 1  **12.** $2ab$  **13.** $r^2$

**14.** $29xy = 29 \cdot \boxed{x} \cdot y$
     $3x = 3 \cdot \boxed{x}$
   The GCF is $x$.
   $$29xy - 3x = x(29y) - x(3)$$
   $$= x(29y - 3)$$

**15.** $x^5y = \boxed{x} \cdot x \cdot x \cdot x \cdot x \cdot y$
     $x = \boxed{x}$
   The GCF is $x$.
   $$x^5y - x = x(x^4y) - x(1)$$
   $$= x(x^4y - 1)$$

**16.** $27a^2b = \boxed{3} \cdot \boxed{3} \cdot 3 \cdot a \cdot a \cdot \boxed{b}$
     $9b^3 = \boxed{3} \cdot \boxed{3} \cdot b \cdot b \cdot \boxed{b}$
   The GCF is $9b$.
   $$27a^2b + 9b^3 = 9b(3a^2) + 9b(b^2)$$
   $$= 9b(3a^2 + b^2)$$

**17.** $3c^2d = \boxed{3} \cdot \boxed{c} \cdot \boxed{c} \cdot \boxed{d}$
     $6c^2d^2 = 2 \cdot \boxed{3} \cdot \boxed{c} \cdot \boxed{c} \cdot \boxed{d} \cdot d$
   The GCF is $3c^2d$.
   $$3c^2d - 6c^2d^2 = 3c^2d(1) - 3c^2d(2d)$$
   $$= 3c^2d(1 - 2d)$$

**PAGES 263-264   EXERCISES**

**18.** $y$  **19.** $2x^2$  **20.** $12x$  **21.** $5ab$

**22.**  $11x = \boxed{11} \cdot \boxed{x}$
     $44x^2y = 2 \cdot 2 \cdot \boxed{11} \cdot \boxed{x} \cdot x \cdot y$
   The GCF is $11x$.
   $$11x + 44x^2y = 11x(1) + 11x(4xy)$$
   $$= 11x(1 + 4xy)$$

**23.**  $16y^2 = \boxed{2} \cdot \boxed{2} \cdot \boxed{2} \cdot 2 \cdot y \cdot \boxed{y}$
     $8y = \boxed{2} \cdot \boxed{2} \cdot \boxed{2} \cdot \boxed{y}$
   The GCF is $8y$.
   $$16y^2 + 8y = 8y(2y) + 8y(1)$$
   $$= 8y(2y + 1)$$

**24.**  $14xz = \boxed{2} \cdot 7 \cdot \boxed{x} \cdot \boxed{z}$
     $18xz^2 = \boxed{2} \cdot 3 \cdot 3 \cdot \boxed{x} \cdot \boxed{z} \cdot z$
   The GCF is $2xz$.
   $$14xz - 18xz^2 = 2xz(7) - 2xz(9z)$$
   $$= 2xz(7 - 9z)$$

**25.**  $14mn^2 = \boxed{2} \cdot 7 \cdot \boxed{m} \cdot \boxed{n} \cdot n$
     $2mn = \boxed{2} \cdot \boxed{m} \cdot \boxed{n}$
   The GCF is $2mn$.
   $$14mn^2 + 2mn = 2mn(7n) + 2mn(1)$$
   $$= 2mn(7n + 1)$$

102

26. $18xy^2 = 2 \cdot 3 \cdot 3 \cdot x \cdot y \cdot y$
    $24x^2y = 2 \cdot 2 \cdot 2 \cdot 3 \cdot x \cdot x \cdot y$
    The GCF is $6xy$.
    $18xy^2 - 24x^2y = 6xy(3y) - 6xy(4x)$
    $\qquad\qquad\quad = 6xy(3y - 4x)$

27. $15xy^3 = 3 \cdot 5 \cdot x \cdot y \cdot y \cdot y$
    $y^4 = y \cdot y \cdot y \cdot y$
    The GCF is $y^3$.
    $15xy^3 + y^4 = y^3(15x) + y^3(y)$
    $\qquad\qquad = y^3(15x + y)$

28. $25a^2b^2 = 5 \cdot 5 \cdot a \cdot a \cdot b \cdot b$
    $30ab^3 = 2 \cdot 3 \cdot 5 \cdot a \cdot b \cdot b \cdot b$
    The GCF is $5ab^2$.
    $25a^2b^2 + 30ab^3 = 5ab^2(5a) + 5ab^2(6b)$
    $\qquad\qquad\qquad = 5ab^2(5a + 6b)$

29. $36p^2q^2 = 2 \cdot 2 \cdot 3 \cdot 3 \cdot p \cdot p \cdot q \cdot q$
    $12pq = 2 \cdot 2 \cdot 3 \cdot p \cdot q$
    The GCF is $12pq$.
    $36p^2q^2 - 12pq = 12pq(3pq) - 12pq(1)$
    $\qquad\qquad\qquad = 12pq(3pq - 1)$

30. $17a = 17 \cdot a$
    $41a^3b = 41 \cdot a \cdot a \cdot a \cdot b$
    The GCF is $a$.
    $17a - 41a^3b = a(17) - a(41a^2b)$
    $\qquad\qquad\quad = a(17 - 41a^2b)$

31. $2m^3n^2 = 2 \cdot m \cdot m \cdot m \cdot n \cdot n$
    $16m^2n^3 = 2 \cdot 2 \cdot 2 \cdot 2 \cdot m \cdot m \cdot n \cdot n \cdot n$
    $8mn = 2 \cdot 2 \cdot 2 \cdot m \cdot n$
    The GCF is $2mn$.
    $2m^3n^2 - 16m^2n^3 + 8mn = 2mn(m^2n) - 2mn(8mn^2)$
    $\qquad\qquad\qquad\qquad\qquad + 2mn(4)$
    $\qquad\qquad\qquad\qquad = 2mn(m^2n - 8mn^2 + 4)$

32. $3x^3y = 3 \cdot x \cdot x \cdot x \cdot y$
    $9xy^2 = 3 \cdot 3 \cdot x \cdot y \cdot y$
    $36xy = 2 \cdot 2 \cdot 3 \cdot 3 \cdot x \cdot y$
    The GCF is $3xy$.
    $3x^3y + 9xy^2 + 36xy = 3xy(x^2) + 3xy(3y) + 3xy(12)$
    $\qquad\qquad\qquad\qquad = 3xy(x^2 + 3y + 12)$

33. $28a^2b^2c^2 = 2 \cdot 2 \cdot 7 \cdot a \cdot a \cdot b \cdot b \cdot c \cdot c$
    $21a^2bc^2 = 3 \cdot 7 \cdot a \cdot a \cdot b \cdot c \cdot c$
    $14abc = 2 \cdot 7 \cdot a \cdot b \cdot c$
    The GCF is $7abc$.
    $28a^2b^2c^2 + 21a^2bc^2 - 14abc$
    $= 7abc(4abc) + 7abc(3ac) - 7abc(2)$
    $= 7abc(4abc + 3ac - 2)$

34. $12ax = 2 \cdot 2 \cdot 3 \cdot a \cdot x$
    $20bx = 2 \cdot 2 \cdot 5 \cdot b \cdot x$
    $32cx = 2 \cdot 2 \cdot 2 \cdot 2 \cdot 2 \cdot c \cdot x$
    The GCF is $4x$.
    $12ax + 20bx + 32cx = 4x(3a) + 4x(5b) + 4x(8c)$
    $\qquad\qquad\qquad\qquad = 4x(3a + 5b + 8c)$

35. $a = a$
    $a^2b = a \cdot a \cdot b$
    $a^3b^3 = a \cdot a \cdot a \cdot b \cdot b \cdot b$
    The GCF is $a$.
    $a + a^2b + a^3b^3 = a(1) + a(ab) + a(a^2b^3)$
    $\qquad\qquad\qquad = a(1 + ab + a^2b^3)$

36. $A = (a + 4)(b + 4) - ab$
    $\quad = ab + 4a + 4b + 16 - ab$
    $\quad = 4a + 4b + 16$
    $\quad = 4(a + b + 4)$

37. $A = (a + 6)^2 - a^2 + 3b$
    $\quad = a^2 + 12a + 36 - a^2 + 3b$
    $\quad = 12a + 3b + 36$
    $\quad = 3(4a + b + 12)$

38. $A = 2(4 + c + 4) + 4(a + 2) + (d + 2)(c + 4) - cd$
    $\quad = 8 + 2c + 8 + 4a + 8 + cd + 2c + 4d + 8 - cd$
    $\quad = 4a + 4c + 4d + 32$
    $\quad = 4(a + c + d + 8)$

39. $A = (a + 2d + 8)(c + 8) - a(c - b) - 2cd - 4b$
    $\quad = ac + 2cd - 8c + 8a + 16d + 64 - ac +$
    $\qquad\quad ab - 2cd - 4b$
    $\quad = 8a + 12b - 4b + 8c + 16d + 64$
    $\quad = 8a + 8b + 8c + 16d + 64$
    $\quad = 8(a + b + c + 2d + 8)$

40. $ax^3 = a \cdot x \cdot x \cdot x$
    $5bx^3 = 5 \cdot b \cdot x \cdot x \cdot x$
    $9cx^3 = 3 \cdot 3 \cdot c \cdot x \cdot x \cdot x$
    The GCF is $x^3$.
    $ax^3 + 5bx^3 + 9cx^3 = x^3(a + 5b + 9c)$

41. $y^5 = y \cdot y \cdot y \cdot y \cdot y$
    $5y^4 = 5 \cdot y \cdot y \cdot y \cdot y$
    $3y^2 = 3 \cdot y \cdot y$
    $2y = 2 \cdot y$
    The GCF is $y$.
    $y^5 + 5y^4 + 3y^2 + 2y = y(y^4 + 5y^3 + 3y + 2)$

42. $\frac{2}{3}x = 2 \cdot \frac{1}{3} \cdot x$
    $\frac{1}{3}x^2 = \frac{1}{3} \cdot x \cdot x$
    $\frac{4}{3}xy^2 = 2 \cdot 2 \cdot \frac{1}{3} \cdot x \cdot y \cdot y$
    The GCF is $\frac{1}{3}x$.
    $\frac{2}{3}x + \frac{1}{3}x^2 - \frac{4}{3}xy^2 = \frac{1}{3}x(2 + x - 4y^2)$

43. $\frac{4}{5}a^2b = 2 \cdot 2 \cdot \frac{1}{5} \cdot a \cdot a \cdot b$
    $\frac{3}{5}ab^2 = 3 \cdot \frac{1}{5} \cdot a \cdot b \cdot b$
    $\frac{1}{5}ab = \frac{1}{5} \cdot a \cdot b$
    The GCF is $\frac{1}{5}ab$.
    $\frac{4}{5}a^2b - \frac{3}{5}ab^2 - \frac{1}{5}ab = \frac{1}{5}ab(4a - 3b - 1)$

**44.** $A = \left(\dfrac{16a + 20b}{4}\right)^2$

$= \dfrac{256a^2 + 640ab + 400b^2}{16}$

$= 16a^2 + 40ab + 25b^2$

$\dfrac{16a + 20b}{4}$

$\dfrac{16a + 20b}{4}$

**45.** If $x = -1$, $A = [2(-1) + 3][9 - 4(-1)]$

$\qquad = 1 \cdot 13$

$\qquad = 13$

If $x = 0$, $A = [2(0) + 3][9 - 4(0)]$

$\qquad = 3 \cdot 9$

$\qquad = 27$

If $x = 1$, $A = [2(1) + 3][9 - 4(1)]$

$\qquad = 5 \cdot 5$

$\qquad = 25$

If $x = 2$, $A = [2(2) + 3][9 - 4(2)]$

$\qquad = 7 \cdot 1$

$\qquad = 7$

**46.** Let $w$ = original width.

Original length = $2w + 5$

$A_1 = w(2w + 5) = 2w^2 + 5w$

$A_2 = 2w(2w + 5 + 4) = 4w^2 + 18w$

$A_2 - A_1 = 4w^2 + 18w - (2w^2 + 5w)$

$\qquad = 2w^2 + 13w$

$\qquad = w(2w + 13)$

Additional area = $w(2w + 13)$ square ft.

**47.** sales during 1st hour = $4x$

sales during 2nd hour = $8(x - 5)$

total sales = $4x + 8(x - 5)$

$\qquad = 4x + 8x - 40$

$\qquad = 12x - 40$

$\dfrac{12x - 40}{4} = 3x - 10$

She would have had to sell $3x - 10$ shares at \$4 per share.

**48.** $x \le -3$

**49.** Let $x$ = original price.

$\dfrac{1}{3}x - 8 = 525$

$\dfrac{1}{3}x = 533$

$x = 3(533)$

$x = \$1599$

**50.** $\dfrac{2}{11} = \dfrac{x - 5}{x + 3}$

$2(x + 3) = 11(x - 5)$

$2x + 6 = 11x - 55$

$9x = 61$

$x = \dfrac{61}{9}$

**51.** $\dfrac{7.8 \times 10^4}{2.6 \times 10^2}$

$= \dfrac{78,000}{260}$

$= 300$

$= 3 \times 10^2$

**52.** $2mx^4 - 3x^5 + 4m^5 + 6x^3$

$= -3x^5 + 2mx^4 + 6x^3 + 4m^5$

**53.** $38ab^3 = \boxed{2} \cdot 19 \cdot \boxed{a} \cdot b \cdot b \cdot \boxed{b}$

$-74a^3b = -1 \cdot \boxed{2} \cdot 37 \cdot \boxed{a} \cdot a \cdot a \cdot \boxed{b}$

The GCF is $2ab$.

---

$\boxed{7\text{-}3}$ ## Factoring by Grouping

PAGES 266-267    CHECKING FOR UNDERSTANDING

**1.** distributive, associative, cummulative

**2.** $(7mn + 14n) + (5m + 10)$

$= 7n(m + 2) + 5(m + 2)$

$= (7n + 5)(m + 2)$

$(7mn + 5m) + (14n + 10)$

$= m(7n + 5) + 2(7n + 5)$

$= (7n + 5)(m + 2)$

**3.** $b - 3a^2$

**4.** $k(r + s) - m(r + s)$

$= (k - m)(r + s)$

**5.** $t(t - s) + s(t - s)$

$= (t + s)(t - s)$

**6.** $3ab(a - 4) - 8(a - 4)$

$= (3ab - 8)(a - 4)$

**7.** $8m(x + y) + (x + y)$

$= (8m + 1)(x + y)$

**8.** $x + y$  **9.** $3x + 2y$  **10.** $a + 3b$  **11.** $2y - 5$

**12.** $rx + 2ry + kx + 2ky$

$= (rx + 2ry) + (kx + 2ky)$

$= r(x + 2y) + k(x + 2y)$

$= (r + k)(x + 2y)$

**13.** $ay - ab + cb - cy$

$= (ay - ab) + (cb - cy)$

$= a(y - b) + c(b - y)$

$= a(y - b) - c(y - b)$

$= (a - c)(y - b)$

**14.** $a^2 - 4ac + ab - 4bc$

$= (a^2 - 4ac) + (ab - 4bc)$

$= a(a - 4c) + b(a - 4c)$

$= (a + b)(a - 4c)$

**15.** $5a + 10a^2 + 2b + 4ab$

$= (5a + 10a^2) + (2b + 4ab)$

$= 5a(1 + 2a) + 2b(1 + 2a)$

$= (5a + 2b)(1 + 2a)$

16. $5x - 3y$    17. $x^2 + 1$    18. $4m - 3p$    19. $5k - 7p$

20. $2ax + 6xc + ba + 3bc$

$= (2ax + 6xc) + (ba + 3bc)$

$= 2x(a + 3c) + b(a + 3c)$

$= (2x + b)(a + 3c)$

21. $6mx - 4m + 3rx - 2r$

$= (6mx - 4m) + (3rx - 2r)$

$= 2m(3x - 2) + r(3x - 2)$

$= (2m + r)(3x - 2)$

22. $2my + 7x + 7m + 2xy$

$= (2my + 7m) + (2xy + 7x)$

$= m(2y + 7) + x(2y + 7)$

$= (m + x)(2y + 7)$

23. $3my - ab + am - 3by$

$= (3my + am) - (ab + 3by)$

$= m(3y + a) - b(3y + a)$

$= (m - b)(3y + a)$

24. $3ax - 6bx + 8b - 4a$

$= (3ax - 6bx) + (8b - 4a)$

$= 3x(a - 2b) + 4(2b - a)$

$= 3x(a - 2b) - 4(a - 2b)$

$= (3x - 4)(a - 2b)$

25. $a^2 - 2ab + a - 2b$

$= (a^2 + a) - (2ab + 2b)$

$= a(a + 1) - 2b(a + 1)$

$= (a - 2b)(a + 1)$

26. $2ab + 2am - b - m$

$= (2ab - b) + (2am - m)$

$= b(2a - 1) + m(2a - 1)$

$= (b + m)(2a - 1)$

27. $3m^2 - 5m^2p + 3p^2 - 5p^3$

$= (3m^2 - 5m^2p) + (3p^2 - 5p^3)$

$= m^2(3 - 5p) + p^2(3 - 5p)$

$= (m^2 + p^2)(3 - 5p)$

28. $5a^2 - 4ab + 12b^3 - 15ab^2$

$= (5a^2 - 4ab) + (12b^3 - 15ab^2)$

$= a(5a - 4b) + 3b^2(4b - 5a)$

$= a(5a - 4b) - 3b^2(5a - 4b)$

$= (a - 3b^2)(5a - 4b)$

29. $4ax - 14bx + 35by - 10ay$

$= (4ax - 14bx) + (35by - 10ay)$

$= 2x(2a - 7b) + 5y(7b - 2a)$

$= 2x(2a - 7b) - 5y(2a - 7b)$

$= (2x - 5y)(2a - 7b)$

30. $6a^2 - 6ab + 3cb - 3ca$

$= (6a^2 - 6ab) + (3cb - 3ca)$

$= 6a(a - b) + 3c(b - a)$

$= 6a(a - b) - 3c(a - b)$

$= (6a - 3c)(a - b)$

$= 3(2a - c)(a - b)$

31. $ax + a^2x - a - 2a^2$

$= (a^2x - 2a^2) + (ax - a)$

$= a(ax - 2a) + a(x - 1)$

$= a(ax - 2a + x - 1)$

32. $a^3 - a^2b + ab^2 - b^3$

$= (a^3 - a^2b) + (ab^2 - b^3)$

$= a^2(a - b) + b^2(a - b)$

$= (a^2 + b^2)(a - b)$

33. $2x^3 - 5xy^2 - 2x^2y + 5y^3$

$= (2x^3 - 5xy^2) + (-2x^2y + 5y^3)$

$= x(2x^2 - 5y^2) + y(5y^2 - 2x^2)$

$= x(2x^2 - 5y^2) - y(2x^2 - 5y^2)$

$= (x - y)(2x^2 - 5y^2)$

34. $5xy + 15x - 6y - 18$

$= (5xy + 15x) - (6y + 18)$

$= 5x(y + 3) - 6(y + 3)$

$= (5x - 6)(y + 3)$

The dimensions are $5x - 6$ cm by $y + 3$ cm.

35. $4z^2 - 24z - 18m + 3mz$

$= (4z^2 - 24z) - (18m - 3mz)$

$= 4z(z - 6) - 3m(6 - z)$

$= 4z(z - 6) + 3m(z - 6)$

$= (4z + 3m)(z - 6)$

The dimensions are $4z + 3m$ ft by $z - 6$ ft.

36. $zr + 6q + rq + 6z$

$= (zr + rq) + (6q + 6z)$

$= r(z + q) + 6(q + z)$

$= (r + 6)(z + q)$

37. $4ax + 3ay + 4bx + 3by$

$= (4ax + 4bx) + (3ay + 3by)$

$= 4x(a + b) + 3y(a + b)$

$= (4x + 3y)(a + b)$

38. $x^2 + ax + 5xy + 5ay$

$= (x^2 + ax) + (5xy + 5ay)$

$= x(x + a) + 5y(x + a)$

$= (x + 5y)(x + a)$

39. $7xa + 7xb + 3ma + 3mb - 4b - 4a$

$= (7xa + 3ma - 4a) + (7xb + 3mb - 4b)$

$= a(7x + 3m - 4) + b(7x + 3m - 4)$

$= (a + b)(7x + 3m - 4)$

40. $ax - ay - 4yb + 4xb + 5x - 5y$

$= (ax + 4sb + 5x) - (ay + 4yb + 5y)$

$= x(a + 4b + 5) - y(a + 4b + 5)$

$= (x - y)(a + 4b + 5)$

41. $2ax + bx - 6ay - 3by - bz - 2az$

$= (2ax - 6ay - 2az) + (bx - 3by - bz)$

$= 2a(x - 3y - z) + b(x - 3y - z)$

$= (2a + b)(x - 3y - z)$

42. $ar - 3ya + br - 3by + 3cy - rc$

$= (ar + br - rc) - (3ya + 3by - 3cy)$

$= r(a + b - c) - 3y(a + b - c)$

$= (r - 3y)(a + b - c)$

43. $A_1 = (x + 2y)(4xy + 1)$

    $A_2 = (x + 4xy)(2y + 1)$

    $A_3 = (x + 1)(2y + 4xy)$

        $= 2(x + 1)(y + 2xy)$

44. a. $96 = ②·②·②· 2 · 2 · 3$

      $56 = ②·②·②· 7$

      $72 = ②·②·②· 3 · 3$

      $2 · 2 · 2$ groups or 8 groups

   b. $\dfrac{96 + 56 + 72}{8}$

      $= 28$ students per group

45. Let $s$ = width of garden;

    $2s - 3$ = length of garden;

    $s + 8$ = width of garden and path.

    $A = (s + 8)(2s - 3)$

46. $5 - 2n < 3n$

    $-1 \longrightarrow 5 - 2(-1) \overset{?}{<} 3(-1)$

            $7 < 3$

    $0 \longrightarrow 5 - 2(0) \overset{?}{<} 3(0)$

            $5 < 0$

    $1 \longrightarrow 5 - 2(1) \overset{?}{<} 3(1)$

            $3 < 4$

    $2 \longrightarrow 5 - 2(2) \overset{?}{<} 3(2)$

            $1 < 6$

    $3 \longrightarrow 5 - 2(3) \overset{?}{<} 3(3)$

           $-1 < 9$

    $\{2, 3\}$

47. Let $x$ = original price.

    $x - 0.20x = 476.79$

    $x(1 - 0.20) = 476.79$

    $0.80x = 476.79$

    $x = \dfrac{476.79}{0.80}$

    $= 595.99$

   Original price is \$595.99.

48. 61

49. $(2x + 5)(3x - 8)$

    $= 6x^2 - 16x + 15x - 40$

    $= 6x^2 - x - 40$

50. $10x^4 = ②· 5 ·ⓧ·ⓧ· x · x$

    $6x^3y = ②· 3 ·ⓧ·ⓧ· x · y$

    $8x^2y^2 = ②· 2 · 2 ·ⓧ·ⓧ· y · y$

   The GCF is $2x^2$.

    $10x^4 - 6x^3y - 8x^2y^2$

    $= 2x^2(5x^2 - 3xy - 4y^2)$

---

7-4  **Problem-Solving Strategy:**
**Guess and Check**

PAGE 269   CHECKING FOR UNDERSTANDING

1. trial and error

2. You do not waste time by making the same guess twice. Also you can see patterns developing.

3. $4 · (5 - 2) + 7 = 19$

4. $25 - 4 · (2 + 3) = 5$

5.

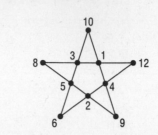

6. $(3 · 8 · 4) = 384$

   The number is 384.

7. 631, 542

PAGE 270   EXERCISES

8. Let $p$ = number of people.

   Let $e$ = number of elephants.

      $2p + 4e = 100$

      $3p + e = 100$

         $e = 100 - 3p$

   $2p + 4(100-3p) = 100$

   $2p + 400 - 12p = 100$

        $10p = 300$

          $p = 30$

          $e = 100 - 3p$

            $= 100 - 90 = 10$

   30 people and 10 elephants

9.
```
        3
   x   5 4
   1 6 2
```

10. 12, 30, 33, 40, 45, 50, 54, 56, 60, 70, 81, 88, 90

11. July 9 and September 7

PAGE 270   COOPERATIVE LEARNING ACTIVITY

1.

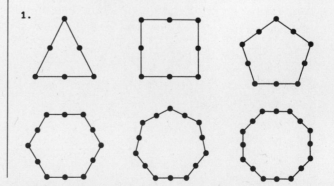

106

2.

| Figurate Number | Shape of Figure | $n$ | | | | | | | | | |
|---|---|---|---|---|---|---|---|---|---|---|---|
| | | 1 | 2 | 3 | 4 | 5 | 6 | 7 | 8 | 9 | 10 |
| triangular | 3-sided | 1 | 3 | 6 | 10 | 15 | 21 | 28 | 36 | 45 | 55 |
| square | 4-sided | 1 | 4 | 9 | 16 | 25 | 36 | 49 | 64 | 81 | 100 |
| pentagonal | 5-sided | 1 | 5 | 12 | 22 | 35 | 51 | 70 | 92 | 117 | 145 |
| hexagonal | 6-sided | 1 | 6 | 15 | 28 | 45 | 66 | 91 | 120 | 153 | 190 |
| heptagonal | 7-sided | 1 | 7 | 18 | 34 | 55 | 81 | 112 | 148 | 189 | 235 |
| octagonal | 8-sided | 1 | 8 | 21 | 40 | 65 | 96 | 133 | 176 | 225 | 280 |

3. $n = 1$, The numbers do not increase.

   $n = 2$, The numbers increase by 1 each time.

   $n = 3$, The numbers increase by 3 each time.

   $n = 4$, The numbers increase by 6 each time.

   $n = 5$, The numbers increase by 10 each time.

   $n = 6$, The numbers increase by 15 each time.

   $n = 7$, The numbers increase by 21 each time.

   $n = 8$, The numbers increase by 28 each time.

   $n = 9$, The numbers increase by 36 each time.

   $n = 10$, The numbers increase by 45 each time.

   The numbers in each column increase by the triangular number in the column directly to the left.

4. $n^2$

## 7-5  Factoring Trinomials

PAGE 274    CHECKING FOR UNDERSTANDING

1. product   2. 18   3. negative   4. prime   5. 2, 9

6. 2, 12   7. 2, 7   8. 9, -4   9. -2, -6

10. -15, 2   11. 10   12. 7   13. 9   14. $4r -$

15. $(x + 5)(x - 3)$     16. $(n - 3)(n - 5)$

17. $(b + 5)(b + 7)$     18. $(2x + 7)(x - 3)$

PAGES 274-275    EXERCISES

19. $- 3$                20. $4y +$

21. $2z, 3$              22. $3, 3n$

23. $(y + 3)(y + 9)$     24. $(a + 21)(a + 1)$

25. $(c + 3)(c - 1)$     26. prime

27. $(x - 8)(x + 3)$     28. $(3y + 5)(y + 1)$

29. $(7a + 1)(a + 3)$    30. $(4m - 3)(2m - 1)$

31. $(3y - 4)(2y - 1)$   32. $(2r + 7)(r - 2)$

33. $(2x + 3)(x - 4)$    34. $(2q + 3)(q - 6)$

35. prime                36. $(3m + 2)(2m + 5)$

37. $(9 - y)(4 - y)$     38. $(x - 5y)(x + y)$

39. $(a + 3b)(a - b)$    40. $(3x - 2y)(5x - y)$

41. $(3s + 2t)(s - 4t)$  42. $(3k + 5m)(3k + 5m)$

43. prime

44. $3x^2 + 14x + 15$

   $= (3x + 5)(x + 3)$

   So $(3x + 5 - 3)(x + 3 - 3)$

   $= (3x + 2)(x)$

   $= 3x^2 + 2x$

   Area of new rectangle is $3x^2 + 2xm^2$.

45. 7, -7, 11, -11          46. 5, -5, 7, -7

47. 12, -12

48. 10, -10, 11, -11, 14, -14, 25, -25

49. 1, -1, 11, -11, 19, -19, 41, -41

50. 4, -4, 7, -7, 11, -11, 17, -17, 28, -28, 59, -59

51. $40x^4 - 116x^3 + 84x^2$

   $= 4x^2(10x^2 - 29x + 21)$

   $= 4x^2(5x - 7)(2x - 3)$

52. $20a^4b - 59a^3b^2 + 42a^2b^3$

   $= a^2b(20a^2 - 59ab + 42b^2)$

   $= a^2b(4a - 7b)(5a - 6b)$

53. $2a^2x + 3a^2y - 14ax - 21ay + 24x + 36y$

   $= (2a^2x - 14ax + 24x) + (3a^2y - 21ay + 36y)$

   $= 2x(a^2 - 7a + 12) + 3y(a^2 - 7a + 12)$

   $= (2x + 3y)(a^2 - 7a + 12)$

   $= (2x + 3y)(a - 4)(a - 3)$

54. $4ax^2 - 12bx^2 - ax + 3bx - 18a + 54b$

   $= (4ax^2 - ax - 18a) - (12bx^2 - 3bx - 54b)$

   $= a(4x^2 - x - 18) - 3b(4x^2 - x - 18)$

   $= (a - 3b)(4x^2 - x - 18)$

   $= (a - 3b)(4x - 9)(x + 2)$

55. $A = \frac{1}{2}b \cdot h, \; b = \frac{2A}{h}$

   $b = \frac{2(7.5x^2 + 15.5x - 12)}{3x + 8}$

   $= \frac{15x^2 + 31x - 24}{3x + 8}$

   $= \frac{(3x + 8)(5x - 3)}{(3x + 8)} = 5x - 3$

   If $x = 1$, $5x - 3 = 5(1) - 3$

   $\qquad\qquad = 2$

   2 is the least possible measure of its base.

56. $V = \ell \cdot w \cdot h$

   $45x^2 - 174x + 144 = \ell \cdot w \cdot 3$

   $\ell \cdot w = \frac{45x^2 - 174x + 144}{3}$

   $= 15x^2 - 58x + 48$

   $= (3x - 8)(5x - 6)$

   If $x = 3$, $\ell \cdot w = 1 \cdot 9$

   $V = 1 \cdot 9 \cdot 3 = 27$ or 27 ft$^3$

57. Let $w$ = width;

   length = $w + 20$.

   $w(w + 20) = (w - 10)(w + 20 + 16)$

   $w^2 + 20w = w^2 + 26w - 360$

   $\qquad 6w = 360$

   $\qquad w = 60$

   Length = $w + 20 = 80$.

   60 $m$ by 80 $m$

107

**58.**

|        | Amount      | Yearly Interest       |
|--------|-------------|------------------------|
| At 5%  | $x$         | $0.05x$                |
| At 7%  | $11,700 - x$ | $0.07(11,700-x)$      |

$$0.05x + 0.07(11,000 - x) = 733$$
$$0.05x + 819 - 0.07x = 733$$
$$-0.02x + 819 = 733$$
$$0.02x = 86$$
$$x = 4300$$
$$11,700 - x = 11,700 - 4300 = 7400$$
$4300 at 5%; $7400 at 7%

**59.** $2n - 6 > n + 8.2$

$n > 14.2$

$\{n/n > 14.2\}$

**60.** $12x^6 y^8$

**61.** $x^2 - 15x + 10$

**62.** $15a + 6b + 10a^2 + 4ab$

$= (15a + 6b) + (10a^2 + 4ab)$

$= 3(5a + 2b) + 2a(5a + 2b)$

$= (3 + 2a)(5a + 2b)$

**63.** 60 guests

## 7-6 Factoring Differences of Squares

PAGE 278    CHECKING FOR UNDERSTANDING

1. Each term of the binomial is a perfect square, and the binomial can be written as a difference of terms.

2. Yes; write the binomial as a trinomial where the coefficient of the middle term is 0, and then factor this trinomial.

3. $\dfrac{15}{16} \cdot \dfrac{17}{16}$

$= \left(1 + \dfrac{1}{16}\right)\left(1 - \dfrac{1}{16}\right)$

$= 1^2 - \left(\dfrac{1}{16}\right)^2$

$= 1 - \dfrac{1}{256}$

$= \dfrac{255}{256}$

4. yes    5. yes    6. no    7. yes    8. no    9. yes

10. c    11. d    12. b    13. a

PAGES 279-280    EXERCISES

14. $(a - 3)(a + 3)$

15. $(x - 7)(x + 7)$

16. $(2x - 3y)(2x + 3y)$

17. $(x - 6y)(x + 6y)$

18. $(1 - 3y)(1 + 3y)$

19. $(4a - 3b)(4a + 3b)$

20. $(7 - ab)(7 + ab)$

21. prime

22. $4(2x^2 - 3y^2)$

23. $2(z^2 - 49)$

$= 2(z - 7)(z + 7)$

24. $12(a^2 - 4)$

$= 12(a - 2)(a + 2)$

25. $2(4x^2 - 9)$

$= 2(2x - 3)(2x + 3)$

26. $5(9x^2 - 4y^2z^2)$

$= 5(3x - 2yz)(3x + 2yz)$

27. $(5y - 7z^2)(5y + 7z^2)$

28. $17(1 - 4a^2)$

$= 17(1 - 2a)(1 + 2a)$

29. $(0.1n - 1.3r)(0.1n + 1.3r)$

30. $(ax - .8y)(ax + .8y)$

31. prime

32. $(3x^2 - 4y)(3x^2 + 4y)$

33. $(7x - 4)(7x + 4)$

34. $9(-x^2 + 9)$

$= 9(3 - x)(3 + x)$

35. $\left(\dfrac{1}{4}x - 5z\right)\left(\dfrac{1}{4}x + 5z\right)$

36. $\dfrac{1}{2}(3a - 7b)(3a + 7b)$

37. $\left(\dfrac{1}{2}n - 4\right)\left(\dfrac{1}{2}n + 4\right)$

38. $(a + b - m)(a + b + m)$

39. prime

40. $(x - y - y)(x - y + y)$

$= x(x - 2y)$

41. 4 and 1

$4 - 1 = 3$

$16 - 1 = 15$

The sum is 5.

42. $x^3 + x^2 - x - 1$

$= x(x^2 - 1) + (x^2 - 1)$

$= (x + 1)(x - 1)(x + 1)$

$x + 1, \ x - 1, \ x + 1$

43. $9a^3 + 18a^2 - 4a - 8$

$= 9a^2(a + 2) - 4(a + 2)$

$= (9a^2 - 4)(a + 2)$

$= (3a - 2)(3a + 2)(a + 2)$

$3a - 2, \ 3a + 2, \ a + 2$

44. $7mp^2 + 2np^2 - 7mr^2 - 2nr^2$

$= p^2(7m + 2n) - r^2(7m + 2n)$

$= (p^2 - r^2)(7m + 2n)$

$= (p - r)(p + r)(7m + 2n)$

45. $5a^3 - 125ab^2 - 75b^3 + 3a^2b$

$= 5a(a^2 - 25b^2) - 3b(25b^2 - a^2)$

$= 5a(a^2 - 25b^2) + 3b(a^2 - 25b^2)$

$= (5a + 3b)(a^2 - 25b^2)$

$= (5a + 3b)(a - 5b)(a + 5b)$

46. $(x^2 - y^2)(x^2 + y^2)$

$= (x - y)(x + y)(x^2 + y^2)$

47. $(4 - a^2)(4 + a^2)$

$= (2 - a)(2 + a)(4 + a^2)$

48. $(3x^2 - 5y^2)(3x^2 + 5y^2)$

49. $3x(16x^4 - y^4)$

$= 3x(4x^2 - y^2)(4x^2 + y^2)$

$= 3x(2x - y)(2x + y)(4x^2 + y^2)$

50. $3st(16s^4 - 81t^4)$

$= 3st(4s^2 - 9t^2)(4s^2 + 9t^2)$

$= 3st(2s - 3t)(2s + 3t)(4s^2 + 9t^2)$

51. $(x^4 - 1)(x^4 + 1)$

$= (x^2 - 1)(x^2 + 1)(x^4 + 1)$

$= (x - 1)(x + 1)(x^2 + 1)(x^4 + 1)$

**52.** Let $x$ = side of square;

$x + 5$ = length of rectangle;

$x - 5$ = width of rectangle.

**a.** $A(\text{square}) = x^2$

$A(\text{rectangle} = (x + 5)(x - 5)$

$= x^2 - 25 \text{ cm}^2$

The square has the greater area.

**b.** $x^2 - (x^2 - 25)$

$= x^2 - x^2 + 25 = 25 \text{ cm}^2$

**53.** $m = 6$, $n = 5$

**54.** $m = 8$, $n = 7$; $m = 4$, $n = 1$

**55.** $m = 9$, $n = 6$; $m = 7$, $n = 2$; $m = 23$, $n = 22$

**56.** $m = 11$, $n = 4$; $m = 13$, $n = 8$; $m = 19$, $n = 16$;

$m = 53$, $n = 52$

**57.** Let $x$ = side of original square.

$x^2 - 64 = (x - 4)(x - 2)$

$x^2 - 64 = x^2 - 6x + 8$

$6x = 72$

$x = 12$

Original dimensions were 12 in. by 12 in.

**58.**

|          | Amount    | Yearly Interest   |
|----------|-----------|-------------------|
| At 8.5%  | $x$       | $0.085x$          |
| At 7.5%  | $x + 800$ | $0.075(x + 800)$  |

$0.085x = 0.075(x + 800)$

$0.085x - 0.075x + 60$

$0.01x = 60$

$x = 6000$

$x + 800 = 6800$

Maria invested $6000.

Juanita invested $6800.

**59.** $\frac{8}{3}x = \frac{4}{9}$

$x = \frac{4}{9} \cdot \frac{3}{8}$

$= \frac{12}{72} = \frac{1}{6}$

**60.**

|          | $d$       | $r$ | $t$     |
|----------|-----------|-----|---------|
| To Beach | $42x$     | 42  | $x$     |
| To Home  | $56(7 - x)$ | 56 | $7 - x$ |

$42x = 56(7 - x)$

$42x = 392 - 56x$

$98x = 392$

$x = 4$

Distance is $4 \cdot 42$ or 168 miles.

**61.** $12x + 71 < 11$

$2x + 7 > -11 \qquad 2x + 7 < 11$

$2x > -18 \qquad\quad 2x < 4$

$x > -9 \qquad\qquad x < 2$

$\{x \mid -9 < x < 2\}$

**62.** $\dfrac{-8a^3b^7}{a^2b^6} = -8ab$

**63.** The degree is 7.

**64.** $(8x - 5)(2x + 3)$

---

**1.** $39a^2 = 3 \cdot 13 \cdot a \cdot a$

$13a^3 = 13 \cdot a \cdot a \cdot a$

The GCF is $13a^2$.

**2.** $64a^2c^2 = 2 \cdot 2 \cdot 2 \cdot 2 \cdot 2 \cdot 2 \cdot a \cdot a \cdot c \cdot c$

$4ab^2c^4 = 2 \cdot 2 \cdot a \cdot b \cdot b \cdot c \cdot c \cdot c \cdot c$

The GCF is $4ac^2$.

**3.** $55m^3n = 5 \cdot 11 \cdot m \cdot m \cdot m \cdot n$

$275m^5n^2 = 5 \cdot 5 \cdot 11 \cdot m \cdot m \cdot m \cdot m \cdot m \cdot n \cdot n$

$165m^2n^3 = 3 \cdot 5 \cdot 11 \cdot m \cdot m \cdot n \cdot n \cdot n$

The GCF is $55m^2n$.

**4.** $(y - 7)(y - 1)$

**5.** $25m^3n = 5 \cdot 5 \cdot m \cdot m \cdot m \cdot n$

$15m^2n^2 = 3 \cdot 5 \cdot m \cdot m \cdot n \cdot n$

The GCF is $5m^2n$.

$25m^3n + 15m^2n^2 = 5m^2n(5m + 3n)$

**6.** $(r + 6)(r - 3)$

**7.** Prime

**8.** $5a^3 = 5 \cdot a \cdot a \cdot a$

$45a^2 = 3 \cdot 3 \cdot 5 \cdot a \cdot a$

$15a = 3 \cdot 5 \cdot a$

The GCF is $5a$.

$5a^3 + 45a^2 - 15a = 5a(a^2 + 9a - 3)$

**9.** $(2p + 3)(3p - 1)$

**10.** $8(k^2 - 9z^2)$

$= 8(k - 3z)(k + 3z)$

**11.** $7a^2b^2 = 7 \cdot a \cdot a \cdot b \cdot b$

$77a^3b^2 = 7 \cdot 11 \cdot a \cdot a \cdot a \cdot b \cdot b$

$77ab^3 = 7 \cdot 11 \cdot a \cdot b \cdot b \cdot b$

The GCF is $7ab^2$.

$-7a^2b^2 - 77a^3b^2 + 77ab^3$

$= 7ab^2(-a - 11a^2 + 11b)$

**12.** $(5x - 14)(x - 1)$

**13.** $(y^2m + y^2n) - (4m + 4n)$

$= y^2(m + n) = 4(m + n)$

$= (y^2 - 4)(m + n)$

$= (y - 2)(y + 2)(m + n)$

**14.** $41,312,432$ or $23,421,314$

**15.** $4x^2 - 196$

$= (2x - 14)(2x + 14)$

$(2x - 14 + 9)(2x + 14 + 9)$

$= (2x - 5)(2x + 23)$

$= 4x^2 + 36x - 115$

Area of new rectangle is $4x^2 + 36x - 115 \text{ m}^2$.

1. 0, 1, 4, 5, 6, 9
2. No; a negative integer can never be a perfect square.
3. false   **4.** 5   **5.** 7   **6.** 12   **7.** $8b$
8. $9n$   **9.** $6x$   **10.** $a^2 + 4a + 4$
$$= a^2 + (2)(2)(a) + 4$$
$$= (a + 2)^2$$

11. no   **12.** no   **14.** $4x^2 - 4x + 1$
13. $b^2 - 14b + 49$   $\qquad = 4x^2 + (2)(2)(x) + 1$
$\quad = b^2 - (2)(7)(b) + 49$   $\quad = (2x + 1)^2$
$\quad = (b - 7)^2$

15. no

16. no   **17.** $p^2 + 12p + 36$
$$= p^2 + (2)(6)(p) + 36$$
$$= (p + 6)^2$$

18. $9b^2 - 6b + 1$
$$= 9b^2 - (2)(3)(b) + 1$$
$$= (3b - 1)^2$$

19. no   **20.** no

21. $4a^2 - 20a + 25$
$$= 4a^2 - (2)(10)(a) + 25$$
$$= (2a - 5)^2$$

22. $x^2 + 16x + 64$
$$= x^2 + (2)(8)(x) + 64$$
$$= (x + 8)^2$$

23. $n^2 - 8m + 16$
$$= n^2 - (2)(4)(n) + 16$$
$$= (n - 4)^2$$

24. $a^2 + 22a + 121$
$$= a^2 + (2)(11)(a) + 121$$
$$= (a + 11)^2$$

25. $4k^2 - 4k + 1$
$$= 4k^2 - (2)(2)(k) + 1$$
$$= (2k - 1)^2$$

26. $100x^2 + 20x + 1$
$$= 100x^2 + (2)(10)(x) + 1$$
$$= (10x + 1)^2$$

27. prime   **28.** prime

29. $1 - 10z + 25z^2$
$$= 1 - (2)(5)(z) + 25z^2$$
$$= (1 - 5z)^2$$

30. $4 - 28r + 49r^2$
$$= 4 - (2)(14)(r) + 49r^2$$
$$= (2 - 7r)^2$$

31. $50x^2 + 40x + 8$
$$= 2(25x^2 + 20x + 4)$$
$$= 2[25x^2 + (2)(10)(x) + 4]$$
$$= 2(5x + 2)^2$$

32. $18a^2 - 48a + 32$
$$= 2(9a^2 - 24a + 16)$$
$$= 2[9a^2 - (2)(12)(a) + 16]$$
$$= 2(3a - 4)^2$$

33. $49m^2 - 126m + 81$   $\qquad$   **34.** prime
$$= 49m^2 - (2)(63)(m) + 81$$
$$= (7m - 9)^2$$

35. $25x^2 - 120x + 144$
$$= 25x^2 - (2)(60)(x) + 144$$
$$= (5x - 12)^2$$

36. $9x^2 + 24xy + 16y^2$
$$= 9x^2 + (2)(12)xy + 16y^2$$
$$= (3x + 4y)^2$$

37. $m^2 + 16mn + 64n^2$
$$= m^2 + (2)(8)mn + 64n^2$$
$$= (m + 8n)^2$$

38. $16p^2 - 40pr + 25r^2$
$$= 16p^2 - (2)(20)pr + 25r^2$$
$$= (4p - 5r)^2$$

39. $4x^2 + 4xz^2 + z^4$
$$= 4x^2 + (2)(2)xz^2 + z^4$$
$$= (2x + z^2)^2$$

40. $16m^4 - 72m^2n^2 + 81n^4$
$$= 16m^4 - (2)(36)m^2n^2 + 81n^4$$
$$= (4m^2 - 9n^2)^2$$
$$= (2m - 3n)^2 (2m + 3n)^2$$

41. $\frac{1}{4}a^2 + 3a + 9$
$$= \frac{1}{4}a^2 + (2)\left(\frac{3}{2}\right)(a) + 9$$
$$= \left(\frac{1}{2}a + 3\right)^2$$

42. $\frac{4}{9}x^2 - \frac{16}{3}x + 16$
$$= \frac{4}{9}x^2 - (2)\left(\frac{8}{3}\right)(x) + 16$$
$$= \left(\frac{2}{3}x - 4\right)^2$$

43. $121y^2 + 22y + 1$
$$= 121y^2 + (2)(11)(y) + 1$$
$$= (11y + 1)^2$$
side = $11y + 1$

44. $64x^2 - 80x + 25$   $\qquad$   **45.** no
$$= 64x^2 - (2)(40)(x) + 25$$
$$= (8x - 5)^2$$
side = $8x - 5$

46. $4b^2 - 24bc + 36c^2$   $\qquad$   **47.** $c = 4$
$$= 4b^2 - (2)(12)bc + 36c^2$$
$$= (2b - 6c)^2$$
side = $2(b - 3c)$

**48.** $c = 100$ **49.** $c = 4b^2$ **50.** $c = 42; -42$

**51.** $c = 40; -40$ **52.** $c = y^2$

**53.** $a^2 + 4a + 4 - 9b^2$
$= (a + 2)^2 - 9b^2$
$= (a + 2 - 3b)(a + 2 + 3b)$

**54.** $x^2 + 2xy + y^2 - r^2$
$= (x + y)^2 - r^2$
$= (x + y - r)(x + y + r)$

**55.** $m^2 - k^2 + 6k - 9$
$= m^2 - (k - 3)^2$
$= (m - k + 3)(m + k - 3)$

**56.** $16 - 9x^2 - 12xz - 4z^2$
$= 16 - (3x + 2z)^2$
$= (4 - 3x - 2z)(4 + 3x + 2z)$

**57.** $a^2m - 2a^2 + 6am - 12a + 9m - 18$
$= (a^2m + 6am + 9m) - (2a^2 + 12a + 18)$
$= m(a^2 + 6a + 9) - 2(a^2 + 6a + 9)$
$= m(a + 3)^2 - 2(a + 3)^2$
$= (m - 2)(a + 3)^2$

**58.** $8ay^2 + 12y^2 + 40ay + 60y + 50a + 75$
$= (8ay^2 + 40ay + 50a) + (12y^2 + 60y + 75)$
$= 2a(4y^2 + 20y + 25) + 3(4y^2 + 20y + 25)$
$= 2a(2y + 5)^2 + 3(2y + 5)^2$
$= (2a + 3)(2y + 5)^2$

**59.** $A = \pi r^2$
$(9y^2 + 78y + 169)\pi = \pi r^2$
$r^2 = 9y^2 + 78y + 169$
$r^2 = (3y + 13)^2$
$r = 3y + 13$
$d = 2 \cdot r = 2(3y + 13)$
$= 6y + 26$

**60.** $25x^2 - 90x + 81$
$= (5x - 9)^2$
Length of side is $5x - 9$.
If $x = 2$, $5x - 9 = 5(2) - 9 = 1$
Smallest possible perimeter is $4 \cdot 1 = 4$.

**61.** Let $x$ = side of frame.
$x^2 - 184 = (x - 4)^2$
$x^2 - 184 = x^2 - 8x + 16$
$8x - 200 = 0$
$8(x - 25) = 0$
$x = 25$
$x - 4 = 25 - 4 = 21$
Dimensions of photo are 21 in. by 21 in.

**62.** Let $w$ = original width;
$w + 60$ = original length.
$w(w + 60) = w^2 + 60w$ = original area
$w^2 + 60w + 900$ = new area
$= (w + 30)^2$
Length of side is $(w + 30)$ yards.

**63.** $0.40 \cdot x = 15$
$x = \dfrac{15}{0.40}$
$x = \dfrac{75}{2}$

**64.** $\dfrac{8}{264} = \dfrac{1}{33}$ gal/mile
$500 \cdot \dfrac{1}{33} = \dfrac{500}{33} = 15\dfrac{5}{33}$ gal

**65.** 7, 8, 9      **66.** $(3x - 2)(3x + 2)$
$= 9x^2 - 6x + 6x - 4$
$= 9x^2 - 4$

**67.** $(8t - 3)(2t + 5)$
$= 16t^2 - 6t + 40t - 15$
$= 16t^2 + 34t - 15$

**68.** $5(x^2 - 16y^4)$
$= 5(x - 4y^2)(x + 4y^2)$

**69.** $15x^3y^4 = 2 \cdot \boxed{3} \cdot \boxed{5} \cdot x \cdot \boxed{x} \cdot \boxed{x} \cdot \boxed{y} \cdot y \cdot y \cdot y$
$30x^2yz = 2 \cdot \boxed{3} \cdot \boxed{5} \cdot \boxed{x} \cdot \boxed{x} \cdot \boxed{y} \cdot z$
The GCF is $15x^2y$.
$15x^3y^4 - 30x^2yz = 15x^2y(xy^3 - 2z)$

## Technology: Factoring

**PAGE 285   EXERCISES**

**1.** $16xy$   **2.** $5x$   **3.** $4(3x - 4)(3x + 4)$   **4.** $(5y + 1)^2$

**5.** $(3z - 5)(3z + 5)(9z^2 + 25)$   **6.** $a(4a - 1)(9a + 1)$

### ⬛ 7-8   Summary of Factoring

**PAGE 288   CHECKING FOR UNDERSTANDING**

**1.** GCF   **2.** trinomial   **3.** 4 or more   **4.** prime

**5.** greatest common factor

**6.** difference of squares

**7.** perfect square trinomial

**8.** greatest common factor

**9.** trinomial that has two binomial factors

**10.** pairs of terms that have a common monomial factor

**11.** $3(x^2 + 5)$      **12.** $mn(8n - 13m)$

**13.** $(a - 3b)(a + 3b)$      **14.** $(x - 3)(x - 2)$

**15.** $(a + 4)^2$      **16.** $3ab(a + 2 + 3b)$

**PAGES 288-289   EXERCISES**

**17.** $12a^2 + 18ay^2$      **18.** $2a^2 - 72$
$= 6a(2a + 3y^2)$          $= 2(a^2 - 36)$
                      $= 2(a - 6)(a + 6)$

**19.** $3y^2 - 147$      **20.** $2k^2 + 3k + 1$
$= 3(y^2 - 49)$          $= (2k + 1)(k + 1)$
$= 3(y - 7)(y + 7)$

**21.** $m^3 + 6m^2 + 9m$      **22.** $2y^3 + 12y^2 + 18y$
$= m(m^2 + 6m + 9)$      $= 2y(y^2 + 6y + 9)$
$= m(m + 3)^2$          $= 2y(y + 3)^2$

23. $6r^2 + 13r + 6$

$\quad = (2r + 3)(3r + 2)$

24. $4x^3 - 3x^2 - 12x + 9$

$\quad = (4x^3 - 3x^2) - (12x - 9)$

$\quad = x^2(4x - 3) - 3(4x - 3)$

$\quad = (x^2 - 3)(4x - 3)$

25. $m^4 - p^2$

$\quad = (m^2 - p)(m^2 + p)$

26. $4a^3 - 36a$

$\quad = 4a(a^2 - 9)$

$\quad = 4a(a - 3)(a + 3)$

27. $3x^3 - 27x$

$\quad = 3x(x^2 - 9)$

$\quad = 3x(x - 3)(x + 3)$

28. $3y^2 + 21y - 24$

$\quad = 3(y^2 + 7y - 8)$

$\quad = 3(y - 1)(y + 8)$

29. $20n^2 + 34n + 6$

$\quad = 2(10n^2 + 17n + 3)$

$\quad = 2(2n + 3)(5n + 1)$

30. $m^2 + 8mn + 16n^2$

$\quad = (m + 4n)^2$

31. $4a^2 + 12ab + 9b^2$

$\quad = (2a + 3b)^2$

32. $4y^3 - 12y^2 + 8y$

$\quad = 4y(y^2 - 3y + 2)$

$\quad = 4y(y - 2)(y - 1)$

33. $9t^3 + 66t^2 - 48t$

$\quad = 3t(3t^2 + 22t - 16)$

$\quad = 3t(3t - 2)(t + 8)$

34. $a^2b^3 - 25b$

$\quad = b(a^2b^2 - 25)$

$\quad = b(ab - 5)(ab + 5)$

35. $m^3n^2 - 49m$

$\quad = m(m^2n^2 - 49)$

$\quad = m(mn - 7)(mn + 7)$

36. $0.4r^2 + 1.6r + 1.6$

$\quad = 0.4(r^2 + 4r + 4)$

$\quad = 0.4(r + 2)^2$

37. $0.7y^2 - 3.5y + 4.2$

$\quad = 0.7(y^2 - 5y + 6)$

$\quad = 0.7(y - 3)(y - 2)$

38. $\frac{1}{3}b^2 + 2b + 3$

$\quad = \frac{1}{3}(b^2 + 6b + 9)$

$\quad = \frac{1}{3}(b + 3)^2$

39. $m^2 + \frac{5}{12}m - \frac{1}{6}$

$\quad = \frac{1}{12}(12m^2 + 5m - 2)$

$\quad = \frac{1}{12}(3m + 2)(4m - 1)$

40. $\frac{1}{4}x^2 + \frac{3}{2}x + 2$

$\quad = \frac{1}{4}(x^2 + 6x + 8)$

$\quad = \frac{1}{4}(x + 2)(x + 4)$

41. $x^3y + 2x^2 + 8xy + 16$

$\quad = (x^3y + 2x^2) + (8xy + 16)$

$\quad = x^2(xy + 2) + 8(xy + 2)$

$\quad = (x^2 + 8)(xy + 2)$

42. $4a^3 + 3a^2b^2 + 8a + 6b^2$

$\quad = (4a^3 + 3a^2b^2) + (8a + 6b^2)$

$\quad = a^2(4a + 3b^2) + 2(4a + 3b^2)$

$\quad = (a^2 + 2)(4a + 3b^2)$

43. $x^2y^2 - z^2 - y^2 + x^2z^2$

$\quad = (x^2y^2 - y^2) + (x^2z^2 - z^2)$

$\quad = y^2(x^2 - 1) + z^2(x^2 - 1)$

$\quad = (y^2 + z^2)(x^2 - 1)$

$\quad = (y^2 + z^2)(x - 1)(x + 1)$

44. $20a^2x - 4a^2y - 45xb^2 + 9yb^2$

$\quad = (20a^2x - 4a^2y) - (45xb^2 - 9yb^2)$

$\quad = 4a^2(5x - y) - 9b^2(5x - y)$

$\quad = (4a^2 - 9b^2)(5x - y)$

$\quad = (2a - 3b)(2a + 3b)(5x - y)$

45. $(x + y)^2 - (a - b)^2$

$\quad = (x + y - a + b)(x + y + a - b)$

46. $x^2 + 6x + 9 - y^2$

$\quad = (x + 3)^2 - y^2$

$\quad = (x + 3 - y)(x + 3 + y)$

47. $(x + 1)^2 - 3(x + 1) + 2$

$\quad = (x + 1 - 2)(x + 1 - 1)$

$\quad = x(x - 1)$

48. $(2x - 3)^2 - 4(2x - 3) - 5$

$\quad = (2x - 3 - 5)(2x - 3 + 1)$

$\quad = (2x - 8)(2x - 2)$

$\quad = 4(x - 4)(x - 1)$

49. $x^4 + 6x^3 + 9x^2 - 3x^2y - 18xy - 27y$

$\quad = (x^4 + 6x^3 + 9x^2) - (3x^2y + 18xy + 27y)$

$\quad = x^2(x^2 + 6x + 9) - 3y(x^2 + 6x + 9)$

$\quad = (x^2 - 3y)(x + 3)^2$

50. $12mp^2 - 15np^2 - 16m + 20np - 16mp + 20n$

$\quad = (12mp^2 - 16mp - 16m) - (15mp^2 - 20np - 20n)$

$\quad = 4m(3p^2 - 4p - 4) - 5n(3p^2 - 4p - 4)$

$\quad = (4m - 5n)(3p^2 - 4p - 4)$

$\quad = (4m - 5n)(3p + 2)(p - 2)$

51. $x^3y - 63y^2 + 7x^2 - 9xy^3$

$\quad = (x^3y + 7x^2) - (9xy^3 + 63y^2)$

$\quad = x^2(xy + 7) - 9y^2(xy + 7)$

$\quad = (x^2 - 9y^2)(xy + 7)$

$\quad = (x - 3y)(x + 3y)(xy + 7)$

Dimensions are $x - 3y$ by $x + 3y$ by $xy + 7$.

52. 24, 30, 54, 60, 84

53.

$\qquad w = $ original width

$\qquad w + 12 = $ original length

$\qquad w(w + 12) = $ original area

$(w + 2)(w + 12 - 5) = w(w + 12) - 55$

$\quad (w + 2)(w + 7) = w(w = 12) - 55$

$\quad w^2 + 9w + 14 = w^2 + 12w - 55$

$\qquad\qquad 3w = 69$

$\qquad\qquad w = \frac{69}{3} = 23$

$\qquad w + 12 = 23 + 12 = 35$

Original dimensions were 23 by 35.

54. a. 4

b. $\frac{32 + 24 + 20}{4} = \frac{76}{4} = 19$

1 extra seat at each meeting.

55. Increase is \$25.

$\qquad 85x = 25$

$\qquad x = \frac{25}{85}$

$\qquad\quad = \frac{5}{17}$

$\qquad\quad = .294$

Increase is 29.4%.

56. $50 - 2(14.20)$
    $= \$21.60$

57.

| Team | Teams to Play |
|------|---------------|
| 1 | 2, 3, 4, 5, 6, 7, 8 |
| 2 | 3, 4, 5, 6, 7, 8 |
| 3 | 4, 5, 6, 7, 8 |
| 4 | 5, 6, 7, 8 |
| 5 | 6, 7, 8 |
| 6 | 7, 8 |
| 7 | 8 |
| 8 | |

28 games

58. $-0.008x^9y^3$

59. $\dfrac{4a^{-2}b^4}{4a^{-3}b}$

$= \dfrac{a^3b^3}{a^2}$

$= ab^3$

60. $9s^2 - 42s + 49$
    $= (3s - 7)^2$

Perimeter $= 4(3s - 7)$
$= 12s - 28$

## 7-9    Solving Equations by Factoring

PAGE 293    CHECKING FOR UNDERSTANDING

1. For all numbers $a$ and $b$, if $ab = 0$, then $a = 0$, $b = 0$, or both $a$ and $b$ equal 0.

2. At least one of the factors must equal 0.

3. No; when solving an equation you should not divide by expressions that contain a variable because you may be dividing by 0.

4. $x = 0$ or $x + 3 = 0$

5. $3r = 0$ or $r - 4 = 0$

6. $3t = 0$ or $4t - 32 = 0$

7. $x - 6 = 0$ or $x + 4 = 0$

8. $2y + 8 = 0$ or $3y + 24 = 0$

9. $4x - 7 = 0$ or $3x + 5 = 0$

10. $n = 0$ or $n - 3 = 0$
    $n = 3$
    The solution set is $\{0, 3\}$.

11. $8c = 0$ or $c + 4 = 0$
    $c = 0$     $c = -4$
    The solution set is $\{0, -4\}$.

12. $3x\left(x - \dfrac{1}{4}\right) = 0$
    $3x = 0$    or    $x - \dfrac{1}{4} = 0$
    $x = 0$         $x = \dfrac{1}{4}$
    The solution set is $\left\{0, \dfrac{1}{4}\right\}$.

13. $7y(y - 2) = 0$
    $7y = 0$    or    $y - 2 = 0$
    $y = 0$         $y = 2$
    The solution set is $\{0, 2\}$.

14. $4a(2a + 1) = 0$
    $4a = 0$    or    $2a + 1 = 0$
    $a = 0$         $2a = -1$
                     $a = -\dfrac{1}{2}$
    The solution set is $\left\{0, -\dfrac{1}{2}\right\}$.

15. $13x(2x - 1)$
    $13x = 0$    or    $2x - 1 = 0$
    $x = 0$         $2x = 1$
                     $x = \dfrac{1}{2}$
    The solution set is $\left\{0, \dfrac{1}{2}\right\}$.

**PAGES 293-294    EXERCISES**

16. $y = 0$    or    $y - 12 = 0$
                     $y = 12$
    The solution set is $\{0, 12\}$.

17. $7a = 0$    or    $a + 6 = 0$
    $a = 0$         $a = -6$
    The solution set is $\{-6, 0\}$.

18. $2x = 0$    or    $5x - 10 = 0$
    $x = 0$         $5x = 10$
                     $x = 2$
    The solution set is $\{0, 2\}$.

19. $b - 3 = 0$    or    $b - 5 = 0$
    $b = 3$         $b = 5$
    The solution set is $\{3, 5\}$.

20. $t - 5 = 0$    or    $t + 5 = 0$
    $t = 5$         $t = -5$
    The solution set is $\{-5, 5\}$.

21. $4x + 4 = 0$    or    $2x + 6 = 0$
    $4x = -4$         $2x = -6$
    $x = -1$         $x = -3$
    The solution set is $\{-1, -3\}$.

22. $p - 8 = 0$    or    $2p + 7 = 0$
    $p = 8$         $2p = -7$
                     $p = -\dfrac{7}{2}$
    The solution set is $\left\{-\dfrac{7}{2}, 8\right\}$.

23. $3x - 5 = 0$
    $3x = 5$
    $x = \dfrac{5}{3}$
    The solution set is $\left\{\dfrac{5}{3}\right\}$.

24. $x(x - 6) = 0$
    $x = 0$    or    $x - 6 = 0$
                     $x = 6$
    The solution set is $\{0, 6\}$.

25. $m(m + 36) = 0$

$m = 0$      or      $m + 36 = 0$

$m = -36$

The solution set is {-36, 0}.

26. $2x(x + 2) = 0$

$2x = 0$      or      $x + 2 = 0$

$x = 0$          $x = -2$

The solution set is {-2, 0}.

27. $4s(s + 9) = 0$

$4s = 0$      or      $s + 9 = 0$

$s = 0$          $s = -9$

The solution set is {-9, 0}.

28. $y^2 - 7y = 0$

$y(y - 7) = 0$

$y = 0$      or      $y - 7 = 0$

$y = 7$

The solution set is {0, 7}.

29. $x^2 + 8x = 0$

$x(x + 8) = 0$

$x = 0$      or      $x + 8 = 0$

$x = -8$

The solution set is {-8, 0}.

30. $3y^2 + 6y = 0$

$3x(y + 2) = 0$

$3y = 0$      or      $y + 2 = 0$

$y = 0$          $y = -2$

The solution set is {-2, 0}.

31. $z^2 + 5z = 0$

$z(z + 5) = 0$

$z = 0$      or      $z + 5 = 0$

$z = -5$

The solution set is {-5, 0}.

32. $\frac{1}{2}y\left(y - \frac{1}{2}\right) = 0$

$\frac{1}{2}y = 0$      or      $y - \frac{1}{2} = 0$

$y = 0$          $y = \frac{1}{2}$

The solution set is $\left\{0, \frac{1}{2}\right\}$.

33. $\frac{1}{3}x(x - 2) = 0$

$\frac{1}{3}x = 0$      or      $x - 2 = 0$

$x = 0$          $x = 2$

The solution set is {0, 2}.

34. $\frac{5}{6}x^2 - \frac{2}{3}x = 0$

$\frac{1}{6}x(5x - 4) = 0$

$\frac{1}{6}x = 0$      or      $5x - 4 = 0$

$x = 0$          $5x = 4$

$x = \frac{4}{5}$

The solution set is $\left\{0, \frac{4}{5}\right\}$.

35. $\frac{3}{4}a^2 - \frac{1}{8}a = 0$

$\frac{1}{8}a(6a - 1) = 0$

$\frac{1}{8}a = 0$      or      $6a - 1 = 0$

$a = 0$          $6a = 1$

$a = \frac{1}{6}$

The solution set is $\left\{0, \frac{1}{6}\right\}$.

36. $(x - 5)(x + 7) = 0$

$x - 5 = 0$      or      $x + 7 = 0$

$x = 5$          $x = -7$

The number is -7.

37. $(2x - 32)(5x + 6) = 0$

$2x - 32 = 0$      or      $5x + 6 = 0$

$2x = 32$          $5x = -6$

$x = 16$          $x = -\frac{6}{5}$

Randy is 16 years old.

38. Let $n$ = the number.

$8n - n^2 = 2n$

$n^2 - 6n = 0$

$n(n - 6) = 0$

$n = 0$      or      $n - 6 = 0$

$n = 6$

The number is 0 or 6.

39. Let $n$ = 1st integer.

$n + 1$ = next consecutive integer.

$n + (n + 1)^2 = 1$

$n + n^2 + 2n + 1 = 1$

$n^2 + 3n = 0$

$n(n + 3) = 0$

$n = 0$      or      $n + 3 = 0$

$n = -3$

1st integer is 0, next consecutive integer is 1; or 1st integer is -3, next consecutive integer is -2.

40. $x(x - 7)(x + 3) = 0$

$x(x^2 + 3x - 7x - 21) = 0$

$x(x^2 - 4x - 21) = 0$

$x^3 - 4x^2 - 21x = 0$

41. Let $w$ = original width.

$3w^2 = w(w + 18)$

$3w^2 = w^2 + 18w$

$2w^2 - 18w = 0$

$2w(w - 9) = 0$

$2w = 0$      or      $w - 9 = 0$

$w = 0$          $w = 9$

The original dimensions were 9 ft by 9 ft.

**42.** Let $w$ = original width;

$3w - 10$ = original length.

$(w - 15)(3w - 10 - 35) = 675$

$(w - 15)(3w - 45) = 675$

$3w^2 - 45w - 45w + 675 = 675$

$3w^2 - 90w = 0$

$3w(w - 30) = 0$

$3w = 0$ or $w - 30 = 0$

$w = 0$ $\qquad\qquad w = 30$

The original dimensions are 30 yd by 80 yd.

**43.** $192t - 16t^2 = 0$

$16t(12 - t) = 0$

$16t = 0$ or $12 - t = 0$

$t = 0$ $\qquad\qquad t = 12$

12 seconds

**44.** $120t - 16t^2 = 0$

$8t(15 - 2t) = 0$

$8t = 0$ or $15 - 2t = 0$

$t = 0$ $\qquad\qquad 15 = 2t$

$\qquad\qquad\qquad t = \dfrac{15}{2} = 7\dfrac{1}{2}$

$7\dfrac{1}{2}$ seconds

**45.** $x + y = 167$, $x = 167 - y$

$255x + 198y = 40{,}191$

$255(167 - y) + 198y = 40{,}191$

$42{,}535 - 255y + 198y = 40{,}191$

$42{,}585 - 57y = 40{,}191$

$57y = 2394$

$y = 42$

$x = 167 - 10 = 106$

125 first class tickets

**46.** $-\dfrac{5s}{8} \geq \dfrac{15}{4}$

$-10s \geq 60$

$s \leq -6$

**47.** $8mn^2 + 3mn - n - 3n^3$

**48.** $2700 = 2 \cdot 2 \cdot 3 \cdot 3 \cdot 3 \cdot 5 \cdot 5$

**49.** $0$, $6$, $-6$, $15$, $-15$

**50.** $12c^2 + 10cd - 42d^2$

$= 2(6c^2 + 5cd - 21d^2)$

$= 2(2c - 3d)(3c + 7d)$

## 7-10  More Solving Equations by Factoring

PAGE 297    CHECKING FOR UNDERSTANDING

**1.** When the equation can be written as a product of factors equal to 0.

**2.** A solution to the equation may not be a reasonable answer to the original problem. Also, you may have written an incorrect equation.

**3.** $35 = (8 - x)(6 - x)$

$35 = 48 - 14x + x^2$

$x^2 - 14x + 13 = 0$

$(x - 13)(x - 1) = 0$

$x - 13 = 0$ or $x - 1 = 0$

$x = 13$ $\qquad\qquad x = 1$

The solution set is $\{1, 13\}$.

She should reduce the original length and width by 1 cm.

**4.** $(a - 3)(a + 7) = 0$

$a - 3 = 0$ or $a + 7 = 0$

$a = 3$ $\qquad\qquad a = -7$

The solution set is $\{-7, 3\}$.

**5.** $(2y + 1)(y + 2) = 0$

$2y + 1 = 0$ or $y + 2 = 0$

$2y = -1$ $\qquad\qquad y = -2$

$y = -\dfrac{1}{2}$

The solution set is $\left\{-2, -\dfrac{1}{2}\right\}$.

**6.** $(2m - 1)(5m + 3) = 0$

$2m - 1 = 0$ or $5m + 3 = 0$

$2m = 1$ $\qquad\qquad 5m = -3$

$m = \dfrac{1}{2}$ $\qquad\qquad m = -\dfrac{3}{5}$

The solution set is $\left\{-\dfrac{3}{5}, \dfrac{1}{2}\right\}$.

**7.** $(y - 4)(y + 4) = 0$

$y - 4 = 0$ or $y + 4 = 0$

$y = 4$ $\qquad\qquad y = -4$

The solution set is $\{-4, 4\}$.

**8.** $7x^2 - 70x + 175 = 0$

$(7x - 35)(x - 5) = 0$

$7x - 35 = 0$ or $x - 5 = 0$

$7x = 35$ $\qquad\qquad x = 5$

$x = 5$

The solution set is $\{5\}$.

**9.** $x^3 + 29x^2 + 28x = 0$

$x(x^2 + 29x + 28) = 0$

$x(x + 28)(x + 1) = 0$

$x = 0$ or $x + 28 = 0$ or $x + 1 = 0$

$\qquad\qquad x = -28$ $\qquad\qquad x = -1$

The solution set is $\{-28, -1, 0\}$.

**10.** Let $n$ = 1st consecutive integer.

$n(n + 1) = 110$

**11.** Let $x$ = one of the integers.

$x(15 - x) = 44$

**12.** Let $w$ = width.

$w(w + 3) = 40$

**13.** Let $x$ = amount length and width are increased.

$(4 + x)(7 + x) = 28 + 26$

14. $(x + 4)(x + 9) = 0$

$x + 4 = 0$     or     $x + 9 = 0$

    $x = -4$           $x = -9$

The solution set is $\{-9, -4\}$.

15. $(a + 8)(a - 7) = 0$

$a + 8 = 0$     or     $a - 7 = 0$

    $a = -8$           $a = 7$

The solution set is $\{-8, 7\}$.

16. $(b - 11)(b + 3) = 0$

$b - 11 = 0$     or     $b + 3 = 0$

    $b = 11$           $b = -3$

The solution set is $\{-3, 11\}$.

17. $(y - 8)(y + 8) = 0$

$y - 8 = 0$     or     $y + 8 = 0$

    $y = 8$           $y = -8$

The solution set is $\{-8, 8\}$.

18. $(c - 12)(c - 5) = 0$

$c - 12 = 0$     or     $c - 5 = 0$

    $c = 12$           $c = 5$

The solution set is $\{5, 12\}$.

19. $(m - 12)(m - 12) = 0$

$m - 12 = 0$

    $m = 12$

The solution set is $\{12\}$.

20. $p^2 - 5p - 24 = 0$

$(p - 8)(p + 3) = 0$

$p - 8 = 0$     or     $p + 3 = 0$

    $p = 8$           $p = -3$

The solution set is $\{-3, 8\}$.

21. $r^2 - 7r - 18 = 0$

$(r - 9)(r + 2) = 0$

$r - 9 = 0$     or     $r + 2 = 0$

    $r = 9$           $r = -2$

The solution set is $\{-2, 9\}$

22. $6z^2 + 17z + 5 = 0$

$(3z + 1)(2z + 5) = 0$

$3z + 1 = 0$     or     $2z + 5 = 0$

    $3z = -1$           $2z = -5$

    $z = -\dfrac{1}{3}$           $z = -\dfrac{5}{2}$

The solution set is $\left\{-\dfrac{5}{2}, -\dfrac{1}{3}\right\}$.

23. $3y^2 + 16y - 35 = 0$

$(3y - 5)(y + 7) = 0$

$3y - 5 = 0$     or     $y + 7 = 0$

    $3y = 5$           $y = -7$

    $y = \dfrac{5}{3}$

The solution set is $\left\{-7, \dfrac{5}{3}\right\}$.

24. $\dfrac{1}{12}(x^2 - 8x - 48) = 0$

$\dfrac{1}{12}(x - 12)(x + 4) = 0$

$x - 12 = 0$     or     $x + 4 = 0$

    $x = 12$           $x = -4$

The solution set is $\{-4, 12\}$.

25. $\dfrac{1}{6}(6x^2 - x - 35) = 0$

$\dfrac{1}{6}(3x + 7)(2x - 5) = 0$

$3x + 7 = 0$     or     $2x - 5 = 0$

    $3x = -7$           $2x = 5$

    $x - -\dfrac{7}{3}$           $x = \dfrac{5}{2}$

The solution set is $\left\{-\dfrac{7}{3}, \dfrac{5}{2}\right\}$.

26. $m(m^2 - 81) = 0$

$m(m - 9)(m + 9) = 0$

$m = 0$    or    $m - 9 = 0$    or    $m + 9 = 0$

           $m = 9$           $m = -9$

The solution set is $\{-9, 0, 9\}$.

27. $5b^3 + 34b^2 - 7b = 0$

$b(5b^2 + 34b - 7) = 0$

$b(5b - 1)(b + 7) = 0$

$b = 0$    or    $5b - 1 = 0$    or    $b + 7 = 0$

           $5b = 1$           $b = -7$

           $b = \dfrac{1}{5}$

The solution set is $\left\{-7, 0, \dfrac{1}{5}\right\}$.

28. $81n^3 + 36n^2 + 4n = 0$

$n(81n^2 + 36n + 4) = 0$

$n(9n + 2)^2 = 0$

$n = 0$     or     $9n + 2 = 0$

           $9n = -2$

           $n = -\dfrac{2}{9}$

The solution set is $\left\{-\dfrac{2}{9}, 0\right\}$.

29. $x^2 + 9x + 20 = 0$

$(x + 4)(x + 5) = 0$

$x + 4 = 0$     or     $x + 5 = 0$

    $x = -4$           $x = -5$

The solution set is $\{-5, -4\}$.

30. $r^2 - 2r - 35 = 0$

$(r - 7)(r + 5) = 0$

$r - 7 = 0$     or     $r + 5 = 0$

    $r = 7$           $r = -5$

The solution set is $\{-5, 7\}$.

31. $3y^2 + 10y - 8 = 0$

$(3y - 2)(y + 4) = 0$

$3y - 2 = 0$     or     $y + 4 = 0$

    $3y = 2$           $y = -4$

    $y = \dfrac{2}{3}$

The solution set is $\left\{-4, \dfrac{2}{3}\right\}$.

32. $4s^2 + 28s + 49$

   $= (2s + 7)(2s + 7)$

   $4(2s + 7) = 60$

   $8s + 28 = 60$

   $8s = 32$

   $s = 4$

33. Let $n$ = 1st integer.

   $n(n + 2) = 120$

   $n^2 + 2n - 120 = 0$

   $(n - 10)(n + 12) = 0$

   $n - 10 = 0$     or     $n + 12 = 0$

       $n = 10$           $n = -12$

   Integers are 10, 12; -12, -10.

34. Let $x$ = one of the integers.

   $x(11 - x) = 24$

   $11x - x^2 = 24$

   $x^2 - 11x + 24 = 0$

   $(x - 3)(x - 8) = 0$

   $x - 3 = 0$     or     $x - 8 = 0$

       $x = 3$           $x = 8$

   The integers are 3 and 8.

35. Let $x$ = one of the integers.

   $x(x + 3) = 88$

   $x^2 + 3x = 88$

   $x^2 + 3x - 88 = 0$

   $(x - 8)(x + 11) = 0$

   $x - 8 = 0$     or     $x + 11 = 0$

       $x = 8$           $x = -11$

   The integers are 8, 11; -8, -11.

36. Let $x$ = 1st integer.

   $x^2 + (x + 2)^2 = 202$

   $2x^2 + 4x - 198 = 0$

   $2(x^2 + 2x - 99) = 0$

   $2(x - 9)(x + 11) = 0$

   $x - 9 = 0$     or     $x + 11 = 0$

       $x = 9$           $x = -11$

   The integers are 9, 11.

37. Let $x$ = 1st integer.

   $(x + 2)^2 + 2x = 76$

   $x^2 + 6x - 72 = 0$

   $(x - 6)(x + 12) = 0$

   $x - 6 = 0$     or     $x + 12 = 0$

       $x = 6$           $x = -12$

   The integers are 6, 8; -12, -10.

38. $(h^3 + h^2) - (4h + 4) = 0$

   $h^2(h + 1) - 4(h + 1) = 0$

   $(h^2 - 4)(h + 1) = 0$

   $(h - 2)(h + 2)(h + 1) = 0$

   $h - 2 = 0$   or   $h + 2 = 0$   or   $h + 1 = 0$

      $h = 2$         $h = -2$         $h = -1$

   The solution set is {-2, -1, 2}.

39. $(9m^3 - m) - (18m^2 - 2) = 0$

   $m(9m^2 - 1) - 2(9m^2 - 1) = 0$

   $(m - 2)(3m - 1)(3m + 1) = 0$

   $m - 2 = 0$   or   $3m - 1 = 0$   or   $3m + 1 = 0$

      $m = 2$         $3m = 1$         $3m = -1$

                   $m = \dfrac{1}{3}$         $m = -\dfrac{1}{3}$

   The solution set is $\left\{ -\dfrac{1}{3},\ \dfrac{1}{3},\ 2 \right\}$.

40. $(xy - 3y) + (4x - 12) = 0$

   $y(x - 3) + 4(x - 3) = 0$

   $(y + 4)(x - 3) = 0$

   $y + 4 = 0$     or     $x - 3 = 0$

      $y = -4$           $x = 3$

   The solution is $x = 3$ or $y = -4$.

41. $(4pz - z) + (12p - 3) = 0$

   $z(4p - 1) + 3(4p - 1) = 0$

   $(z + 3)(4p - 1) = 0$

   $z + 3 = 0$     or     $4p - 1 = 0$

   $z = -3$           $4p = 1$

                   $p = \dfrac{1}{4}$

   The solution is $p = \dfrac{1}{4}$ or $z = -3$.

42. $(x + 3)(x - 5) = 0$

   $x^2 - 2x - 15 = 0$

43. $\left( x - \dfrac{2}{3} \right)(x + 1) = 0$

   $x^2 + \dfrac{1}{3}x - \dfrac{2}{3} = 0$

   $3x^2 + x - 2 = 0$

44. $(x + 2)(x - 2)(x - 5) = 0$

   $(x^2 - 4)(x - 5) = 0$

   $x^3 - 5x^2 - 4x + 20 = 0$

45. Let $w$ = width;

   $w + 5$ = length.

   $w(w + 5) = 234$

   $w^2 + 5w - 234 = 0$

   $(w + 18)(w - 13) = 0$

   $w + 18 = 0$     or     $w - 13 = 0$

      $w = -18$           $w = 13$

   Dimensions are 13 yd by 18 yd.

46. Let $x$ = amount length and width are increased.

   $(8 + x)(12 + x) = 96 + 69$

   $x^2 + 20x - 69 = 0$

   $(x + 23)(x - 3) = 0$

   $x + 23 = 0$     or     $x - 3 = 0$

      $x = -23$           $x = 3$

   New dimensions are 11 cm by 15 cm.

**47.** Let $x$ = width of 2 strips.

$$12 \cdot 9 \cdot \frac{1}{2} = (12 - x)(9 - x)$$
$$54 = x^2 - 21x + 108$$
$$x^2 - 21x + 54 = 0$$
$$(x - 18)(x - 3) = 0$$

$x - 18 = 0$     or     $x - 3 = 0$

$x = 18$          $x = 3$

Width of strip is $\frac{3}{2}$ or 1.5 km.

**48.**
$$3000 = 440t - 16t^2$$
$$16t^2 - 440t + 3000 = 0$$
$$8(2t^2 - 55t + 375) = 0$$
$$8(2t - 25)(t - 15) = 0$$

$2t - 25 = 0$     or     $t - 15 = 0$

$2t = 25$          $t = 15$

$t = \frac{25}{2}$

12.5 seconds

**49.**
$$40{,}000 = 2320t - 16t^2$$
$$16(t^2 - 145t + 2500) = 0$$
$$16(t - 125)(t - 20) = 0$$

$t - 125 = 0$     or     $t - 20 = 0$

$t = 125$          $t = 20$

20 seconds

**50.** $50.4 \times 82 = 4133$ points

**51.** $9(x + 2) = 4(x - 3)$

$9x + 18 = 4x - 12$

$5x = -30$

$x = -6$

**52.**     $xy = k$        **53.** $5t - (t - 3) < 6t + 7$

$20 \cdot 24 = 480$            $4t + 3 < 6t + 7$

$330y = 480$              $-2t < 4$

$y = 16$                 $t > -2$

$$\{t \mid t > -2\}$$

**54.** $56c^3d^3 - 8c^2d^3 + 8cd^4$     **55.** 16 or $-16$

**56.**        $0 = 128t - 16t^2$

$16t(t - 8) = 0$

$t = 0$     or     $t - 8 = 0$

$t = 8$

8 seconds

# Chapter 7    Summary and Review

**PAGES 300-302**    SKILLS AND CONCEPTS

**1.** $35 = (5) \cdot 7$

$30 = 2 \cdot 3 \cdot (5)$

The GCF is 5.

**2.** $12ab = (2) \cdot (2) \cdot 3 \cdot (a) \cdot (b)$

$-4a^2b^2 = -1 \cdot (2) \cdot (2) \cdot (a) \cdot a \cdot (b) \cdot b$

The GCF is $4ab$.

**3.** $12 = (2) \cdot 2 \cdot 3$

$18 = (2) \cdot 3 \cdot 3$

$40 = (2) \cdot 2 \cdot 2 \cdot 5$

The GCF is 2.

**4.** $16mrt = (2) \cdot 2 \cdot 2 \cdot 2 \cdot (m) \cdot (r) \cdot t$

$30m^2r = (2) \cdot 3 \cdot 5 \cdot m \cdot (m) \cdot (r)$

The GCF is $2mr$.

**5.** $20n^2 = (2) \cdot (2) \cdot 5 \cdot (n) \cdot n$

$24np^5 = (2) \cdot (2) \cdot 2 \cdot 3 \cdot (n) \cdot p \cdot p \cdot p \cdot p \cdot p$

The GCF is $4n$.

**6.** $60x^2y^2 = 2 \cdot 2 \cdot 3 \cdot (5) \cdot (x) \cdot x \cdot y \cdot y$

$35xz^3 = (5) \cdot 7 \cdot (x) \cdot z \cdot z \cdot z$

The GCF is $5x$.

**7.** $2m^2n^3p = 2 \cdot m \cdot (m) \cdot n \cdot (n) \cdot n \cdot (p)$

$8mn^2p^3 = 2 \cdot 2 \cdot 2 \cdot (m) \cdot (n) \cdot n \cdot (p) \cdot p \cdot p$

$5m^2np^3 = 5 \cdot m \cdot (m) \cdot (n) \cdot p \cdot p \cdot (p)$

The GCF is $mnp$.

**8.** $13x = (13) \cdot x$

$26y = 2 \cdot (13) \cdot y$

The GCF is 13.

$13x + 26y = 13(x + 2y)$

**9.** $6x^2y = (2) \cdot (3) \cdot x \cdot x \cdot y$

$12xy = (2) \cdot 2 \cdot (3) \cdot x \cdot y$

$6 = (2) \cdot (3)$

The GCF is 6.

$6x^2y + 12xy + 6 = 6(x^2y + 2xy + 1)$

**10.** $24a^2b^2 = (2) \cdot 2 \cdot 2 \cdot (3) \cdot (a) \cdot a \cdot (b) \cdot b$

$18ab = (2) \cdot 3 \cdot (3) \cdot (a) \cdot (b)$

The GCF is $6ab$.

$24a^2b^2 - 18ab = 6ab(4ab - 3)$

**11.** $26ab = (2) \cdot 13 \cdot (a) \cdot b$

$18ac = (2) \cdot 3 \cdot 3 \cdot (a) \cdot c$

$32a^2 = (2) \cdot 2 \cdot 2 \cdot 2 \cdot 2 \cdot (a) \cdot a$

The GCF is $2a$.

$26ab + 18ac + 32a^2 = 2a(13b + 9c + 16a)$

**12.**       $m = (m)$

$m^2n = (m) \cdot m \cdot n$

$m^3n^3 = (m) \cdot m \cdot m \cdot n \cdot n \cdot n$

The GCF is $m$.

$m + m^2n + m^3n^3 = m(1 + mn + m^2n^3)$

**13.** $\frac{3}{5}a = (3) \cdot (\frac{1}{5}) \cdot a$

$\frac{3}{5}b = (3) \cdot (\frac{1}{5}) \cdot b$

$\frac{6}{5}c = 2 \cdot (3) \cdot (\frac{1}{5}) \cdot c$

The GCF is $\frac{3}{5}$.

$\frac{3}{5}a - \frac{3}{5}b + \frac{6}{5}c = \frac{3}{5}(a - b + 2c)$

**14.** $(a^2 - 4ac) + (ab - 4bc)$

$= a(a - 4c) + b(a - 4c)$

$= (a + b)(a - 4c)$

Check: $(a + b)(a - 4c)$

       $= a^2 - 4ac + ab - 4bc$ ✓

**15.** $(24am - 9an) + (40bm - 15bn)$

$= 3a(8m - 3n) + 5b(8m - 3n)$

$= (3a + 5b)(8m - 3n)$

Check: $(3a + 5b)(8m - 3n)$

       $= 24am - 9an + 40bm - 15bn$ ✓

16. $(2rs + 6ps) + (mr + 3mp)$

    $= 2s(r + 3p) + m(r + 3p)$

    $= (2s + m)(r + 3p)$

    Check: $(2s + m)(r + 3p)$

           $= 2rs + 6ps + mr + 3mp$ ✓

17. $(16k^3 - 4k^2p^2) + (7p^3 - 28kp)$

    $= 4k^2(4k - p^2) + 7p(p^2 - 4k)$

    $= 4k^2(4k - p^2) - 7p(4k - p^2)$

    $= (4k^2 - 7p)(4k - p^2)$

    Check: $(4k^2 - 7p)(4k - p^2)$

           $= 16k^3 - 4k^2p^2 - 28kp + 7p^3$ ✓

18. $(dm + 7d) + (mr + 7r)$

    $= d(m + 7) + r(m + 7)$

    $= (d + r)(m + 7)$

    Check: $(d + r)(m + 7)$

           $= dm + 7d + rm + 7r$

           $= dm + 7r + mr + 7d$ ✓

19. $y^2 + 7y + 12$

    $= (y + 3)(y + 4)$

20. $x^2 - 9x - 36$

    $= (x - 12)(x + 3)$

21. $b^2 + 5b - 6$

    $= (b + 6)(b - 1)$

22. $2r^2 - 3r - 20$

    $= (2r + 5)(r - 4)$

23. $3a^2 - 13a + 14$

    $= (3a - 7)(a - 2)$

24. prime

25. $a^2 - 10ab + 9b^2$

    $= (a - b)(a - 9b)$

26. $r^2 - 8rs - 65s^2$

    $= (r + 5s)(r - 13s)$

27. $56m^2 - 93mn + 27n^2$

    $= (8m - 3n)(7m - 9n)$

28. $b^2 - 16$

    $= (b - 4)(b + 4)$

29. $25 - 9y^2$

    $= (5 - 3y)(5 + 3y)$

30. $16a^2 - 81b^4$

    $= (4a - 9b^2)(4a + 9b^2)$

31. $2y^3 - 128y$

    $= 2y(y^2 - 64)$

    $= 2y(y - 8)(y + 8)$

32. $\frac{1}{4}n^2 - \frac{9}{16}r^2$

    $= \left(\frac{1}{2}n - \frac{3}{4}r\right)\left(\frac{1}{2}n + \frac{3}{4}r\right)$

33. $81x^4 - 16$

    $= (9x^2 - 4)(9x^2 + 4)$

    $= (3x - 2)(3x + 2)(9x^2 + 4)$

34. $a^2 + 18a + 81$

    $= a^2 + 2 \cdot 9 \cdot a + 9^2$

    $= (a + 9)^2$

35. $16x^2 - 8x + 1$

    $= (4x)^2 - 2 \cdot 4 \cdot x + 1$

    $= (4x - 1)^2$

36. $9k^2 - 12k + 4$

    $= (3k)^2 - 2 \cdot 3 \cdot k + 2^2$

    $= (3k - 2)^2$

37. $32n^2 - 80n + 50$

    $= 2(16n^2 - 40n + 25)$

    $= 2[(4n)^2 - 2 \cdot 20 \cdot n + 5^2]$

    $= 2(4n - 5)^2$

38. $6b^3 - 24b^2g + 24bg^2$

    $= 6b(b^2 - 4bg + 4g^2)$

    $= 6b[b^2 - 2 \cdot 2 \cdot b \cdot g + (2g)^2]$

    $= 6b(b - 2g)^2$

39. $y^2 - \frac{3}{2}yz^2 + \frac{9}{16}z^4$

    $= y^2 - 2 \cdot \frac{3}{4}yz^2 + \left(\frac{3}{4}z^2\right)^2$

    $= \left(y - \frac{3}{4}z^2\right)^2$

40. $3x^2 - 12$

    $= 3(x^2 - 4)$

    $= 3(x - 2)(x + 2)$

41. $28y^2 - 13y - 6$

    $= (7y + 2)(4y - 3)$

42. $56a^2 - 93a + 27$

    $= (8a - 3)(7a - 9)$

43. $6m^3 + m^2 - 15m$

    $= m(6m^2 + m - 15)$

    $= m(3m + 5)(2m - 3)$

44. $15ay^2 + 37ay + 20a$

    $= a(15y^2 + 37y + 20)$

    $= a(5y + 4)(3y + 5)$

45. $2r^3 - 18r^2 + 30r$

    $= 2r(r^2 - 9r + 15)$

46. $12mx + 3xb + 4my + by$

    $= (12mx + 3xb) + (4my + by)$

    $= 3x(4m + b) + y(4m + b)$

    $= (3x + y)(4m + b)$

47. $mx^2 + bx^2 - 49m - 49b$

    $= (mx^2 + bx^2) - (49m + 49b)$

    $= x^2(m + b) - 49(m + b)$

    $= (x^2 - 49)(m + b)$

    $= (x - 7)(x + 7)(m + b)$

48. $y = 0$     or    $y + 11 = 0$

                         $y = -11$

    The solution set is $\{-11, 0\}$.

49. $4t = 0$     or    $2t - 10 = 0$

    $t = 0$                    $2t = 10$

                             $t = 5$

    The solution set is $\{0, 5\}$.

50. $3x - 2 = 0$     or    $4x + 7 = 0$

       $3x = 2$             $4x = -7$

         $x = \frac{2}{3}$             $x = -\frac{7}{4}$

    The solution set is $\left\{-\frac{7}{4}, \frac{2}{3}\right\}$.

51. $a(2a - 9) = 0$

           $a = 0$ or $2a - 9 = 0$

                      $2a = 9$

                       $a = \frac{9}{2}$

    The solution set is $\left\{0, \frac{9}{2}\right\}$.

52. $n^2 + 17n = 0$

$n(n + 17) = 0$

$n = 0 \quad$ or $\quad n + 17 = 0$

$n = -17$

The solution set is $\{-17, 0\}$.

53. $\frac{1}{2}y^2 - \frac{3}{4}y = 0$

$\frac{1}{4}y(2y - 3) = 0$

$\frac{1}{4}y = 0$

$y = 0$ or $2y - 3 = 0$

$2y = 3$

$y = \frac{3}{2}$

The solution set is $\left\{0, \frac{3}{2}\right\}$.

54. $(y + 5)(y + 8) = 0$

$y + 5 = 0 \quad$ or $\quad y + 8 = 0$

$y = -5 \qquad\qquad y = -8$

The solution set is $\{-8, -5\}$.

55. $2(a^2 - 49) = 0$

$2(a - 7)(a + 7) = 0$

$a - 7 = 0 \quad$ or $\quad a + 7 = 0$

$a = 7 \qquad\qquad a = -7$

The solution set is $\{-7, 7\}$.

56. $2m^2 + 13m - 24 = 0$

$(2m - 3)(m + 8) = 0$

$2m - 3 = 0 \quad$ or $\quad m + 8 = 0$

$2m = 3 \qquad\qquad m = -8$

$m = \frac{3}{2}$

The solution set is $\left\{-8, \frac{3}{2}\right\}$.

57. $25r^2 + 20r + 4 = 0$

$(5r)^2 + 2 \cdot 10 \cdot r + 2^2 = 0$

$(5r + 2)^2 = 0$

$5r + 2 = 0$

$5r = -2$

$r = -\frac{2}{5}$

The solution set is $\left\{-\frac{2}{5}\right\}$.

58. $x^2 + 5x - 6 - 78 = 0$

$x^2 + 5x - 84 = 0$

$(x + 12)(x - 7) = 0$

$x + 12 = 0 \quad$ or $\quad x - 7 = 0$

$x = -12 \qquad\qquad x = 7$

The solution set is $\{-12, 7\}$.

59. $x(6x^2 + 29x + 28) = 0$

$x(2x + 7)(3x + 4) = 0$

$x = 0 \quad$ or $\quad 2x + 7 = 0 \quad$ or $\quad 3x + 4 = 0$

$2x = -7 \qquad\qquad 3x = -4$

$x = -\frac{7}{2} \qquad\qquad x = -\frac{4}{3}$

The solution set is $\left\{-\frac{7}{2}, -\frac{4}{3}, 0\right\}$.

60. $1063

61. 5 of the 24, 3 of the 36

62. length of side $= \dfrac{20m + 32p}{4}$

$= 5m + 8p$

$A = (5m + 8p)^2$

$= 25m^2 + 80mp + 64p^2$

63. $A = (4x - 3)(4x + 3)$

$P = 2(4x - 3) + 2(4x + 3)$

$= 8x - 6 + 8x + 6$

$= 16x$

64. $(4m^2 - 4m) - (3mp - 3p)$

$= 4m(m - 1) - 3p(m - 1)$

$= (4m - 3p)(m - 1)$

Dimensions are $4m - 3p$ by $m - 1$.

65. Let $x$ = 1st integer.

$x(x + 2) = 99$

$x^2 + 2x - 99 = 0$

$(x + 11)(x - 9) = 0$

$x + 11 = 0 \quad$ or $\quad x - 9 = 0$

$x = -11 \qquad\qquad x = 9$

$-11, -9 \quad$ or $\quad 9, 11$

66.

height = 3

$w$ = width

$2w$ = length

Volume = length · width · height

$1350 = 2w \cdot w \cdot 3$

$6w^2 - 1350 = 0$

$6(w^2 - 225) = 0$

$6(w - 15)(w + 15) = 0$

$w - 15 = 0 \quad$ or $\quad w + 15 = 0$

$w = 15 \qquad\qquad w = -15$

$2w = 30$

Dimensions are 3 in. by 15 in. by 30 in.

# Chapter 7    Test

PAGE 303

1. $18a^2b = 2 \cdot 3 \cdot 3 \cdot a \cdot a \cdot b$

$28a^3b^2 = 2 \cdot 2 \cdot 7 \cdot a \cdot a \cdot a \cdot b \cdot b$

The GCF is $2a^2b$.

2. $6x^2y^3 = 2 \cdot 3 \cdot x \cdot x \cdot y \cdot y \cdot y$

$12x^2y^2z = 2 \cdot 2 \cdot 3 \cdot x \cdot x \cdot y \cdot y \cdot z$

$15x^2y = 3 \cdot 5 \cdot x \cdot x \cdot y$

The GCF is $3x^2y$.

3. $25y^2 - 49w^2$

$= (5y - 7w)(5y + 7w)$

4. $t^2 - 16t + 64$

$= t^2 - 2 \cdot 8 \cdot t + 8^2$

$= (t - 8)^2$

5. $x^2 + 14x + 24$

$= (x + 2)(x + 12)$

6. $28m^2 + 18m$

$= 2m(14m + 9)$

7. $12x^2 + 23x - 24$
   $= (4x - 3)(3x + 8)$

8. $a^2 - 11ab + 18b^2$
   $= (a - 2b)(a - 9b)$

9. prime

10. $6x^3 + 15x^2 - 9x$
    $= 3x(2x^2 + 5x - 3)$
    $= 3x(2x - 1)(x + 3)$

11. $36m^2 + 60mn + 25n^2$
    $= (6m)^2 + 2 \cdot 30 \cdot mn + (5n)^2$
    $= (6m + 5n)^2$

12. $9ab^3(4a - 5b)$

13. $4my - 20m + 15p - 3py$
    $= (4my - 20m) + (15p - 3py)$
    $= 4m(y - 5) + 3p(5 - y)$
    $= 4m(y - 5) - 3p(y - 5)$
    $= (4m - 3p)(y - 5)$

14. $x^3 - 5x^2 - 9x + 45$
    $= (x^3 - 5x^2) - (9x - 45)$
    $= x^2(x - 5) - 9(x - 5)$
    $= (x^2 = 9)(x - 5)$
    $= (x - 3)(x + 3)(x - 5)$

15. $A = (2x - 5)(x + 4)$
    $P = 2(2x - 5) + 2(x + 4)$
    $= 4x - 10 + 2x + 8$
    $= 6x - 2$

16. $18s(s + 4) = 0$
    $18s = 0$ or $s + 4 = 0$
    $s = 0$      $s = -4$
    The solution set is $\{-4, 0\}$.

17. $4x^2 - 36 = 0$
    $4(x^2 - 9) = 0$
    $4(x - 3)(x + 3) = 0$
    $x - 3 = 0$ or $x + 3 = 0$
    $x = 3$      $x = -3$
    The solution set is $\{-3, 3\}$.

18. $t^2 - 10t + 25 = 0$
    $t^2 - 2 \cdot 5 \cdot t + 5^2 = 0$
    $(t - 5)^2 = 0$
    $t - 5 = 0$
    $t = 5$
    The solution set is $\{5\}$.

19. $(a - 13)(a + 4) = 0$
    $a - 13 = 0$ or $a + 4 = 0$
    $a = 13$      $a = -4$
    The solution set is $\{-4, 13\}$.

20. $12x^2 - x - 6 = 0$
    $(3x + 2)(4x - 3) = 0$
    $3x + 2 = 0$ or $4x - 3 = 0$
    $3x = -2$      $4x = 3$
    $x = -\frac{2}{3}$      $x = \frac{3}{4}$
    The solution set is $\left\{-\frac{2}{3}, \frac{3}{4}\right\}$.

21. $x(x^2 - 5x - 66) = 0$
    $x(x + 6)(x - 11) = 0$
    $x = 0$ or $x + 6 = 0$ or $x - 11 = 0$
                $x = -6$      $x = 11$
    The solution set is $\{-6, 0, 11\}$.

22. Let $n =$ one of the integers;
    $21 - n =$ the other integer.
    $n(21 - n) = 104$
    $n^2 - 21n + 104 = 0$
    $(n - 13)(n - 8) = 0$
    $n - 13 = 0$ or $n - 8 = 0$
    $n = 13$      $n = 8$
    The two integers are 8, 13.

23. Let $x =$ amount of increase in length and width.
    $(x + 4)(x + 7) = 4 \cdot 7 + 26$
    $x^2 + 11x + 28 = 28 + 26$
    $x^2 + 11x - 26 = 0$
    $(x + 13)(x - 2) = 0$
    $x + 13 = 0$ or $x - 2 = 0$
    $x = -13$      $x = 2$
    New dimensions are 9 in. by 6 in.

24. $78,400 = 2240t - 16t^2$
    $16t^2 - 2240t + 78,400 = 0$
    $16(t^2 - 140t + 4900) = 0$
    $16(t - 70)(t - 70) = 0$
    $t - 70 = 0$
    $t = 70$ seconds

25. Let $x =$ width of walk.
    $(24 - 2x)(32 - 2x) = 425$
    $768 - 112x + 4x^2 = 425$
    $4x^2 - 112x + 343 = 0$
    $(2x - 7)(2x - 49) = 0$
    $2x - 7 = 0$ or $2x - 49 = 0$
    $2x - 7$      $2x - 49$
    $x = \frac{7}{2} = 3.5$      $x = \frac{49}{2}$
    Width of walk will be 3.5 ft.

PAGE 303   BONUS
$A = 12x^2 + x - 20$
$= (3x + 4)(4x - 5)$
$P = 2(3x + 4) + 2(4x - 5)$
$= 6x + 8 + 8x - 10$
$= 14x - 2$
Smallest possible perimeter is $14(2) - 2 = 26$.

# Chapter 8 Rational Expressions

## Simplifying Rational Expressions

PAGE 308     CHECKING FOR UNDERSTANDING

1. Factor the numerator and denominator.

2. Factor the denominator. Then use the Zero product property to find the excluded values.

3. $-4$ and $9$

4. $\dfrac{x}{(x + 2)(x - 3)(x - 7)}$

   Answers may vary.

5. $\dfrac{42y}{18xy}$

   $= \dfrac{2 \cdot 3 \cdot 7 \cdot y}{2 \cdot 3 \cdot 3 \cdot x \cdot y}$     The GCF is $6y$.

   $= \dfrac{7}{3x}$

   $x \neq 0,\ y \neq 0$

6. $\dfrac{-3x^2y^5}{18x^5y^2}$

   $= \dfrac{3 \cdot x \cdot x \cdot y \cdot y \cdot y \cdot y \cdot y}{2 \cdot 3 \cdot 3 \cdot x \cdot x \cdot x \cdot x \cdot x \cdot y \cdot y}$

   $= \dfrac{-y^3}{6x^3}$     The GCF is $3x^2y^2$.

   $x \neq 0,\ y \neq 0$

7. $\dfrac{x(y + 1)}{x(y - 2)}$     The GCF $= x$.

   $= \dfrac{y + 1}{y - 2}$

   $x \neq 0,\ y \neq 2$

8. $\dfrac{-6a^3 + 8a^2 + 12a}{2a}$

   $= \dfrac{-6a^3}{2a} + \dfrac{8a^2}{2a} + \dfrac{12a}{2a}$     The GCF is $2a$.

   $= \dfrac{-3 \cdot 2 \cdot a \cdot a^2}{2 \cdot a} + \dfrac{2 \cdot 4 \cdot a \cdot a}{2 \cdot a} + \dfrac{2 \cdot 6 \cdot a}{2 \cdot a}$

   $= -3a^2 + 4a + 6$

   $2a \neq 0$, thus $a \neq 0$

9. $\dfrac{(a + b)(a - b)}{(a - b)(a - b)}$     The GCF is $a - b$.

   $= \dfrac{a + b}{a - b}$

   $a - b \neq 0$

   $a \neq b$

10. $\dfrac{y - 4}{y^2 - 16}$

    $= \dfrac{y - 4}{(y - 4)(y + 4)}$     The GCF is $y - 4$

    $= \dfrac{1}{y + 4}$

    $y - 4 \neq 0,\ y + 4 \neq 0$

    $y \neq 4 \qquad y \neq -4$

11. $\dfrac{13x}{39x^2}$

    $= \dfrac{13x}{3 \cdot 13x^2}$

    $= \dfrac{1}{3x}$

    $x \neq 0$

12. $\dfrac{14y^2z}{49yz^3}$

    $= \dfrac{2 \cdot 7y^2z}{7 \cdot 7yz^3}$

    $= \dfrac{2y}{7z^2}$

    $y \neq 0,\ z \neq 0$

13. $\dfrac{38a^2}{42ab}$

    $= \dfrac{2 \cdot 19a^2}{2 \cdot 3 \cdot 7ab}$

    $= \dfrac{19a}{21b}$

    $a \neq 0,\ b \neq 0$

14. $\dfrac{79a^2b}{158a^3bc}$

    $= \dfrac{79a^2b}{2 \cdot 79a^3bc}$

    $= \dfrac{1}{2ac}$

    $a \neq 0,\ b \neq 0,\ c \neq 0$

15. $\dfrac{m + 5}{2(m + 5)}$

    $= \dfrac{1}{2}$

    $m + 5 \neq 0$

    $m \neq -5$

16. $\dfrac{9z^4 - 6z^3 + 4z^2 - 15}{3z}$

    $= \dfrac{9z^4}{3z} - \dfrac{6z^3}{3z} + \dfrac{4z^2}{3z} - \dfrac{15}{3z}$

    $= 3z^3 - 2z^2 + \dfrac{4}{3}z - \dfrac{5}{z}$

    $z \neq 0$

17. $\dfrac{y + 4}{(y - 4)(y + 4)}$

    $= \dfrac{1}{y - 4}$

    $y - 4 \neq 0,\ y + 4 \neq 0$

    $y \neq 4 \qquad y \neq -4$

18. $\dfrac{(a - 4)(a + 4)}{(a - 2)(a - 4)}$

    $= \dfrac{a + 4}{a - 2}$

    $a - 2 \neq 0,\ a - 4 \neq 0$

    $a \neq 2 \qquad a \neq 4$

19. $\dfrac{-1(3w - 2)}{(3w - 2)(w + 4)}$

    $= \dfrac{-1}{(w + 4)}$

    $3w - 2 \neq 0,\ w + 4 \neq 0$

    $w \neq \dfrac{2}{3} \qquad w \neq -4$

20. $\dfrac{a + b}{a^2 - b^2}$

    $\dfrac{a + b}{(a - b)(a + b)}$

    $= \dfrac{1}{a - b}$

    $a - b \neq 0,\ a + b \neq 0$

    $a \neq b \qquad a \neq -b$

21. $\dfrac{c^2 - 4}{(c + 2)^2}$

    $= \dfrac{(c - 2)(c + 2)}{(c + 2)(c + 2)}$

    $= \dfrac{c - 2}{c + 2}$

    $c + 2 \neq 0$

    $c \neq -2$

22. $\dfrac{a^2 - a}{a - 1}$

    $= \dfrac{a(a - 1)}{a - 1}$

    $= a$

    $a - 1 \neq 0$

    $a \neq 1$

23. $\dfrac{m^2 - 2m}{m - 2}$

$= \dfrac{m(m - 2)}{m - 2}$

$= m$

$m - 2 \neq 0$

$\quad m \neq 2$

24. $\dfrac{x^2 + 4}{x^4 - 16}$

$= \dfrac{x^2 + 4}{(x^2 - 4)(x^2 + 4)}$

$= \dfrac{x^2 + 4}{(x - 2)(x + 2)(x^2 + 4)}$

$= \dfrac{1}{(x - 2)(x + 2)}$

$= \dfrac{1}{x^2 - 4}$

$x - 2 \neq 0, \; x + 2 \neq 0$

$\quad x \neq 2, \qquad x \neq -2$

25. $\dfrac{r^3 - r^2}{r - 1}$

$= \dfrac{r^2(r - 1)}{r - 1}$

$= r^2$

$r - 1 \neq 0$

$\quad r \neq 1$

26. $\dfrac{4n^2 - 8}{4n - 4}$

$= \dfrac{4(n^2 - 2)}{4(n - 1)}$

$= \dfrac{n^2 - 2}{n - 1}$

$n - 1 \neq 0$

$\quad n \neq 1$

27. $\dfrac{3m^3}{6m^2 - 3m}$

$= \dfrac{m^3}{3m(2m - 1)}$

$= \dfrac{m^2}{2m - 1}$

$m \neq 0, \; 2m - 1 \neq 0$

$\qquad m \neq \dfrac{1}{2}$

28. $\dfrac{6y^3 - 12y^2}{12y - 18}$

$= \dfrac{6y^2(y - 2)}{6(2y - 3)}$

$= \dfrac{y^2(y - 2)}{2y - 3}$

$2y - 3 \neq 0$

$y \neq \dfrac{3}{2}$

29. $\dfrac{-4y^2}{2y^2 - 4y^3}$

$= \dfrac{-4y^2}{2y^2(1 - 2y)}$

$= \dfrac{-2}{1 - 2y}$

$y^2 \neq 0, \; 1 - 2y \neq 0$

$\quad y \neq 0 \qquad y \neq \dfrac{1}{2}$

30. $\dfrac{3a^3}{3a^3 + 6a^2 b}$

$= \dfrac{3a^3}{3a^2(a + 2b)}$

$= \dfrac{a}{a + 2b}$

$a^2 \neq 0, \; a + 2b \neq 0$

$\quad a \neq 0 \qquad a \neq -2b$

31. $\dfrac{7a^3 b^2}{21a^2 b + 49ab^3}$

$= \dfrac{7a^3 b^2}{7ab(3a + 7b^2)}$

$= \dfrac{a^2 b}{3a + 7b^2}$

$a \neq 0, \; b \neq 0, \; 3a + 7b^2 \neq 0$

$\qquad\qquad\qquad 3a \neq -7b^2$

$\qquad\qquad\qquad\quad a \neq -\dfrac{7}{3}b^2$

32. $\dfrac{12s^5 - 15s^4 + 20s^2 - 7s}{-5s^3}$

$= \dfrac{12s^5}{-5s^3} + \dfrac{15s^4}{-5s^3} + \dfrac{20s^2}{-5s^3}$

$\quad - \dfrac{7s}{-5s^3}$

$= -\dfrac{12}{5}s^2 - 3s - \dfrac{4}{s} + \dfrac{7}{5s^2}$

$s \neq 0$

33. $\dfrac{x + y}{x^2 + 2xy + y^2}$

$= \dfrac{x + y}{(x + y)(x + y)}$

$= \dfrac{1}{x + y}$

$x + y \neq 0$

$x \neq -y$

34. $\dfrac{x - 3}{x^2 + x - 12}$

$= \dfrac{x - 3}{(x - 3)(x + 4)}$

$= \dfrac{1}{x + 4}$

$x - 3 \neq 0, \; x + 4 \neq 0$

$\quad x \neq 3 \qquad x \neq -4$

35. $\dfrac{6x^2 + 24x}{x^2 + 8x + 16}$

$= \dfrac{6x(x + 4)}{(x + 4)(x + 4)}$

$= \dfrac{6x}{x + 4}$

$x + 4 \neq 0$

$\quad x \neq -4$

36. $\dfrac{3 - x}{6 - 17x + 5x^2}$

$= \dfrac{3 - x}{(3 - x)(2 - 5x)}$

$= \dfrac{1}{2 - 5x}$

$3 - x \neq 0, \; 2 - 5x \neq 0$

$\quad x \neq 3 \qquad x \neq \dfrac{2}{5}$

37. $\dfrac{2x - 14}{x^2 - 4x - 21}$

$= \dfrac{2(x - 7)}{(x - 7)(x + 3)}$

$= \dfrac{2}{x + 3}$

$x - 7 \neq 0, \; x + 3 \neq 0$

$\quad x \neq 7 \qquad x \neq -3$

38. $\dfrac{x^2 - x^2 y}{x^3 - x^3 y}$

$= \dfrac{x^2(1 - y)}{x^3(1 - y)}$

$= \dfrac{1}{x}$

$x^3 \neq 0, \; 1 - y \neq 0$

$\quad x \neq 0 \qquad y \neq 1$

39. $\dfrac{5x^2 + 10x + 5}{3x^2 + 6x + 3}$

$= \dfrac{5(x + 1)(x + 1)}{3(x + 1)(x + 1)}$

$= \dfrac{5}{3}$

$x + 1 \neq 0$

$\quad x \neq -1$

40. $\dfrac{6x^4 y + 8x^3 y^2 + 3x^2 y^3}{2xy}$

$= \dfrac{6x^4 y}{2xy} + \dfrac{8x^3 y^2}{2xy} + \dfrac{3x^2 y^3}{2xy}$

$= 3x^3 + 4x^2 y + \dfrac{3}{2}xy^2$

$x \neq 0, \; y \neq 0$

41. $\dfrac{4k^2 - 25}{4k^2 - 20k + 25}$

$= \dfrac{(2k - 5)(2k + 5)}{(2k - 5)(2k - 5)}$

$= \dfrac{2k + 5}{2k - 5}$

$2k - 5 \neq 0$

$\quad k \neq \dfrac{5}{2}$

123

42. $\dfrac{2x^2 - 5x + 3}{3x^2 - 5x + 2}$

$= \dfrac{(2x - 3)(x - 1)}{(3x - 2)(x - 1)}$

$= \dfrac{2x - 3}{3x - 2}$

$3x - 2 \neq 0, \quad x - 1 \neq 0$

$\qquad x \neq \dfrac{3}{2} \qquad x \neq 1$

43. $\dfrac{b^2 - 5b + 6}{b^4 - 13b^2 + 36}$

$= \dfrac{(b - 2)(b - 3)}{(b - 2)(b + 2)(b - 3)(b + 3)}$

$= \dfrac{1}{(b + 2)(b + 3)}$

$b - 2 \neq 0, \ b + 2 \neq 0, \ b - 3 \neq 0, \ b + 3 \neq 0$

$\quad b \neq 2 \qquad b \neq -2 \qquad b \neq 3 \qquad b \neq -3$

44. $\dfrac{25 - x^2}{x^2 + x - 30}$

$= \dfrac{(5 - x)(5 + x)}{(x + 6)(x - 5)}$

$= \dfrac{-(x - 5)(x + 5)}{(x + 6)(x - 5)}$

$= -\dfrac{x + 5}{x + 6}$

$x + 6 \neq 0, \quad x - 5 \neq 0$

$\quad x \neq -6 \qquad x \neq 5$

45. $\dfrac{n^2 - 8n + 12}{n^3 - 12n^2 + 36n}$

$= \dfrac{(n - 2)(n - 6)}{n(n - 6)(n - 6)}$

$= \dfrac{n - 2}{n(n - 6)}$

$n \neq 0, \ n - 6 \neq 0$

$\qquad\qquad n \neq 6$

46. $\dfrac{16a^3 - 24a^2 - 160a}{8a^4 - 36a^3 + 16a^2}$

$= \dfrac{8a(2a^2 - 3a - 20)}{4a^2(2a^2 - 9a + 4)}$

$= \dfrac{8a(2a + 5)(a - 4)}{4a^2(2a - 1)(a - 4)}$

$= \dfrac{2(2a + 5)}{a(2a - 1)}$

$a^2 \neq 0, \ 2a - 1 \neq 0, \ a - 4 \neq 0$

$\quad a \neq 0 \qquad a \neq \dfrac{1}{2} \qquad a \neq 4$

47. $\dfrac{-x^2 + 6x - 9}{x^2 - 6x + 9}$

$= \dfrac{-(x - 3)(x - 3)}{(x - 3)(x - 3)}$

$= -1$

$x - 3 \neq 0$

$\quad x \neq 3$

48. $\dfrac{x^3y^3 + 5x^3y^2 + 6x^3y}{xy^5 + 5xy^4 + 6xy^3}$

$= \dfrac{x^3y(y + 3)(y + 2)}{xy^3(y + 3)(y + 2)}$

$= \dfrac{x^2}{y^2}$

$x \neq 0, \ y \neq 0, \ y + 3 \neq 0, \ y + 2 \neq 0$

$\qquad\qquad\qquad y \neq -3 \qquad y \neq -2$

49. $\dfrac{x^4 - 16}{x^4 - 8x^2 + 16}$

$= \dfrac{(x - 2)(x + 2)(x^2 + 4)}{(x - 2)(x + 2)(x - 2)(x + 2)}$

$= \dfrac{x^2 + 4}{x^2 - 4}$

$x - 2 \neq 0, \ x + 2 \neq 0$

$\quad x \neq 2 \qquad x \neq -2$

50. In $\dfrac{x^2 - 4}{x + 2}$, $x \neq -2$.

51. $\left(\dfrac{1}{90} + \dfrac{1}{60}\right) \cdot x = 1$

$\qquad \dfrac{5}{180}x = 1$

$\qquad x = \dfrac{180}{5} = 36$ seconds

52. $1050 \cdot 1 \overset{?}{\leq} 205 \cdot 5$

$\quad 1050 \not\leq 1025$

Chico will not be able to lift the rock.

53. $29,002$ ft $= \dfrac{29,002}{5280}$ mi

$\qquad\qquad = 5.5$ mi

$\dfrac{212 - 159.8}{5.5}$

$\approx 9.5°$F

54. 1 mile = 5280 ft

Area of sidewalk $= 2 \cdot 10 \cdot 5280$

$\qquad\qquad\qquad = 105,600$ ft$^2$

$\dfrac{105,600 \text{ ft}^2}{4 \text{ ft}^2/\text{person}}$

$= 26,400$ people

55. $\qquad \dfrac{5}{12} = \dfrac{2 - x}{3 + x}$

$5(3 + x) = 12(2 - x)$

$\quad 15 + 5x = 24 - 12x$

$\qquad\quad 17x = 9$

$\qquad\qquad x = \dfrac{9}{17}$

56. $150\% \times 4 = 6$ years

57. $9q + 2 \leq 7q - 25$

$\quad 2q \leq -27$

$\quad q \leq -\dfrac{27}{2}$

$\left\{q \mid q \leq -\dfrac{27}{2}\right\}$

58. $a^3 + b^2 - (c^2 + abcde) - a + b + d + e + c$

$= 2^3 + \left(\dfrac{1}{3}\right)^2 - \left[(2.2)^2 + 2 \cdot \dfrac{1}{3} \cdot 2.2 \cdot 4 \cdot \dfrac{2}{5}\right] - 2$

$+ \dfrac{1}{3} + 4 + \dfrac{2}{5} + 2.2$

$= 8 + \dfrac{1}{9} - (4.4 + 2.3) - 6 + 10 + 2.2$

$= 8 + \dfrac{1}{9} - 6.7 - 6 + 10 + 2.2$

$= 7.12$

59. $(-5x^3)(4x^4) = -20x^7$

60. $(3a^2b + 2ab^3) + (6ab + 4b^3)$

$3a^2b + 2ab^3 = ab(3a + 2b^2)$

$6ab + 4b^3 = 2b(3a + 2b^2)$

Common factor is $3a + 2b^2$.

61. $\quad x^2 + 22 = 58$

$\quad\quad x^2 - 36 = 0$

$(x - 6)(x + 6) = 0$

$\quad x - 6 = 0$ or $x + 6 = 0$

$\quad\quad x = 6 \quad\quad x = -6$

The solution set is $\{6, -6\}$.

## 8-2 Multiplying Rational Expressions

PAGE 313    CHECKING FOR UNDERSTANDING

1. $b$ = any number except 0

2. Only factors can be cancelled, not terms.

3. $\dfrac{3b}{4a}$

4. $\dfrac{6ax}{5y}$

5. $\dfrac{abc}{acd}$

$= \dfrac{b}{d}$

6. $\dfrac{72a^2n^2}{72an^2}$

$= a$

7. $\dfrac{14(y - 3)}{7(y - 3)}$

$= 2$

8. $\dfrac{9(m - 3)(m + 3)}{12(m - 3)}$

$= \dfrac{3(m + 3)}{4}$

$= \dfrac{3m + 9}{4}$

PAGES 313-314    EXERCISES

9. $\dfrac{a^2b}{b^2c} \cdot \dfrac{c}{d}$

$= \dfrac{a^2bc}{b^2cd}$

$= \dfrac{a^2}{bd}$

10. $\dfrac{10n^3}{6x^3} \cdot \dfrac{12n^2x^4}{25n^2x^2}$

$= \dfrac{120n^5x^4}{150n^2x^5}$

$= \dfrac{4n^3}{5x}$

11. $\left(\dfrac{2a}{b}\right)^2 \dfrac{5c}{6a}$

$= \dfrac{4a^2}{b^2} \cdot \dfrac{5c}{6a}$

$= \dfrac{20a^2c}{6ab^2}$

$= \dfrac{10ac}{3b^2}$

12. $\dfrac{8}{m^2}\left(\dfrac{m^2}{2c}\right)^2$

$= \dfrac{8}{m^2} \cdot \dfrac{m^4}{4c^2}$

$= \dfrac{8m^4}{4m^2c^2}$

$= \dfrac{2m^2}{c^2}$

13. $\dfrac{6m^3n}{10a^2} \cdot \dfrac{4a^2m}{9n^3}$

$= \dfrac{24a^2m^4n}{90a^2n^3}$

$= \dfrac{4m^4}{15n^2}$

14. $\dfrac{7xy^3}{11z^2} \cdot \dfrac{44z^3}{21x^2y}$

$= \dfrac{308xy^3z^3}{231x^2yz^2}$

$= \dfrac{4y^2z}{3x}$

15. $\dfrac{5n - 5}{3} \cdot \dfrac{9}{n - 1}$

$= \dfrac{45(n - 1)}{3(n - 1)}$

$= 15$

16. $\dfrac{3a - 3b}{a} \cdot \dfrac{a^2}{a - b}$

$= \dfrac{3a^2(a - b)}{a(a - b)}$

$= 3a$

17. $\dfrac{-(2a + 7c)}{6} \cdot \dfrac{36}{-7c - 2a}$

$= \dfrac{-36(2a + 7c)}{-6(2a + 7c)}$

$= 6$

18. $\dfrac{2a + 4b}{5} \cdot \dfrac{25}{6a + 8b}$

$= \dfrac{50(a + 2b)}{10(3a + 4b)}$

$= \dfrac{5(a + 2b)}{3a + 4b}$

$= \dfrac{5a + 10b}{3a + 4b}$

19. $\dfrac{3x + 30}{2x} \cdot \dfrac{4x}{4x + 40}$

$= \dfrac{12x(x + 10)}{8x(x + 10)}$

$= \dfrac{3}{2}$

20. $\dfrac{3}{x - y} \cdot \dfrac{(x - y)^2}{6}$

$= \dfrac{3(x - y)(x - y)}{6(x - y)}$

$= \dfrac{x - y}{2}$

21. $\dfrac{a^2 - b^2}{4} \cdot \dfrac{16}{a + b}$

$= \dfrac{16(a - b)(a + b)}{4(a + b)}$

$= 4(a - b)$

$= 4a - 4b$

22. $\dfrac{r^2}{r - s} \cdot \dfrac{r^2 - s^2}{s^2}$

$= \dfrac{r^2(r - s)(r + s)}{s^2(r - s)}$

$= \dfrac{r^2(r + s)}{s^2}$

$= \dfrac{r^3 + r^2s}{s^2}$

23. $\dfrac{a^2 - b^2}{a - b} \cdot \dfrac{7}{a + b}$

$= \dfrac{7(a - b)(a + b)}{(a - b)(a + b)}$

$= 7$

24. $\dfrac{x^2 - 16}{9} \cdot \dfrac{x + 4}{x - 4}$

$= \dfrac{(x - 4)(x + 4)(x + 4)}{9(x - 4)}$

$= \dfrac{(x + 4)(x + 4)}{9}$

$= \dfrac{x^2 + 8x + 16}{9}$

25. $\dfrac{x^2 - y^2}{x^2 - 1} \cdot \dfrac{x - 1}{x - y}$

$= \dfrac{(x - y)(x + y)(x - 1)}{(x - 1)(x + 1)(x - y)}$

$= \dfrac{x + y}{x + 1}$

26. $\dfrac{r^2 + s^2}{r^2 - s^2} \cdot \dfrac{r - s}{r + s}$

$= \dfrac{(r - s)(r^2 + s^2)}{(r - s)(r + s)(r + s)}$

$= \dfrac{r^2 + s^2}{r^2 + 2rs + s^2}$

27. $\dfrac{3k + 9}{k} \cdot \dfrac{k^2}{k^2 - 9}$

$= \dfrac{3k^2(k + 3)}{k(k - 3)(k + 3)}$

$= \dfrac{3k}{k - 3}$

28. $\dfrac{3a - 6}{a^2 - 9} \cdot \dfrac{a + 3}{a^2 - 2a}$

$= \dfrac{3(a - 2)(a + 3)}{a(a - 2)(a - 3)(a + 3)}$

$= \dfrac{3}{a(a - 3)}$

$= \dfrac{3}{a^2 - 3a}$

29. $\dfrac{y^2 - x^2}{y} \cdot \dfrac{x}{x - y}$

$= \dfrac{x(y - x)(y + x)}{y(x - y)}$

$= \dfrac{-x(x - y)(y + x)}{y(x - y)}$

$= \dfrac{-x(y + x)}{y}$

$= \dfrac{-xy - x^2}{y}$

30. $\dfrac{b + a}{b - a} \cdot \dfrac{a^2 - b^2}{a}$

$= \dfrac{(a - b)(a + b)(a + b)}{a(b - a)}$

$= \dfrac{(a - b)(a + b)(a + b)}{-a(a - b)}$

$= \dfrac{-(a^2 + 2ab + b^2)}{a}$

$= \dfrac{-a^2 - 2ab - b^2}{a}$

31. $\dfrac{3mn^2 - 3m}{n} \cdot \dfrac{3m}{n^2 - 1}$

$= \dfrac{9m^2(n^2 - 1)}{n(n^2 - 1)}$

$= \dfrac{9m^2}{n}$

32. $\dfrac{x}{x^2 + 8x + 15} \cdot \dfrac{2x + 10}{x^2}$

$= \dfrac{2x(x + 5)}{x^2(x + 3)(x + 5)}$

$= \dfrac{2}{x(x + 3)}$

$= \dfrac{2}{x^2 + 3x}$

33. $\dfrac{x - 5}{x^2 - 7x + 10} \cdot \dfrac{x - 2}{3}$

$= \dfrac{(x - 5)(x - 2)}{3(x - 5)(x - 2)}$

$= \dfrac{1}{3}$

34. $\dfrac{b^2 + 20b + 99}{b + 9} \cdot \dfrac{b + 7}{b^2 + 12b + 11}$

$= \dfrac{(b + 7)(b + 9)(b + 11)}{(b + 9)(b + 11)(b + 1)}$

$= \dfrac{b + 7}{b + 1}$

35. $\dfrac{x + 7}{x^2 - 25} \cdot \dfrac{x^2 + 10x + 25}{x^2 - 49}$

$= \dfrac{(x + 7)(x + 5)(x + 5)}{(x - 5)(x + 5)(x - 7)(x + 7)}$

$= \dfrac{x + 5}{(x - 5)(x - 7)}$

$= \dfrac{x + 5}{x^2 - 12x + 35}$

36. $\dfrac{2x + 3}{x^2} \cdot \dfrac{2x + 3}{x^2}$

$= \dfrac{4x^2 + 12x + 9}{x^4}$

37. $\dfrac{x^2y - x^2}{x^3 - x^3y} \cdot \dfrac{x^2}{xy^2 - y}$

$= \dfrac{x^4(y - 1)}{x^3(1 - y)(xy^2 - y)}$

$= \dfrac{-x^4(1 - y)}{x^3(1 - y)(xy^2 - y)}$

$= \dfrac{-x}{xy^2 - y}$

38. $\dfrac{z^2 - 15z + 50}{z^2 - 9z + 20} \cdot \dfrac{z^2 - 11z + 24}{z^2 - 18z + 80}$

$= \dfrac{(z - 10)(z - 5)(z - 8)(z - 3)}{(z - 4)(z - 5)(z - 10)(z - 8)}$

$= \dfrac{z - 3}{z - 4}$

39. $\dfrac{y^2 + 3y^3}{y^2 - 4} \cdot \dfrac{2y + y^2}{y + 4y^2 + 3y^3}$

$= \dfrac{y^2(1 + 3y) \cdot y(2 + y)}{(y - 2)(y + 2)y(3y^2 + 4y + 1)}$

$= \dfrac{y^3(1 + 3y)(2 + y)}{y(y - 2)(y + 2)(3y + 1)(y + 1)}$

$= \dfrac{y^2}{(y - 2)(y + 1)}$

$= \dfrac{y^2}{y^2 - y - 2}$

40. $\dfrac{3t^3 - 14t^2 + 8t}{2t^2 - 3t - 20} \cdot \dfrac{16t^2 + 34t - 15}{24t^2 - 25t + 6}$

$= \dfrac{t(3t - 2)(t - 4)(2t + 5)(8t - 3)}{(2t + 5)(t - 4)(3t - 2)(8t - 3)}$

$= t$

41. $\dfrac{6y^2 - 5y - 6}{3y^2 - 20y - 7} \cdot \dfrac{y^2 - 49}{12y^3 + 23y^2 + 10y}$

$= \dfrac{(3y + 2)(2y - 3)(y - 7)(y + 7)}{(3y + 1)(y - 7)y(4y + 5)(3y + 2)}$

$= \dfrac{(2y - 3)(y + 7)}{y(3y + 1)(4y + 5)}$

$= \dfrac{2y^2 + 11y - 21}{12y^3 + 19y^2 + 5y}$

42. $\dfrac{2m^2 - 9m + 9}{3m^2 + 19m - 14} \cdot \dfrac{m^2 + 14m + 49}{9 - 6m + m^2} \cdot$

$= \dfrac{(2m - 3)(m - 3)(m + 7)(m + 7)}{(3m - 2)(m + 7)(m - 3)(m - 3)}$

$= \dfrac{(2m - 3)(m + 7)}{(3m - 2)(m - 3)}$

$= \dfrac{2m^2 + 11m - 21}{3m^2 - 11m + 6}$

**43.** $\dfrac{a^2x - b^2x}{y} \cdot \dfrac{y^2 + y}{a - 2} \cdot \dfrac{4 - 2a}{axy - bxy}$

$= \dfrac{x(a - b)(a + b) \cdot y(y + 1) \cdot 2(2 - a)}{y(a - 2) \cdot xy(a - b)}$

$= \dfrac{-2xy(a - b)(a + b)(a - 2)(y + 1)}{xy^2(a - 2)(a - b)}$

$= \dfrac{-2(a + b)(y + 1)}{y}$

$= \dfrac{-2ay - 2by - 2a - 2b}{y}$

**44.** $\dfrac{x^2y}{x^2 + 4xy + 4y^2} \cdot \dfrac{x^2 + 2xy}{xy} \cdot \dfrac{y}{x^4 - 9x^2}$

$= \dfrac{x^2y \cdot x(x + 2y) \cdot y}{(x + 2y)(x + 2y) \cdot xy \cdot x^2(x + 3)(x - 3)}$

$= \dfrac{y}{(x + 2y)(x + 3)(x - 3)}$

$= \dfrac{y}{x^3 + 2x^2y - 9x - 18y}$

**45.** Answers may vary. Sample answer:

$\dfrac{6x - 18}{x + 7}, \dfrac{x + 2}{x - 4}$ and $\dfrac{x - 3}{x + 7}, \dfrac{6x + 12}{x - 4}$

**46.** Let $x$ = original price.

$(0.10x + x) - 0.10(0.10x + x)$
$\qquad\qquad + 0.10\,[(0.10x + x) - 0.10(0.10x + x)]$

$= 0.10x + x - 0.01x - 0.10x$
$\qquad\qquad + 0.10(0.10x + x - 0.01x - 0.10x)$

$= 0.10x + x - 0.01x - 0.10x + 0.01x + 0.10x$
$\qquad\qquad - 0.001x - 0.01x$

$= x + 0.10x - 0.001x - 0.01x$

$= x(1 + 0.10 - 0.001 - 0.01)$

$= 1.089x$

Increase is 8.9%

**47.** $V = \dfrac{5(18 + 15)}{2} \cdot 9$

$\qquad = 742.5 \text{ ft}^3$

**48.** $\dfrac{500}{2\frac{1}{2}}$

$= \dfrac{500}{\frac{5}{2}}$

$= 500 \cdot \dfrac{2}{5}$

$= 200 \text{ laps}$

**49.**

| 1 | 1 | 11 | 21 | 21 | 41 | 31 | 61 | 41 | 81 |
|---|---|----|----|----|----|----|----|----|----|
| 2 | 3 | 12 | 23 | 22 | 43 | 32 | 63 | 42 | 83 |
| 3 | 5 | 13 | 25 | 23 | 45 | 33 | 65 | 43 | 85 |
| 4 | 7 | 14 | 27 | 24 | 47 | 34 | 67 | 44 | 87 |
| 5 | 9 | 15 | 29 | 25 | 49 | 35 | 69 | 45 | 89 |
| 6 | 11 | 16 | 31 | 26 | 51 | 36 | 71 | 46 | 91 |
| 7 | 13 | 17 | 33 | 27 | 53 | 37 | 73 | 47 | 93 |
| 8 | 15 | 18 | 35 | 28 | 55 | 38 | 75 | 48 | 95 |
| 9 | 17 | 19 | 37 | 29 | 57 | 39 | 77 | 49 | 97 |
| 10 | 19 | 20 | 39 | 30 | 59 | 40 | 79 | 50 | 99 |

9, 25, 2500

**50.** $h < -18 \cdot -25$

$h < 450$

$\{h \mid h < 450\}$

**51.** 7,600,000

$= 7.6 \times 10^6$

---

**52.** $15x^2 + 35x - 3x - 7$

$= 15x^2 + 32x - 7$

**53.** $6(y^2 - 4x^2)$

$= 6(y - 2x)(y + 2x)$

**54.** $\dfrac{x}{x^2 - 4}$

## Technology:  Rational Expressions

**1.** $\dfrac{2p}{3q^2}$  **2.** $\dfrac{y + 3}{y - 3}$  **3.** $\dfrac{x - 2}{(x - 1)(x + 1)}$

**4.** $\dfrac{y - 1}{y}$  **5.** $\dfrac{x + 4}{x - 15}$

## 8-3   Dividing Rational Expressions

**1.** true

**2.** Zero can be represented as $\dfrac{0}{1}$. The reciprocal of $\dfrac{0}{1}$ is $\dfrac{1}{0}$, which is not defined.

**3.** $\dfrac{2}{m}$  **4.** $\dfrac{4}{x^2}$  **5.** $-\dfrac{3n}{8}$  **6.** $\dfrac{1}{x}$

**7.** $\dfrac{5}{2m^2}$  **8.** $\dfrac{1}{2bc}$  **9.** $\dfrac{x - y}{x + y}$  **10.** $\dfrac{1}{x - 2}$

**11.** $\dfrac{y}{5} \cdot \dfrac{5 - y}{y^2 - 25}$

$= \dfrac{-y(y - 5)}{5(y - 5)(y + 5)}$

$= \dfrac{-y}{5y + 25}$

**12.** $\dfrac{m^2 + 2m + 1}{?} \cdot \dfrac{m - 1}{m + 1}$

$= \dfrac{(m + 1)(m + 1)(m - 1)}{2(m + 1)}$

$= \dfrac{(m - 1)(m + 1)}{2}$

$= \dfrac{m^2 - 1}{2}$

**13.** $\dfrac{a^2}{b^2} \cdot \dfrac{a^2}{b^2}$

$= \dfrac{a^4}{b^4}$

**14.** $\dfrac{a^2}{b} \cdot \dfrac{b^2}{a^2}$

$= b$

**15.** $\dfrac{(-a)^2}{b} \cdot \dfrac{b}{a}$

$= \dfrac{a^2}{a}$

$= a$

**16.** $\dfrac{3m}{m + 1} \cdot \dfrac{1}{m - 2}$

$= \dfrac{3m}{m^2 - m - 2}$

**17.** $\dfrac{b^2 - 9}{4b} \cdot \dfrac{1}{b - 3}$

$= \dfrac{(b - 3)(b + 3)}{4b(b - 3)}$

$= \dfrac{b + 3}{4b}$

127

18. $\dfrac{y^2 + 8y + 16}{y^2} \cdot \dfrac{1}{y + 4}$

$= \dfrac{(y + 4)(y + 4)}{y^2(y + 4)}$

$= \dfrac{y + 4}{y^2}$

19. $\dfrac{2a^3}{a + 1} \cdot \dfrac{a + 1}{a^2}$

$= 2a$

20. $\dfrac{p^2}{y^2 - 4} \cdot \dfrac{2 - y}{p}$

$= \dfrac{-p^2(y - 2)}{p(y - 2)(y + 2)}$

$= \dfrac{-p}{y + 2}$

21. $\dfrac{x^2 - 16}{16 - x^2} \cdot \dfrac{x}{7}$

$= \dfrac{x(x - 4)(x + 4)}{-7(x^2 - 16)}$

$= \dfrac{x(x - 4)(x + 4)}{-7(x - 4)(x + 4)}$

$= \dfrac{x}{-7}$

22. $\dfrac{x^2 - 4x + 4}{3} \cdot \dfrac{2x}{x^2 - 4}$

$= \dfrac{2x(x - 2)(x - 2)}{3(x - 2)(x + 2)}$

$= \dfrac{2x(x - 2)}{3(x + 2)}$

$= \dfrac{2x^2 - 4x}{3x + 6}$

23. $\dfrac{a^2 + 2ab + b^2}{2x} \cdot \dfrac{x^2}{a + b}$

$= \dfrac{x^2(a + b)(a + b)}{2x(a + b)}$

$= \dfrac{x(a + b)}{2}$

$= \dfrac{ax + bx}{2}$

24. $\dfrac{k^2 - 81}{k^2 - 36} \cdot \dfrac{k + 6}{k - 9}$

$= \dfrac{(k - 9)(k + 9)(k + 6)}{(k - 6)(k + 6)(k - 9)}$

$= \dfrac{k + 9}{k - 6}$

25. $\dfrac{t^2 + 8t + 16}{w^2 - 6w + 9} \cdot \dfrac{3w - 9}{2t + 8}$

$= \dfrac{3(t + 4)(t + 4)(w - 3)}{2(w - 3)(w - 3)(t + 4)}$

$= \dfrac{3(t + 4)}{2(w - 3)}$

$= \dfrac{3t + 12}{2w - 6}$

26. $\dfrac{k + 2}{m^2 + 4m + 4} \cdot \dfrac{m + 4}{4k + 8}$

$= \dfrac{(k + 2)(m + 4)}{4(m + 2)(m + 2)(k + 2)}$

$= \dfrac{m + 4}{4(m + 2)^2}$

$= \dfrac{m + 4}{4m^2 + 16m + 16}$

27. $\dfrac{x}{x + 2} \cdot \dfrac{x^2 + 5x + 6}{x^2}$

$= \dfrac{x(x + 3)(x + 2)}{x^2(x + 2)}$

$= \dfrac{x + 3}{x}$

28. $\dfrac{x^2 + x - 2}{x^2 + 5x + 6} \cdot \dfrac{x^2 + 7x + 12}{x^2 + 2x - 3}$

$= \dfrac{(x + 2)(x - 1)(x + 4)(x + 3)}{(x + 2)(x + 3)(x + 3)(x - 1)}$

$= \dfrac{x + 4}{x + 3}$

29. $\dfrac{2m^2 + 7m - 15}{m + 5} \cdot \dfrac{3m + 2}{9m^2 - 4}$

$= \dfrac{(2m - 3)(m + 5)(3m + 2)}{(m + 5)(3m - 2)(3m + 2)}$

$= \dfrac{2m - 3}{3m - 2}$

30. $\dfrac{2x^2 - x - 15}{x^2 - 2x - 3} \cdot \dfrac{1 - x^2}{2x^2 + 3x - 5}$

$= \dfrac{(2x + 5)(x - 3)(1 - x)(1 + x)}{(x - 3)(x + 1)(2x + 5)(x - 1)}$

$= \dfrac{1 - x}{x - 1}$

$= \dfrac{-(x - 1)}{x - 1}$

$= -1$

31. $\dfrac{x^2 + 5x + 6}{x^2 - x - 12} \cdot \dfrac{x - 4}{x^2 + 11x + 18} \cdot \dfrac{x^2 + 14x + 45}{x + 7}$

$= \dfrac{(x + 2)(x + 3)(x - 4)(x + 5)(x + 9)}{(x - 4)(x + 3)(x + 2)(x + 9)(x + 7)}$

$= \dfrac{x + 5}{x + 7}$

32. $\dfrac{2x - 3}{2x^2 - 7x + 6} \cdot \dfrac{x^2 + 3x - 10}{5x + 1} \cdot \dfrac{3x^2 + 2x - 1}{3x^2 + 14x - 5}$

$= \dfrac{(2x - 3)(x + 5)(x - 2)(3x - 1)(x + 1)}{(2x - 3)(x - 2)(5x + 1)(3x - 1)(x + 5)}$

$= \dfrac{x + 1}{5x + 1}$

33. $\dfrac{(x - 1)(x + 1)}{2(x + 1)(x + 6)} \div \dfrac{(2x - 1)(x - 1)}{4(2x - 3)(x + 6)}$

$\qquad \cdot \dfrac{(x + 4)(x - 1)}{(x + 6)(x - 1)}$

$= \dfrac{(x - 1)}{2(x + 6)} \div \dfrac{(2x - 1)(x - 1)}{4(2x - 3)(x + 6)} \cdot \dfrac{(x + 4)}{(x + 6)}$

$= \dfrac{(x - 1)}{2(x + 6)} \cdot \dfrac{4(2x - 3)(x + 6)}{(2x - 1)(x - 1)} \cdot \dfrac{(x + 4)}{(x + 6)}$

$= \dfrac{2(2x - 3)}{(2x - 1)} \cdot \dfrac{(x + 4)}{(x + 6)}$

$= \dfrac{2(2x^2 + 5x - 12)}{2x^2 + 11x - 6}$

$= \dfrac{4x^2 + 10x - 24}{2x^2 + 11x - 6}$

34. $\dfrac{x^2 - y^2}{2} \div 2x + 2y$

$= \dfrac{x^2 - y^2}{2} \cdot \dfrac{1}{2x + 2y}$

$= \dfrac{(x - y)(x + y)}{4(x + y)}$

$= \dfrac{x - y}{4} = \text{width}$

35. Let $a$ = original allowance.

$\dfrac{2a + 3}{2} = 10$

$2a + 3 = 20$

$2a = 17$

$a = 8.5$

$\$8.50$

128

**36.** $40,000 + .15(40,000)$

$= 40,000 + 6000$

$= 46,000$

Total for 2 years $= 2(46,000)$

$\qquad = \$92,000$

or

$2[40,000 + 0.075(40,000)] + 0.075[40,000$

$+ 0.075(40,000)]$

$= 2(43,000) + 0.075(43,000)$

$= 86,000 + 3225$

$= 89,225$

Total for 2 years $= \$89,225$

JoAnn should choose 15% option.

**37.** $\frac{7}{8}$ below water

$\frac{1}{8}$ above water

$\frac{1}{8} = .125$

12.5% above water

**38.** 1 minute to get completely in; 1 minute to get completely out; 2 minutes

**39.**

| | Amount | Yearly Interest |
|---|---|---|
| At 9% | 5000 | .09(5000) |
| At 8% | $x$ | .08$x$ |

$.09(5000) + .08x = 810$

$450 + .08x = 810$

$.08x = 360$

$x = 4500$

Marta invested $4500.

**40.** $x + 3 < -17$      **41.** $9m^4 + 12m^2n + 4n^2$

$\quad x < -20$

**42.** $\frac{1}{2}x^2 = 2 \cdot \frac{1}{4} \cdot x \cdot x$

$\frac{1}{4}ax = \frac{1}{4} \cdot a \cdot x$

$\frac{1}{2}x^2 - \frac{1}{4}ax = \frac{1}{4}x(2x - a)$

**43.** $\frac{m^2 - 4}{2} \cdot \frac{4}{m - 2}$

$= \frac{(m - 2)(m + 2) \cdot 4}{2(m - 2)}$

$= 2(m + 2)$

$= 2m + 4$

**PAGE 318    EXTRA**

In step 6 dividing by $a - b$ is the fallacy because $a - b = 0$.

---

**8-4**    **Dividing Polynomials**

**1.** degree of dividend - degree of divisor

$\quad$ = degree of quotient

**2.** A factor is a number that is being multiplied.

$\quad$ no; yes

**3.** $a$    **4.** $b$    **5.** $4m^2$    **6.** $x$    **7.** $x^2$    **8.** $x^2$

**9.**
$$x + 3 \overline{\smash{\big)}\ x^2 + 7x + 12}$$
quotient: $x + 4$
$$\underline{x^2 + 3x}$$
$$4x + 12$$
$$\underline{4x + 12}$$
$$0$$

**10.**
$$x + 5 \overline{\smash{\big)}\ x^2 + 9x + 20}$$
quotient: $x + 4$
$$\underline{x^2 + 5x}$$
$$4x + 20$$
$$\underline{4x + 20}$$
$$0$$

**PAGES 320-321     EXERCISES**

**11.**
$$a - 7 \overline{\smash{\big)}\ a^2 - 2a - 35}$$
quotient: $a + 5$
$$\underline{a^2 - 7a}$$
$$5a - 35$$
$$\underline{5a - 35}$$
$$0$$

**12.**
$$x - 2 \overline{\smash{\big)}\ x^2 + 6x - 16}$$
quotient: $x + 8$
$$\underline{x^2 - 2x}$$
$$8x - 16$$
$$\underline{8x - 16}$$
$$0$$

**13.**
$$c + 9 \overline{\smash{\big)}\ c^2 + 12c + 36}$$
quotient: $c + 3 \; R9$
$$\underline{c^2 + 9c}$$
$$3c + 36$$
$$\underline{3c + 27}$$
$$9$$

**14.**
$$y + 7 \overline{\smash{\big)}\ y^2 - 2y - 30}$$
quotient: $y - 9 \; R33$
$$\underline{y^2 + 7y}$$
$$-9y - 30$$
$$\underline{-9y - 63}$$
$$33$$

**15.**
$$2r + 7 \overline{\smash{\big)}\ 2r^2 - 3r - 35}$$
quotient: $r - 5$
$$\underline{2r^2 + 7r}$$
$$-10r - 35$$
$$\underline{-10r - 35}$$
$$0$$

**16.**
$$3t + 4 \overline{\smash{\big)}\ 3t^2 - 14t - 24}$$
quotient: $t - 6$
$$\underline{3t^2 + 4t}$$
$$-18t - 24$$
$$\underline{-18t - 24}$$
$$0$$

**17.**
$$5x + 7 \overline{\smash{\big)}\ 10x^2 + 29x + 21}$$
quotient: $2x + 3$
$$\underline{10x^2 + 14x}$$
$$15x + 21$$
$$\underline{15x + 21}$$
$$0$$

**18.**
$$6n + 3 \overline{\smash{\big)}\ 12n^2 + 36n + 15}$$
quotient: $2n + 5$
$$\underline{12n^2 + 6n}$$
$$30n + 15$$
$$\underline{30n + 15}$$
$$0$$

**19.**
$$x - 2 \overline{\smash{\big)}\ x^3 + 0x^2 - 7x + 6}$$
quotient: $x^2 + 2x - 3$
$$\underline{x^3 - 2x^2}$$
$$2x^2 - 7x$$
$$\underline{2x^2 - 4x}$$
$$-3x + 6$$
$$\underline{-3x + 6}$$
$$0$$

**20.**

$$\begin{array}{r}
2m^2 + 3m + 7 \\
2m - 3 \enclose{longdiv}{4m^3 + 0m^2 + 5m - 21} \\
\underline{4m^3 - 6m^2}\phantom{+ 5m - 21} \\
6m^2 + 5m\phantom{- 21} \\
\underline{6m^2 - 9m}\phantom{- 21} \\
14m - 21 \\
\underline{14m - 21} \\
0
\end{array}$$

**21.**

$$\begin{array}{r}
t^2 + 4t - 1 \\
4t - 1 \enclose{longdiv}{4t^3 + 17t^2 + 0t - 1} \\
\underline{4t^3 + \phantom{1}t^2}\phantom{+ 0t - 1} \\
16t^2 + 0t\phantom{- 1} \\
\underline{16t^2 + 4t}\phantom{- 1} \\
-4t - 1 \\
\underline{-4t - 1} \\
0
\end{array}$$

**22.**

$$\begin{array}{r}
2a^2 + 3a - 4 \\
a + 3 \enclose{longdiv}{2a^3 + 9a^2 + 5a - 12} \\
\underline{2a^3 + 6a^2}\phantom{+ 5a - 12} \\
3a^2 + 5a\phantom{- 12} \\
\underline{3a^2 + 9a}\phantom{- 12} \\
-4a - 12 \\
\underline{-4a - 12.} \\
0
\end{array}$$

**23.**

$$\begin{array}{r}
3c - 2 + \dfrac{4}{9c - 2} \\
9c - 2 \enclose{longdiv}{27c^2 - 24c + 8} \\
\underline{27c^2 - \phantom{1}6c}\phantom{+ 8} \\
-18c + 8 \\
\underline{-18c + 4} \\
4
\end{array}$$

**24.**

$$\begin{array}{r}
4b + 1 + \dfrac{8}{12b - 1} \\
12b - 1 \enclose{longdiv}{48b^2 + 8b + 7} \\
\underline{48b^2 - 4b}\phantom{+ 7} \\
12b + 7 \\
\underline{12b - 1} \\
8
\end{array}$$

**25.**

$$\begin{array}{r}
3n^2 - 2n + 3 + \dfrac{3}{2n + 3} \\
2n + 3 \enclose{longdiv}{6n^3 + 5n^2 + 0n + 12} \\
\underline{6n^3 + 9n^2}\phantom{+ 0n + 12} \\
-4n^2 + 0n\phantom{+ 12} \\
\underline{-4n^2 - 6n}\phantom{+ 12} \\
6n + 12 \\
\underline{6n + 9} \\
3
\end{array}$$

**26.**

$$\begin{array}{r}
t^2 + 4t - 3 - \dfrac{3}{t - 4} \\
t - 4 \enclose{longdiv}{t^3 + 0t^2 - 19t + 9} \\
\underline{t^3 - 4t^2}\phantom{- 19t + 9} \\
4t^2 - 19t\phantom{+ 9} \\
\underline{4t^2 - 16t}\phantom{+ 9} \\
-3t + 9 \\
\underline{-3t + 12} \\
-3
\end{array}$$

**27.**

$$\begin{array}{r}
3s^2 + 2s - 3 - \dfrac{1}{s + 2} \\
s + 2 \enclose{longdiv}{3s^3 + 8s^2 + s - 7} \\
\underline{3s^3 + 6s^2}\phantom{+ s - 7} \\
2s^2 + s\phantom{- 7} \\
\underline{2s^2 + 4s}\phantom{- 7} \\
-3s - 7 \\
\underline{-3s - 6} \\
-1
\end{array}$$

**28.**

$$\begin{array}{r}
3d^2 + 2d + 3 - \dfrac{2}{3d - 2} \\
3d - 2 \enclose{longdiv}{9d^3 + 0d^2 + 5d - 8} \\
\underline{9d^3 - 6d^2}\phantom{+ 5d - 8} \\
6d^2 + 5d\phantom{- 8} \\
\underline{6d^2 - 4d}\phantom{- 8} \\
9d - 8 \\
\underline{9d - 6} \\
-2
\end{array}$$

**29.**

$$\begin{array}{r}
5t^2 - 3t - 2 \\
4t - 3 \enclose{longdiv}{20t^3 - 27t^2 + t + 6} \\
\underline{20t^3 - 15t^2}\phantom{+ t + 6} \\
-12t^2 + t\phantom{+ 6} \\
\underline{-12t^2 + 9t}\phantom{+ 6} \\
-8t + 6 \\
\underline{-8t + 6} \\
0
\end{array}$$

**30.**

$$\begin{array}{r}
3x^2 - 2 \\
2x - 3 \enclose{longdiv}{6x^3 - 9x^2 - 4x + 6} \\
\underline{6x^3 - 9x^2}\phantom{- 4x + 6} \\
0 - 4x + 6 \\
\underline{-4x + 6} \\
0
\end{array}$$

**31.**

$$\begin{array}{r}
8x^2 - 9 \\
7x + 4 \enclose{longdiv}{56x^3 + 32x^2 - 63x - 36} \\
\underline{56x^3 + 32x^2}\phantom{- 63x - 36} \\
0 - 63x - 36 \\
\underline{-63x - 36} \\
0
\end{array}$$

**32.**

$$\begin{array}{r}
x^2 + 5x - 3 \\
x + 2 \enclose{longdiv}{x^3 + 7x^2 + 7x + k} \\
\underline{x^3 + 2x^2}\phantom{+ 7x + k} \\
5x^2 + 7x\phantom{+ k} \\
\underline{5x^2 + 10x}\phantom{+ k} \\
-3x + k \\
\underline{-3x - 6} \\
0
\end{array}$$

$$k - (-6) = 0$$
$$k + 6 = 0$$
$$k = -6$$

**33.**

$$\begin{array}{r}
m^2 + 4 \\
2m - 5 \enclose{longdiv}{2m^3 - 5m^2 + 8m + k} \\
\underline{2m^3 - 5m^2}\phantom{+ 8m + k} \\
0 + 8m + k \\
\underline{8m - 20} \\
0
\end{array}$$

$$k - (-20) = 0$$
$$k + 20 = 0$$
$$k = -20$$

130

**34.**

$$\begin{array}{r}
x^2 - 5x - 6 \\
x - 2 \overline{\smash{\big)}\ x^3 - 7x^2 + 4x + k} \\
\underline{x^3 - 2x^2} \\
-5x^2 + 4x \\
\underline{-5x^2 + 10x} \\
-6x + k \\
\underline{-6x + 12} \\
15
\end{array}$$

$$k - 12 = 15$$
$$k = 27$$

**35.** Area of football field

$= 160 \text{ ft} \times 100 \text{ yds}$

$= 160 \text{ ft} \times 300 \text{ ft}$

$= 48{,}000 \text{ ft}^2$

Area of polo field

$= 160 \text{ yds} \times 300 \text{ yds}$

$= 480 \text{ ft} \times 900 \text{ ft}$

$= 432{,}000 \text{ ft}^2$

$\dfrac{432{,}000}{48{,}000} = 9$ football fields

**36. a.** 22 h/wk $\cdot$ 52 wks = 1144 h

$\qquad$ = 47 days 16 h

**b.** 20% $\times$ 1144 h

$\qquad$ = 228 h 48 min

$\qquad$ = 9 days 12 h 48 min

**37. a.** $3x + 11 + \dfrac{24}{x - 2}$  **38.** $50x = 75(16 - x)$

**b.** $3x + 1$ $\qquad\qquad\qquad 50x = 1200 - 75x$

**c.** $x^2 + 4x + 4$ $\qquad\qquad 125x = 1200$

**d.** $x^2 + 4$ $\qquad\qquad\qquad\quad x = 9.6$

**e.** $2x^3 + 3x^2 + x + 4 + \dfrac{5}{x - 1}$ $\qquad$ 9.6 ft from the fulcrum

**39.**

```
                              ┌ 31
        End of Day 9        ─ ┤ 30
                              ├ 28
                              ├ 26
  Beginning of Day 9 ─       ├ 24
  Beginning of Day 8 ═       ├ 22
                              ├ 20
  Beginning of Day 7 ─       ├ 18
                              ├ 16
  Beginning of Day 6 ═       ├ 14
                              ├ 12
  Beginning of Day 5 ─       ├ 10
                              ├ 8
  Beginning of Day 4 ═       ├ 6
                              ├ 4
  Beginning of Day 3 ─       ├ 2
  Beginning of Day 2 ═
  Beginning of Day 1 └          9 days
```

**40.** $\dfrac{9yz^5}{x^3}$  **41.** $(p + 5)(p + 5)$  **42.** $\dfrac{y^2}{x^2} \cdot \dfrac{x^2}{a^2}$

$\qquad\qquad\qquad\qquad\qquad\qquad\qquad\quad = \dfrac{y^2}{a^2}$

PAGE 324 $\qquad$ CHECKING FOR UNDERSTANDING

**1.** They are additive inverses.

**2.** No; division by zero is undefined.

**3.** $\dfrac{1}{5} + \dfrac{4}{5} = \dfrac{5}{5} = 1$ $\qquad$ **4.** $\dfrac{7}{8}$

Answers may vary.

**5.** $\dfrac{7}{a}$ $\qquad$ **6.** $\dfrac{b + 2}{x}$ $\qquad$ **7.** $\dfrac{-2}{2z}$ $\qquad$ **8.** $\dfrac{1}{11}$

$\qquad\qquad\qquad\qquad\qquad\qquad\quad = \dfrac{-1}{z}$

**9.** $\dfrac{-1}{16}$ $\qquad$ **10.** $\dfrac{a - b}{5}$ $\qquad$ **11.** $\dfrac{5k}{5m}$

$\qquad\qquad\qquad\qquad\qquad\qquad\qquad\quad = \dfrac{k}{m}$

PAGES 324-325 $\qquad$ EXERCISES

**12.** $\dfrac{2y}{2}$ $\quad$ **13.** $\dfrac{3a}{12}$ $\quad$ **14.** $\dfrac{2x}{24}$ $\quad$ **15.** $\dfrac{-t}{t}$

$= y$ $\qquad\quad = \dfrac{a}{4}$ $\qquad = \dfrac{x}{12}$ $\qquad = -1$

**16.** $\dfrac{2y - 6}{2}$ $\qquad$ **17.** $\dfrac{2m + 3}{5}$ $\qquad$ **18.** $\dfrac{a + 2 - a - 3}{6}$

$= \dfrac{2(y - 3)}{2}$ $\qquad\qquad\qquad\qquad\qquad = \dfrac{-1}{6}$

$= y - 3$

**19.** $\dfrac{x + 1}{x + 1}$ $\qquad$ **20.** $\dfrac{2}{y - 2}$ $\qquad$ **21.** $\dfrac{-y}{b + 6}$

$= 1$

**22.** $\dfrac{2n}{2n - 5} - \dfrac{5}{2n - 5}$ $\qquad$ **23.** $\dfrac{x + y}{y - 2} - \dfrac{x - y}{y - 2}$

$= \dfrac{2n - 5}{2n - 5}$ $\qquad\qquad\qquad = \dfrac{x + y - x + y}{y - 2}$

$= 1$ $\qquad\qquad\qquad\qquad\quad = \dfrac{2y}{y - 2}$

**24.** 0 $\qquad\qquad\qquad\qquad$ **25.** $\dfrac{a + b}{x - 3} - \dfrac{a + b}{x - 3}$

$\qquad\qquad\qquad\qquad\qquad\quad = \dfrac{a + b - a - b}{x - 3}$

$\qquad\qquad\qquad\qquad\qquad\quad = 0$

**26.** $\dfrac{a + b}{x - 3} + \dfrac{a + b}{x - 3}$ $\qquad$ **27.** $\dfrac{r^2 + s^2}{r - s}$

$= \dfrac{2a + 2b}{x - 3}$

**28.** $\dfrac{x^2 - y^2}{x - y}$ $\qquad\qquad$ **29.** $\dfrac{m^2 + 2mn + n^2}{m + n}$

$= \dfrac{(x - y)(x + y)}{x - y}$ $\qquad = \dfrac{(m + n)(m + n)}{m + n}$

$= x + y$ $\qquad\qquad\qquad = m + n$

**30.** $\dfrac{x^2 - 2xy - y^2}{x - y}$ $\qquad$ **31.** $\dfrac{12n + 8}{3n + 2}$

$\qquad\qquad\qquad\qquad\qquad\quad = \dfrac{4(3n + 2)}{3n + 2}$

$\qquad\qquad\qquad\qquad\qquad\quad = 4$

32. $\dfrac{6x + 6y}{x + y}$

$= \dfrac{6(x + y)}{x + y}$

$= 6$

33. $\dfrac{a^2 - b^2}{a - b}$

$= \dfrac{(a - b)(a + b)}{a - b}$

$= a + b$

34. $\dfrac{r^2}{r - 3} - \dfrac{9}{r - 3}$

$= \dfrac{r^2 - 9}{r - 3}$

$= \dfrac{(r - 3)(r + 3)}{r - 3}$

$= r + 3$

35. $\dfrac{x^2 + 2x + 1}{x^2 - 1}$

$= \dfrac{(x + 1)(x + 1)}{(x - 1)(x + 1)}$

$= \dfrac{x + 1}{x - 1}$

36. $\dfrac{x^2 + 2x + 1}{(x + 1)^2}$

$= \dfrac{(x + 1)^2}{(x + 1)^2}$

$= 1$

37. $\dfrac{x - 1 - x + 1}{(x + 1)^2}$

$= 0$

38. $\dfrac{25 - k^2}{k + 5}$

$= \dfrac{(5 - k)(k + 5)}{k + 5}$

$= 5 - k$

39. $\dfrac{x + 1}{x^2 + 2x + 1}$

$= \dfrac{x + 1}{(x + 1)(x + 1)}$

$= \dfrac{1}{x + 1}$

40. $\dfrac{8y + 12}{4y^2 + 12y + 9}$

$= \dfrac{4(2y + 3)}{(2y + 3)^2}$

$= \dfrac{4}{2y + 3}$

41. $\dfrac{2 - t}{t^2 - t - 2}$

$= \dfrac{2 - t}{(t - 2)(t + 1)}$

$= \dfrac{-(t - 2)}{(t - 2)(t + 1)}$

$= \dfrac{-1}{t + 1}$

42. $P = 2\left(\dfrac{3t - 6}{t^2 + t - 6}\right) + 2\left(\dfrac{t^2 - 2t}{t^2 + t - 6}\right)$

$= \dfrac{6t - 12 + 2t^2 - 4t}{t^2 + t - 6}$

$= \dfrac{2t^2 + 2t - 12}{t^2 + t - 6}$

$= \dfrac{2(t^2 + t - 6)}{t^2 + t - 6}$

$= 2$

43. $P = 2\left(\dfrac{-1}{x - 2}\right) + 2\left(\dfrac{x^2 - 5}{2 - x}\right)$

$= \dfrac{-2}{x - 2} + \dfrac{2x^2 - 10}{2 - x}$

$= \dfrac{-2}{x - 2} - \dfrac{2x^2 - 10}{x - 2}$

$= \dfrac{-2 - 2x^2 + 10}{x - 2}$

$= \dfrac{-2x^2 + 8}{x - 2}$

$= \dfrac{-2(x^2 - 4)}{x - 2}$

$= \dfrac{-2(x - 2)(x + 2)}{x - 2}$

$= -2(x + 2)$

$= -2x - 4$

44. $P = 2\left(\dfrac{x - 1}{x^2 + 2x + 1}\right) + 2\left(\dfrac{x + 1}{x^2 + 2x + 1}\right)$

$= \dfrac{2x - 2 + 2x + 2}{x^2 + 2x + 1}$

$= \dfrac{4x}{x^2 + 2x + 1}$

45. yes; yes; no

46. $\dfrac{20 \cdot 12{,}500 \cdot \frac{2}{3}}{5}$

$= \$33{,}333.33$

47. $T = 24(1 + .05)^{368}$

$= \$1{,}506{,}167{,}664$

48.

| | $d$ | $r$ | $t$ |
|---|---|---|---|
| Alma | $x$ | 35 mph | $\dfrac{x}{35}$ |
| Reiko | $266 - x$ | 42 mph | $\dfrac{x}{35} - 1$ |

$266 - x = 42\left(\dfrac{x}{35} - 1\right)$

$266 - x = \dfrac{42x}{35} - 42$

$266 - x = \dfrac{6}{5}x - 42$

$\dfrac{11}{5}x = 308$

$x = 140$

$\dfrac{x}{35} = \dfrac{140}{35} = 4$

It will take Alma 4 hrs and Reiko 3 hrs. They
will be 266 miles apart at 12:00 noon.

49. $-\dfrac{1}{2} < r < \dfrac{8}{3}$

50. $56m + 16$

51. $1000 = 2 \cdot 2 \cdot 2 \cdot 5 \cdot 5 \cdot 5$

$= 2^3 \cdot 5^3$

**52.**

$$m - 4 \overline{\smash{\big)}\, m^3 - 6m^2 - m + 32} \quad \leftarrow m^2 - 2m - 9 - \frac{4}{m - 4}$$

$$\underline{m^3 - 4m^2}$$
$$-2m^2 - m$$
$$\underline{-2m^2 + 8m}$$
$$-9m + 32$$
$$\underline{-9m + 36}$$
$$-4$$

## PAGE 325   MID-CHAPTER REVIEW

**1.** $\dfrac{a - 7}{(a + 1)(a - 7)} = \dfrac{1}{a + 1}$

$a + 1 \neq 0, \quad a - 7 \neq 0$

$a \neq -1 \qquad a \neq 7$

**2.** $\dfrac{y - 3}{y^2 - 9}$

$= \dfrac{y - 3}{(y - 3)(y + 3)}$

$= \dfrac{1}{y + 3}$

$y - 3 \neq 0, \quad y + 3 \neq 0$

$\qquad y \neq 3 \qquad\qquad y \neq -3$

**3.** $\dfrac{4y^2 + 7y - 2}{8y^2 + 15y - 2}$

$= \dfrac{(4y - 1)(y + 2)}{(8y - 1)(y + 2)}$

$= \dfrac{4y - 1}{8y - 1}$

$8y - 1 \neq 0, \quad y + 2 \neq 0$

$\qquad 8y \neq 1 \qquad\qquad y \neq -2$

$\qquad y \neq \dfrac{1}{8}$

**4.** $\dfrac{y^2 - 4}{y^2 - 1} \cdot \dfrac{y + 1}{y + 2}$

$= \dfrac{(y - 2)(y + 2)(y + 1)}{(y - 1)(y + 1)(y + 2)}$

$= \dfrac{y - 2}{y - 1}$

**5.** $\dfrac{m^2 + 16}{m^2 - 16} \cdot \dfrac{m - 4}{m + 4}$

$= \dfrac{(m^2 + 16)(m - 4)}{(m - 4)(m + 4)(m + 4)}$

$= \dfrac{m^2 + 16}{m^2 + 8m + 16}$

**6.** $\dfrac{x + 3}{x + 4} \cdot \dfrac{x}{x^2 + 7x + 12}$

$= \dfrac{x(x + 3)}{(x + 4)(x + 3)(x + 4)}$

$= \dfrac{x}{x^2 + 8x + 16}$

**7.** $\dfrac{a^2}{b} \div \dfrac{a^2}{b^2}$

$= \dfrac{a^2}{b} \cdot \dfrac{b^2}{a^2}$

$= b$

**8.** $\dfrac{q}{y^2 - 4} \div \dfrac{q^2}{y + 2}$

$= \dfrac{q}{y^2 - 4} \cdot \dfrac{y + 2}{q^2}$

$= \dfrac{q(y + 2)}{(y - 2)(y + 2)q^2}$

$= \dfrac{1}{q(y - 2)}$

$= \dfrac{1}{qy - 2q}$

**9.** $\dfrac{m^2 + 2mn + n^2}{3m} \div \dfrac{m^2 - n^2}{2}$

$= \dfrac{m^2 + 2mn + n^2}{3m} \cdot \dfrac{2}{m^2 - n^2}$

$= \dfrac{2(m + n)(m + n)}{3m(m - n)(m + n)}$

$= \dfrac{2(m + n)}{3m(m - n)}$

$= \dfrac{2m + 2n}{3m^2 - 3mn}$

**10.**

$$m + 3 \overline{\smash{\big)}\, 2m^2 + 5m - 3} \quad \leftarrow 2m - 1$$

$$\underline{2m^2 + 6m}$$
$$-m - 3$$
$$\underline{-m - 3}$$
$$0$$

**11.**

$$3t + 1 \overline{\smash{\big)}\, 3t^3 - 11t^2 - 31t + 7} \quad \leftarrow t^2 - 4t - 9 + \frac{16}{3t + 1}$$

$$\underline{3t^2 + t^2}$$
$$-12t^2 - 31t$$
$$\underline{-12t^2 - 4t}$$
$$-27t + 7$$
$$\underline{-27t - 9}$$
$$16$$

## 8-6   Problem-Solving Strategy: List Possibilities

### PAGE 327   CHECKING FOR UNDERSTANDING

**1.** They are all multiplies of 12 and 12 = 3 · 4.

**2.** look for a pattern, make a table or chart, make a diagram, guess and check

**3.** 0, 8, 16, 24, 32, 40, 48

0, 12, 24, 36, 48

0, 24, and 48 are divisible by both 8 and 12.

**4.**

| Total Points | 3 Points | 4 Points | 8 Points |
|---|---|---|---|
| 9 | 3 | 0 | 0 |
| 12 | 0 | 3 | 0 |
| 24 | 0 | 0 | 3 |
| 10 | 2 | 1 | 0 |
| 14 | 2 | 0 | 1 |
| 11 | 1 | 2 | 0 |
| 16 | 0 | 2 | 1 |
| 19 | 1 | 0 | 2 |
| 20 | 0 | 1 | 2 |
| 15 | 1 | 1 | 1 |

10 point totals are possible.

**5.**

| | | |
|---|---|---|
| 111 | 122 | 223 |
| 222 | 212 | 232 |
| 333 | 221 | 322 |
| 112 | 133 | 123 |
| 121 | 313 | 132 |
| 211 | 331 | 213 |
| 113 | 233 | 231 |
| 131 | 323 | 312 |
| 311 | 332 | 321 |

27 different codes

**6.**

| | | |
|---|---|---|
| 12:00 | 12:49, 12:58, 12:59 | 3 |
| 1:00 | | 0 |
| 2:00 | 2:59 | 1 |
| 3:00 | 3:49, 3:58, 3:59 | 3 |
| 4:00 | 4:39, 4:48, 4:49, 4:57, 4:58, 4:59 | 6 |
| 5:00 | 5:29, 5:38, 5:39, 5:47, 5:48, 5:49, 5:56, 5:57, 5:58, 5:59 | 10 |
| 6:00 | 6:19, 6:28, 6:29, 6:37, 6:38, 6:39, 6:46, 6:47, 6:48, 6:49, 6:55, 6:56, 6:57, 6:58, 6:59 | 15 |
| 7:00 | 7:09, 7:18, 7:19, 7:27, 7:28, 7:29, 7:36, 7:37, 7:38, 7:39, 7:45, 7:46, 7:47, 7:48, 7:49, 7:54, 7:55, 7:56, 7:57, 7:58, 7:59 | 21 |
| 8:00 | 8:08, 8:09, 8:17, 8:18, 8:19, 8:26, 8:27, 8:28, 8:29, 8:35, 8:36, 8:37, 8:38, 8:39, 8:44, 8:45, 8:46, 8:47, 8:48, 8:49, 8:53, 8:54, 8:55, 8:56, 8:57, 8:58, 8:59 | 27 |
| 9:00 | 9:07, 9:08, 9:09, 9:16, 9:17, 9:18, 9:19, 9:25, 9:26, 9:27, 9:28, 9:29, 9:34, 9:35, 9:36, 9:37, 9:38, 9:39, 9:43, 9:44, 9:45, 9:46, 9:47, 9:48, 9:49, 9:52, 9:53, 9:54, 9:55, 9:56, 9:57, 9:58, 9:59 | 33 |
| 10:00 | | 0 |
| 11:00 | 11:59 | 1 |

120 times

**7.** Let $e$ = total value of estate.

$$e - \frac{1}{2}e - 50,000 - \frac{1}{2}\left(e - \frac{1}{2}e - 50,000\right)$$

$$- \frac{1}{2}\left[e - \frac{1}{2}e - 50,000 - \frac{1}{2}\left(e - \frac{1}{2}e - 50,000\right)\right]$$

$$= 10,000$$

$$\frac{1}{2}e - 50,000 - \frac{1}{2}e + \frac{1}{4}e + 25,000 - \frac{1}{2}e + \frac{1}{4}e$$

$$+ 25,000 + \frac{1}{4}\left(e - \frac{1}{2}e - 50,000\right) = 10,000$$

$$\frac{1}{4}e - \frac{1}{8}e - 12,500 = 10,000$$

$$\frac{1}{8}e = 22,500$$

$$e = \$180,000$$

**8.**

| p | vp | s | t |
|---|---|---|---|
| p | vp | t | s |
| p | t | vp | s |
| p | t | s | vp |
| p | s | vp | t |
| p | s | t | vp |

6 arrangements with president in 1st chair.
So 6 × 4 = 24 total arrangements.

**9.** Since Ed was freshly shaved and neatly trimmed and there are only two barbers, we can assume that Floyd did it. Therefore the visitor went to Floyd's.

**10.** yes

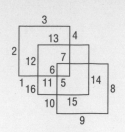

**11.** Let $a$ = # of people ahead of Felicia
Let $b$ = # of people behind Felicia

$$a = b + 2$$
$$1 + a + b = 3b$$
$$1 + (b + 2) + b = 3b$$
$$2b + 3 = 3b$$
$$3 = b, \quad a = 5$$

5 people

**12.**

| 1st Square Space | Possible 2nd Square Space | Number of Dominoes |
|---|---|---|
| blank | blank, 1, 2, 3, 4, 5, 6 | 7 |
| 1 | 1, 2, 3, 4, 5, 6 | 6 |
| 2 | 2, 3, 4, 5, 6 | 5 |
| 3 | 3, 4, 5, 6 | 4 |
| 4 | 4, 5, 6 | 3 |
| 5 | 5, 6 | 2 |
| 6 | 6 | 1 |

28 dominoes

**13. a.** It is also happy because it contains the same digits.

**b.** 1, 7, 10, 13, 19, 23, 28, 31, 32, 44, 49, 68, 70, 79, 82, 86, 91, 94, 97

**PAGE 328    COOPERATIVE LEARNING ACTIVITY**

**1.** The first five are 6, 28, 496, 8128, and 33550336.

**2.** true

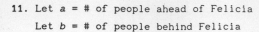

**8-7    Rational Expressions with Unlike Denominators**

**PAGE 331    CHECKING FOR UNDERSTANDING**

**1.** Yes; when one denominator is a factor of the other.

**2.** You cannot add fractions by adding numerators and adding denominators. To add, first write each term with the LCD, $11(x - 1)$. Then add the numerators.

**3.** $a^2 = a \cdot a$
$a = a$
The LCD is $a^2$.

**4.** $b^3 = b \cdot b \cdot b$
$ab = ab$
The LCD is $ab^3$.

5. $20a^2 = 2 \cdot 2 \cdot 5 \cdot a \cdot a$

   $24ab^3 = 2 \cdot 2 \cdot 2 \cdot 3 \cdot a \cdot b \cdot b \cdot b$

   The LCD is $2^3 \cdot 3 \cdot 5 \cdot a^2 \cdot b^3 = 120a^2b^3$.

6. $12an^2 = 2 \cdot 2 \cdot 3 \cdot a \cdot n \cdot n$

   $40a^4 = 2 \cdot 2 \cdot 2 \cdot 5 \cdot a \cdot a \cdot a \cdot a$

   The LCD is $2^3 \cdot 3 \cdot 5 \cdot a^4 \cdot n^2 = 120a^4n^2$.

7. $56x^3y = 2 \cdot 2 \cdot 2 \cdot 7 \cdot x \cdot x \cdot x \cdot y$

   $49ax^2 = 7 \cdot 7 \cdot a \cdot x \cdot x$

   The LCD is $2^3 \cdot 7^2 \cdot a \cdot x^3 \cdot y = 392ax^3y$.

8. LCD is $(a + 5)(a - 3)$.

9. LCD is $n(m + n)$.

10. $3x - 6 = 3 \cdot (x - 2)$

    $x - 2 = x - 2$

    The LCD is $3(x - 2)$.

11. $\dfrac{m - n}{m + n} \cdot \dfrac{1}{m^2 - n^2}$

    $m + n = m + n$

    $m^2 - n^2 = (m - n)(m + n)$

    The LCD is $(m - n)(m + n)$.

    $\dfrac{m - n}{m - n} \cdot \dfrac{m - n}{m + n} - \dfrac{1}{(m - n)(m + n)}$

    $= \dfrac{m^2 - 2mn - n^2 - 1}{(m - n)(m + n)}$

    $= \dfrac{m^2 - 2mn - n^2 - 1}{m^2 - n^2}$

12. $\dfrac{a}{a - b} + \dfrac{b}{2b + 3a}$

    $a - b = a - b$

    $2b + 3a = 2b + 3a$

    The LCD is $(a - b)(2b + 3a)$.

    $\dfrac{2b + 3a}{2b + 3a} \cdot \dfrac{a}{a - b} + \dfrac{a - b}{a - b} \cdot \dfrac{b}{2b + 3a}$

    $= \dfrac{2ab + 3a^2 + ab - b^2}{(a - b)(2b + 3a)}$

    $= \dfrac{3a^2 + 3ab - b^2}{3a^2 - ab - 2b^2}$

**PAGES 332–333    EXERCISES**

13. $\dfrac{t}{3} + \dfrac{2t}{7}$

    The LCD is 21.

    $\dfrac{7}{7} \cdot \dfrac{t}{3} + \dfrac{3}{3} \cdot \dfrac{2t}{7}$

    $= \dfrac{7t + 6t}{21}$

    $= \dfrac{13t}{21}$

14. $\dfrac{2n}{5} - \dfrac{3m}{4}$

    The LCD is 20.

    $\dfrac{4}{4} \cdot \dfrac{2n}{5} - \dfrac{5}{5} \cdot \dfrac{3m}{4}$

    $= \dfrac{8n - 15m}{20}$

15. $\dfrac{5}{2a} + \dfrac{-3}{6a}$

    $2a = 2 \cdot a$

    $6a = 2 \cdot 3 \cdot a$

    The LCD is $2 \cdot 3 \cdot a = 6a$.

    $\dfrac{3}{3} \cdot \dfrac{5}{2a} + \dfrac{-3}{6a}$

    $= \dfrac{15 - 3}{6a}$

    $= \dfrac{12}{6a}$

    $= \dfrac{2}{a}$

16. $\dfrac{7}{3a} - \dfrac{3}{6a^2}$

    $3a = 3 \cdot a$

    $6a^2 = 2 \cdot 3 \cdot a \cdot a$

    The LCD is $6a^2$.

    $\dfrac{2a}{2a} \cdot \dfrac{7}{3a} - \dfrac{3}{6a^2}$

    $= \dfrac{14a - 3}{6a^2}$

17. $\dfrac{5}{xy} + \dfrac{6}{yz}$

    $xy = x \cdot y$

    $yz = y \cdot z$

    The LCD is $xyz$.

    $\dfrac{z}{z} \cdot \dfrac{5}{xy} + \dfrac{x}{x} \cdot \dfrac{6}{yz}$

    $= \dfrac{5z + 6x}{xyz}$

18. $\dfrac{3z}{7w^2} - \dfrac{2z}{w}$

    $7w^2 = 7 \cdot w \cdot w$

    $w = w$

    The LCD is $7w^2$.

    $\dfrac{3z}{7w^2} - \dfrac{7w}{7w} \cdot \dfrac{2z}{w}$

    $= \dfrac{3z - 14wz}{7w^2}$

19. $\dfrac{2}{t} + \dfrac{t + 3}{s}$

    The LCD is $st$.

    $\dfrac{s}{s} \cdot \dfrac{2}{t} + \dfrac{t}{t} \cdot \dfrac{t + 3}{s}$

    $= \dfrac{2s + t^2 + 3t}{st}$

20. $\dfrac{m}{1(m - n)} - \dfrac{5}{m}$

    The LCD is $m(m - n)$.

    $\dfrac{m}{m} \cdot \dfrac{m}{m - n} - \dfrac{m - n}{m - n} \cdot \dfrac{5}{m}$

    $= \dfrac{m^2 - 5m - 5n}{m(m - n)}$

21. $\dfrac{4a}{2a + 6} + \dfrac{3}{a + 3}$

    $2a + 6 = 2(a + 3)$

    $a + 3 = a + 3$

    The LCD is $2(a + 3) = 2a + 6$.

    $\dfrac{4a}{2a + 6} + \dfrac{2}{2} \cdot \dfrac{3}{a + 3}$

    $= \dfrac{4a + 6}{2a + 6}$

    $= \dfrac{2(2a + 3)}{2(a + 3)}$

    $= \dfrac{2a + 3}{a + 3}$

22. $\dfrac{-3}{a - 5} + \dfrac{-6}{a^2 - 5a}$

$a - 5 = a - 5$

$a^2 - 5a = a(a - 5)$

The LCD is $a(a - 5)$.

$\dfrac{a}{a} \cdot \dfrac{-3}{a - 5} + \dfrac{-6}{a^2 - 5a}$

$= \dfrac{-3a - 6}{a^2 - 5a}$

23. $\dfrac{2y}{y^2 - 25} + \dfrac{y + 5}{y - 5}$

$y^2 - 25 = (y - 5)(y + 5)$

$y - 5 = y - 5$

The LCD is $(y - 5)(y + 5)$.

$\dfrac{2y}{y^2 - 25} + \dfrac{y + 5}{y + 5} \cdot \dfrac{y + 5}{y - 5}$

$= \dfrac{2y + y^2 + 10y + 25}{y^2 - 25}$

$= \dfrac{y^2 + 12y + 25}{y^2 - 25}$

24. $\dfrac{3a + 2}{3a - 6} - \dfrac{a + 2}{a^2 - 4}$

$3a - 6 = 3(a - 2)$

$a^2 - 4 = (a - 2)(a + 2)$

The LCD is $3(a - 2)(a + 2)$.

$\dfrac{a + 2}{a + 2} \cdot \dfrac{3a + 2}{3a - 6} - \dfrac{3}{3} \cdot \dfrac{a + 2}{a^2 - 4}$

$= \dfrac{3a^2 + 8a + 4 - 3a - 6}{3(a - 2)(a + 2)}$

$= \dfrac{3a^2 + 5a - 2}{3(a - 2)(a + 2)}$

$= \dfrac{(3a - 1)(a + 2)}{3(a - 2)(a + 2)}$

$= \dfrac{3a - 1}{3a - 6}$

25. $\dfrac{x^2 - 1}{x + 1} + \dfrac{x^2 + 1}{x - 1}$

The LCD is $(x - 1)(x + 1)$.

$\dfrac{x - 1}{x - 1} \cdot \dfrac{x^2 - 1}{x + 1} + \dfrac{x + 1}{x + 1} \cdot \dfrac{x^2 + 1}{x - 1}$

$= \dfrac{x^3 - x^2 - x + 1 + x^3 + x^2 + x + 1}{(x - 1)(x + 1)}$

$= \dfrac{2x^3 + 2}{x^2 - 1}$

$= \dfrac{2(x^3 + 1)}{x^2 - 1}$

26. $\dfrac{k}{2k + 1} - \dfrac{2}{k + 2}$

The LCD is $(2k + 1)(k + 2)$.

$\dfrac{k + 2}{k + 2} \cdot \dfrac{k}{2k + 1} - \dfrac{2k + 1}{2k + 1} \cdot \dfrac{2}{k + 2}$

$= \dfrac{k(k + 2) - 2(2k + 1)}{(k + 2)(2k + 1)}$

$= \dfrac{k^2 + 2k - 4k - 2}{(k + 2)(2k + 1)}$

$= \dfrac{k^2 - 2k - 2}{(k + 2)(2k + 1)}$

27. $\dfrac{-18}{y^2 - 9} + \dfrac{7}{3 - y}$

$= \dfrac{-18}{y^2 - 9} - \dfrac{7}{y - 3}$

$y^2 - 9 = (y - 3)(y + 3)$

$y - 3 = y - 3$

The LCD is $(y - 3)(y + 3)$.

$\dfrac{-18}{(y - 3)(y + 3)} - \dfrac{y + 3}{y + 3} \cdot \dfrac{7}{y - 3}$

$= \dfrac{-18 - 7y - 21}{(y - 3)(y + 3)}$

$= \dfrac{-7y - 39}{y^2 - 9}$

28. $\dfrac{a - 1}{4ab} + \dfrac{a^2 - a}{16b^2}$

$4ab = 2 \cdot 2 \cdot a \cdot b$

$16b^2 = 2 \cdot 2 \cdot 2 \cdot 2 \cdot b \cdot b$

The LCD is $2^4 ab^2 = 16ab^2$

$\dfrac{4b}{4b} \cdot \dfrac{a - 1}{4ab} + \dfrac{a}{a} \cdot \dfrac{a^2 - a}{16b^2}$

$= \dfrac{4ab - 4b + a^3 - a^2}{16ab^2}$

$= \dfrac{4b(a - 1) + a^2(a - 1)}{16ab^2}$

$= \dfrac{(4b + a^2)(a - 1)}{16ab^2}$

29. $\dfrac{x - 1}{3xy} - \dfrac{x^2 - x}{9y^2}$

$3xy = 3 \cdot x \cdot y$

$9y^2 = 3 \cdot 3 \cdot y \cdot y$

The LCD is $3^2 \cdot x \cdot y^2 = 9xy^2$.

$\dfrac{3y}{3y} \cdot \dfrac{x - 1}{3xy} - \dfrac{x}{x} \cdot \dfrac{x^2 - x}{9y^2}$

$= \dfrac{3xy - 3y - x^3 + x^2}{9xy^2}$

136

30. $a^2 + 4a + 4 = (a + 2)^2$

$\qquad a - 2 = a - 2$

The LCD is $(a + 2)^2(a - 2)$.

$= \dfrac{a - 2}{(a + 2)^2} \cdot \dfrac{a - 2}{a - 2} + \dfrac{a + 2}{a - 2} \cdot \dfrac{a^2 + 4a + 4}{(a + 2)^2}$

$= \dfrac{a^2 - 4a + 4 + a^3 + 6a^2 + 12a + 8}{(a + 2)^2(a - 2)}$

$= \dfrac{a^3 + 7a^2 + 8a + 12}{(a + 2)^2(a - 2)}$

31. $\dfrac{x^2}{4x^2 - 9} + \dfrac{x}{(2x + 3)^2}$

$\qquad 4x^2 - 9 = (2x - 3)(2x + 3)$

$\qquad (2x + 3)^2 = (2x + 3)(2x + 3)$

The LCD is $(2x + 3)^2(2x - 3)$.

$\dfrac{2x + 3}{2x + 3} \cdot \dfrac{x^2}{(2x - 3)(2x + 3)} + \dfrac{2x - 3}{2x - 3} \cdot \dfrac{x}{(2x + 3)^2}$

$= \dfrac{2x^3 + 3x^2 + 2x^2 - 3x}{(2x - 3)(2x + 3)^2}$

$= \dfrac{2x^3 + 5x^2 - 3x}{(2x - 3)(2x + 3)^2}$

32. $\dfrac{y}{y^2 - 2y + 1} - \dfrac{1}{y - 1}$

$\qquad y^2 - 2y + 1 = (y - 1)(y - 1)$

$\qquad\qquad y - 1 = y - 1$

The LCD is $(y - 1)^2$.

$\dfrac{y}{(y - 1)(y - 1)} - \dfrac{y - 1}{y - 1} \cdot \dfrac{1}{y - 1}$

$= \dfrac{y - y + 1}{(y - 1)(y - 1)}$

$= \dfrac{1}{y^2 - 2y + 1}$

33. $\dfrac{x^2 + 4x - 5}{x^2 - 2x - 3} + \dfrac{2}{x + 1}$

$\qquad x^2 - 2x - 3 = (x - 3)(x + 1)$

$\qquad\qquad x + 1 = x + 1$

The LCD is $(x - 3)(x + 1)$.

$\dfrac{x^2 + 4x - 5}{(x - 3)(x + 1)} + \dfrac{(x - 3)}{(x - 3)} \cdot \dfrac{2}{x + 1}$

$= \dfrac{x^2 + 4x - 5 + 2x - 6}{x^2 - 2x - 3}$

$= \dfrac{x^2 + 6x - 11}{x^2 - 2x - 3}$

34. $\dfrac{a + 2}{a^2 - 9} - \dfrac{2a}{6a^2 - 17a - 3}$

$\qquad a^2 - 9 = (a - 3)(a + 3)$

$\qquad 6a^2 - 17a - 3 = (6a + 1)(a - 3)$

The LCD is $(a - 3)(a + 3)(6a + 1)$.

$\dfrac{6a + 1}{6a + 1} \cdot \dfrac{a + 2}{a^2 - 9} - \dfrac{a + 3}{a + 3} \cdot \dfrac{2a}{6a^2 - 17a - 3}$

$= \dfrac{6a^2 + 13a + 2 - 2a^2 - 6a}{(a - 3)(a + 3)(6a + 1)}$

$= \dfrac{4a^2 + 7a + 2}{(a - 3)(a + 3)(6a + 1)}$

35. $\dfrac{3m}{m^2 + 3m + 2} - \dfrac{3m - 6}{m^2 + 4m + 4}$

$\qquad m^2 + 3m + 2 = (m + 1)(m + 2)$

$\qquad m^2 + 4m + 4 = (m + 2)(m + 2)$

The LCD is $(m + 1)(m + 2)(m + 2)$.

$\dfrac{m + 2}{m + 2} \cdot \dfrac{3m}{m^2 + 3m + 2} - \dfrac{m + 1}{m + 1} \cdot \dfrac{3m - 6}{m^2 + 4m + 4}$

$= \dfrac{3m^2 + 6m - 3m^2 + 3m + 6}{(m + 1)(m + 2)^2}$

$= \dfrac{9m + 6}{(m + 1)(m + 2)^2}$

36. $\dfrac{4a}{6a^2 - a - 2} - \dfrac{5a + 1}{2 - 3a}$

$= \dfrac{4a}{6a^2 - a - 2} + \dfrac{5a + 1}{2a - 2}$

$\qquad 6a^2 - a - 2 = (2a - 3)(3a + 1)$

$\qquad 3a - 2 = 3a - 2$

The LCD is $(3a - 2)(2a + 1)$.

$\dfrac{4a}{6a^2 - a - 2} + \dfrac{(2a + 1)}{(2a + 1)} \cdot \dfrac{5a + 1}{3a - 2}$

$= \dfrac{4a + 10a^2 + 7a + 1}{(3a - 2)(2a + 1)}$

$= \dfrac{10a^2 + 11a + 1}{(3a - 2)(2a + 1)}$

37. $\dfrac{2x + 1}{(x - 1)^2} + \dfrac{x - 2}{(1 - x)(x + 4)}$

$= \dfrac{2x + 1}{(x - 1)^2} - \dfrac{x - 2}{(x - 1)(x + 4)}$

$\qquad (x - 1)^2 = (x - 1)(x - 1)$

$\qquad (x - 1)(x + 4) = (x - 1)(x + 4)$

The LCD is $(x - 1)^2(x + 4)$.

$\dfrac{x + 4}{x + 4} \cdot \dfrac{2x + 1}{(x - 1)^2} - \dfrac{x - 1}{x - 1} \cdot \dfrac{x - 2}{(x - 1)(x + 4)}$

$= \dfrac{2x^2 + 9x + 4 - x^2 + 3x - 2}{(x + 4)(x - 1)^2}$

$= \dfrac{x^2 + 12x + 2}{(x + 4)(x - 1)^2}$

38. $\dfrac{a + 3}{3a^2 - 10a - 8} + \dfrac{2a}{a^2 - 8a + 16}$

$3a^2 - 10a - 8 = (3a + 2)(a - 4)$

$a^2 - 8a + 16 = (a - 4)(a - 4)$

The LCD is $(a - 4)^2(3a + 2)$.

$\dfrac{a - 4}{a - 4} \cdot \dfrac{a + 3}{(3a + 2)(a - 4)} + \dfrac{3a + 2}{3a + 2} \cdot \dfrac{2a}{(a - 4)^2}$

$= \dfrac{a^2 - a - 12 + 6a^2 + 4a}{(3a + 2)(a - 4)^2}$

$= \dfrac{7a^2 + 3a - 12}{(3a + 2)(a - 4)^2}$

39. a. $18 \cdot 20 = 360$

   $18 = \boxed{2} \cdot 3 \cdot 3$

   $20 = \boxed{2} \cdot 2 \cdot 5$

   GCF of 18 and 20 = 2

   LCM of 18 and 20 = 180

   GCF $\cdot$ LCM = $2 \cdot 180 = 360$

   b. $16 \cdot 48 = 768$

   $16 = \boxed{2} \cdot \boxed{2} \cdot \boxed{2} \cdot \boxed{2}$

   $48 = \boxed{2} \cdot \boxed{2} \cdot \boxed{2} \cdot \boxed{2} \cdot 3$

   GCF of 16 and 48 = 16

   LCM of 16 and 48 = 48

   GCF $\cdot$ LCM = 768

   c. The product of the numbers is equal to the product of the GCF and the LCM.

   d. Divide the product of the two numbers by the LCM.

40. $1 = 1$

   $12 = 2 \cdot 2 \cdot 3$

   $30 = 3 \cdot 5$

   The LCM is $1 \cdot 2^2 \cdot 3 \cdot 5 = 60$.

   It will happen again in 60 years or in 2042.

41. eldest: $\dfrac{1}{2} \cdot 18 = 9$ cows

   second: $\dfrac{1}{3} \cdot 18 = 6$ cows

   youngest: $\dfrac{1}{9} \cdot 18 = 2$ cows

42. $6 = 2 \cdot 3$

   $7 = 7$

   $8 = 2 \cdot 2 \cdot 2$

   The LCM is $2^3 \cdot 3 \cdot 7 = 168$.

   168 members

43. 3 tables of 5 people and 8 tables of 8 people or 11 tables of 5 people and 3 tables of 8 people

44. $? = \dfrac{1}{3}x + \dfrac{1}{6}x + 12 + \dfrac{1}{2}\left[x - \left(\dfrac{1}{3}x + \dfrac{1}{6}x + 12\right)\right]$

   $\quad + \dfrac{1}{4}\left[x - \left(\dfrac{1}{3}x + \dfrac{1}{6}x + 12\right)\right]$

   $\quad + \dfrac{1}{4}\left[x - \left(\dfrac{1}{3}x + \dfrac{1}{6}x + 12\right)\right]$

   $= \dfrac{1}{3}x + \dfrac{1}{6}x + 12 + \left(\dfrac{1}{4}x - 6\right) + \left(\dfrac{1}{8}x - 3\right) + \left(\dfrac{1}{8}x - 3\right)$

   Find common multiples of 3, 4, 6, and 8.

   $3 = 3$

   $4 = 2 \cdot 2$

   $6 = 2 \cdot 3$

   $8 = 2 \cdot 2 \cdot 2$

   LCM = 12; other common multiples are 24, 36, 48, and so on. Recall that George must have lived more than 45 years.

   $\dfrac{1}{3}(48) + \dfrac{1}{6}(48) + 12 = 36$   $\dfrac{1}{3}(72) + \dfrac{1}{6}(72) + 12 = 48$

   $\dfrac{1}{3}(60) + \dfrac{1}{6}(60) + 12 = 42$   George lived 72 years.

45. 60% more than 20 $= 20 + (.6 \times 20)$

   $\qquad\qquad\qquad\quad = 20 + 12$

   $\qquad\qquad\qquad\quad = 32$

   25% less than 32 $= 32 - (.25 \times 32)$

   $\qquad\qquad\qquad\quad = 32 - 8$

   $\qquad\qquad\qquad\quad = 24$

   24 is 50% more than 16.

46. 16 ounces per pound

   $\dfrac{1}{10}x = 16$

   $x = 160$ balls

47. 7

48. $3.16, $1.50, $1.25, $1.20

49. $\dfrac{y}{y - 1} - \dfrac{1}{y - 1}$

   $= \dfrac{y - 1}{y - 1}$

   $= 1$

50. Let $p$ = penny

   $n$ = nickel

   $d$ = dime

   $q$ = quarter

   $q + 2d + n$

   $q + 2d + 5p$

   $q + d + 3n$

   $q + d + 2n + 5p$

   $q + d + n + 10p$

   $q + d + 15p$

   6 ways

# Mixed Expressions and Complex Fractions

1. Yes, if it equals 1 or -1.    2. 1

3. $4 + \dfrac{2}{x}$

$= \dfrac{x}{x} \cdot 4 + \dfrac{2}{x}$

$= \dfrac{4x + 2}{x}$

4. $8 + \dfrac{5}{3y}$

$= \dfrac{3y}{3y} \cdot 8 + \dfrac{5}{3y}$

$= \dfrac{24y + 5}{3y}$

5. $2m + \dfrac{4 + m}{m}$

$= \dfrac{m}{m} \cdot 2m + \dfrac{4 + m}{m}$

$= \dfrac{2m^2 + m + 4}{m}$

6. $3a + \dfrac{a + 1}{2a}$

$= \dfrac{2a}{2a} \cdot 3a + \dfrac{a + 1}{2a}$

$= \dfrac{6a^2 + a + 1}{2a}$

7. $b^2 + \dfrac{2}{b - 2}$

$= \dfrac{(b - 2)}{(b - 2)} \cdot b^2 + \dfrac{2}{b - 2}$

$= \dfrac{b^3 - 2b^2 + 2}{b - 2}$

8. $3r^2 + \dfrac{4}{2r + 1}$

$= \dfrac{2r + 1}{2r + 1} \cdot 3r^2 + \dfrac{4}{2r + 1}$

$= \dfrac{6r^3 + 3r^2 + 4}{2r + 1}$

9. $\dfrac{3\frac{1}{2}}{4\frac{3}{4}}$

$= \dfrac{\frac{7}{2}}{\frac{19}{4}}$

$= \dfrac{7}{2} \cdot \dfrac{4}{19}$

$= \dfrac{14}{19}$

10. $\dfrac{\frac{x^2}{y}}{\frac{y}{x^3}}$

$= \dfrac{x^2}{y} \cdot \dfrac{x^3}{y}$

$= \dfrac{x^5}{y^2}$

11. $\dfrac{\frac{x + 4}{y - 2}}{\frac{x^2}{y^3}}$

$= \dfrac{x + 4}{y - 2} \cdot \dfrac{y^3}{x^2}$

$= \dfrac{y^3(x + 4)}{x^2(y - 2)}$

12. $\dfrac{\frac{x^3}{y^2}}{\frac{x + y}{x - y}}$

$= \dfrac{x^3}{y^2} \cdot \dfrac{x - y}{x + y}$

$= \dfrac{x^3(x - y)}{y^2(x + y)}$

13. $\dfrac{\frac{x + y}{a + b}}{\frac{x^2 - y^2}{a^2 - b^2}}$

$= \dfrac{x + y}{a + b} \cdot \dfrac{a^2 - b^2}{x^2 - y^2}$

$= \dfrac{(x + y)(a - b)(a + b)}{(a + b)(x - y)(x + y)}$

$= \dfrac{a - b}{x - y}$

14. $\dfrac{\frac{x - y}{x + y}}{\frac{x + y}{x - y}}$

$= \dfrac{x - y}{x + y} \cdot \dfrac{x - y}{x + y}$

$= \dfrac{(x - y)^2}{(x + y)^2}$

15. $\dfrac{\frac{1}{x} + \frac{1}{y}}{\frac{1}{y} - \frac{1}{x}}$

$= \dfrac{xy}{xy} \cdot \left( \dfrac{\frac{1}{x} + \frac{1}{y}}{\frac{1}{y} - \frac{1}{x}} \right)$

$= \dfrac{y + x}{x - y}$

16. $\dfrac{\frac{a + b}{x}}{\frac{a - b}{y}}$

$= \dfrac{a + b}{x} \cdot \dfrac{y}{a - b}$

$= \dfrac{y(a + b)}{x(a - b)}$

17. $\dfrac{\frac{x^2 + 8x + 15}{x^2 + x - 6}}{\frac{x^2 + 2x - 15}{x^2 - 2x - 3}}$

$= \dfrac{x^2 + 8x + 15}{x^2 + x - 6} \cdot \dfrac{x^2 - 2x - 3}{x^2 + 2x - 15}$

$= \dfrac{(x + 3)(x + 5)(x - 3)(x + 1)}{(x + 3)(x - 2)(x + 5)(x - 3)}$

$= \dfrac{x + 1}{x - 2}$

18. $\dfrac{\frac{a^2 - 6a + 5}{a^2 + 13a + 42}}{\frac{a^2 - 4a + 3}{a^2 + 3a - 18}}$

$= \dfrac{a^2 - 6a + 5}{a^2 + 13a + 42} \cdot \dfrac{a^2 + 3a - 18}{a^2 - 4a + 3}$

$= \dfrac{(a - 5)(a - 1)(a - 3)(a + 6)}{(a + 7)(a + 6)(a - 3)(a - 1)}$

$= \dfrac{a - 5}{a + 7}$

19. $\dfrac{\frac{y^2 - 1}{y^2 + 3y - 4}}{y + 1}$

$= \dfrac{y^2 - 1}{y^2 + 3y - 4} \cdot \dfrac{1}{y + 1}$

$= \dfrac{(y - 1)(y + 1)}{(y + 4)(y - 1)(y + 1)}$

$= \dfrac{1}{y + 4}$

20. $\dfrac{\frac{a^2 - 2a - 3}{a^2 - 1}}{a - 3}$

$= \dfrac{a^2 - 2a - 3}{a^2 - 1} \cdot \dfrac{1}{a - 3}$

$= \dfrac{(a - 3)(a + 1)}{(a - 1)(a + 1)(a - 3)}$

$= \dfrac{1}{a - 1}$

**21.** $\dfrac{\dfrac{a^2 + 2a}{a^2 + 9a + 18}}{\dfrac{a^2 - 5a}{a^2 + a - 30}}$

$= \dfrac{a^2 + 2a}{a^2 + 9a + 18} \cdot \dfrac{a^2 + a - 30}{a^2 - 5a}$

$= \dfrac{a(a + 2)(a + 6)(a - 5)}{a(a - 5)(a + 3)(a + 6)}$

$= \dfrac{a + 2}{a + 3}$

**22.** $\dfrac{\dfrac{x^2 + 4x - 21}{x^2 - 9x + 18}}{\dfrac{x^2 + 3x - 28}{x^2 - 10x + 24}}$

$= \dfrac{x^2 + 4x - 21}{x^2 - 9x + 18} \cdot \dfrac{x^2 - 10x + 24}{x^2 + 3x - 28}$

$= \dfrac{(x + 7)(x - 3)(x - 6)(x - 4)}{(x - 6)(x - 3)(x + 7)(x - 4)}$

$= 1$

**23.** $\dfrac{x - \dfrac{15}{x - 2}}{x - \dfrac{20}{x - 1}}$

$= \dfrac{\dfrac{x - 2}{x - 2} \cdot x - \dfrac{15}{x - 2}}{\dfrac{x - 1}{x - 1} \cdot x - \dfrac{20}{x - 1}}$

$= \dfrac{\dfrac{x^2 - 2x - 15}{x - 2}}{\dfrac{x^2 - x - 20}{x - 1}}$

$= \dfrac{x^2 - 2x - 15}{x - 2} \cdot \dfrac{x - 1}{x^2 - x - 20}$

$= \dfrac{(x - 5)(x + 3)(x - 1)}{(x - 2)(x - 5)(x + 4)}$

$= \dfrac{(x + 3)(x - 1)}{(x - 2)(x + 4)}$

**24.** $\dfrac{m + \dfrac{35}{m + 12}}{m - \dfrac{63}{m - 2}}$

$= \dfrac{\dfrac{m + 12}{m + 12} \cdot m + \dfrac{35}{m + 12}}{\dfrac{m - 2}{m - 2} \cdot m - \dfrac{63}{m - 2}}$

$= \dfrac{\dfrac{m^2 + 12m + 35}{m + 12}}{\dfrac{m^2 - 2m - 63}{m - 2}}$

$= \dfrac{m^2 + 12m + 35}{m + 12} \cdot \dfrac{m - 2}{m^2 - 2m - 63}$

$= \dfrac{(m + 5)(m + 7)(m - 2)}{(m + 12)(m - 9)(m + 7)}$

$= \dfrac{(m + 5)(m - 2)}{(m + 12)(m - 9)}$

**25.** $7 + \dfrac{x^2 + y^2}{x^2 - 4y^2}$

$= \dfrac{x^2 - 4y^2}{x^2 - 4y^2} \cdot 7 + \dfrac{x^2 + y^2}{x^2 - 4y^2}$

$= \dfrac{7x^2 - 28y^2 + x^2 + y^2}{x^2 - 4y^2}$

$= \dfrac{8x^2 - 27y^2}{x^2 - 4y^2}$

**26.** $5 + \dfrac{a^2 + 11}{a^2 - 1}$

$= \dfrac{a^2 - 1}{a^2 - 1} \cdot 5 + \dfrac{a^2 + 11}{a^2 - 1}$

$= \dfrac{5a^2 - 5 + a^2 + 11}{a^2 - 1}$

$= \dfrac{6a^2 + 6}{a^2 - 1}$

**27.** $\dfrac{x + 2 + \dfrac{2}{x + 5}}{x + 6 + \dfrac{6}{x + 1}}$

$= \dfrac{\dfrac{x + 5}{x + 5} \cdot x + \dfrac{x + 5}{x + 5} \cdot 2 + \dfrac{2}{x + 5}}{\dfrac{x + 1}{x + 1} \cdot x + \dfrac{x + 1}{x + 1} \cdot 6 + \dfrac{6}{x + 1}}$

$= \dfrac{\dfrac{x^2 + 5x + 2x + 10 + 2}{x + 5}}{\dfrac{x^2 + x + 6x + 6 + 6}{x + 1}}$

$= \dfrac{x^2 + 7x + 12}{x + 5} \cdot \dfrac{x + 1}{x^2 + 7x + 12}$

$= \dfrac{x + 1}{x + 5}$

**28.** $\dfrac{x + 5 + \dfrac{3}{x + 1}}{x - 1 - \dfrac{3}{x + 1}}$

$= \dfrac{\dfrac{x + 1}{x + 1} \cdot x + \dfrac{x + 1}{x + 1} \cdot 5 + \dfrac{3}{x + 1}}{\dfrac{x + 1}{x + 1} \cdot x - \dfrac{x + 1}{x + 1} \cdot 1 - \dfrac{3}{x + 1}}$

$= \dfrac{\dfrac{x^2 + x + 5x + 5 + 3}{x + 1}}{\dfrac{x^2 + x - x - 1 - 3}{x + 1}}$

$= \dfrac{\dfrac{x^2 + 6x + 8}{x + 1}}{\dfrac{x^2 - 4}{x + 1}}$

$= \dfrac{x^2 + 6x + 8}{x + 1} \cdot \dfrac{x + 1}{x^2 - 4}$

$= \dfrac{(x + 2)(x + 4)}{(x - 2)(x + 2)}$

$= \dfrac{x + 4}{x - 2}$

29. $\dfrac{\dfrac{a^2 - a - 1}{a - 1}}{a - \dfrac{1}{a - 1}}$

$= \dfrac{\dfrac{a^2 - a - 1}{a - 1}}{\dfrac{a - 1}{a - 1} \cdot a - \dfrac{1}{a - 1}}$

$= \dfrac{\dfrac{a^2 - a - 1}{a - 1}}{\dfrac{a^2 - a - 1}{a - 1}}$

$= \dfrac{a^2 - a - 1}{a - 1} \cdot \dfrac{a - 1}{a^2 - a - 1}$

$= 1$

30. $\dfrac{1}{1 - \dfrac{1}{1 + a}} - \dfrac{1}{\dfrac{1}{1 - a} - 1}$

$= \dfrac{1}{\dfrac{1 + a}{1 + a} \cdot 1 - \dfrac{1}{1 + a}} - \dfrac{1}{\dfrac{1}{1 - a} - \dfrac{1 - a}{1 - a} \cdot 1}$

$= \dfrac{1}{\dfrac{a}{1 + a}} - \dfrac{1}{\dfrac{a}{1 - a}}$

$= \dfrac{1 + a}{a} - \dfrac{1 - a}{a}$

$= \dfrac{2a}{a}$

$= 2$

31. $1854 + 26 + 4 + 4$

$= 1888$

32. New Jersey $\dfrac{7,721,000}{7,468}$

$= 1034$ people/mi$^2$

Alaska $\dfrac{524,000}{570,833}$

$= 1$ person/mi$^2$

$1034 - 1 = 1033$ people

33.

| | Pounds | Price |
|---|---|---|
| Apples at 64¢ | $x$ | $0.64x$ |
| Apples at 49¢ | 30 | $0.49 \cdot 30$ |

$\dfrac{0.64x + 0.49(30)}{x + 30} = 0.58$

$\dfrac{0.64x + 14.7}{x + 30} = 0.58$

$0.64x + 14.7 = 0.58(x + 30)$

$0.64x + 14.7 = 0.58x + 17.4$

$0.06x = 2.7$

$x = 45$

45 pounds

34. $\dfrac{6}{9} = 0.\overline{6}$

$\dfrac{57}{99} = 0.\overline{57}$

$\dfrac{253}{999} = 0.\overline{253}$

$\dfrac{6001}{9999} = 0.\overline{6001}$

35. $12a^2 - 12$

$= 12(a^2 - 1)$

$= 12(a - 1)(a + 1)$

36. $\dfrac{5b}{7x} + \dfrac{3a}{21x^2}$

$7x = 7 \cdot x$

$21x^2 = 3 \cdot 7 \cdot x \cdot x$

The LCD is $3 \cdot 7 \cdot x^2 = 21x^2$.

$\dfrac{3x}{3x} \cdot \dfrac{5b}{7x} + \dfrac{3a}{21x^2}$

$= \dfrac{15bx + 3a}{21x^2}$

## 8-9 Solving Rational Equations

1. It would go backwards.

2. It would make the denominator zero.

3. LCD is 6.          4. LCD is 15.

5. LCD is 8.          6.  $x = x$

$x + 1 = x + 1$

LCD is $x(x + 1)$.

7. $r^2 - 1 = (r - 1)(r + 1)$

$r - 1 = r - 1$

LCD is $(r - 1)(r + 1)$.

$= r^2 - 1$

8. $2m^2 + 3m - 35 = (2m - 7)(m + 5)$

$2m - 7 = 2m - 7$

LCD is $(2m - 7)(m + 5)$.

9. $k + 5 = k + 5$          10. $h + 1 = h + 1$

$k + 3 = k + 3$                $2 = 2$

$k + 3 = k + 3$              $h - 1 = h - 1$

LCD is $(k + 3)(k + 5)$.   LCD is $2(h + 1)(h - 1)$.

11. $4x^2 - 1 = (2x - 1)(2x + 1)$

$3 = 3$

$2x + 1 = 2x + 1$

LCD is $3(2x - 1)(2x + 1)$.

12. a. $\dfrac{1}{8}$          13. a. $\dfrac{1}{n}$

b. $\dfrac{3}{8}$          b. $\dfrac{4}{n}$

c. $\dfrac{x}{8}$          c. $\dfrac{x}{n}$

14. a. $\dfrac{1}{8}, \dfrac{x}{8}$

b. $\dfrac{1}{10}, \dfrac{x}{10}$

c. $\dfrac{1}{8}, \dfrac{1}{10}$          $\dfrac{x}{8} + \dfrac{1}{10}$

$= \dfrac{5 + 4}{40}$          $= \dfrac{5x + 4x}{40}$

$= \dfrac{9}{40}$          $= \dfrac{9x}{40}$

141

15. $\dfrac{2a - 3}{6} = \dfrac{2a}{3} + \dfrac{1}{2}$

$6\left(\dfrac{2a - 3}{6}\right) = 6\left(\dfrac{2a}{3} + \dfrac{1}{2}\right)$

$2a - 3 = \dfrac{12a}{3} + \dfrac{6}{2}$

$2a - 3 = 4a + 3$

$-2a = 6$

$a = -3$

16. $\dfrac{3x}{5} + \dfrac{3}{2} = \dfrac{7x}{10}$

$10\left(\dfrac{3x}{5} + \dfrac{3}{2}\right) = 10\left(\dfrac{7x}{10}\right)$

$\dfrac{30x}{5} + \dfrac{30}{2} = \dfrac{70x}{10}$

$6x + 15 = 7x$

$15 = x$

17. $\dfrac{2b - 3}{7} - \dfrac{b}{2} = \dfrac{b + 3}{14}$

$14\left(\dfrac{2b - 3}{7} - \dfrac{b}{2}\right) = 14\left(\dfrac{b + 3}{14}\right)$

$\dfrac{28b - 42}{7} - \dfrac{14b}{2} = b + 3$

$4b - 6 - 7b = b + 3$

$-4b = 9$

$b = -\dfrac{9}{4}$

18. $\dfrac{x + 1}{x} + \dfrac{x + 4}{x} = 6$

$x\left(\dfrac{x + 1}{x} + \dfrac{x + 4}{x}\right) = 6 \cdot x$

$x + 1 + x + 4 = 6x$

$4x = 5$

$x = \dfrac{5}{4}$

19. $\dfrac{18}{b} = \dfrac{3}{b} + 3$

$b\left(\dfrac{18}{b}\right) = b\left(\dfrac{3}{b} + 3\right)$

$18 = 3 + 3b$

$15 = 3 + 3b$

$b = 5$

20. $\dfrac{3}{5x} + \dfrac{7}{2x} = 1$

$10x\left(\dfrac{3}{5x} + \dfrac{7}{2x}\right) = 1 \cdot 10x$

$\dfrac{30x}{5x} + \dfrac{70x}{2x} = 10x$

$6 + 35 = 10x$

$41 = 10x$

$x = \dfrac{41}{10}$

21. $\dfrac{5x}{x + 1} + \dfrac{1}{x} = 5$

$x(x + 1)\left(\dfrac{5x}{x + 1} + \dfrac{1}{x}\right) = 5 \cdot x(x + 1)$

$5x^2 + x + 1 = 5x(x + 1)$

$5x^2 + x + 1 = 5x^2 + 5x$

$-4x = -1$

$x = \dfrac{1}{4}$

22. $\dfrac{2}{3r} - \dfrac{3r}{r - 2} = -3$

$3r(r - 2)\left(\dfrac{2}{3r} - \dfrac{3r}{r - 2}\right) = -3 \cdot 3r(r - 2)$

$2(r - 2) - 3r \cdot 3r = -9r(r - 2)$

$2r - 4 - 9r^2 = -9r^2 + 18r$

$-16r = 4$

$r = -\dfrac{4}{16}$

$r = -\dfrac{1}{4}$

23. $\dfrac{m}{m + 1} + \dfrac{5}{m - 1} = 1$

$(m - 1)(m + 1)\left(\dfrac{m}{m + 1} + \dfrac{5}{m - 1}\right) = 1 \cdot (m - 1)(m + 1)$

$m(m - 1) + 5(m + 1) = (m - 1)(m + 1)$

$m^2 - m + 5m + 5 = m^2 - 1$

$4m = -6$

$m = -\dfrac{6}{4}$

$m = -\dfrac{3}{2}$

24. $\dfrac{r - 1}{r + 1} - \dfrac{2r}{r - 1} = -1$

$(r - 1)(r + 1)\left(\dfrac{r - 1}{r + 1} - \dfrac{2r}{r - 1}\right) = -1 \cdot (r - 1)(r + 1)$

$(r - 1)^2 - 2r(r + 1) = -(r - 1)(r + 1)$

$r^2 - 2r + 1 - 2r^2 - 2r = -r^2 + 1$

$-4r = 0$

$r = 0$

25. $\dfrac{4x}{2x + 3} - \dfrac{2x}{2x - 3} = 1$

$(2x + 3)(2x - 3)\left(\dfrac{4x}{2x + 3} - \dfrac{2x}{2x - 3}\right)$

$= 1 \cdot (2x + 3)(2x - 3)$

$4x(2x - 3) - 2x(2x + 3) = (2x + 3)(2x - 3)$

$8x^2 - 12x - 4x^2 - 6x = 4x^2 - 9$

$-18x = -9$

$x = \dfrac{-9}{-18}$

$x = \dfrac{1}{2}$

26. $\dfrac{5}{5 - P} - \dfrac{P^2}{5 - P} = -2$

$\dfrac{5 - p^2}{5 - p} = -2$

$5 - p^2 = -2(5 - p)$

$5 - p^2 = -10 + 2p$

$p^2 + 2p - 15 = 0$

$(p + 5)(p - 3) = 0$

$p = -5, \; 3$

27. $\dfrac{14}{b-6} = \dfrac{1}{2} + \dfrac{6}{b-8}$

$2(b-6)(b-8)\left(\dfrac{14}{b-6}\right)$

$= 2(b-6)(b-8)\left(\dfrac{1}{2} + \dfrac{6}{b-8}\right)$

$28(b-8) = (b-6)(b-8) + 12(b-6)$

$28b - 224 = b^2 - 14b + 48 + 12b - 72$

$28b - 224 = b^2 - 2b - 24$

$b^2 - 30b + 200 = 0$

$(b-10)(b-20) = 0$

$b = 10, \ 20$

28. $\dfrac{2a-3}{a-3} - 2 = \dfrac{12}{a+3}$

$(a-3)(a+3)\left(\dfrac{2a-3}{a-3} - 2\right)$

$= (a-3)(a+3) \cdot \dfrac{12}{a+3}$

$(2a-3)(a+3) - 2(a-3)(a+3) = 12(a-3)$

$2a^2 + 3a - 9 - 2a^2 + 18 = 12a - 36$

$9a = 45$

$a = 5$

29. $\dfrac{r}{3r+6} - \dfrac{r}{5r+10} = \dfrac{2}{5}$

$\dfrac{r}{3(r+2)} - \dfrac{r}{5(r+2)} = \dfrac{2}{5}$

$15(r+2)\left[\dfrac{r}{3(r+2)} - \dfrac{r}{5(r+2)}\right] = 15(r+2) \cdot \dfrac{2}{5}$

$5r - 3r = 6(r+2)$

$2r = 6r + 12$

$-4r = 12$

$r = -3$

30. $\dfrac{x-2}{x} - \dfrac{x-3}{x-6} = \dfrac{1}{x}$

$x(x-6)\left(\dfrac{x-2}{x} - \dfrac{x-3}{x-6}\right) = x(x-6) \cdot \dfrac{1}{x}$

$(x-6)(x-2) - x(x-3) = x - 6$

$x^2 - 8x + 12 - x^2 + 3x = x - 6$

$6x = 18$

$x = 3$

31. $\dfrac{z+3}{z-1} + \dfrac{z+1}{z-3} = 2$

$(z-1)(z-3)\left(\dfrac{z+3}{z-1} + \dfrac{z+1}{z-3}\right)$

$= 2 \cdot (z-1)(z-3)$

$(z-3)(z+3) + (z-1)(z+1) = 2(z-1)(z-3)$

$z^2 - 9 + z^2 - 1 = 2z^2 - 8z + 6$

$8z = 16$

$z = 2$

32. $\dfrac{x+2}{x-2} - \dfrac{2}{x+2} = \dfrac{-7}{3}$

$3(x-2)(x+2)\left(\dfrac{x+2}{x-2} - \dfrac{2}{x+2}\right)$

$= \dfrac{-7}{3} \cdot 3(x-2)(x+2)$

$3(x+2)^2 - 6(x-2) = -7(x-2)(x+2)$

$3(x^2 + 4x + 4) - 6x + 12 = -7(x^2 - 4)$

$3x^2 + 12x + 12 - 6x + 12 = -7x^2 + 28$

$10x^2 + 6x - 4 = 0$

$2(5x^2 + 3x - 2) = 0$

$2(5x - 2)(x + 1) = 0$

$5x - 2 = 0, \ x + 1 = 0$

$5x = 2 \qquad x = -1$

$x = \dfrac{2}{5}$

33. $\dfrac{7}{x^2 - 5x} + \dfrac{3}{5 - x} = \dfrac{4}{x}$

$\dfrac{7}{x(x-5)} - \dfrac{3}{x-5} = \dfrac{4}{x}$

$x(x-5)\left[\dfrac{7}{x(x-5)} - \dfrac{3}{x-5}\right] = x(x-5) \cdot \dfrac{4}{x}$

$7 - 3x = 4(x-5)$

$7 - 3x = 4x - 20$

$-7x = -27$

$x = \dfrac{27}{7}$

34. $\dfrac{6}{z+2} + \dfrac{3}{z^2 - 4} = \dfrac{2z-7}{z-2}$

$\dfrac{6}{z+2} + \dfrac{3}{(z-2)(z+2)} = \dfrac{2z-7}{z-2}$

$(z-2)(z+2)\left[\dfrac{6}{z+2} + \dfrac{3}{(z-2)(z+2)}\right]$

$= (z-2)(z+2)\left(\dfrac{2z-7}{z-2}\right)$

$6(z-2) + 3 = (z+2)(2z-7)$

$6z - 12 + 3 = 2z^2 - 3z - 14$

$2z^2 - 9z - 5 = 0$

$(2z+1)(z-5) = 0$

$2z + 1 = 0, \ z - 5 = 0$

$2z = -1 \qquad z = 5$

$z = -\dfrac{1}{2}$

35. $\dfrac{3w}{w^2 - 5w + 4} = \dfrac{2}{w-4} + \dfrac{3}{w-1}$

$\dfrac{3w}{(w-4)(w-1)} = \dfrac{2}{w-4} + \dfrac{3}{w-1}$

$(w-4)(w-1)\left[\dfrac{3w}{(w-4)(w-1)}\right]$

$= (w-4)(w-1)\left(\dfrac{2}{w-4} + \dfrac{3}{w-1}\right)$

$3w = 2(w-1) + 3(w-4)$

$3w = 2w - 2 + 3w - 12$

$2w = 14$

$w = 7$

36. $\dfrac{4}{k^2 - 8k + 12} = \dfrac{k}{k - 2} + \dfrac{1}{k - 6}$

$\dfrac{4}{(k - 2)(k - 6)} = \dfrac{k}{k - 2} + \dfrac{1}{k - 6}$

$(k - 2)(k - 6)\left[\dfrac{4}{(k - 2)(k - 6)}\right]$

$= (k - 2)(k - 6)\left(\dfrac{k}{k - 2} + \dfrac{1}{k - 6}\right)$

$4 = k(k - 6) + k - 2$

$4 = k^2 - 6k + k - 2$

$k^2 - 5k - 6 = 0$

$(k + 1)k - 6) = 0$

$k + 1 = 0, \ k - 6 = 0$

$k = -1 \qquad k = 6$

But $k = 6$ is an excluded value so the only solution is $k = -1$.

37. $\dfrac{m + 3}{m + 5} + \dfrac{2}{m - 9} = \dfrac{-20}{m^2 - 4m - 45}$

$\dfrac{m + 3}{m + 5} + \dfrac{2}{m - 9} = \dfrac{-20}{(m - 9)(m + 5)}$

$(m + 5)(m - 9)\left[\dfrac{m + 3}{m + 5} + \dfrac{2}{m - 9}\right]$

$= (m + 5)(m - 9)\left[\dfrac{-20}{(m + 5)(m - 9)}\right]$

$(m + 3)(m - 9) + 2(m + 5) = -20$

$m^2 - 6m - 27 + 2m + 10 = -20$

$m^2 - 4m + 3 = 0$

$(m - 3)(m - 1) = 0$

$m - 3 = 0, \ m - 1 = 0$

$m = 3 \qquad m = 1$

38. $\dfrac{h^2 - 7h - 8}{3h^2 + 2h - 8} + \dfrac{1}{h + 2} = 0$

$\dfrac{h^2 - 7h - 8}{(3h - 4)(h + 2)} + \dfrac{1}{h + 2} = 0$

$(3h - 4)(h + 2)\left[\dfrac{h^2 - 7h - 8}{(3h - 4)(h + 2)} + \dfrac{1}{h + 2}\right]$

$= 0 \cdot (3h - 4)(h + 2)$

$h^2 - 7h - 8 + 3h - 4 = 0$

$h^2 - 4h - 12 = 0$

$(h - 6)(h + 2) = 0$

$h - 6 = 0, \ h + 2 = 0$

$h = 6 \qquad h = -2$

But $h = -2$ is an excluded value so the only solution is $h = 6$.

39. $\dfrac{2}{11} + \dfrac{7}{7} = \dfrac{9}{18} = \dfrac{1}{2}$

40.

|  | $r$ | $t$ | $w$ |
|---|---|---|---|
| Jane | $\frac{1}{4}$ | $t$ | $\frac{t}{4}$ |
| Jaime | $\frac{1}{6}$ | $l$ | $\frac{t}{6}$ |

$\dfrac{t}{4} + \dfrac{t}{6} = 1$

$12\left(\dfrac{t}{4} + \dfrac{t}{6}\right) = 12 \cdot 1$

$3t + 2t = 12$

$5t = 12$

$t = \dfrac{12}{5}$

$t = 2\dfrac{2}{5}$

$2\dfrac{2}{5}$ hours

41.

|  | $r$ | $t$ | $w$ |
|---|---|---|---|
| Pipe 1 | $\frac{1}{10}$ | $t$ | $\frac{t}{10}$ |
| Pipe 2 | $\frac{-1}{15}$ | $t$ | $\frac{-t}{15}$ |

$\dfrac{t}{10} - \dfrac{t}{15} = 1$

$30\left(\dfrac{t}{10} - \dfrac{t}{15}\right) = 30 \cdot 1$

$3t - 2t = 30$

$t = 30$

30 hours

42.

|  | $r$ | $t$ | $w$ |
|---|---|---|---|
| Kiko | $\frac{1}{6}$ | $\frac{18}{5}$ | $\frac{3}{5}$ |
| Marcus | $r$ | $\frac{18}{5}$ | $\frac{18r}{5}$ |

$\dfrac{3}{5} + \dfrac{18r}{5} = 1$

$\dfrac{18r + 3}{5} = 1$

$18r + 3 = 5$

$18r = 2$

$r = \dfrac{1}{9}$

It would take Marcus 9 hours.

43.

|  | $d$ | $r$ | $t$ |
|---|---|---|---|
| With Wind | 30 | $r + 3$ | $\frac{30}{r + 3}$ |
| Against Wind | 18 | $r - 3$ | $\frac{18}{r - 3}$ |

$\dfrac{30}{r + 3} = \dfrac{18}{r - 3}$

$30(r - 3) = 18(r + 3)$

$30r - 90 = 18r + 54$

$12r = 144$

$r = 12$

12 mph

44.

|  | $d$ | $r$ | $t$ |
|---|---|---|---|
| Up River | 36 | $r - 3$ | $\frac{36}{r - 3}$ |
| Down River | 36 | $r + 3$ | $\frac{36}{r + 3}$ |

$\dfrac{36}{r - 3} = \dfrac{36}{r + 3} + 1$

$(r - 3)(r + 3)\left(\dfrac{36}{r - 3}\right) = (r - 3)(r + 3)\left(\dfrac{36}{r + 3} + 1\right)$

$36(r + 3) = 36(r - 3) + (r - 3)(r + 3)$

$36r + 108 = 36r - 108 + r^2 - 9$

$r^2 = 225$

$r = 15$

15 mph

**45.**

|  | $d$ | $r$ | $t$ |
|---|---|---|---|
| With Wind | 2520 | $600 + r$ | $\dfrac{2520}{600 + r}$ |
| Against Wind | 2280 | $600 - r$ | $\dfrac{2280}{600 - r}$ |

$$\frac{2520}{600 + r} = \frac{2280}{600 - r}$$

$$2520(600 - r) = 2280(600 + r)$$

$$1{,}512{,}000 - 2520r = 1{,}368{,}000 + 2280r$$

$$4800r = 144{,}000$$

$$48r = 1440$$

$$r = 30$$

30 mph

**46.**

|  | $d$ | $r$ | $t$ |
|---|---|---|---|
| Upstream | 10 | $r - 5$ | $\dfrac{10}{r - 5}$ |
| Downstream | 10 | $r + 5$ | $\dfrac{10}{r + 5}$ |

$$\frac{2}{3} \cdot \frac{10}{r - 5} = \frac{10}{r + 5}$$

$$\frac{20}{3r - 15} = \frac{10}{r + 5}$$

$$20(r + 5) = 10(3r - 15)$$

$$20r + 100 = 30r - 150$$

$$10r = 250$$

$$r = 25$$

25 mph

**47.** $\dfrac{22{,}996 \text{ ft}}{5280 \text{ ft/mi}} = 4.355$ miles

4.355 min or about 4 min 21 s

**48.** $126x = 154(16 - x)$

$126x = 2464 - 154x$

$280x = 2464$

$x = 8.8$

8.8 ft

**49.** $(4a + 2a) + (6b + 3b)$

$= 6a + 9b$

**50.** $(a + 6)^2$

**51.** $\dfrac{y}{y} \cdot x + \dfrac{x}{y}$

$= \dfrac{xy + x}{y}$

---

## 8-10   Application:   Formulas

1. Multiply each side by 2. Divide each side by $h$. Subtract $b$ from each side.

2. Multiply each side by 2. Divide each side by $h$. Subtract $a$ from each side.

3. Multiply each side by $abf$. Subtract $af$ from each side. Factor and divide by $b - f$.

4. Multiply each side by $abf$. Subtract $bf$ from each side. Factor and divide by $a - f$.

**5.**

$$\frac{1}{R_T} = \frac{1}{8} + \frac{1}{6}$$

$$24 \cdot \frac{1}{R_T} = 24\left(\frac{1}{8} + \frac{1}{6}\right)$$

$$\frac{24}{R_T} = 3 + 4$$

$$\frac{24}{R_T} = 7$$

$$24 = 7R_T$$

$$R_T = \frac{24}{7}$$

$$R_T = 3.429 \text{ ohms}$$

**6.**

$$\frac{1}{R_T} = \frac{1}{4.5} + \frac{1}{3.5}$$

$$\frac{1}{R_T} = \frac{1}{\frac{9}{2}} + \frac{1}{\frac{7}{2}}$$

$$\frac{1}{R_T} = \frac{2}{9} + \frac{2}{7}$$

$$63 \cdot \frac{1}{R_T} = 63\left(\frac{2}{9} + \frac{2}{7}\right)$$

$$\frac{63}{R_T} = 14 + 18$$

$$63 = R_T \cdot 32$$

$$R_T = \frac{63}{32}$$

$$R_T = 1.969 \text{ ohms}$$

**7.**

$$\frac{1}{2.\overline{2}} = \frac{1}{R_1} + \frac{1}{5}$$

$$\frac{1}{2.\overline{2}} - \frac{1}{5} = \frac{1}{R_1}$$

$$\frac{9}{20} - \frac{4}{20} = \frac{1}{R_1}$$

$$\frac{5}{20} = \frac{1}{R_1}$$

$$\frac{1}{4} = \frac{1}{R_1}$$

$$R_1 = 4 \text{ ohms}$$

**8.**

$$\frac{1}{3\frac{3}{7}} = \frac{1}{R_1} + \frac{1}{8}$$

$$\frac{1}{\frac{24}{7}} - \frac{1}{8} = \frac{1}{R_1}$$

$$\frac{7}{24} - \frac{1}{8} = \frac{1}{R_1}$$

$$\frac{7}{24} - \frac{3}{24} = \frac{1}{R_1}$$

$$\frac{4}{24} = \frac{1}{R_1}$$

$$\frac{1}{6} = \frac{1}{R_1}$$

$$R_1 = 6 \text{ ohms}$$

**9.**

$$\frac{1}{2.\overline{6}} = \frac{1}{2R_2} + \frac{1}{R_2}$$

$$\frac{3}{8} = \frac{1}{2R_2} + \frac{2}{2} \cdot \frac{1}{R_2}$$

$$\frac{3}{8} = \frac{1 + 2}{2R_2}$$

$$\frac{3}{8} = \frac{3}{2R_2}$$

$$3 \cdot 2R_2 = 3 \cdot 8$$

$$6R_2 = 24$$

$$R_2 = 4 \text{ ohms}$$

$$R_1 = 2 \cdot R_2$$

$$= 2 \cdot 4$$

$$= 8 \text{ ohms}$$

**10.**

$$\frac{1}{2.25} = \frac{1}{R_1} + \frac{1}{3R_1}$$

$$\frac{1}{\frac{9}{4}} = \frac{3}{3} \cdot \frac{1}{R_1} + \frac{1}{3R_1}$$

$$\frac{4}{9} = \frac{3 + 1}{3R_1}$$

$$\frac{4}{9} = \frac{4}{3R_1}$$

$$4 \cdot 3R_1 = 4 \cdot 9$$

$$12R_1 = 36$$

$$R_1 = 3 \text{ ohms}$$

$$R_2 = 3 \cdot R_1$$

$$= 3 \cdot 3$$

$$= 9 \text{ ohms}$$

**11.** $a = \dfrac{v}{t}$

$at = v$

$t = \dfrac{v}{a}$

**12.** $v = r + at$

$v - r = at$

$a = \dfrac{v - r}{t}$

**13.** $s = vt + \frac{1}{2}at^2$

$vt = s - \frac{1}{2}at^2$

$v = \frac{s - \frac{1}{2}at^2}{t}$

$v = \frac{2s - at^2}{2t}$

**14.** $s = vt + \frac{1}{2}at^2$

$s - vt = \frac{1}{2}at^2$

$2(s - vt) = at^2$

$a = \frac{2(s - vt)}{t^2}$

$a = \frac{2s - 2vt}{t^2}$

**15.** $F = G\left(\frac{Mm}{d^2}\right)$

$Fd^2 = GMm$

$\frac{Fd^2}{Gm} = M$

$M = \frac{Fd^2}{Gm}$

**16.** $f = \frac{W}{g} \cdot \frac{v^2}{R}$

$fgR = Wv^2$

$R = \frac{Wv^2}{fg}$

**17.** $A = p + prt$

$A = p(1 + rt)$

$p = \frac{A}{1 + rt}$

**18.** $I = prt$

$r = \frac{I}{pt}$

**19.** $I = \left(\frac{100 - P}{P}\right)\frac{365}{R}$

$\frac{IR}{365} = \frac{100 - P}{P}$

$PIR = 365(100 - P)$

$PIR = 36,500 - 365P$

$PIR + 365P = 36,500$

$P(IR + 365) = 36,500$

$P = \frac{36,500}{IR + 365}$

**20.** $I = \frac{365d}{360 - dr}$

$I(360 - dr) = 365d$

$360I - dIr = 365d$

$365d + dIr = 360I$

$d(365 + Ir) = 360I$

$d = \frac{360I}{Ir + 365}$

**21.** $a = \frac{r}{2y} - 0.25$

$a + 0.25 = \frac{r}{2y}$

$2y(a + 0.25) = r$

$y = \frac{r}{2(a + 0.25)}$

$y = \frac{r}{2a + 0.5}$

**22.** $c = \frac{P - 100}{P}$

$cP = P - 100$

$P - cP = 100$

$P(1 - c) = 100$

$P = \frac{100}{1 - c}$

**23.** $H = (0.24)I^2Rt$

$R = \frac{H}{0.24I^2t}$

**24.** $P = \frac{E^2}{R}$

$PR = E^2$

$R = \frac{E^2}{P}$

**25.** $\frac{1}{R_T} = \frac{1}{R_1} + \frac{1}{R_2}$

$\frac{1}{R_T} - \frac{1}{R_2} = \frac{1}{R_1}$

$R_TR_2\left(\frac{1}{R_T} - \frac{1}{R_2}\right) = \frac{R_TR_2}{R_1}$

$R_2 - R_T = \frac{R_TR_2}{R_1}$

$R_1 = \frac{R_TR_2}{R_2 - R_T}$

**26.** $I = \frac{E}{r + R}$

$I(r + R) = E$

$Ir + IR = E$

$IR = E - Ir$

$R = \frac{E - Ir}{I}$

**27.** $I = \frac{nE}{nr + R}$

$I(nr + R) = nE$

$Inr + IR = nE$

$n(Ir - E) = -IR$

$n = \frac{-IR}{IR - E}$

$n = \frac{IR}{E - Ir}$

**28.** $I = \frac{E}{\frac{r}{n} + R}$

$I\left(\frac{r}{n} + R\right) = E$

$\frac{Ir}{n} + IR = E$

$\frac{Ir}{n} = E - IR$

$Ir = n(E - IR)$

$r = \frac{n(E - IR)}{I}$

$r = \frac{En - IRn}{I}$

**29.** $y = mx + b$

$y - b = mx$

$m = \frac{y - b}{x}$

**30.** $S = \frac{n}{2}(A + t)$

$2S = n(A + t)$

$n = \frac{2S}{A + t}$

**31.** $m = \frac{y_2 - y_1}{x_2 - x_1}$

$m(x_2 - x_1) = y_2 - y_1$

$y^2 = mx_2 - mx_1 + y_1$

**32.** $m = \frac{y_2 - y_1}{x_2 - x_1}$

$m(x_2 - x_1) = y_2 - y_1$

$x_2 - x_1 = \frac{y_2 - y_1}{m}$

$-x_1 = \frac{y_2 - y_1}{m} - x_2$

$x_1 = x_2 - \left(\frac{y_2 - y_1}{m}\right)$

$x_1 = \frac{mx_2 - y_2 + y_1}{m}$

**33.** $\frac{P}{D} = Q + \frac{R}{D}$

$\frac{P}{D} - Q = \frac{R}{D}$

$R = D\left(\frac{P}{D} - Q\right)$

$R = P - DQ$

**34.** $\frac{P}{D} = Q + \frac{R}{D}$

$\frac{P}{D} - \frac{R}{D} = Q$

$\frac{P - R}{D} = Q$

$D = \frac{P - R}{Q}$

**35.** $R_2 + R_3$

$= 4 + 3 = 7$ ohms

$\dfrac{1}{R_T} = \dfrac{1}{5} + \dfrac{1}{7}$

$35 \cdot \dfrac{1}{R_T} = \dfrac{1}{5} + \dfrac{1}{7}$

$\dfrac{35}{R_T} = 7 + 5$

$\dfrac{35}{R_T} = 12$

$12R_T = 35$

$R_T = 2.91\overline{6}$ ohms

**36.** $\dfrac{1}{2\frac{10}{13}} = \dfrac{1}{R_1} + \dfrac{1}{3+6}$

$\dfrac{13}{36} = \dfrac{1}{R_1} + \dfrac{1}{9}$

$\dfrac{1}{R_1} = \dfrac{13}{36} - \dfrac{1}{9}$

$36R_1 \cdot \dfrac{1}{R_1} = 36R_1 \cdot \left(\dfrac{13}{36} - \dfrac{1}{9}\right)$

$36 = 13R_1 - 4R_1$

$36 = 9R_1$

$R_1 = 4$ ohms

**37.**

$\dfrac{1}{3.5} = \dfrac{1}{5} + \dfrac{1}{4 + R_2}$

$\dfrac{1}{3.5} - \dfrac{1}{5} = \dfrac{1}{4 + R_2}$

$\dfrac{1}{\frac{7}{2}} - \dfrac{1}{5} = \dfrac{1}{4 + R_2}$

$\dfrac{2}{7} - \dfrac{1}{5} = \dfrac{1}{4 + R_2}$

$35\left(\dfrac{2}{7} - \dfrac{1}{5}\right) = \dfrac{35}{4 + R_2}$

$10 - 7 = \dfrac{35}{4 + R_2}$

$3(4 + R_2) = 35$

$12 + 3R_2 = 35$

$3R_2 = 23$

$R_2 = 7.\overline{6}$ ohms

**38.** $3 + 6 + 9$

$= 18$ ohms

**39.** $8 \cdot 12 = 96$ ohms

**40.** $\dfrac{1}{R_T} = \dfrac{1}{3} + \dfrac{1}{4} + \dfrac{1}{6}$

$\dfrac{1}{R_T} = \dfrac{8 + 6 + 4}{24}$

$R_T = \dfrac{24}{18} = \dfrac{4}{3} = 1.\overline{3}$ ohms

**41.** $\dfrac{1}{R_T} = \dfrac{1}{60} + \dfrac{1}{20} + \dfrac{1}{80}$

$\dfrac{1}{R_T} = \dfrac{4 + 12 + 3}{240}$

$\dfrac{1}{R_T} = \dfrac{19}{240}$

$R_T = \dfrac{240}{19}$

$R_T = 12.632$ ohms

**42.** $\dfrac{1}{R_{23}} = \dfrac{1}{R_2} + \dfrac{1}{R_3}$

$\dfrac{1}{R_{23}} = \dfrac{R_2 R_3}{R_2 R_3} \cdot \left(\dfrac{1}{R_2} + \dfrac{1}{R_3}\right)$

$\dfrac{1}{R_{23}} = \dfrac{R_3 + R_2}{R_2 R_3}$

$R_{23} = \dfrac{R_2 R_3}{R_2 + R_3}$

$R_T = R_1 + \dfrac{R_2 R_3}{R_2 + R_3}$

**43.** $R_T = 5 + \dfrac{4 \cdot 6}{4 + 6}$

$R_T = 5 + \dfrac{24}{10}$

$R_T = 5 + 2.4$

$R_T = 7.4$ ohms

**44.** $C = \dfrac{5}{9}(59 - 32)$

$C = \dfrac{5}{9} \cdot 27$

$C = 15$

$15°C$

**45.** $-14 \le 4x + 4 \le 14$

$-7 \le 2x + 2 \le 7$

$-9 \le 2x \le 5$

$-\dfrac{9}{2} \le x \le \dfrac{5}{2}$

$\left\{ x \mid -\dfrac{9}{2} \le x \le \dfrac{5}{2} \right\}$

**46.** $256\left[\dfrac{1 - (1 + 0.01)^{20-60}}{0.01}\right]$

$= 256\left[\dfrac{1 - (1.01)^{-40}}{0.01}\right]$

$= \$8405.68$

**47.** $d = r \cdot t$

$t = \dfrac{d}{r}$

$t = \dfrac{1.5 \times 10^8}{3 \times 10^6}$

$t = 50$ hrs or about two days.

**48.** $2(m^2 - 16n^2)$

$= 2(m - 4n)(m + 4n)$

**49.**

| | $r$ | $t$ | $w$ |
|---|---|---|---|
| Hugo | $\frac{1}{40}$ | 24 | $\frac{24}{40}$ |
| Denise | $\frac{1}{x}$ | 24 | $\frac{24}{x}$ |

$\dfrac{24}{40} + \dfrac{24}{x} = 1$

$40x\left(\dfrac{24}{40} + \dfrac{24}{x}\right) = 40x$

$24x + 24 \cdot 40 = 40x$

$16x = 960$

$x = 60$

It would take Denise 60 min.

# Chapter 8    Summary and Review

PAGES 348-350    SKILLS AND CONCEPTS

**1.** $\dfrac{3x^2 y}{12xy^3 z} = \dfrac{x}{4y^2 z}$

$x \neq 0,\ y \neq 0,\ z \neq 0$

**2.** $\dfrac{z^2 - 3z}{z - 3}$

$= \dfrac{z(z - 3)}{z - 3}$

$= z$

$z - 3 \neq 0$

$z \neq 3$

**3.** $\dfrac{a^2 - 25}{a^2 + 3a - 10}$

$= \dfrac{(a - 5)(a + 5)}{(a + 5)(a - 2)}$

$= \dfrac{a - 5}{a - 2}$

$a + 5 \neq 0,\ a - 2 \neq 0$

$a \neq -5 \qquad a \neq 2$

4. $\dfrac{x^2 + 10x + 21}{x^3 + x^2 - 42x}$

$= \dfrac{(x + 7)(x + 3)}{x(x^2 + x - 42)}$

$= \dfrac{(x + 7)(x + 3)}{x(x - 6)(x + 7)}$

$= \dfrac{x + 3}{x(x - 6)}$

$x \neq 0,\ x - 6 \neq 0,\ x + 7 \neq 0$

$\qquad\qquad x \neq 6 \qquad x \neq -7$

5. $\dfrac{7a^2}{9b}$

6. $\dfrac{3axy}{10}$

7. $\dfrac{x^2 + x - 12}{x + 2} \cdot \dfrac{x + 4}{x^2 - x - 6}$

$= \dfrac{(x + 4)(x - 3)(x + 4)}{(x + 2)(x - 3)(x + 2)}$

$= \dfrac{(x + 4)^2}{(x + 2)^2}$

8. $\dfrac{b^2 + 19b + 84}{b - 3} \cdot \dfrac{b^2 - 9}{b^2 + 15b + 36}$

$= \dfrac{(b + 7)(b + 12)(b - 3)(b + 3)}{(b - 3)(b + 12)(b + 3)}$

$= b + 7$

9. $\dfrac{p^3}{2q} \div \dfrac{-(p^2)}{4q}$

$= \dfrac{p^3}{2q} \cdot \dfrac{4q}{-p^2}$

$= -2p$

10. $\dfrac{n^2}{n - 3} \div (n + 4)$

$= \dfrac{n^2}{n - 3} \cdot \dfrac{1}{n + 4}$

$= \dfrac{n^2}{(n - 3)(n + 4)}$

11. $\dfrac{7a^2 b}{x^2 + x - 30} \div \dfrac{3a}{x^2 + 15x + 54}$

$= \dfrac{7a^2 b}{x^2 + x - 30} \cdot \dfrac{x^2 + 15x + 54}{3a}$

$= \dfrac{7ab(x + 6)(x + 9)}{(x + 6)(x - 5) \cdot 3}$

$= \dfrac{7ab(x + 9)}{3(x - 5)}$

12. $\dfrac{m^2 + 4m - 21}{m^2 + 8m + 15} \div \dfrac{m^2 - 9}{m^2 + 12m + 35}$

$= \dfrac{m^2 + 4m - 21}{m^2 + 8m + 15} \cdot \dfrac{m^2 + 12m + 35}{m^2 - 9}$

$= \dfrac{(m + 7)(m - 3)(m + 7)(m + 5)}{(m + 3)(m + 5)(m - 3)(m + 3)}$

$= \dfrac{(m + 7)^2}{(m + 3)^2}$

13.
$$
\begin{array}{r}
x^2 + 4x - 2 \\
x + 3\,\overline{\smash{)}\,x^3 + 7x^2 + 10x - 6} \\
\underline{x^3 + 3x^2\phantom{00000000000}} \\
4x^2 + 10x\phantom{0000} \\
\underline{4x^2 + 12x\phantom{0000}} \\
-2x - 6 \\
\underline{-2x - 6} \\
0
\end{array}
$$

14.
$$
\begin{array}{r}
x^3 + 5x^2 + 12x + 23 + \dfrac{52}{x - 2} \\
x - 2\,\overline{\smash{)}\,x^4 + 3x^3 + 2x^2 - x + 6} \\
\underline{x^4 - 2x^3\phantom{0000000000000}} \\
5x^3 + 2x^2\phantom{000000} \\
\underline{5x^3 - 10x^2\phantom{000000}} \\
12x^2 - x\phantom{000} \\
\underline{12x^2 - 24x\phantom{000}} \\
23x + 6 \\
\underline{23x - 46} \\
52
\end{array}
$$

15.
$$
\begin{array}{r}
2a^2 + 18a + 159 + \dfrac{1422}{a - 9} \\
a - 9\,\overline{\smash{)}\,2a^3 - 0a^2 - 3a - 9} \\
\underline{2a^3 - 18a^2\phantom{0000000}} \\
18a^2 - 3a\phantom{000} \\
\underline{18a^2 - 162a\phantom{000}} \\
159a - 9 \\
\underline{159a - 1431} \\
1422
\end{array}
$$

16.
$$
\begin{array}{r}
3a^2 - 2a - 4 - \dfrac{5}{2a - 5} \\
2a - 5\,\overline{\smash{)}\,6a^3 - 19a^2 + 2a + 15} \\
\underline{6a^3 - 15a^2\phantom{0000000}} \\
-4a^2 + 2a\phantom{000} \\
\underline{-4a^2 + 10a\phantom{000}} \\
-8a + 15 \\
\underline{-8a + 20} \\
-5
\end{array}
$$

17. $\dfrac{7 + a}{x^2}$

18. $\dfrac{a^2 - b^2}{a^2 - b^2}$

$= 1$

19. $\dfrac{2x - 6}{x - 3}$

$\dfrac{2(x - 3)}{x - 3}$

$= 2$

20. $\dfrac{x + 1}{x^2 - 1}$

$= \dfrac{x + 1}{(x - 1)(x + 1)}$

$= \dfrac{1}{x - 1}$

21. $\dfrac{2}{x - y} + \dfrac{x}{y - x}$

$= \dfrac{2}{x - y} - \dfrac{x}{x - y}$

$= \dfrac{2 - x}{x - y}$

**22.** $\dfrac{x}{x+3} - \dfrac{5}{x-2}$

$= \dfrac{(x+3)(x-2)}{(x+3)(x-2)}\left(\dfrac{x}{x+3} - \dfrac{5}{x-2}\right)$

$= \dfrac{x(x-2) - 5(x+3)}{(x+3)(x-2)}$

$= \dfrac{x^2 - 2x - 5x - 15}{x^2 + x - 6}$

$= \dfrac{x^2 - 7x - 15}{x^2 + x - 6}$

**23.** $\dfrac{2x+3}{x^2-4} + \dfrac{6}{x+2}$

$= \dfrac{2x+3}{(x-2)(x+2)} + \dfrac{6}{x+2}$

$= \dfrac{(x-2)(x+2)}{(x-2)(x+2)}\left[\dfrac{2x+3}{(x+2)(x-2)} + \dfrac{6}{x+2}\right]$

$= \dfrac{2x+3 + 6(x-2)}{(x-2)(x+2)}$

$= \dfrac{2x+3 + 6x - 12}{x^2 - 4}$

$= \dfrac{8x - 9}{x^2 - 4}$

**24.**

$\dfrac{m-n}{m^2 + 2mn + n^2} - \dfrac{m+n}{m-n}$

$= \dfrac{m-n}{(m+n)^2} - \dfrac{m+n}{m-n}$

$= (m+n)^2(m-n)\left[\dfrac{m-n}{(m+n)^2} - \dfrac{m+n}{m-n}\right]$

$= \dfrac{(m-n)(m-n) - (m+n)(m+n)^2}{(m+n)^2(m-n)}$

$= \dfrac{m^2 - 2mn + n^2 - (m+n)(m^2 + 2mn + n^2)}{(m+n)^2(m-n)}$

$= \dfrac{m^2 - 2mn + n^2 - m^3 - 2m^2n - mn^2 - m^2n - 2mn^2 - n^3}{(m+n)^2(m-n)}$

$= \dfrac{-m^3 + m^2 - 3m^2n - 3mn^2 - 2mn + n^2 - n^3}{(m+n)^2(m-n)}$

**25.** $\dfrac{\dfrac{x^2}{y^2}}{\dfrac{3x}{9y^2}}$

$= \dfrac{x^2}{y^3} \cdot \dfrac{9y^2}{3x}$

$= \dfrac{9x}{3y}$

$= \dfrac{3x}{y}$

**26.** $\dfrac{\dfrac{a^2 - 13a + 40}{a^2 - 4a - 32}}{\dfrac{a-5}{a+7}}$

$= \dfrac{a^2 - 13a + 40}{a^2 - 4a - 32} \cdot \dfrac{a+7}{a-5}$

$= \dfrac{(a-5)(a-8)(a+7)}{(a-8)(a+4)(a-5)}$

$= \dfrac{a+7}{a+4}$

**27.** $\dfrac{x - \dfrac{35}{x+2}}{x + \dfrac{42}{x+13}}$

$= \dfrac{\dfrac{x+2}{x+2} \cdot x - \dfrac{35}{x+2}}{\dfrac{x+13}{x+13} \cdot x + \dfrac{42}{x+13}}$

$= \dfrac{\dfrac{x(x+2) - 35}{x+2}}{\dfrac{x(x+13) + 42}{x+13}}$

$= \dfrac{x(x+2) - 35}{x+2} \cdot \dfrac{x+13}{x(x+13) + 42}$

$= \dfrac{(x^2 + 2x - 35)(x+13)}{(x+2)(x^2 + 13x + 42)}$

$= \dfrac{(x+7)(x-5)(x+13)}{(x+2)(x+6)(x+7)}$

$= \dfrac{(x-5)(x+13)}{(x+2)(x+6)}$

$= \dfrac{x^2 + 8x - 65}{x^2 + 8x + 12}$

**28.** $\dfrac{4x}{3} + \dfrac{7}{2} = \dfrac{7x}{12}$

$12\left(\dfrac{4x}{3} + \dfrac{7}{2}\right) = 12 \cdot \dfrac{7x}{12}$

$16x + 42 = 7x$

$-9x = 42$

$x = -\dfrac{42}{9}$

$x = -\dfrac{14}{3}$

**29.** $\dfrac{1}{h+1} + \dfrac{2}{3} = \dfrac{2h+5}{h-1}$

$3(h-1)(h+1)\left(\dfrac{1}{h+1} + \dfrac{2}{3}\right) = 3(h-1)(h+1)\left(\dfrac{2h+5}{h-1}\right)$

$3(h-1) + 2(h-1)(h+1) = 3(h+1)(2h+5)$

$3h - 3 + 2h^2 - 2 = 2(2h^2 + 7h + 5)$

$2h^2 + 3h - 5 = 6h^2 + 21h + 15$

$4h^2 + 18h + 20 = 0$

$2(2h^2 + 9h + 10) = 0$

$2(2h+5)(h+2) = 0$

$2h + 5 = 0, \quad h + 2 = 0$

$2h = -5 \qquad h = -2$

$h = -\dfrac{5}{2}$

**30.** $\dfrac{3x+2}{(x+6)(x+1)} = \dfrac{1}{x+6} + \dfrac{4}{x+1}$

$(x+6)(x+1)\left[\dfrac{3x+2}{(x+6)(x+1)}\right]$

$= (x+6)(x+1)\left(\dfrac{1}{x+6} + \dfrac{4}{x+1}\right)$

$3x + 2 = x + 1 + 4(x+6)$

$3x + 2 = x + 1 + 4x + 24$

$3x + 2 = 5x + 25$

$2x = -23$

$x = -\dfrac{23}{2}$

**31.**

$$\frac{3m - 2}{2m^2 - 5m - 3} - \frac{2}{2m + 1} = \frac{4}{m - 3}$$

$$\frac{3m - 2}{(2m + 1)(m - 3)} - \frac{2}{(2m + 1)} = \frac{4}{m - 3}$$

$$(2m + 1)(m - 3)\left[\frac{3m - 2}{(2m + 1)(m - 3)} - \frac{2}{(2m + 1)}\right]$$

$$= (2m + 1)(m - 3)\left(\frac{4}{m - 3}\right)$$

$$3m - 2 - 2(m - 3) = 4(2m + 1)$$

$$3m - 2 - 2m + 6 = 8m + 4$$

$$m + 4 = 8m + 4$$

$$7m = 0$$

$$m = 0$$

**32.** $\frac{1}{2}n + b = n$

$$n - \frac{1}{2}n = b$$

$$\frac{1}{2}n = b$$

$$n = 2b$$

**33.** $\frac{n}{x} = \frac{y}{r}$

$$n = \frac{xy}{r}$$

**34.** $\frac{n}{a} + \frac{b}{c} = d$

$$\frac{n}{a} = d - \frac{b}{c}$$

$$n = a\left(d - \frac{b}{c}\right)$$

$$n = ad - \frac{ab}{c} = \frac{acd - ab}{c}$$

**35.** $\frac{a}{c} = n + bn$

$$\frac{a}{c} = n(1 + b)$$

$$n = \frac{a}{c} \cdot \frac{1}{1 + b}$$

$$n = \frac{a}{c + cb}$$

**PAGE 350  APPLICATIONS AND CONNECTIONS**

**36.** $\frac{6x^2 + 9x - 27}{x + 5} \cdot \frac{2x^2 + 13x + 15}{4x^2 - 12x + 9}$

$$= \frac{3(2x^2 + 3x - 9)(2x + 3)(x + 5)}{(x + 5)(2x - 3)(2x - 3)}$$

$$= \frac{3(2x - 3)(x + 3)(2x + 3)(x + 5)}{(x + 5)(2x - 3)(2x - 3)}$$

$$= \frac{3(x + 3)(2x + 3)}{(2x - 3)}$$

$$= \frac{3(2x^2 + 9x + 9)}{2x - 3}$$

$$A = \frac{6x^2 + 27x + 27}{2x - 3}$$

**37.** $\frac{x^2 + 5x + 6}{x^2 + 4x + 4} \cdot \frac{x^2 + 3x - 10}{x^2 + 8x + 15}$

$$= \frac{(x + 3)(x + 2)(x + 5)(x - 2)}{(x + 2)^2(x + 3)(x + 5)}$$

$$A = \frac{x - 2}{x + 2}$$

**38.** $\left(\frac{3x - 7}{4x}\right)^2$

$$A = \frac{9x^2 - 42x + 49}{16x^2}$$

**39.**  $3 \rightarrow 3,\ 6,\ 9,\ 12,\ 15,\ 18,\ 21,\ 24,\ 27,\ 30,\ 33,$
  $36,\ 39,\ 42,\ 45,\ 48,\ 51,\ 54,\ 57,\ 60,\ 63,\ 66,$
  $69,\ 72,\ 75,\ 78,\ 81,\ 84,\ 87,\ 90,\ 93,\ 96,\ 99$

  $11 \rightarrow 11,\ 22,\ 33,\ 44,\ 55,\ 66,\ 77,\ 88,\ 99$
  $33,\ 66,\ 99$

**40. a.** $4 + 6 = 10$ ohms

**b.** $\frac{1}{R_T} = \frac{1}{4} + \frac{1}{6}$

$$\frac{1}{R_T} = \frac{3}{12} + \frac{2}{12}$$

$$\frac{1}{R_T} = \frac{5}{12}$$

$$R_T = \frac{12}{5}$$

$$R_T = 2.4 \text{ ohms}$$

## Chapter 8    Test

**PAGE 351**

**1.** $\dfrac{\frac{5}{9}}{\frac{2}{3}} = \frac{5}{9} \cdot \frac{3}{2}$

$$= \frac{5}{6}$$

**2.** $\frac{21x^2y}{28ax} = \frac{3xy}{4a}$

**3.** $\frac{x^2 + 7x - 18}{x^2 + 12x + 27}$

$$= \frac{(x - 2)(x + 9)}{(x + 3)(x + 9)}$$

$$= \frac{x - 2}{x + 3}$$

**4.** $\frac{x^2 - x - 56}{x^2 + x - 42}$

$$= \frac{(x - 8)(x + 7)}{(x - 6)(x + 7)}$$

$$= \frac{x - 8}{x - 6}$$

**5.** $\frac{7x^2 - 28}{5x^3 - 20x}$

$$= \frac{7(x^2 - 4)}{5x(x^2 - 4)}$$

$$= \frac{7}{5x}$$

**6.** $\frac{2x^2 - 5x - 3}{x^2 - 2x - 15}$

$$= \frac{(2x + 1)(x - 3)}{(x + 5)(x - 3)}$$

$$= \frac{2x + 1}{x + 5}$$

**7.** $\frac{3x}{x + 3} + \frac{5x}{x + 3}$

$$= \frac{8x}{x + 3}$$

**8.** $\frac{2x}{x - 7} - \frac{14}{x - 7}$

$$= \frac{2x - 14}{x - 7}$$

$$= \frac{2(x - 7)}{x - 7}$$

$$= 2$$

**9.** $\frac{2x}{x + 7} + \frac{4}{x + 4}$

$$= \frac{x + 7)(x + 4)}{x + 7)(x + 4)} \cdot \left(\frac{2x}{x + 7} + \frac{4}{x + 4}\right)$$

$$= \frac{2x^2(x + 4) + 4(x + 7)}{(x + 4)(x + 7)}$$

$$= \frac{2x^2 + 8x + 4x + 28}{x^2 + 11x + 28}$$

$$= \frac{2x^2 + 12x + 28}{x^2 + 11x + 28}$$

10. $\dfrac{2a + 1}{2a - 3} + \dfrac{a - 3}{3a + 2}$

$= (2a - 3)(3a + 2)\left(\dfrac{2a + 1}{2a - 3} + \dfrac{a - 3}{3a + 2}\right)$

$= \dfrac{(3a + 2)(2a + 1) + (a - 3)(2a - 3)}{(2a - 3)(3a + 2)}$

$= \dfrac{6a^2 + 7a + 2 + 2a^2 - 9a + 9}{6a^2 - 5a - 6}$

$= \dfrac{8a^2 - 2a + 11}{6a^2 - 5a - 6}$

11. $\dfrac{x + 5}{x + 2} + 6$

$= \dfrac{x + 5}{x + 2} + 6 \cdot \dfrac{x + 2}{x + 2}$

$= \dfrac{x + 5 + 6x + 12}{x + 2}$

$= \dfrac{7x + 17}{x + 2}$

12. $\dfrac{x - 2}{x - 8} + x + 5$

$= \dfrac{x - 2}{x - 8} + \dfrac{x - 8}{x - 8} \cdot x + \dfrac{x - 8}{x - 8} \cdot 5$

$= \dfrac{x - 2 + x(x - 8) + 5(x - 8)}{x - 8}$

$= \dfrac{x - 2 + x^2 - 8x + 5x - 40}{x - 8}$

$= \dfrac{x^2 - 2x - 42}{x - 8}$

13. $\dfrac{3x + 2}{4x + 1} + \dfrac{7}{x}$

$= \dfrac{x(4x + 1)}{x(4x + 1)}\left(\dfrac{3x + 2}{4x + 1} + \dfrac{7}{x}\right)$

$= \dfrac{x(3x + 2) + 7(4x + 1)}{x(4x + 1)}$

$= \dfrac{3x^2 + 2x + 28x + 7}{4x^2 + x}$

$= \dfrac{3x^2 + 30x + 7}{4x^2 + x}$

14. $\dfrac{x}{x + 1} + \dfrac{1}{x + 1}$

$= \dfrac{x + 1}{x + 1}$

$= 1$

15. $\dfrac{3x - 8}{x + 4} + \dfrac{9}{x + 1}$

$= \dfrac{(x + 1)(x + 4)}{(x + 1)(x + 4)}\left(\dfrac{3x - 8}{x + 4} + \dfrac{9}{x + 1}\right)$

$= \dfrac{(x + 1)(3x - 8) + 9(x + 4)}{(x + 1)(x + 4)}$

$= \dfrac{3x^2 - 5x - 8 + 9x + 36}{x^2 + 5x + 4}$

$= \dfrac{3x^2 + 4x + 28}{x^2 + 5x + 4}$

16. $\dfrac{x^2 + 4x - 32}{x + 5} \cdot \dfrac{x - 3}{x^2 - 7x + 12}$

$= \dfrac{(x + 8)(x - 4)(x - 3)}{(x + 5)(x - 3)(x - 4)}$

$= \dfrac{x + 8}{x + 5}$

17. $\dfrac{3x^2 + 2x - 8}{x^2 - 4} \div \dfrac{6x^2 + 13x - 28}{2x^2 - 3x - 35}$

$= \dfrac{3x^2 + 2x - 8}{x^2 - 4} \cdot \dfrac{2x^2 - 3x - 35}{6x^2 + 13x - 28}$

$= \dfrac{(3x - 4)(x + 2)(2x + 7)(x - 5)}{(x - 2)(x + 2)(3x - 4)(2x + 7)}$

$= \dfrac{x - 5}{x - 2}$

18. $\dfrac{4x^2 + 11x + 6}{x^2 - x - 6} \div \dfrac{x^2 + 8x + 16}{x^2 + x - 12}$

$= \dfrac{4x^2 + 11x + 6}{x^2 - x - 6} \cdot \dfrac{x^2 + x - 12}{x^2 + 8x + 16}$

$= \dfrac{(4x + 3)(x + 2)(x + 4)(x - 3)}{(x - 3)(x + 2)(x + 4)^2}$

$= \dfrac{4x + 3}{x + 4}$

19. $\dfrac{3x^2 + 5x - 28}{x^2 - 3x - 28} \cdot \dfrac{x^2 - 8x + 7}{3x - 7}$

$= \dfrac{(3x - 7)(x + 4)(x - 7)(x - 1)}{(x - 7)(x + 4)(3x - 7)}$

$= x - 1$

20. $\dfrac{x - \dfrac{24}{x + 5}}{x - \dfrac{72}{x - 1}}$

$= \dfrac{\dfrac{x + 5}{x + 5} \cdot x - \dfrac{24}{x + 5}}{\dfrac{x - 1}{x - 1} \cdot x - \dfrac{72}{x - 1}}$

$= \dfrac{\dfrac{x(x + 5) - 24}{x + 5}}{\dfrac{x(x - 1) - 72}{x - 1}}$

$= \dfrac{\dfrac{x^2 + 5x - 24}{x + 5}}{\dfrac{x^2 - x - 72}{x - 1}}$

$= \dfrac{x^2 + 5x - 24}{x + 5} \cdot \dfrac{x - 1}{x^2 - x - 72}$

$= \dfrac{(x + 8)(x - 3)(x - 1)}{(x + 5)(x + 8)(x - 9)}$

$= \dfrac{(x - 3)(x - 1)}{(x - 9)(x + 5)}$

21.
$$\dfrac{\dfrac{x^2 - x - 6}{x^2 + 2x - 15}}{\dfrac{x^2 - 2x - 8}{x^2 + x - 20}}$$

$$= \dfrac{x^2 - x - 6}{x^2 + 2x - 15} \cdot \dfrac{x^2 + x - 20}{x^2 - 2x - 8}$$

$$= \dfrac{(x - 3)(x + 2)(x + 5)(x - 4)}{(x + 5)(x - 3)(x - 4)(x + 2)}$$

$$= 1$$

22.
$$\dfrac{\dfrac{2}{3m} + \dfrac{3}{m^2}}{\dfrac{2}{5m} + \dfrac{5}{m}}$$

$$= \dfrac{15m^3\left(\dfrac{2}{3m} + \dfrac{3}{m^2}\right)}{15m^3\left(\dfrac{2}{5m} + \dfrac{5}{m}\right)}$$

$$= \dfrac{2 \cdot 5m^2 + 15 \cdot 3m}{2 \cdot 3m^2 + 15 \cdot 5m^2}$$

$$= \dfrac{10m^2 + 45m}{6m^2 + 75m^2}$$

$$= \dfrac{5m(2m + 9)}{81m^2}$$

$$= \dfrac{5(2m + 9)}{81m}$$

23.
$$\dfrac{y + 3}{6} = \dfrac{y + 2}{12} - \dfrac{2}{5}$$

$$60\left(\dfrac{y + 3}{6}\right) = 60\left(\dfrac{y + 2}{12} - \dfrac{2}{5}\right)$$

$$10(y + 3) = 5(y + 2) - 12 \cdot 2$$

$$10y + 30 = 5y + 10 - 24$$

$$5y = -44$$

$$y = \dfrac{-44}{5}$$

24.
$$\dfrac{x + 1}{x} + \dfrac{6}{x} = x + 7$$

$$\dfrac{x + 1 + 6}{x} = x + 7$$

$$x + 7 = x(x + 7)$$

$$x + 7 = x^2 + 7x$$

$$x^2 + 6x - 7 = 0$$

$$(x + 7)(x - 1) = 0$$

$$x + 7 = 0, \quad x - 1 = 0$$

$$x = -7 \qquad x = 1$$

25.
$$\dfrac{4m}{m - 3} + \dfrac{6}{3 - m} = m$$

$$\dfrac{4m}{m - 3} - \dfrac{6}{m - 3} = m$$

$$\dfrac{4m - 6}{m - 3} = m$$

$$4m - 6 = m(m - 3)$$

$$4m - 6 = m^2 - 3m$$

$$m^2 - 7m + 6 = 0$$

$$(m - 6)(m - 1) = 0$$

$$m - 6 = 0, \quad m - 1 = 0$$

$$m = 6 \qquad m = 1$$

26.
$$\dfrac{-2b - 9}{b^2 + 7b + 12} = \dfrac{b}{b + 3} + \dfrac{2}{b + 4}$$

$$\dfrac{-2b - 9}{(b + 3)(b + 4)} = \dfrac{b}{b + 3} + \dfrac{2}{b + 4}$$

$$(b + 3)(b + 4)\left[\dfrac{-2b - 9}{(b + 3)(b + 4)}\right]$$

$$= (b + 3)(b + 4)\left(\dfrac{b}{b + 3} + \dfrac{2}{b + 4}\right)$$

$$-2b - 9 = b(b + 4) + 2(b + 3)$$

$$-2b - 9 = b^2 + 4b + 2b + 6$$

$$b^2 + 8b + 15 = 0$$

$$(b + 3)(b + 5) = 0$$

$$b + 3 = 0, \quad b + 5 = 0$$

$$b = -3 \qquad b = -5$$

But $b = -3$ is an excluded value so the only solution is $b = -5$.

27.
$$\dfrac{1}{y - 4} - \dfrac{2}{y - 8} = \dfrac{-1}{y + 6}$$

$$(y - 4)(y - 8)(y + 6)\left(\dfrac{1}{y - 4} - \dfrac{2}{y - 8}\right)$$

$$= (y - 4)(y - 8)(y + 6)\left(\dfrac{-1}{y + 6}\right)$$

$$(y - 8)(y + 6) - 2(y - 4)(y + 6) = -(y - 4)(y - 8)$$

$$y^2 - 2y - 48 - 2(y^2 + 2y - 24) = -(y^2 - 12y + 32)$$

$$y^2 - 2y - 48 - 2y^2 - 4y + 48 = -y^2 + 12y - 32$$

$$18y = 32$$

$$y = \dfrac{32}{18}$$

$$y = \dfrac{16}{9}$$

28.
$$\dfrac{m + 3}{m - 1} + \dfrac{m + 1}{m - 3} = \dfrac{22}{3}$$

$$3(m - 1)(m - 3)\left(\dfrac{m + 3}{m - 1} + \dfrac{m + 1}{m - 3}\right)$$

$$= 3(m - 1)(m - 3) \cdot \dfrac{22}{3}$$

$$3(m - 3)(m + 3) + 3(m - 1)(m + 1) = 22(m - 1)(m - 3)$$

$$3(m^2 - 9) + 3(m^2 - 1) = 22(m^2 - 4m + 3)$$

$$3m^2 - 27 + 3m^2 - 3 = 22m^2 - 88m + 66$$

$$16m^2 - 88m + 96 = 0$$

$$8(2m^2 - 11m + 12) = 0$$

$$8(2m - 3)(m - 4) = 0$$

$$2m - 3 = 0, \quad m - 4 = 0$$

$$2m = 3 \qquad m = 4$$

$$m = \dfrac{3}{2}$$

29. $F = G\left(\dfrac{Mm}{d^2}\right)$

$$G = \dfrac{Fd^2}{Mm}$$

**30.**

$$\frac{1}{R_T} = \frac{1}{R_1} + \frac{1}{R_2}$$

$$\frac{1}{R_T} - \frac{1}{R_1} = \frac{1}{R_2}$$

$$\frac{1}{R_2} = \frac{R_T R_1}{R_T R_1}\left(\frac{1}{R_T} - \frac{1}{R_1}\right)$$

$$\frac{1}{R_2} = \frac{R_1 - R_T}{R_T R_1}$$

$$R_2 = \frac{R_1 R_T}{R_1 - R_T}$$

**31.**

|        | $r$           | $t$ | $w$           |
|--------|---------------|-----|---------------|
| Willie | $\frac{1}{6}$ | $t$ | $\frac{t}{6}$ |
| Myra   | $\frac{1}{\frac{9}{2}}$ | $t$ | $\frac{t}{\frac{9}{2}}$ |

$$\frac{t}{6} + \frac{t}{\frac{9}{2}} = 1$$

$$\frac{t}{6} + \frac{2t}{9} = 1$$

$$18\left(\frac{t}{6} + \frac{2t}{9}\right) = 18 \cdot 1$$

$$3t + 4t = 18$$

$$7t = 18$$

$$t = \frac{18}{7}$$

$$t = 2\frac{4}{7} \text{ days}$$

**32.**

|            | $d$ | $r$     | $t$              |
|------------|-----|---------|------------------|
| Downstream | 21  | $5 + c$ | $\frac{21}{5+c}$ |
| Upstream   | 9   | $5 - c$ | $\frac{9}{5-c}$  |

$$\frac{21}{5 + c} = \frac{9}{5 - c}$$

$$21(5 - c) = 9(5 + c)$$

$$105 - 21c = 45 + 9c$$

$$-30c = -60$$

$$c = 2$$

2 mph

**33.**

$$\frac{1}{R_T} = \frac{1}{120} + \frac{1}{20} + \frac{1}{12}$$

$$\frac{1}{R_T} = \frac{120}{120}\left(\frac{1}{120} + \frac{1}{20} + \frac{1}{12}\right)$$

$$\frac{1}{R_T} = \frac{1 + 6 + 10}{120}$$

$$\frac{1}{R_T} = \frac{17}{120}$$

$$R_T = \frac{120}{17}$$

$$R_T = 7\frac{1}{17} \text{ ohms}$$

**PAGE 351     BONUS**

$$\frac{1}{x - y} + \frac{2}{y - x} + \frac{3}{x - y} + \frac{4}{y - x} + \frac{5}{x - y} + \frac{6}{y - x} +$$

$$\frac{7}{x - y} + \frac{8}{y - x} = \frac{?}{x - y}$$

$$\frac{1}{x - y} - \frac{2}{x - y} + \frac{3}{x - y} - \frac{4}{x - y} + \frac{5}{x - y} - \frac{6}{x - y} +$$

$$\frac{7}{x - y} - \frac{8}{x - y} = \frac{?}{x - y}$$

$$\frac{-4}{x - y} = \frac{?}{x - y}$$

$$? = -4$$

# Chapter 9   Functions and Graphs

| 9-1 |   Ordered Pairs |

1.

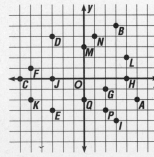

2. (5, 3) represents a point 5 units to the right and 3 units up from the origin. (3, 5) represents a point 3 units to the right and 5 units up from the origin.

3. Each point in the plane is named by exactly one ordered pair, and each ordered pair names exactly one point in the plane.

4. (0, 0), (-1, 0), (0, 2)
   Answers may vary.

5. (1, 4)      6. (-3, 3)      7. (-1, -2)
8. (4, 0)      9. (3, -1)     10. (0, -5)
11. I          12. III        13. II
14. none       15. none       16. IV

17. (-1, 1)    18. (-4, -3)   19. (3, -2)
20. (4, 2)     21. (1, 1)     22. (0, -1)
23. (-1, -1)   24. (-3, 0)    25. (2, -3)
26. (-3, -4)   27. (-4, 1)    28. (5, 1)
29. IV         30. III        31. II
32. none       33. IV         34. III
35. II         36. I          37. none

38-53.

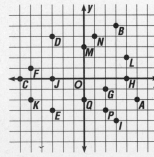

54.

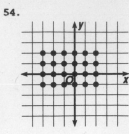

55.

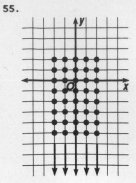

56. Umbrella

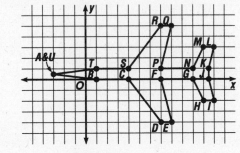

57. Airplane

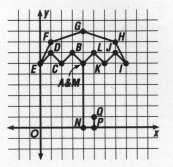

58. I or III      59. II or IV      60. x or y axis
61. Irving        62. (F, 6)
63. (B, 4), (B, 5), (C, 4), (C, 5)
64. I-20
65. (A, 3), (B, 3), (C, 3), (D, 3), (E, 3), (E, 4), (F, 4)
66. $10x^2 + 3y + z^2$      67. $0.75 \times 720$
                              $= 540$ seats
68. $25a^2 - 10ab + b^2$

69.

$$-3\ -2\ -1\ \ 0\ \ 1\ \ 2\ \ 3\ \ 4$$

70. $5 \times 10^5$ or 500,000

71. $4(x^2 - 16y^2) = 4(x - 4y)(x + 4y)$

72. $\dfrac{(z + 3)(z + 13)(z + 5)}{(z + 6)(z + 3)(z + 5)(z + 13)} = \dfrac{1}{z + 6}$

## 9-2 Relations

PAGE 361    CHECKING FOR UNDERSTANDING

1. {(322, 1965), (381, 1970), (542, 1975), (909, 1980), (1817, 1985), (2601, 1990)}

2. set of ordered pairs, table, mapping, graph

3. The domain is the set of all first coordinates while the range is the set of all second coordinates.

4. {0, 1, 2}, {2, -2, 4}

5. {5, 0, -9}, {2, 0, -1}

6. {-4, -2, 0, 2}, {2, 0, 4}

7. {7, -2, 4, 5, -9}, {5, -3, 0, -7, 2}

8. {3.1, -4.7, 2.4, -9}, {-1, 3.9, -3.6, 12.12}

9. $\left\{\dfrac{1}{2}, 1\dfrac{1}{2}, -3, -5\dfrac{1}{4}\right\}$, $\left\{\dfrac{1}{4}, \dfrac{-2}{3}, \dfrac{2}{5}, -6\dfrac{2}{7}\right\}$

10. {(1, 5), (2, 7), (3, 9), (4, 11)}
    {1, 2, 3, 4}
    {5, 7, 9, 11}
    {(5, 1), (7, 2), (9, 3), (11, 4)}

11. {(1, 3), (2, 2), (4, 9), (6, 5)}
    {1, 2, 4, 6}
    {3, 2, 9, 5}
    {(3, 1), (2, 2), (9, 4), (5, 6)}

12. (1, 4), (3, -2), (4, 4), (6, -2)}
    {1, 3, 4, 6}
    {4, -2}
    {(4, 1), (-2, 3), (4, 4), (-2, 6)}

PAGES 362-363    EXERCISES

13. {(1, 7), (2, 2), (-3, 1), (5, 2)}

14. {(1, 7), (-2, 7), (3, 7)}

15. {(5, 4), (5, 8), (2, 9), (-7, 2), (3, 2), (3, 4)}

16. {(-1, 5), (-2, 5), (-2, 4), (-2, 1), (-6, 1)}

17.

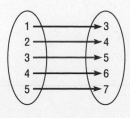

{(1, 3), (2, 4), (3, 5), (4, 6), (5, 7)}
{(3, 1), (4, 2), (5, 3), (6, 4), (7, 5)}

18.

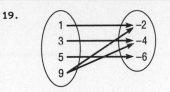

{(-4, 1), (-2, 3), (0, 1), (2, 3), (4, 1)}
{(1, -4), (3, -2), (1, 0), (3, 2), (1, 4)}

19.

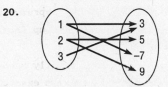

{(1, -2), (3, -4), (5, -6), (9, -4), (9, -2)}
{(-2, 1), (-4, 3), (-6, 5), (-4, 9), (-2, 9)}

20.

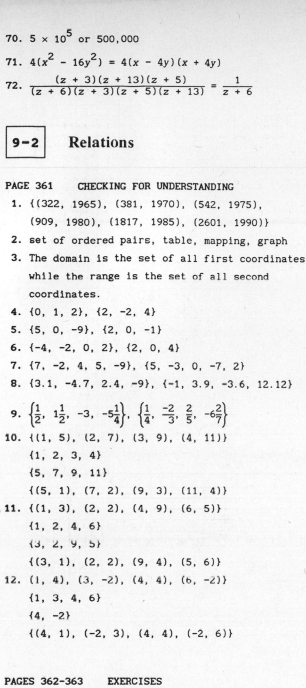

{(1, 3), (2, 5), (1, -7), (2, 9), (3, 3)}
{(3, 1), (5, 2), (-7, 1), (9, 2), (3, 3)}

21. {(-2, 2), (-1, 1), (0, 1), (1, 1), (3, 1), (1, -1), (2, -1)}
    {-2, -1, 0, 1, 3, 2}
    {2, 1, -1}

22. {(-3, -2), (-2, -1), (1, 1)}
    {-3, -2, 1}
    {-2, -1, 1}

23. {(-3, 0), (-2, 2), (-1, 3), (0, 1), (1, -1), (1, -2), (1, -3), (3, -2)}
    {-3, -2, -1, 0, 1, 3}
    {0, 2, 3, 1, -1, -2, -3}

24. {(-3, -1), (-2, 0), (-1, 3), (0, -1), (1, 0), (1, 1), (2, 2), (3, 1), (3, 2)}
    {-3, -2, -1, 0, 1, 2, 3}
    {-1, 0, 3, 1, 2}

25. {(-3, 3), (-1, 2), (1, 1), (1, 3), (2, 0), (2, -1), (3, -1)}
    {-3, -1, 1, 2, 3}
    {3, 2, 1, 0, -1}

26. {(-3, 1), (-2, 1), (-1, 1), (0, 1), (0, 0), (0, -1), (1, -1), (2, -2), (3, -2)}
    {-3, -2, -1, 0, 1, 2, 3}
    {1, 0, -1, -2}

27. {(2, -2), (1, -1), (1, 0), (1, 1), (1, 3), (-1, 1), (-1, 2)}

28. {(-2, -3), (-1, -2), (1, 1)}

29. {(0, -3), (2, -2), (3, -1), (1, 0), (-1, 1), (-2, 1), (-3, 1), (-2, 3)}

30. {(-1, -3), (0, -2), (3, -1), (-1, 0), (0, 1), (1, 1), (2, 2), (1, 3), (2, 3)}

**31.** {(3, -3), (2, -1), (1, 1), (3, 1), (0, 2), (-1, 2), (-1, 3)}

**32.** {(1, -3), (1, -2), (1, -1), (1, 0), (0, 0), (-1, 0), (-1, 1), (-2, 2), (-2, 3)}

**33.**

| Sum | Possibilities | Number of Possibilities |
|---|---|---|
| 2 | (1, 1) | 1 |
| 3 | (2, 1), (1, 2) | 2 |
| 4 | (1, 3), (3, 1), (2, 2) | 3 |
| 5 | (1, 4), (4, 1), (2, 3), (3, 2) | 4 |
| 6 | (1, 5), (5, 1), (3, 3), (4, 2), (2, 4) | 5 |
| 7 | (1, 6), (6, 1), (3, 4), (4, 3), (2, 5), (5, 2) | 6 |
| 8 | (4, 4), (2, 6), (6, 2), (3, 5), (5, 3) | 5 |
| 9 | (4, 5), (5, 4), (3, 6), (6, 3) | 4 |
| 10 | (5, 5), (6, 4), (4, 6) | 3 |
| 11 | (5, 6), (6, 5) | 2 |
| 12 | (6, 6) | 1 |

**34.** The numbers start at 1 and increase by 1's up to 6. Then they decrease by 1's back to 1.

**35.**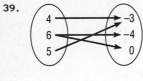

**36.**

**37.**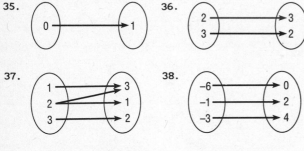

**38.**

**39.**

**40.**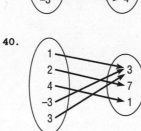

**41.**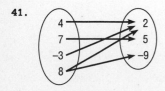

**42.**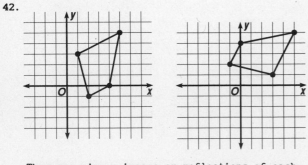

They are mirror images or reflections of each other.

**43.**

**44.** {(8, 4), (9, 3), (10, 2), (11, 1), (12, 0)}

**45.** $10 - 16n = -12 - 16n$

$10 \neq -12$

no solution

**46.**

| | Amount of solution (mL) | Amount of 40% solution |
|---|---|---|
| 25% solution | 800 | 0.25(800) |
| 100% solution | $x$ | $x$ |
| 40% solution (mixture) | $800 + x$ | $0.40(800 + x)$ |

$0.25(800) + x = 0.40(800 + x)$

$200 + x = 320 + 0.40x$

$0.60x = 120$

$x = 200 \text{ mL}$

**47.** $7a^6b^2 - 35a^4b^3 + 42a^2b^4$

**48.** $(12n + 7)^2$

**49.** $\dfrac{1}{R_T} = \dfrac{1}{4} + \dfrac{1}{6} + \dfrac{1}{15}$

$\dfrac{1}{R_T} = \dfrac{60}{60}\left(\dfrac{1}{4} + \dfrac{1}{6} + \dfrac{1}{15}\right)$

$\dfrac{1}{R_T} = \dfrac{15 + 10 + 4}{60}$

$\dfrac{1}{R_T} = \dfrac{29}{60}$

$R_T = \dfrac{60}{29}$

$R_T = 2\dfrac{2}{29} \text{ ohms}$

**50.**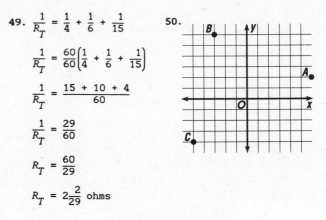

## 9-3 Equations as Relations

PAGE 367 CHECKING FOR UNDERSTANDING

1. She can solve the equation $1900 = 80x + 500$.

2. All of the solutions of this equation form a set of ordered pairs.

3. {-1, 0}

4.

| $x$ | $y$ | $(x, y)$ |
|---|---|---|
| -3 | -15 | (-3, -15) |
| -2 | -11 | (-2, -11) |
| -1 | -7 | (-1, -7) |
| 0 | -3 | (0, -3) |
| 2 | 5 | (2, 5) |
| 4 | 13 | (4, 13) |

**5.**

| $m$ | $n$ | $(m, n)$ |
|---|---|---|
| $-4$ | $-1$ | $(-4, -1)$ |
| $-2$ | $\frac{1}{3}$ | $(-2, \frac{1}{3})$ |
| $0$ | $\frac{5}{3}$ | $(0, \frac{5}{3})$ |
| $1$ | $\frac{7}{3}$ | $(1, \frac{7}{3})$ |
| $3$ | $\frac{11}{3}$ | $(3, \frac{11}{3})$ |

**6.** $a, c$   **7.** $b, c$   **8.** $a, d$

**9.** $y = 5 - x$   **10.** $y = 7 - 3x$   **11.** $b = 3 + 5a$

**12.** $n = 7 - 4m$

### PAGES 367-368   EXERCISES

**13.** $a, b, c$   **14.** $c, d$   **15.** $a$

**16.** $2y = 6 - 8x$        **17.** $3y = 12 - 6x$
    $y = 3 - 4x$            $y = 4 - 2x$

**18.** $3b = 7 - 4a$        **19.** $5s = 2 - 6r$
    $b = \dfrac{7 - 4a}{3}$     $s = \dfrac{2 - 6r}{5}$

**20.** $3y = 6x - 2$        **21.** $7b = 3a - 8$
    $y = \dfrac{6x - 2}{3}$     $b = \dfrac{3a - 8}{7}$

**22.** $2r = 7 - 4p$        **23.** $7r = 5n + 4$
    $r = \dfrac{7 - 4p}{2}$     $r = \dfrac{5n + 4}{7}$

**24.** $\{(-2, -6), (-1, -3), (0, 0), (2, 6), (5, 15)\}$

**25.** $\{(-2, -3), (-1, -1), (0, 1), (2, 5), (5, 11)\}$

**26.** $\{(-2, 9), (-1, 8), (0, 7), (2, 5), (5, 2)\}$

**27.** $\{(-2, -6), (-1, -5), (0, -4), (2, -2), (5, 1)\}$

**28.** $\{(-2, 14), (-1, 9), (0, 4), (2, -6), (5, -21)\}$

**29.** $\{(-2, \frac{17}{3})\ \ (-1, 5), (0, \frac{13}{3}), (2, 3), (5, 1)\}$

**30.** $\{(-2, 8, ), (-1, \frac{20}{3}), (0, \frac{16}{3}), (2, \frac{8}{3}), (5, -\frac{4}{3})\}$

**31.** $\{(-2, \frac{13}{2}), (-1, 4), (0, \frac{3}{2}), (2, -\frac{7}{2}), (5, -11)\}$

**32.** $\{(-2, -7), (-1, -2), (0, 3), (2, 13), (5, 28)\}$

**33.** $\{(-2, \frac{-11}{2}), (-1, -4), (0, \frac{-5}{2}), (2, \frac{1}{2}), (5, 5)\}$

**34.** $\{(-2, \frac{9}{2}), (-1, \frac{13}{4}), (0, 2), (2, \frac{-1}{2}), (5, \frac{-17}{4})\}$

**35.** $\{(-2, 5), (-1, \frac{31}{6}), (0, \frac{16}{3}), (2, \frac{17}{3}), (5, \frac{37}{6})\}$

**36.** $\{(\frac{-3}{2}, -3), (\frac{-1}{2}, -1), (0, 0), (1, 2), (\frac{3}{2}, 3)\}$

**37.** $\{(\frac{-4}{5}, -3), (\frac{-2}{5}, -1), (\frac{-1}{5}, 0), (\frac{1}{5}, 2), (\frac{2}{5}, 3)\}$

**38.** $\{(\frac{7}{2}, -3), (\frac{5}{2}, -1), (2, 0), (1, 2), (\frac{1}{2}, 3)\}$

**39.** $\{(\frac{11}{2}, -3), (4, -1), (\frac{13}{4}, 0), (\frac{7}{4}, 2), (1, 3)\}$

**40.** $\{(\frac{23}{4}, -3), (\frac{13}{4}, -1), (2, 0), (\frac{-1}{2}, 2), (\frac{-7}{4}, 3)\}$

**41.** $\{(-1, -3), (\frac{-2}{3}, -1), (\frac{-1}{2}, 0), (\frac{-1}{6}, 2), (0, 3)\}$

**42.** $x = \pm\sqrt{y}$
    $\{-6, -2, 0, 2, 6\}$

**43.** $y = 2x - 4$   or   $y = -2x - 4$
    $x = \dfrac{y + 4}{2}$       $x = \dfrac{y + 4}{-2}$
    $\{-20, -4, -2, 2, 4, 20\}$

**44.** $y = 2x - 4$   or   $y = 4 - 2x$
    $x = \dfrac{y + 4}{2}$       $x = \dfrac{y - 4}{-2}$
    $\{-16, 0, 2, 4, 20\}$

**45.** 4 m by 4 m
    (by guess and check)

**46.**

| t(sec) | h(ft) |
|---|---|
| 0 | 0 |
| 1 | 80 |
| 2 | 128 |
| 3 | 144 |
| 4 | 128 |
| 5 | 80 |
| 6 | 0 |

3 seconds; 6 seconds

**47.** $s < -6.9$
    $\{s \mid s < -6.9\}$

**48.** $6xy^2 - 3x^2y - 2y^2$

**49.** $3a(14bc - 4ab^2 + ac^2)$

**50.** $5m(m + 1) = 0$
    $5m = 0$ or $m + 1 = 0$
    $m = 0$        $m = -1$
    $\{-1, 0\}$

**51.**

|  | $r$ | $t$ | $w$ |
|---|---|---|---|
| Pipe 1 | $\frac{1}{12}$ | $t$ | $\frac{t}{12}$ |
| Pipe 2 | $\frac{1}{4}$ | $t$ | $\frac{t}{4}$ |

$\dfrac{t}{12} + \dfrac{t}{4} = 1$

$\dfrac{t}{12} + \dfrac{3t}{12} = 1$

$\dfrac{4t}{12} = 1$

$4t = 12$

$t = 3$

3 hours

**52.** $\{8, 4, 6, 5\}$
    $\{1, 2, -4, -3, 0\}$
    $\{(1, 8), (2, 4), (-4, 6), (-3, 5), (0, 6)\}$

## 9-4   Graphing Linear Relations

### PAGE 371   CHECKING FOR UNDERSTANDING

**1.** $A = 3$, $B = -2$, $C = 0$ or $A = -3$, $B = 2$, $C = 0$

**2.** horizontal   **3.** vertical   **4.** the origin

**5.** yes        **6.** no        **7.** no

**8.** no         **9.** yes       **10.** no

**11.** no        **12.** yes      **13.** yes

**14.** $y = -\dfrac{6x + 7}{14}$        **15.** $y = 8x - 16$

16. $5y = 16 - x$

$y = \dfrac{16 - x}{5}$

17. $4y = 12 - 3x$

$y = \dfrac{12 - 3x}{4}$

18. $-\dfrac{3}{8}y = 1 - 4x$

$y = \dfrac{1 - 4x}{-\frac{3}{8}}$

$y = -\dfrac{8}{3}(1 - 4x)$

$y = \dfrac{32x - 8}{3}$

19. $-\dfrac{2}{3}y = 10 - \dfrac{1}{2}x$

$y = \dfrac{10 - \frac{1}{2}x}{-\frac{2}{3}}$

$y = -\dfrac{3}{2}\left(10 - \dfrac{1}{2}x\right)$

$y = \dfrac{3}{4}x - 15$

20. no    21. yes    22. no
23. no    24. yes    25. yes
26. no    27. yes    28. yes

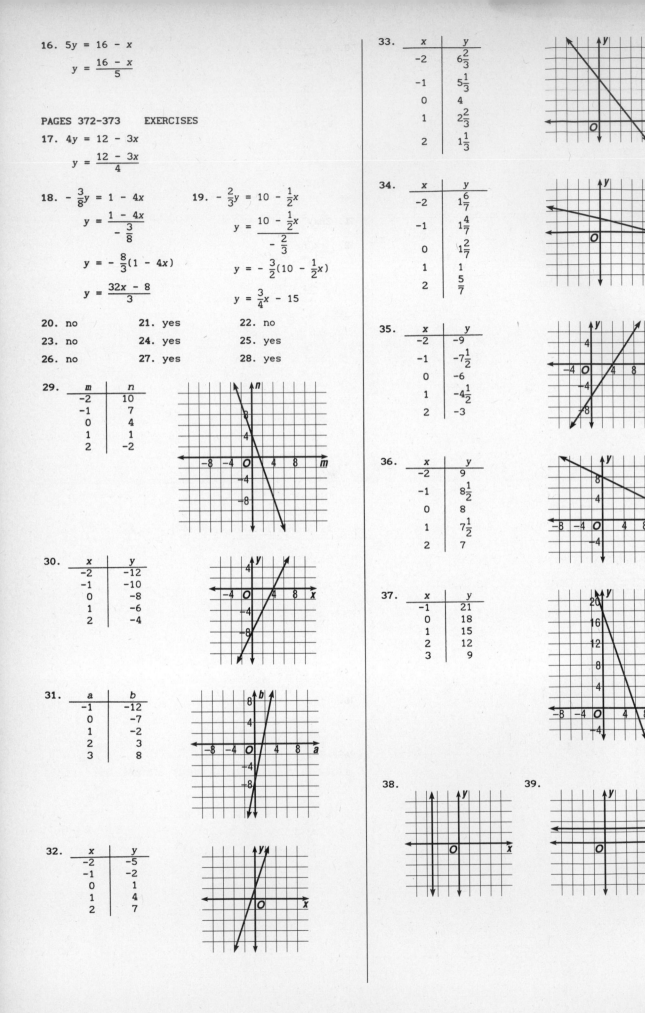

29.

| m | n |
|---|---|
| -2 | 10 |
| -1 | 7 |
| 0 | 4 |
| 1 | 1 |
| 2 | -2 |

30.

| x | y |
|---|---|
| -2 | -12 |
| -1 | -10 |
| 0 | -8 |
| 1 | -6 |
| 2 | -4 |

31.

| a | b |
|---|---|
| -1 | -12 |
| 0 | -7 |
| 1 | -2 |
| 2 | 3 |
| 3 | 8 |

32.

| x | y |
|---|---|
| -2 | -5 |
| -1 | -2 |
| 0 | 1 |
| 1 | 4 |
| 2 | 7 |

33.

| x | y |
|---|---|
| -2 | $6\frac{2}{3}$ |
| -1 | $5\frac{1}{3}$ |
| 0 | 4 |
| 1 | $2\frac{2}{3}$ |
| 2 | $1\frac{1}{3}$ |

34.

| x | y |
|---|---|
| -2 | $1\frac{6}{7}$ |
| -1 | $1\frac{4}{7}$ |
| 0 | $1\frac{2}{7}$ |
| 1 | 1 |
| 2 | $\frac{5}{7}$ |

35.

| x | y |
|---|---|
| -2 | -9 |
| -1 | $-7\frac{1}{2}$ |
| 0 | -6 |
| 1 | $-4\frac{1}{2}$ |
| 2 | -3 |

36.

| x | y |
|---|---|
| -2 | 9 |
| -1 | $8\frac{1}{2}$ |
| 0 | 8 |
| 1 | $7\frac{1}{2}$ |
| 2 | 7 |

37.

| x | y |
|---|---|
| -1 | 21 |
| 0 | 18 |
| 1 | 15 |
| 2 | 12 |
| 3 | 9 |

38.

39.

158

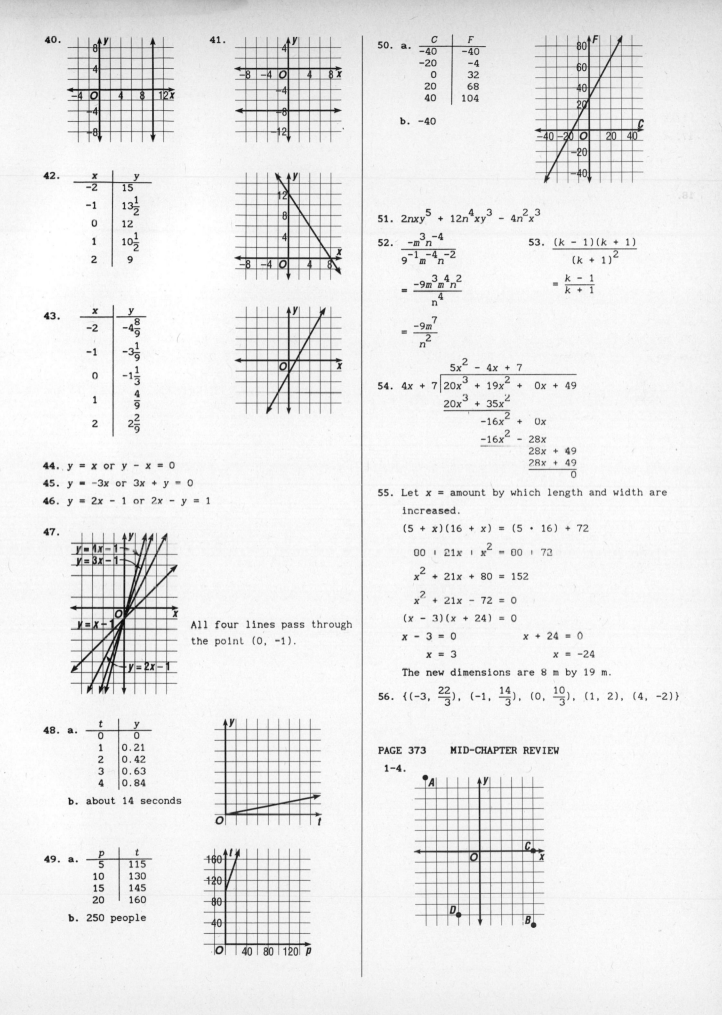

**40.**

**41.**

**42.**

| x | y |
|---|---|
| -2 | 15 |
| -1 | $13\frac{1}{2}$ |
| 0 | 12 |
| 1 | $10\frac{1}{2}$ |
| 2 | 9 |

**43.**

| x | y |
|---|---|
| -2 | $-4\frac{8}{9}$ |
| -1 | $-3\frac{1}{9}$ |
| 0 | $-1\frac{1}{3}$ |
| 1 | $\frac{4}{9}$ |
| 2 | $2\frac{2}{9}$ |

**44.** $y = x$ or $y - x = 0$

**45.** $y = -3x$ or $3x + y = 0$

**46.** $y = 2x - 1$ or $2x - y = 1$

**47.**

$y = 4x - 1$
$y = 3x - 1$
$y = x - 1$
$y = 2x - 1$

All four lines pass through the point (0, -1).

**48. a.**

| t | y |
|---|---|
| 0 | 0 |
| 1 | 0.21 |
| 2 | 0.42 |
| 3 | 0.63 |
| 4 | 0.84 |

**b.** about 14 seconds

**49. a.**

| p | t |
|---|---|
| 5 | 115 |
| 10 | 130 |
| 15 | 145 |
| 20 | 160 |

**b.** 250 people

**50. a.**

| C | F |
|---|---|
| -40 | -40 |
| -20 | -4 |
| 0 | 32 |
| 20 | 68 |
| 40 | 104 |

**b.** -40

**51.** $2nxy^5 + 12n^4xy^3 - 4n^2x^3$

**52.** $\dfrac{-m^3n^{-4}}{9^{-1}m^{-4}n^{-2}}$

$= \dfrac{-9m^3m^4n^2}{n^4}$

$= \dfrac{-9m^7}{n^2}$

**53.** $\dfrac{(k-1)(k+1)}{(k+1)^2}$

$= \dfrac{k-1}{k+1}$

**54.**

$$
\begin{array}{r}
5x^2 - 4x + 7 \\
4x + 7 \overline{\smash{)}\ 20x^3 + 19x^2 + 0x + 49} \\
\underline{20x^3 + 35x^2}\phantom{ + 0x + 49} \\
-16x^2 + 0x\phantom{ + 49} \\
\underline{-16x^2 - 28x}\phantom{ + 49} \\
28x + 49 \\
\underline{28x + 49} \\
0
\end{array}
$$

**55.** Let $x$ = amount by which length and width are increased.

$(5 + x)(16 + x) = (5 \cdot 16) + 72$

$80 + 21x + x^2 = 80 + 72$

$x^2 + 21x + 80 = 152$

$x^2 + 21x - 72 = 0$

$(x - 3)(x + 24) = 0$

$x - 3 = 0 \qquad\qquad x + 24 = 0$

$x = 3 \qquad\qquad x = -24$

The new dimensions are 8 m by 19 m.

**56.** $\{(-3, \frac{22}{3}), (-1, \frac{14}{3}), (0, \frac{10}{3}), (1, 2), (4, -2)\}$

**PAGE 373    MID-CHAPTER REVIEW**

**1-4.**

5. {(4, 2), (1, 3), (3, 3), (6, 4)}
   {4, 1, 3, 6}
   {2, 3, 4}
   {(2, 4), (3, 1), (3, 3), (4, 6)}

6. {(4, 2), (-3, 2), (8, 2), (8, 9), (7, 5)}
   {4, -3, 8, 7)
   {2, 9, 5)
   {(2, 4), (2, -3), (2, 8), (9, 8), (5, 7)}

7. {(-2, 2), (-1, 1), (1, 1), (1, -1), (2, 2),
   (2, -2)}
   {-2, -1, 1, 2}
   {2, 1, -1, -2}
   {(2, -2), (1, -1), (1, 1), (-1, 1), (2, 2),
   (-2, 2)}

8. {(-5, -22), (-2, -7), (0, 3), (1, 8), (3, 18)}

9. {(-5, -17), (-2, -11), (0, -7), (1, -5), (3, -1)}

10. {(-5, $\frac{-4}{3}$), (-2, $\frac{8}{3}$), (0, $\frac{16}{3}$), (1, $\frac{20}{3}$), (3, $\frac{28}{3}$)}

11. {(-5, $\frac{-41}{3}$), (-2, $\frac{-23}{5}$), (0, $\frac{-11}{5}$), (1, -1), (3, $\frac{7}{5}$)}

12. yes

| x | y |
|---|---|
| -2 | -10 |
| -1 | -7 |
| 0 | -4 |
| 1 | -1 |
| 2 | 2 |

13. yes

| a | b |
|---|---|
| -2 | -19 |
| -1 | -12 |
| 0 | -5 |
| 1 | 2 |
| 2 | 9 |

14. no

15. yes

| x | y |
|---|---|
| -2 | $-5\frac{1}{3}$ |
| -1 | $-4\frac{2}{3}$ |
| 0 | -4 |
| 1 | $-3\frac{1}{3}$ |
| 2 | $-2\frac{2}{3}$ |

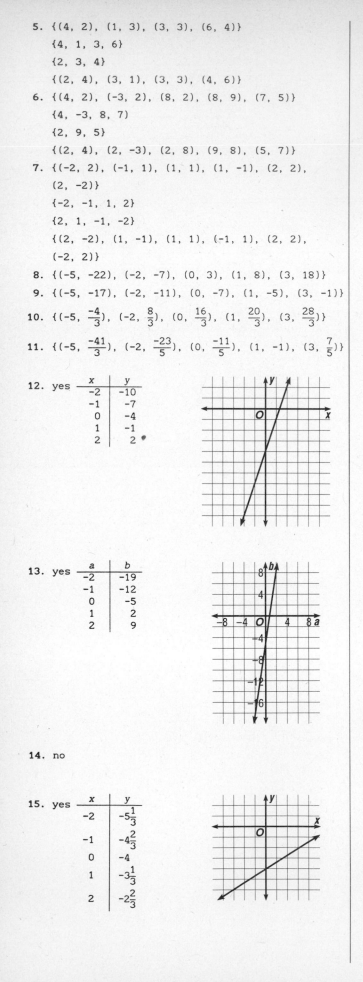

## 9-5 Functions

1. No, since the graph of any linear equation of the form $x = a$ is a vertical line.

2. A relation is a function if no two distinct points on the graph of the relation have the same x-coordinate.

3. Substitute 1 for each $x$ in the equation of $g(x)$ and simplify.

4. {(1, 2), (3, 2)}
   Answers may vary.

5. no          6. yes          7. yes

8. no          9. no          10. yes

11. yes

12. $g(2) = 2(2) - 1$          13. $g(-4) = 2(-4) - 1$
    $= 4 - 1$                       $= -8 - 1$
    $= 3$                           $= -9$

14. $g(0) = 2(0) - 1$          15. $g(\frac{1}{2}) = 2(\frac{1}{2}) - 1$
    $= 0 - 1$                       $= 1 - 1$
    $= -1$                          $= 0$

16. no          17. yes          18. no

19. yes
    {(1, 3), (1, 5), (1, 7)}; no

20. no
    {(3, 1), (5, 1), (7, 1)}; yes

21. no
    {(4, -2), (3, 1), (2, 5), (4, 1)}; no

22. no
    {(-1, 6), (4, 1), (3, 2), (1, 6)} yes

23. yes
    {(4, 5), (5, -6), (5, 4), (4, 0}; no

24. no
    {(-2, 3), (7, 4), (5, -2), (5, 4)}; no

25. yes          26. yes          27. yes

28. yes          29. no          30. no

31. yes          32. no

33. $f(-3) = 3(-3) - 5$          34. $g(3) = 3^2 - 3$
    $= -9 - 5$                        $= 9 - 3$
    $= -14$                           $= 6$

35. $g(\frac{1}{3}) = (\frac{1}{3})^2 - \frac{1}{3}$          36. $f(\frac{2}{3}) = 3(\frac{2}{3}) - 5$
    $= \frac{1}{9} - \frac{1}{3}$                       $= 2 - 5$
    $= -\frac{2}{9}$                                    $= -3$

37. $f(5.5) = 3(5.5) - 5$
    $= 16.5 - 5$
    $= 11.5$

**38.** $3[f(5)] = 3[3(5) - 5]$

$\qquad = 3(15 - 5)$

$\qquad = 3 \cdot 10$

$\qquad = 30$

**39.** $2[g(-2)] = 2[(-2)^2 - (-2)]$

$\qquad = 2(4 + 2)$

$\qquad = 2 \cdot 6$

$\qquad = 12$

**40.** $g(0.5) = (0.5)^2 - 0.5$

$\qquad = 0.25 - 0.5$

$\qquad = -0.25$

**41.** $f(4a) = 3(4a) - 5$

$\qquad = 12a - 5$

**42.** $g(4b) = (4b)^2 - 4b$

$\qquad = 16b^2 - 4b$

**43.** $3[f(2n)] = 3[3(2n) - 5]$

$\qquad = 3(6n - 5)$

$\qquad = 18n - 15$

**44.** $2[f(3n)] = 2[3(3n) - 5]$

$\qquad = 2(9n - 5)$

$\qquad = 18n - 10$

**45.** $3[g(2m)] = 3[(2m)^2 - 2m]$

$\qquad = 3(4m^2 - 2m)$

$\qquad = 12m^2 - 6m$

**46.** $2[g(3m)] = 2[(3m)^2 - 3m]$

$\qquad = 2(9m^2 - 3m)$

$\qquad = 18m^2 - 6m$

**47.** $f(a + 3) = 3(a + 3) - 5$

$\qquad = 3a + 9 - 5$

$\qquad = 3a + 4$

**48.** $g(b - 3) = (b - 3)^2 - (b - 3)$

$\qquad = b^2 - 6b + 9 - b + 3$

$\qquad = b^2 - 7b + 12$

**49.** $3y + 2x = 1$      **50.** $x = -3y^2$

yes                 no

**51.** $3y^2 - x^2 = 3$     **52.** $y + 3x^2 = 3$

no                 yes

**53.** $C(220) = 31 + 0.13(220)$

$\qquad = 31 + 28.6$

$\qquad = \$59.60$

**54.** $P(40) = -0.027(40)^2 + 8(40) - 280$

$\qquad = -\$3.20$

$P(41) = -0.027(41)^2 + 8(41) - 280$

$\qquad = \$2.61$

41 cars

**55. a.**

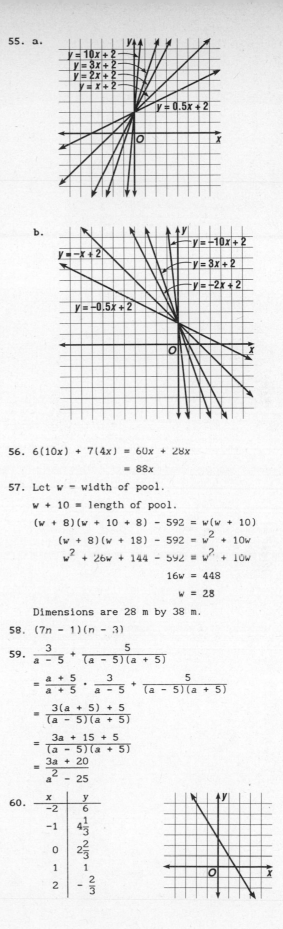

**b.**

**56.** $6(10x) + 7(4x) = 60x + 28x$

$\qquad\qquad\qquad = 88x$

**57.** Let $w =$ width of pool.

$w + 10 =$ length of pool.

$(w + 8)(w + 10 + 8) - 592 = w(w + 10)$

$(w + 8)(w + 18) - 592 = w^2 + 10w$

$w^2 + 26w + 144 - 592 = w^2 + 10w$

$\qquad\qquad\qquad 16w = 448$

$\qquad\qquad\qquad w = 28$

Dimensions are 28 m by 38 m.

**58.** $(7n - 1)(n - 3)$

**59.** $\dfrac{3}{a - 5} + \dfrac{5}{(a - 5)(a + 5)}$

$= \dfrac{a + 5}{a + 5} \cdot \dfrac{3}{a - 5} + \dfrac{5}{(a - 5)(a + 5)}$

$= \dfrac{3(a + 5) + 5}{(a - 5)(a + 5)}$

$= \dfrac{3a + 15 + 5}{(a - 5)(a + 5)}$

$= \dfrac{3a + 20}{a^2 - 25}$

**60.**

| $x$ | $y$ |
|----|----|
| $-2$ | $6$ |
| $-1$ | $4\frac{1}{3}$ |
| $0$ | $2\frac{2}{3}$ |
| $1$ | $1$ |
| $2$ | $-\frac{2}{3}$ |

## 9-6  Graphing Inequalities in Two Variables

PAGES 381-382  CHECKING FOR UNDERSTANDING

1. half-planes  2. closed  3. contains

4. yes  5. yes  6. no

7. *c*  8. *a, c*  9. *b*

10. *a, b*  11. *a, b*  12. *a, b, c*

13. half-plane which contains (0, 0)

14. half-plane which contains (0, 0)

15. half-plane which does not contain (0, 0)

PAGES 382-383  EXERCISES

16. half-plane which contains (0, 0)

17. half-plane which contains (0, 0)

18. half-plane which contains (-1, 1)

19.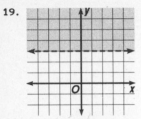

20.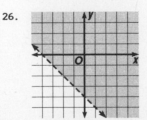

21.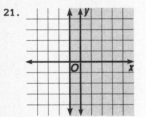

22.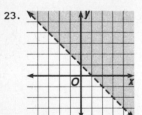

23.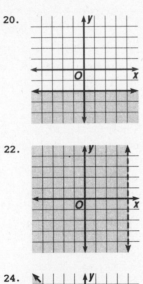

24.

25.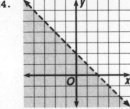

26.

27.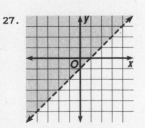

28.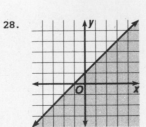

29.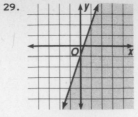

30.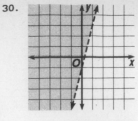

31.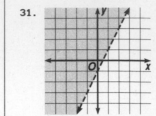

32.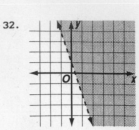

33.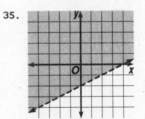

34.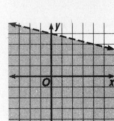

35.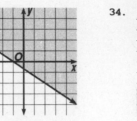

36.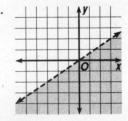

37.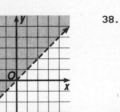

38.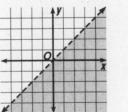

39.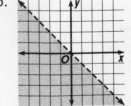

40.

41.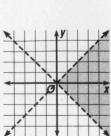

42.

162

**43.**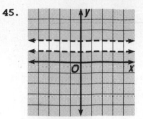

**44.**

**45.**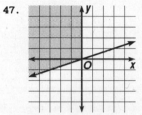

**46.**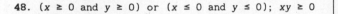

Only one of the two shaded areas will be a solution at any one time.

Only one of the two shaded areas will be a solution at any one time.

**47.**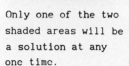

**48.** $(x \geq 0$ and $y \geq 0)$ or $(x \leq 0$ and $y \leq 0)$; $xy \geq 0$

**49. a.**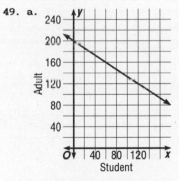

**b.** 200 adult tickets and 0 student tickets
180 adult tickets and 30 student tickets
160 adult tickets and 60 student tickets

**50.** 8 hours = 480 min.

**a.**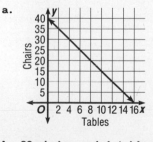

**b.** 30 chairs and 4 tables
35 chairs and 2 tables
40 chairs and 0 tables

**51.** $2x - 8 - 10x \leq 0$
$\quad -8 - 8x \leq 0$
$\quad\quad -8x \leq 8$
$\quad\quad\quad -x \leq 1$
$\quad\quad\quad\quad x \geq -1$
$\{x \mid x \geq -1\}$

**52.** $(r^2xy)(4r^6x^2) = 4r^8x^3y$

**53.** $\dfrac{12n}{3n - 2} - \dfrac{8}{3n - 2} = \dfrac{12n - 8}{3n - 2}$
$\quad\quad\quad\quad\quad\quad = \dfrac{4(3n - 2)}{3n - 2}$
$\quad\quad\quad\quad\quad\quad = 4$

**54.** $\dfrac{x + y}{a + b} \cdot \dfrac{b^2 - a^2}{x^2 - y^2} = \dfrac{(x + y)(b - a)(b + a)}{(a + b)(x - y)(x + y)}$
$\quad\quad\quad\quad\quad\quad\quad = \dfrac{b - a}{x - y}$

**55.** $(15a^2 + 20aqc) - (28bc + 21ab)$
$5a(3a + 4c) - 7b(4c + 3a)$
$= (5a - 7b)(3a + 4c)$

**56.** No; after 4 seconds the ball will be $100 - 4.9(4)^2$ or 21.6 meters above the ground.

## Technology: Graphing Linear Relations

**1.** yes

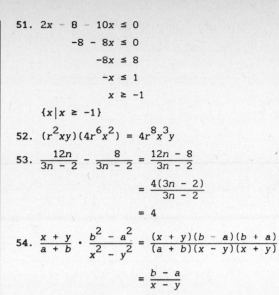

**2.** yes

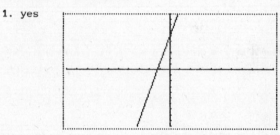

**3.** no

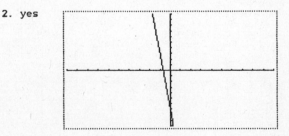

163

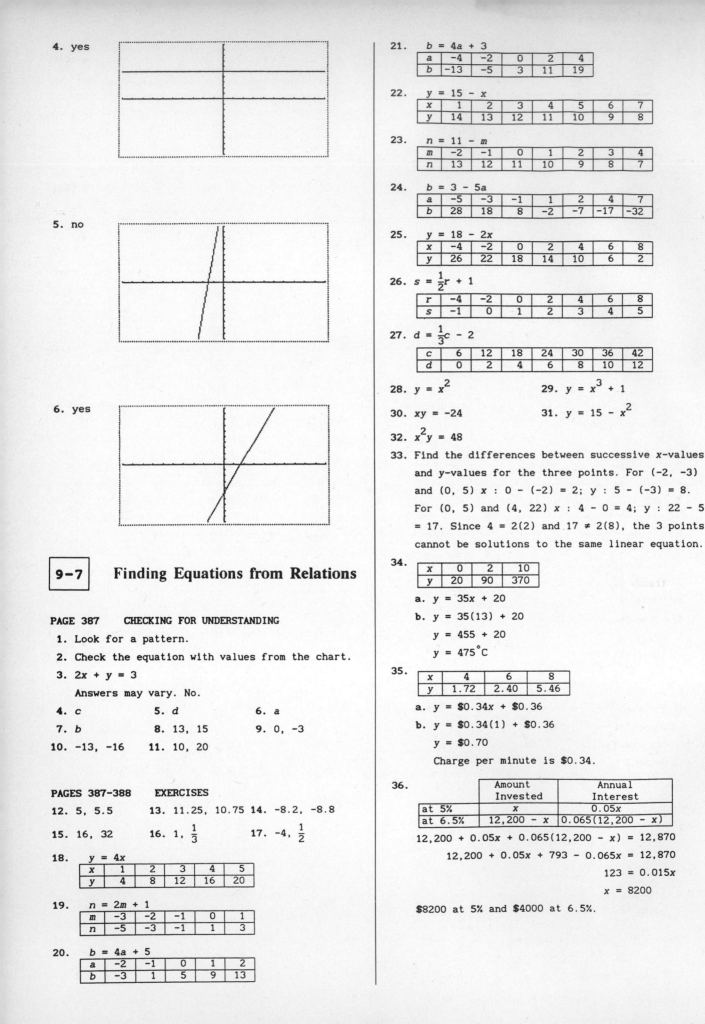

**4. yes**

**5. no**

**6. yes**

---

**9-7** | **Finding Equations from Relations**

PAGE 387    CHECKING FOR UNDERSTANDING

1. Look for a pattern.

2. Check the equation with values from the chart.

3. $2x + y = 3$

   Answers may vary. No.

4. $c$

5. $d$

6. $a$

7. $b$

8. 13, 15

9. 0, -3

10. -13, -16

11. 10, 20

PAGES 387-388    EXERCISES

12. 5, 5.5

13. 11.25, 10.75

14. -8.2, -8.8

15. 16, 32

16. 1, $\frac{1}{3}$

17. -4, $\frac{1}{2}$

18. $y = 4x$

| $x$ | 1 | 2 | 3 | 4 | 5 |
|---|---|---|---|---|---|
| $y$ | 4 | 8 | 12 | 16 | 20 |

19. $n = 2m + 1$

| $m$ | -3 | -2 | -1 | 0 | 1 |
|---|---|---|---|---|---|
| $n$ | -5 | -3 | -1 | 1 | 3 |

20. $b = 4a + 5$

| $a$ | -2 | -1 | 0 | 1 | 2 |
|---|---|---|---|---|---|
| $b$ | -3 | 1 | 5 | 9 | 13 |

21. $b = 4a + 3$

| $a$ | -4 | -2 | 0 | 2 | 4 |
|---|---|---|---|---|---|
| $b$ | -13 | -5 | 3 | 11 | 19 |

22. $y = 15 - x$

| $x$ | 1 | 2 | 3 | 4 | 5 | 6 | 7 |
|---|---|---|---|---|---|---|---|
| $y$ | 14 | 13 | 12 | 11 | 10 | 9 | 8 |

23. $n = 11 - m$

| $m$ | -2 | -1 | 0 | 1 | 2 | 3 | 4 |
|---|---|---|---|---|---|---|---|
| $n$ | 13 | 12 | 11 | 10 | 9 | 8 | 7 |

24. $b = 3 - 5a$

| $a$ | -5 | -3 | -1 | 1 | 2 | 4 | 7 |
|---|---|---|---|---|---|---|---|
| $b$ | 28 | 18 | 8 | -2 | -7 | -17 | -32 |

25. $y = 18 - 2x$

| $x$ | -4 | -2 | 0 | 2 | 4 | 6 | 8 |
|---|---|---|---|---|---|---|---|
| $y$ | 26 | 22 | 18 | 14 | 10 | 6 | 2 |

26. $s = \frac{1}{2}r + 1$

| $r$ | -4 | -2 | 0 | 2 | 4 | 6 | 8 |
|---|---|---|---|---|---|---|---|
| $s$ | -1 | 0 | 1 | 2 | 3 | 4 | 5 |

27. $d = \frac{1}{3}c - 2$

| $c$ | 6 | 12 | 18 | 24 | 30 | 36 | 42 |
|---|---|---|---|---|---|---|---|
| $d$ | 0 | 2 | 4 | 6 | 8 | 10 | 12 |

28. $y = x^2$

29. $y = x^3 + 1$

30. $xy = -24$

31. $y = 15 - x^2$

32. $x^2y = 48$

33. Find the differences between successive $x$-values and $y$-values for the three points. For (-2, -3) and (0, 5) $x$ : $0 - (-2) = 2$; $y$ : $5 - (-3) = 8$. For (0, 5) and (4, 22) $x$ : $4 - 0 = 4$; $y$ : $22 - 5 = 17$. Since $4 = 2(2)$ and $17 \neq 2(8)$, the 3 points cannot be solutions to the same linear equation.

34.

| $x$ | 0 | 2 | 10 |
|---|---|---|---|
| $y$ | 20 | 90 | 370 |

   a. $y = 35x + 20$

   b. $y = 35(13) + 20$

   $y = 455 + 20$

   $y = 475°C$

35.

| $x$ | 4 | 6 | 8 |
|---|---|---|---|
| $y$ | 1.72 | 2.40 | 5.46 |

   a. $y = \$0.34x + \$0.36$

   b. $y = \$0.34(1) + \$0.36$

   $y = \$0.70$

   Charge per minute is \$0.34.

36.

|  | Amount Invested | Annual Interest |
|---|---|---|
| at 5% | $x$ | $0.05x$ |
| at 6.5% | $12,200 - x$ | $0.065(12,200 - x)$ |

$12,200 + 0.05x + 0.065(12,200 - x) = 12,870$

$12,200 + 0.05x + 793 - 0.065x = 12,870$

$123 = 0.015x$

$x = 8200$

\$8200 at 5% and \$4000 at 6.5%.

37. $24x^2y = $ ②·②· 2 · 3 · $x$ · ⓧ · $y$
    $28mnx = $ ②·②· 7 · $m$ · $n$ · ⓧ
    $36nx = $ ②·②· 3 · 3 · $n$ · ⓧ
    The GCF is $4x$.

38. $3x(x^2 + 8xy - 33y^2) = 3x(x + 11y)(x - 3y)$

39. $\dfrac{x^2 + 2x - 15}{x^2 - x - 30} \cdot \dfrac{x^2 - 2x - 24}{x^2 - 3x - 18}$

    $= \dfrac{(x + 5)(x - 3)(x - 6)(x + 4)}{(x - 6)(x + 5)(x - 6)(x + 3)}$

    $= \dfrac{(x - 3)(x + 4)}{(x - 6)(x + 3)}$

    $= \dfrac{x^2 + x - 12}{x^2 - 3x - 18}$

40.
| $x$ | $y$ |
|----|----|
| -2 | 9 |
| -1 | 5 |
| 0 | 1 |
| 1 | -3 |
| 2 | -7 |

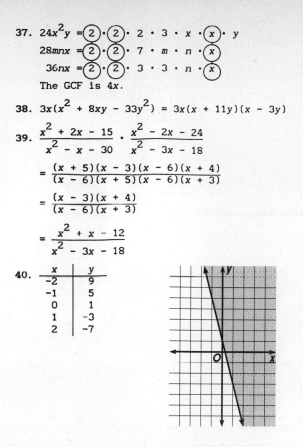

### 9-8 Problem-Solving Strategy: Use a Graph

**PAGES 390-391   CHECKING FOR UNDERSTANDING**

1. how specific quantities compare
2. trends and changes in quantities
3. vertical axis
4. variables represented
5. title
6. horizontal axis
7. yes
8. no
9. In Graph A, Restaurant III does not appear as unpopular as it does in Graph B.
10. The scale of the vertical axis is smaller.
11. Graph A

**PAGE 391   EXERCISES**

12. 2  contain pens and pencils
    2  more contain pencils only
    <u>3</u>  more contain pens only
    7
    10 - 7 = 3 empty boxes

13. 512

    guess and check

14. Paula spends $\frac{1}{3}$ of her income on rent, so after the rent is paid $\frac{2}{3}$ of her income remains.

    $\frac{1}{4}$ of the remaining $\frac{2}{3}$ is spent on food. So, $\frac{2}{3}\left(\frac{1}{4}\right)$ or $\frac{1}{6}$ is spent on food. $\frac{2}{3} - \frac{1}{6}$ or $\frac{1}{2}$ of Paula's income remains.

    $\frac{1}{6}$ of the remaining income is spent on clothes. So, $\frac{1}{2}\left(\frac{1}{6}\right)$ or $\frac{1}{12}$ is spent on clothes. $\frac{1}{2} - \frac{1}{12}$ or $\frac{5}{12}$ of the income remains.

    Entertainment takes $\frac{1}{5}$ of the remaining income. So, $\frac{5}{12}\left(\frac{1}{5}\right)$ or $\frac{1}{12}$ of Paula's income goes to entertainment. $\frac{5}{12} - \frac{1}{12}$ or $\frac{1}{3}$ remains.

    Paula saves $\frac{1}{2}$ of the remaining $\frac{1}{3}$ of her income. So, $\frac{1}{2}$ of $\frac{1}{3}$, or $\frac{1}{6}$ remains.

    After a $200 car payment, $40 of Paula's income remains. If Paula received $x, then $\frac{1}{6}x - 200 = 40$. Solve for $x$.

    $\frac{1}{6}x - 200 = 40$

    $\frac{1}{6}x = 240$

    $x = 1440$.

    Paula's monthly income is $1440.

15. Al is 12 years old, Betty is 14 years old. Carmelita is 7 years old, and Dwayne is 4 years old. (Solved by guess and check.)

**PAGE 391   COOPERATIVE LEARNING ACTIVITY**

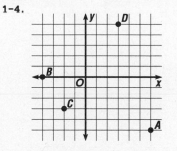

## Chapter 9   Summary and Review

**PAGES 392-394   SKILLS AND CONCEPTS**

1-4.

**5.** I  **6.** III

**7.** II  **8.** none

**9.** {4}

{1, -2, 6, -1}

{(1, 4), (-2, 4), (6, 4), (-1, 4)}

**10.** {-3, 4}

{5, 6}

{(5, -3), (6, -3), (5, 4), (6, 4)}

**11.** {-2, -5, -7}

{1}

{(1, -2), (1, -5), (1, -7)}

**12.** {-3, -2, -1, 0}

{1, 0, 2}

{(1, -3), (0, -2), (1, -1), (2, 0)}

**13.** $y = 7 - 3x$

**14.** $-3y = 9 - 4x$

$-y = \dfrac{9 - 4x}{3}$

$y = \dfrac{4x - 9}{3}$

**15.** $6y = 12 - x$

$y = \dfrac{12 - x}{6}$

**16.** {(-4, -11), (-2, -3), (0, 5), (2, 13), (4, 21)}

**17.** {(-4, -13), (-2, -11), (0, -9), (2, -7), (4, -5)}

**18.** {(-4, $\frac{21}{2}$), (-2, $\frac{15}{2}$), (0, $\frac{9}{2}$), (2, $\frac{3}{2}$), (4, $\frac{-3}{2}$)}

**19.** {(-4, $\frac{-16}{3}$), (-2, $\frac{-8}{3}$), (0, 0), (2, $\frac{8}{3}$), (4, $\frac{16}{3}$)}

**20.**

| x | y |
|---|---|
| -2 | $1\frac{1}{5}$ |
| -1 | 1 |
| 0 | $\frac{4}{5}$ |
| 1 | $\frac{3}{5}$ |
| 2 | $\frac{2}{5}$ |

**21.**

| x | y |
|---|---|
| -2 | $-3\frac{1}{3}$ |
| -1 | $-2\frac{2}{3}$ |
| 0 | -2 |
| 1 | $-1\frac{1}{3}$ |
| 2 | $-\frac{2}{3}$ |

**22.**

| x | y |
|---|---|
| -2 | 10 |
| -1 | $7\frac{1}{2}$ |
| 0 | 5 |
| 1 | $2\frac{1}{2}$ |
| 2 | 0 |

**23.**

| x | y |
|---|---|
| -2 | 12 |
| -1 | $10\frac{1}{2}$ |
| 0 | 9 |
| 1 | $7\frac{1}{2}$ |
| 2 | 6 |

**24.** yes  **25.** no  **26.** yes  **27.** yes

**28.** $g(2) = 2^2 - 2 + 1$  **29.** $g(-1) = (-1)^2 - (-1) + 1$

$= 4 - 2 + 1$  $\qquad = 1 + 1 + 1$

$= 3$  $\qquad = 3$

**30.** $g(\frac{1}{2}) = (\frac{1}{2})^2 - \frac{1}{2} + 1$

$= \frac{1}{4} - \frac{1}{2} + 1$

$= \frac{3}{4}$

**31.** $g(a + 1) = (a + 1)^2 - (a + 1) + 1$

$= a^2 + 2a + 1 - a - 1 + 1$

$= a^2 + a + 1$

**32.** $g(-2a) = (-2a)^2 - (-2a) + 1$

$= 4a^2 + 2a + 1$

**33.**

**34.**

**35.**

**36.**

**37.** $y = 3x + 5$  **38.** $y = x - 4$

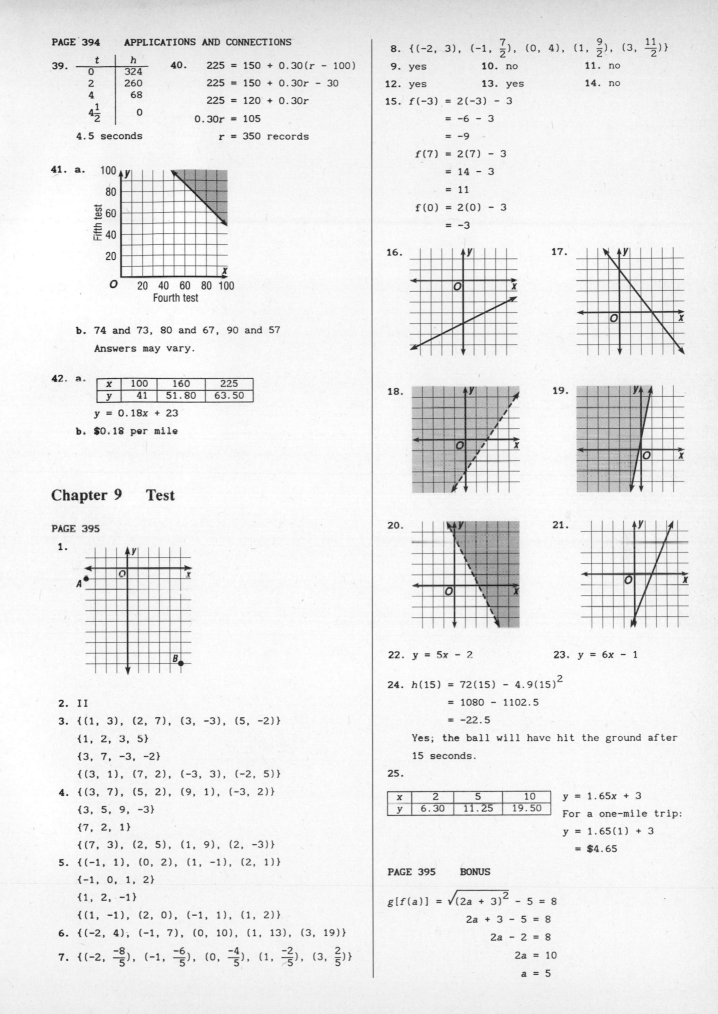

**39.**

| $t$ | $h$ |
|---|---|
| 0 | 324 |
| 2 | 260 |
| 4 | 68 |
| $4\frac{1}{2}$ | 0 |

4.5 seconds

**40.**  $225 = 150 + 0.30(r - 100)$

$225 = 150 + 0.30r - 30$

$225 = 120 + 0.30r$

$0.30r = 105$

$r = 350$ records

**41. a.**

**b.** 74 and 73, 80 and 67, 90 and 57

Answers may vary.

**42. a.**

| $x$ | 100 | 160 | 225 |
|---|---|---|---|
| $y$ | 41 | 51.80 | 63.50 |

$y = 0.18x + 23$

**b.** $0.18 per mile

# Chapter 9    Test

**1.**

**2.** II

**3.** $\{(1, 3), (2, 7), (3, -3), (5, -2)\}$

$\{1, 2, 3, 5\}$

$\{3, 7, -3, -2\}$

$\{(3, 1), (7, 2), (-3, 3), (-2, 5)\}$

**4.** $\{(3, 7), (5, 2), (9, 1), (-3, 2)\}$

$\{3, 5, 9, -3\}$

$\{7, 2, 1\}$

$\{(7, 3), (2, 5), (1, 9), (2, -3)\}$

**5.** $\{(-1, 1), (0, 2), (1, -1), (2, 1)\}$

$\{-1, 0, 1, 2\}$

$\{1, 2, -1\}$

$\{(1, -1), (2, 0), (-1, 1), (1, 2)\}$

**6.** $\{(-2, 4), (-1, 7), (0, 10), (1, 13), (3, 19)\}$

**7.** $\{(-2, \frac{-8}{5}), (-1, \frac{-6}{5}), (0, \frac{-4}{5}), (1, \frac{-2}{5}), (3, \frac{2}{5})\}$

**8.** $\{(-2, 3), (-1, \frac{7}{2}), (0, 4), (1, \frac{9}{2}), (3, \frac{11}{2})\}$

**9.** yes          **10.** no          **11.** no

**12.** yes          **13.** yes          **14.** no

**15.** $f(-3) = 2(-3) - 3$

$= -6 - 3$

$= -9$

$f(7) = 2(7) - 3$

$= 14 - 3$

$= 11$

$f(0) = 2(0) - 3$

$= -3$

**16.**          **17.**

**18.**          **19.**

**20.**          **21.**

**22.** $y = 5x - 2$          **23.** $y = 6x - 1$

**24.** $h(15) = 72(15) - 4.9(15)^2$

$= 1080 - 1102.5$

$= -22.5$

Yes; the ball will have hit the ground after 15 seconds.

**25.**

| $x$ | 2 | 5 | 10 |
|---|---|---|---|
| $y$ | 6.30 | 11.25 | 19.50 |

$y = 1.65x + 3$

For a one-mile trip:

$y = 1.65(1) + 3$

$= \$4.65$

$g[f(a)] = \sqrt{(2a + 3)^2} - 5 = 8$

$2a + 3 - 5 = 8$

$2a - 2 = 8$

$2a = 10$

$a = 5$

167

# Chapter 9    College Entrance
              Exam Preview

1. B

$$\frac{37}{3} = 12\frac{1}{3}$$

2. A

$$\frac{0.4}{20} = 0.02$$

3. B

$$10 + 1\frac{1}{4} - 3 \qquad 10 - 1\frac{1}{4} + 3$$

$$= 8\frac{1}{4} \qquad\qquad = 11\frac{3}{4}$$

4. A      5. D      6. D      7. D

8. C

$$-5(a - b) = 0 \qquad 7(3b - 3a) = 0$$

9. B

$$\frac{3}{4}(6)(0) = 0 \qquad \frac{1}{6}(4)(6) = 4$$

10. C

$$\frac{1}{4} \cdot \frac{4}{7} = \frac{1}{7} \qquad \frac{4}{7} \cdot \frac{1}{4} = \frac{1}{7}$$

11. B

$$0.02 \div 0.2 = 0.1 \qquad 0.2 \div 0.02 = 10$$

12. B

$$2(-2) + 7 \qquad 2(6) - 8$$

$$= -4 + 7 \qquad\quad = 12 - 8$$

$$= 3 \qquad\qquad = 4$$

13. B

14. A

$$x \qquad x + 0.2x - 0.2(x + 0.2x)$$

$$\qquad = 1.2x - 0.2x - 0.04x$$

$$\qquad = 0.96x$$

15. C

16. D

17. B

$$0.2x = 6 \qquad \frac{1}{10} \cdot 310$$

$$x = \frac{6}{0.2} \qquad = 31$$

$$x = 30$$

18. B

x is negative       y is positive

19. B

$$1540 = 2 \cdot 2 \cdot 5 \cdot 7 \cdot 11$$

GPF = 11

$$1530 = 2 \cdot 3 \cdot 3 \cdot 5 \cdot 17$$

GPF = 17

20. C

2, 3, 5, 7            11, 13, 17, 19

4 prime numbers      4 prime numbers

21. C

$$a = b - 2 \qquad\qquad 2b$$

$$c = b + 2$$

$$a + c = b - 2 + b + 2$$

$$a + c = 2b$$

22. B

23. A

$$\frac{2}{5} = \frac{8}{x} \qquad\qquad \frac{2}{5} = \frac{x}{8}$$

$$2x = 40 \qquad\qquad 5x = 16$$

$$x = 20 \qquad\qquad x = 3\frac{1}{16}$$

24. C

|      | Amount Invested | Interest |
|------|------|------|
| 6%   | $x$  | $0.06x$ |
| 8%   | $10,000 - x$ | $0.08(10,000 - x)$ |

$$0.06 + 0.08(10,000 - x) = 700$$

$$0.06x + 800 - 0.08x = 700$$

$$0.02x = 100$$

$$x = 5000$$

$5000 invested at 6%      $5000 invested at 8%

25. B

$$x - 5 < 0 \qquad\qquad 5 - x > 0$$

26. D

27. A

$$f(3) = (3)^2 + 2(3) - 5 \quad f(-3) = (-3)^2 + 2(-3) - 5$$

$$= 9 + 6 - 5 \qquad\qquad = 9 - 6 - 5$$

$$= 10 \qquad\qquad\qquad = -2$$

# Chapter 10    Graphing Linear Equations

## 10-1    Slope of a Line

PAGES 402–403     CHECKING FOR UNDERSTANDING

1. For every 100 feet of horizontal change, there is a vertical change of 5 feet.

2. Slope is a ratio, rise to run, or the change in y to the change in x.

3. Answers may vary.

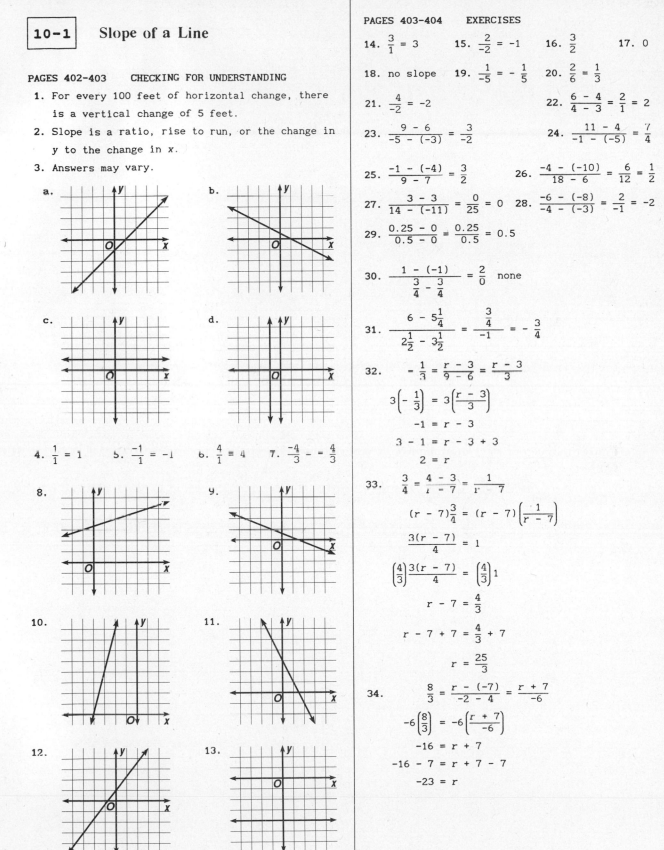

4. $\frac{1}{1} = 1$    5. $\frac{-1}{1} = -1$    6. $\frac{4}{1} = 4$    7. $\frac{-4}{3} = -\frac{4}{3}$

PAGES 403–404     EXERCISES

14. $\frac{3}{1} = 3$    15. $\frac{-2}{2} = -1$    16. $\frac{3}{2}$     17. 0

18. no slope    19. $\frac{1}{-5} = -\frac{1}{5}$   20. $\frac{2}{6} = \frac{1}{3}$

21. $\frac{4}{-2} = -2$         22. $\frac{6 - 4}{4 - 3} = \frac{2}{1} = 2$

23. $\frac{9 - 6}{-5 - (-3)} = \frac{3}{-2}$      24. $\frac{11 - 4}{-1 - (-5)} = \frac{7}{4}$

25. $\frac{-1 - (-4)}{9 - 7} = \frac{3}{2}$    26. $\frac{-4 - (-10)}{18 - 6} = \frac{6}{12} = \frac{1}{2}$

27. $\frac{3 - 3}{14 - (-11)} = \frac{0}{25} = 0$   28. $\frac{-6 - (-8)}{-4 - (-3)} = \frac{2}{-1} = -2$

29. $\frac{0.25 - 0}{0.5 - 0} = \frac{0.25}{0.5} = 0.5$

30. $\frac{1 - (-1)}{\frac{3}{4} - \frac{3}{4}} = \frac{2}{0}$   none

31. $\frac{6 - 5\frac{1}{4}}{2\frac{1}{2} - 3\frac{1}{2}} = \frac{\frac{3}{4}}{-1} = -\frac{3}{4}$

32. $-\frac{1}{3} = \frac{r - 3}{9 - 6} = \frac{r - 3}{3}$

$3\left(-\frac{1}{3}\right) = 3\left(\frac{r - 3}{3}\right)$

$-1 = r - 3$

$3 - 1 = r - 3 + 3$

$2 = r$

33. $\frac{3}{4} = \frac{4 - 3}{r - 7} = \frac{1}{r - 7}$

$(r - 7)\frac{3}{4} = (r - 7)\left(\frac{1}{r - 7}\right)$

$\frac{3(r - 7)}{4} = 1$

$\left(\frac{4}{3}\right)\frac{3(r - 7)}{4} = \left(\frac{4}{3}\right)1$

$r - 7 = \frac{4}{3}$

$r - 7 + 7 = \frac{4}{3} + 7$

$r = \frac{25}{3}$

34. $\frac{8}{3} = \frac{r - (-7)}{-2 - 4} = \frac{r + 7}{-6}$

$-6\left(\frac{8}{3}\right) = -6\left(\frac{r + 7}{-6}\right)$

$-16 = r + 7$

$-16 - 7 = r + 7 - 7$

$-23 = r$

**35.**
$$-4 = \frac{-6 - (-2)}{r - 6} = \frac{-4}{r - 6}$$
$$(r - 6)(-4) = (r - 6)\left(\frac{-4}{r - 6}\right)$$
$$-4r + 24 = -4$$
$$-4r + 24 - 24 = -4 - 24$$
$$-4r = -28$$
$$\frac{-4r}{-4} = \frac{-28}{-4}$$
$$r = 7$$

**36.**
$$-\frac{1}{5} = \frac{r - 7}{11 - r}$$
$$(11 - r)\left(-\frac{1}{5}\right) = (11 - r)\left(\frac{r - 7}{11 - r}\right)$$
$$-\frac{11}{5} + \frac{r}{5} = r - 7$$
$$7 - \frac{11}{5} + \frac{r}{5} = r - 7 + 7$$
$$\frac{24}{5} + \frac{r}{5} = r$$
$$\frac{24}{5} + \frac{r}{5} - \frac{r}{5} = r - \frac{r}{5}$$
$$\frac{24}{5} = \frac{4r}{5}$$
$$\frac{5}{4}\left(\frac{24}{5}\right) = \frac{5}{4}\left(\frac{4r}{5}\right)$$
$$6 = r$$

**37.**
$$-\frac{5}{3} = \frac{r - 2}{4 - r}$$
$$(4 - r)\left(-\frac{5}{3}\right) = (4 - r)\left(\frac{r - 2}{4 - r}\right)$$
$$\frac{-20 + 5r}{3} = r - 2$$
$$(3)\left(\frac{-20 + 5r}{3}\right) = (3)(r - 2)$$
$$-20 + 5r = 3r - 6$$
$$20 - 20 + 5r = 3r - 6 + 20$$
$$5r = 3r + 14$$
$$5r - 3r = 3r - 3r + 14$$
$$2r = 14$$
$$\frac{2r}{2} = \frac{14}{2}$$
$$r = 7$$

**38.**
$$r = \frac{r - 2}{9 - 6} = \frac{r - 2}{3}$$
$$3(r) = 3\left(\frac{r - 2}{3}\right)$$
$$3r = r - 2$$
$$3r - r = r - r - 2$$
$$2r = -2$$
$$\frac{2r}{2} = \frac{-2}{2}$$
$$r = -1$$

**39.**
$$r = \frac{r^2 - (-6)}{8 - 3} = \frac{r^2 + 6}{5}$$
$$5(r) = 5\left(\frac{r^2 + 6}{5}\right)$$
$$5r = r^2 + 6$$
$$5r - 5r = r^2 - 5r + 6$$
$$0 = r^2 - 5r + 6$$
$$0 = (r - 3)(r - 2)$$
$$r = 3 \text{ and } r = 2$$

**40.** The lines go from lower left to upper right.

**41.** The lines go from upper left to lower right.

**42.** $\frac{3}{36} = \frac{1}{12}$

**43.** $0.895\% = 0.00895$
$$0.00895 = \frac{\text{vertical change}}{\text{horizontal change}}$$
$$v = (0.00895)(h)$$
$$v = (0.00895)(8941)$$
$$v = 80$$

The elevation at the end of the tunnel is 11,080 + 80 or 11,160 feet.

**44.** $\frac{8}{12} = \frac{2}{3}$

**45.** $\frac{p}{100} = \frac{\text{vertical change}}{\text{horizontal change}}$
$$\frac{p}{100} = \frac{33,000 - 7000}{50(5280)}$$
$$\frac{p}{100} = 0.098$$
$$p = 9.8\%$$

**46.** Associate property of addition

**47.** $1 + 1 + 5 = 7$

**48.** $5a^3 + 3a^2b - 5ab^2 - 3b^3$
$$= (5a^3 + 3a^2b) + (-5ab^2 - 3b^3)$$
$$= a^2(5a + 3b) + -b^2(5a + 3b)$$
$$= (a^2 - b^2)(5a + 3b)$$
$$= (a - b)(a + b)(5a + 3b)$$

**49.** $\frac{6}{x} - \frac{5}{x^2}$
$$= \frac{6x}{x^2} - \frac{5}{x^2}$$
$$= \frac{6x - 5}{x^2}$$

**50.** Add 5:
$$1,\ 6,\ 11,\ 16,\ 21,\ 26,\ 31$$

---

| **10-2** | **Point-Slope and Standard Forms of Linear Equations** |
|---|---|

PAGES 407-408    CHECKING FOR UNDERSTANDING

1. the coordinates of a point on the line

2. $Ax + By = C$

3. horizontal line with $y$-coordinate $c$.

4. vertical line with $x$-coordinate $c$.

5. 3; (5,2)

6. -2; (-1,-5)

**7.** $-\frac{3}{2}$; $(-5,-6)$    **8.** $2$; $\left(3,-\frac{3}{2}\right)$

**9.** $0$; $(0,3)$    **10.** none; $(1,0)$

**11.** 
$$y - 3 = 2\left(x + \frac{3}{2}\right)$$
$$y - 3 = 2x + 3$$
$$y - y - 3 = 2x - y + 3$$
$$-3 = 2x - y + 3$$
$$-3 - 3 = 2x - y + 3 - 3$$
$$-6 = 2x - y$$
$$2x - y = -6$$

**12.** 
$$y + 5 = -3\left(x - \frac{1}{3}\right)$$
$$y + 5 = -3x + 1$$
$$3x + y + 5 = 3x - 3x + 1$$
$$3x + y + 5 = 1$$
$$3x + y + 5 - 5 = 1 - 5$$
$$3x + y = -4$$

**13.** 
$$y + 1 = \frac{2}{3}(x + 2)$$
$$3(y + 1) = 2(x + 2)$$
$$3y + 3 = 2x + 4$$
$$3 - 4 = 2x - 3y$$
$$-1 = 2x - 3y$$
$$2x - 3y = -1$$

**14.** 
$$y + \frac{3}{2} = \frac{1}{2}(x + 4)$$
$$2\left(y + \frac{3}{2}\right) = 1(x + 4)$$
$$2y + 3 = x + 4$$
$$3 - 4 = x - 2y$$
$$-1 = x - 2y$$
$$x - 2y = -1$$

**PAGES 408-409    EXERCISES**

**15.** 
$$y - y_1 = m(x - x_1)$$
$$y - 4 = -\frac{2}{3}(x - 5)$$
$$3(y - 4) = -2(x - 5)$$
$$3y - 12 = -2x + 10$$
$$2x + 3y = 12 + 10$$
$$2x + 3y = 22$$

**16.** 
$$y - y_1 = m(x - x_1)$$
$$y - (-3) = -\frac{1}{2}[x - (-6)]$$
$$y + 3 = -\frac{1}{2}(x + 6)$$
$$2(y + 3) = -1(x + 6)$$
$$2y + 6 = -x - 6$$
$$x + 2y = -6 - 6$$
$$x + 2y = -12$$

**17.** 
$$y - y_1 = m(x - x_1)$$
$$y - 1 = \frac{2}{3}(x - 9)$$
$$3(y - 1) = 2(x - 9)$$
$$3y - 3 = 2x - 18$$
$$-3 + 18 = 2x - 3y$$
$$15 = 2x - 3y$$
$$2x - 3y = 15$$

**18.** 
$$y - y_1 = m(x - x_1)$$
$$y - (-3) = 2(x - 4)$$
$$y + 3 = 2(x - 4)$$
$$y + 3 = 2x - 8$$
$$3 + 8 = 2x - y$$
$$11 = 2x - y$$
$$2x - y = 11$$

**19.** 
$$y - y_1 = m(x - x_1)$$
$$y - 4 = -3[x - (-2)]$$
$$y - 4 = -3(x + 2)$$
$$y - 4 = -3x - 6$$
$$3x + y = -6 + 4$$
$$3x + y = -2$$

**20.** 
$$y - y_1 = m(x - x_1)$$
$$y - (-2) = \frac{4}{3}(x - 6)$$
$$y + 2 = \frac{4}{3}(x + 6)$$
$$3(y + 2) = 4(x - 6)$$
$$3y + 6 = 4x - 24$$
$$6 + 24 = 4x - 3y$$
$$30 = 4x - 3y$$
$$4x - 3y = 30$$

**21.** 
$$y - y_1 = m(x - x_1)$$
$$y - 6 = 0[x - (-2)]$$
$$y - 6 = 0$$
$$y = 6$$

**22.** $x = 1$

**23.** 
$$y - y_1 = m(x - x_1)$$
$$m = \frac{4 - 3}{5 - 6} = -1$$
$$y - 4 = -1(x - 5)$$
$$y - 4 = -x + 5$$
$$x + y = 5 + 4$$
$$x + y = 9$$

**24.** 
$$y - y_1 = m(x - x_1)$$
$$m = \frac{1 - (-4)}{6 - 7} = -5$$
$$y - 1 = -5(x - 6)$$
$$y - 1 = -5x + 30$$
$$5x + y = 30 + 1$$
$$5x + y = 31$$

**25.** 
$$y - y_1 = m(x - x_1)$$
$$m = \frac{8 - (-2)}{4 - 4} \text{ none}$$
$$x = 4$$

**26.** 
$$y - y_1 = m(x - x_1)$$
$$m = \frac{-2 - (-3)}{4 - 8} = -\frac{1}{4}$$
$$y - (-2) = -\frac{1}{4}(x - 4)$$
$$y + 2 = -\frac{1}{4}(x - 4)$$
$$4(y + 2) = -1(x - 4)$$
$$4y + 8 = -x + 4$$
$$x + 4y = 4 - 8$$
$$x + 4y = -4$$

**27.** 
$$y - y_1 = m(x - x_1)$$
$$m = \frac{2 - 1}{-8 - (-6)} = -\frac{1}{2}$$
$$y - 1 = -\frac{1}{2}[x - (-6)]$$
$$y - 1 = -\frac{1}{2}(x + 6)$$
$$2(y - 1) = -1(x + 6)$$
$$2y - 2 = -x - 6$$
$$x + 2y = -6 + 2$$
$$x + 2y = -4$$

**28.** 
$$y - y_1 = m(x - x_1)$$
$$m = \frac{3 - 3}{5 - (-6)} = 0$$
$$y - 3 = 0(x - 5)$$
$$y - 3 = 0$$
$$y = 3$$

**29.** 
$$y - y_1 = m(x - x_1)$$
$$m = \frac{1 - (-2)}{-5 - 6} = -\frac{3}{11}$$
$$y - 1 = -\frac{3}{11}[x - (-5)]$$
$$y - 1 = -\frac{3}{11}(x + 5)$$
$$11(y - 1) = -3(x + 5)$$
$$11y - 11 = -3x - 15$$
$$3x + 11y = -15 + 11$$
$$3x + 11y = -4$$

171

30. $y - y_1 = m(x - x_1)$

$m = \dfrac{2 - (-2)}{-8 - (-1)} = -\dfrac{4}{7}$

$y - 2 = -\dfrac{4}{7}[x - (-8)]$

$y - 2 = -\dfrac{4}{7}(x + 8)$

$7(y - 2) = -4(x + 8)$

$7y - 14 = -4x - 32$

$4x + 7y = -32 + 14$

$4x + 7y = -18$

31. $y - y_1 = m(x - x_1)$

$m = \dfrac{1 - 0.5}{0.75 - 2} = \dfrac{0.5}{-1.25} = -0.4$

$y - 1 = -0.4(x - 0.75)$

$10(y - 1) = -4(x - 0.75)$

$10y - 10 = -4x + 3$

$4x + 10y = 10 + 3$

$4x + 10y = 13$

32. $y - y_1 = m(x - x_1)$

$m = \dfrac{0.5 - 0.5}{-8 - 9} = \dfrac{0}{-17} = 0$

$y - 0.5 = 0(x - 9)$

$y - 0.5 = 0$

$y = 0.5$

$2y = 1$

33. $y - y_1 = m(x - x_1)$

$m = \dfrac{\frac{1}{3} - 1\frac{1}{2}}{2\frac{1}{2} - \frac{3}{4}} = \dfrac{-\frac{7}{6}}{\frac{7}{4}} = -\dfrac{2}{3}$

$y - \dfrac{1}{3} = -\dfrac{2}{3}\left(x - 2\frac{1}{2}\right)$

$3\left(y - \dfrac{1}{3}\right) = -2\left(x - 2\frac{1}{2}\right)$

$3y - 1 = -2x + 5$

$2x + 3y = 5 + 1$

$2x + 3y = 6$

34. $y - y_1 = m(x - x_1)$

$m = \dfrac{7 - \frac{16}{3}}{-2 - (-2)}$ none

$x = -2$

35. $m = \dfrac{5 - 1}{5 - 9} = \dfrac{4}{-4} = -1$

$y - 5 = -1(x - 5)$

$y - 5 = -x + 5$

$y = -x + 10$

Let $x = 10$.

$y = -(10) + 10$

$y = 0$

Since $y = 0$ when $x = 10$, this line intersects the $x$-axis at $(10,0)$.

36. Let $x$ = the number of algebra books and $y$ = the number of geometry books. Use $(6,18)$ and $(11,14)$.

$m = \dfrac{18 - 14}{6 - 11} = -\dfrac{4}{5}$

$y - 18 = -\dfrac{4}{5}(x - 6)$

$5(y - 18) = -4(x - 6)$

$5y - 90 = -4x + 24$

$4x + 5y = 90 + 24$

$4x + 5y = 114$

37. Let $x$ = the number of weeks that have passed and $y$ = the money he has left. Kyung started with $90 since he had $75 left after 3 weeks. Use $(0,90)$ and $(3,75)$.

$m = \dfrac{90 - 75}{0 - 3} = -5$

$y - 90 = -5(x - 0)$

$y - 90 = -5x$

$5x + y = 90$

38. $7a(8a + 11) = 56a^2 + 77a$

39. $x^2 - 9x + 14 = (x - 7)(x - 2)$

40. $\dfrac{y^2 + 3y^3}{y^2 - 4} \cdot \dfrac{2y + y^2}{y + 4y^2 + 3y^3}$

$= \dfrac{y^2(1 + 3y)}{(y - 2)(y + 2)} \cdot \dfrac{y(2 + y)}{y(3y^2 + 4y + 1)}$

$= \dfrac{y^2(1 + 3y)}{y - 2} \cdot \dfrac{1}{(3y + 1)(y + 1)}$

$= \dfrac{y^2}{(y - 2)(y + 1)}$

$= \dfrac{y^2}{y^2 - y - 2}$

41. Quadrant I

42. $\dfrac{100}{100} = \dfrac{\text{vertical change}}{\text{horizontal change}}$

$1 = \dfrac{1015}{h}$

$h = 1015$ feet

## 10-3 Slope-Intercept Form of Linear Equations

PAGES 412-413   CHECKING FOR UNDERSTANDING

1. No; equations of the form $y = c$ do not.

2. Let $y = 0$ and solve for $x$.

3. $x = c$ ($c$ is any number)

4. $y = c$ ($c$ is any number)

5. $m = 5$; $y = 3$    6. $m = 3$; $y = -7$

7. $m = \dfrac{1}{3}$; $y = 0$    8. $m = \dfrac{3}{5}$; $y = -\dfrac{1}{4}$

9. $2x + 3y = 5$

$3y = -2x + 5$

$y = -\dfrac{2}{3}x + \dfrac{5}{3}$

$m = -\dfrac{2}{3}; \ y = \dfrac{5}{3}$

10. $-x + 4y = 3$

$4y = x + 3$

$y = \dfrac{1}{4}x + \dfrac{3}{4}$

$m = \dfrac{1}{4}; \ y = \dfrac{3}{4}$

11. $y - 6x = 5$

$y = 6x + 5$

$m = 6; \ y = 5$

12. $3y - 8x = 2$

$3y = 8x + 2$

$y = \dfrac{8}{3}x + \dfrac{2}{3}$

$m = \dfrac{8}{3}; \ y = \dfrac{2}{3}$

13. $5y = -8y - 2$

$y = -\dfrac{8}{5}x - \dfrac{2}{5}$

$m = -\dfrac{8}{5}; \ y = -\dfrac{2}{5}$

14. $y = 3x + 1$

15. $y = -3x + 5$

16. $y = 4x - 2$

17. $y = \dfrac{1}{2}x + 5$

18. $y = -3.1x + 0.6$

19. $y = 0x + 14 = 14$

PAGES 413-414    EXERCISES

20. Let $y = 0$.

$3x + 2(0) = 6$

$3x = 6$

$x = 2$

Let $x = 0$.

$3(0) + 2y = 6$

$2y = 6$

$y = 3$

The $x$-intercept is 2.   The $y$-intercept is 3.

21. Let $y = 0$.

$5x + 0 = 10$

$5x = 10$

$x = 2$

Let $x = 0$.

$5(0) + y = 10$

$y = 10$

The $y$-intercept is 10.

The $x$-intercept is 2.

22. Let $y = 0$.

$3x + 4(0) = 24$

$3x - 24$

$x = 8$

Let $x = 0$.

$3(0) + 4y = 24$

$4y = 24$

$y = 6$

The $x$-intercept is 8.   The $y$-intercept is 6.

23. Let $y = 0$.

$2x - 7(0) = 28$

$2x = 28$

$x = 14$

Let $x = 0$.

$2(0) - 7y = 28$

$-7y = 28$

$y = -4$

The $x$-intercept is 14.  The $y$-intercept is -4.

24. Let $y = 0$.

$2x + 5(0) = -11$

$2x = -11$

$x = -\dfrac{11}{2}$

Let $x = 0$.

$2(0) + 5y = -11$

$5y = -11$

$y = -\dfrac{11}{5}$

The $x$-intercept is $-\dfrac{11}{2}$.  The $y$-intercept is $-\dfrac{11}{5}$.

25. The $x$-intercept is -2; there is no $y$-intercept.

26. Let $y = 0$.

$\dfrac{3}{4}x - 2(0) = 7$

$\dfrac{3}{4}x = 7$

$x = \dfrac{28}{3}$ or $9\dfrac{1}{3}$

Let $x = 0$.

$\dfrac{3}{4}(0) - 2y = 7$

$-2y = 7$

$y = -\dfrac{7}{2}$ or $-3\dfrac{1}{2}$

27. No $x$-intercept; the $y$-intercept is 4.

28. Let $y = 0$.

$1.8x - 2.5(0) = 5.4$

$1.8x = 5.4$

$x = 3$

Let $x = 0$.

$1.8(0) - 2.5y = 5.4$

$-2.5y = 5.4$

$y = -2.16$

The $x$-intercept is 3.   The $y$-intercept is -2.16.

29. $2x + 5y = 10$

$A = 2, \ B = 5, \ C = 10$

slope: $-\dfrac{A}{B} = -\dfrac{2}{5}$

$y$-intercept: $\dfrac{C}{B} = \dfrac{10}{5} = 2$

$y = -\dfrac{2}{5}x + 2$

30. $5x - y = 15$

$A = 5, \ B = -1, \ C = 15$

slope: $-\dfrac{A}{B} = -\dfrac{5}{-1} = 5$

$y$-intercept: $\dfrac{C}{B} = \dfrac{15}{-1} = -15$

$y = 5x - 15$

31. $7x + 4y = 8$

$A = 7, \ B = 4, \ C = 8$

slope: $-\dfrac{A}{B} = -\dfrac{7}{4}$

$y$-intercept: $\dfrac{C}{B} = \dfrac{8}{4} = 2$

$y = -\dfrac{7}{4}x + 2$

32. $5x - 4y = 11$

$A = 5, \ B = -4. \ C = 11$

slope: $-\dfrac{A}{B} = -\dfrac{5}{-4} = \dfrac{5}{4}$

$y$-intercept: $\dfrac{C}{B} = \dfrac{11}{-4}$

$y = \dfrac{5}{4}x - \dfrac{11}{4}$

33. $12x + 9y = 15$

$A = 12, \ B = 9. \ C = 15$

slope: $-\dfrac{A}{B} = -\dfrac{12}{9}$ or $-\dfrac{4}{3}$

$y$-intercept: $\dfrac{C}{B} = \dfrac{15}{9}$ or $\dfrac{5}{3}$

$y = -\dfrac{4}{3}x + \dfrac{5}{3}$

34. $13x - 11y = 22$

$A = 13, \ B = -11, \ C = 22$

slope: $-\dfrac{A}{B} = -\dfrac{13}{-11} = \dfrac{13}{11}$

$y$-intercept: $\dfrac{C}{B} = \dfrac{22}{-11} = -2$

$y = \dfrac{13}{11}x - 2$

35. $2x + \frac{1}{3}y = 5$

$A = 2$, $B = \frac{1}{3}$, $C = 5$

slope: $-\frac{A}{B} = -\frac{2}{\frac{1}{3}} = -6$

y-intercept: $\frac{C}{B} = \frac{5}{\frac{1}{3}} = 15$

$y = -6x + 15$

36. $3x - \frac{1}{4}y = 6$

$A = 3$, $B = -\frac{1}{4}$, $C = 6$

slope: $-\frac{A}{B} = -\frac{3}{-\frac{1}{4}} = 12$

y-intercept: $\frac{C}{B} = \frac{6}{-\frac{1}{4}} = -24$

$y = 12x - 24$

37. $\frac{2}{3}x + \frac{1}{6}y = 2$

$A = \frac{2}{3}$, $B = \frac{1}{6}$, $C = 2$

slope: $-\frac{A}{B} = -\frac{\frac{2}{3}}{\frac{1}{6}} = -4$

y-intercept: $\frac{C}{B} = \frac{2}{\frac{1}{6}} = 12$

$y = -4x + 12$

38. $3x = 2y - 7$

$3x - 2y = -7$

$A = 3$, $B = -2$, $C = -7$

slope: $-\frac{A}{B} = -\frac{3}{-2} = \frac{3}{2}$

y-intercept: $\frac{C}{B} = \frac{-7}{-2} = \frac{7}{2}$

$y = \frac{3}{2}x + \frac{7}{2}$

39. $5x = 8 - 2y$

$5x + 2y = 8$

$A = 5$, $B = 2$, $C = 8$

slope: $-\frac{A}{B} = -\frac{5}{2}$

y-intercept: $\frac{C}{B} = \frac{8}{2} = 4$

$y = -\frac{5}{2}x + 4$

40. $8y = 4x + 12$

$4x - 8y = -12$

$A = 4$, $B = -8$, $C = -12$

slope: $-\frac{A}{B} = -\frac{4}{-8} = \frac{1}{2}$

y-intercept: $\frac{C}{B} = \frac{-12}{-8} = \frac{3}{2}$

$y = \frac{1}{2}x + \frac{3}{2}$

41. $1.1x - 0.2y = 3.2$

$11x - 2y = 32$

$A = 11$, $B = -2$, $C = 32$

slope: $-\frac{A}{B} = -\frac{11}{-2} = \frac{11}{2}$

y-intercept: $\frac{C}{B} = \frac{32}{-2} = -16$

$y = \frac{11}{2}x - 16$

42. $3(x - 7) = 2y + 5x + 8$

$3x - 21 = 2y + 5x + 8$

$2x + 2y = 29$

$A = 2$, $B = 2$, $C = 29$

slope: $-\frac{A}{B} = -\frac{2}{2} = -1$

y-intercept: $\frac{C}{B} = \frac{29}{-2}$

$y = -x - \frac{29}{2}$

43. $y - 3x = 6(y + 7x) + 10$

$y - 3x = 6y + 42x + 10$

$45x + 5y = -10$

$A = 45$, $B = 5$, $C = -10$

slope: $-\frac{A}{B} = -\frac{45}{5} = -9$

y-intercept: $\frac{C}{B} = \frac{-10}{5} = -2$

$y = -9x - 2$

44. $4y + x = 9 - 3(2y - 2x)$

$4y + x = 9 - 6y + 6x$

$5x - 10y = -9$

$A = 5$, $B = -10$, $C = -9$

slope: $-\frac{A}{B} = -\frac{5}{-10} = \frac{1}{2}$

y-intercept: $\frac{C}{B} = \frac{-9}{-10} = \frac{9}{10}$

$y = \frac{1}{2}x + \frac{9}{10}$

45. $\frac{4}{5}(2x - y) = 6x + \frac{2}{5}y - 10$

$\frac{8}{5}x - \frac{4}{5}y = 6x + \frac{2}{5}y - 10$

$\frac{22}{5}x + \frac{6}{5}y = 10$

$22x + 6y = 50$

$A = 22$, $B = 6$, $C = 50$

slope: $-\frac{A}{B} = -\frac{22}{6} = -\frac{11}{3}$

y-intercept: $\frac{C}{B} = \frac{50}{6} = \frac{25}{3}$

$y = -\frac{11}{3}x + \frac{25}{3}$

46. $\dfrac{3}{2}(4x + 9y) = 4\left(7x - \dfrac{1}{2}y\right)$

   $6x + \dfrac{27}{2}y = 28x - 2y$

   $22x - \dfrac{31}{2}y = 0$

   $A = 22, \; B = -\dfrac{31}{2}, \; C = 0$

   slope: $-\dfrac{A}{B} = -\dfrac{22}{\frac{-31}{2}} = \dfrac{44}{31}$

   $y$-intercept: $\dfrac{C}{B} = 0$

   $y = \dfrac{44}{31}x$

47. Let $x = 0$.
   $3(0) + 4y = 6$
   $\qquad y = \dfrac{6}{4} = \dfrac{3}{2}$
   The $y$-intercept is $\dfrac{3}{2}$.
   $y = \dfrac{4}{5}x + \dfrac{3}{2}$

48. Let $x = 0$.
   $7(0) - 3y = 12$
   $\qquad y = -4$
   The $y$-intercept is $-4$.
   $y = -\dfrac{3}{5}x - 4$

49. $2x - 5y - 10 = 0$
   $2x - 5y = 10$
   $A = 2, \; B = -5$
   slope: $-\dfrac{A}{B} = -\dfrac{2}{-5} = \dfrac{2}{5}$
   $y = \dfrac{2}{5}x + 12$

50. $\dfrac{1}{2}x - \dfrac{3}{4}y = 6$
   $2x - 3y = 24$
   $A = 2, \; B = -3$
   slope: $-\dfrac{A}{B} = -\dfrac{2}{-3} = \dfrac{2}{3}$
   $y = \dfrac{2}{3}x - 0.65$

51. $\qquad y = 2x$
   $3x - 4(2x) = -20$
   $3x - 8x = -20$
   $\qquad -5x = -20$
   $\qquad\quad x = 4$
   $\qquad\quad y = 8$
   $(4,8)$ is the point.

52. $\qquad y = 3x$
   $4x - 3x = -2$
   $\qquad x = -2$
   $\qquad y = -6$
   $(-2,-6)$ is the point.

53. $\qquad\qquad y = x - 5$
   $x + 2(x - 5) = 11$
   $x + 2x - 10 = 11$
   $\qquad\quad 3x = 21$
   $\qquad\quad\; x = 7$
   $\qquad\quad\; y = 2$
   $(7,2)$ is the point.

54. $\qquad\qquad y = x + 4$
   $7x + 3(x + 4) = 2$
   $7x + 3x + 12 = 2$
   $\qquad\quad 10x = -10$
   $\qquad\quad\; x = -1$
   $\qquad\quad\; y = 3$
   $(-1,3)$ is the point.

55. a. Plan started at
   $w = 0$.
   $s = 5(0) + 56$
   $s = \$56$
   b. He adds \$5 each
   week.

56. a. $g = 2.5(0) + 10$
   $g = 10$
   10 points
   b. 2.5 points

57. $12 + 2.5 = 4.8$
   4 tennis balls

58. $(3x^4)(-2x^4y^3)$
   $= -6x^{4+4}y^3$
   $= -6x^8y^3$

59. $m^4 + 12m^2n^2 + 36n^4$
   $= (m^2 + 6n^2)(m^2 + 6n^2)$
   $= (m^2 + 6n^2)^2$

60. $\dfrac{y^2}{x + 2} \div \dfrac{y}{x + 2}$
   $= \dfrac{y^2}{x + 2} \cdot \dfrac{x + 2}{y} = y$

61. $g(x) = 2x - 1$
   $g\left(\dfrac{5}{2}\right) = 2\left(\dfrac{5}{2}\right) - 1$
   $\qquad\quad = 5 - 1$
   $\qquad\quad = 4$

62. $y = 7$

## 10-4   Graphing Linear Equations

PAGES 416–417    CHECKING FOR UNDERSTANDING

1. 2 points

2. If $A = 0$, the line is parallel to the $x$-axis.
   If $B = 0$, the line is parallel to the $y$-axis.

3. Let $y = 0$.
   $4x + 0 = 8$
   $\qquad 4x = 8$
   $\qquad\; x = 2$
   $\qquad (2,0)$
   Let $x = 0$.
   $4(0) + y = 8$
   $\qquad\quad y = 8$
   $\qquad (0,8)$

4. Let $y = 0$.
   $3x + 4(0) = 6$
   $\qquad\quad 3x = 6$
   $\qquad\quad\; x = 2$
   $\qquad\quad (2,0)$
   Let $x = 0$.
   $3(0) + 4y = 6$
   $\qquad\quad 4y = 6$
   $\qquad\quad\; y = \dfrac{6}{4} \text{ or } 1\dfrac{1}{2}$
   $\qquad \left(0, 1\dfrac{1}{2}\right)$

5. Let $y = 0$.
   $2x - 0 = 8$
   $\qquad 2x = 8$
   $\qquad\; x = 4$
   $\qquad (4,0)$
   Let $x = 0$.
   $2(0) - y = 8$
   $\qquad\quad -y = 8$
   $\qquad\quad\; y = -8$
   $\qquad (0,-8)$

175

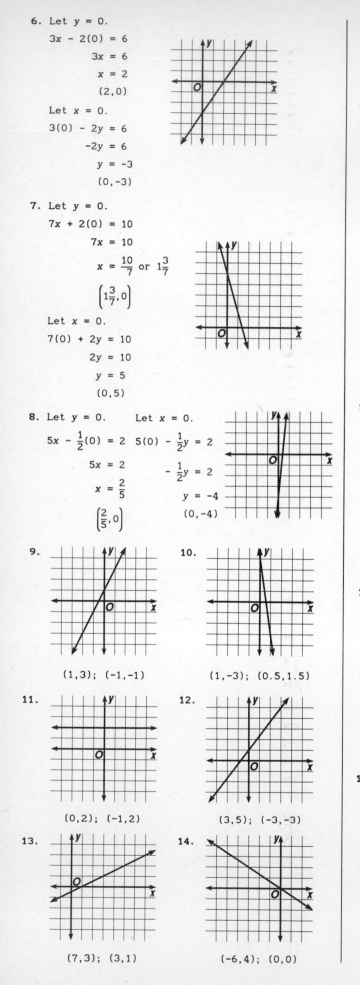

6. Let $y = 0$.

$3x - 2(0) = 6$

$3x = 6$

$x = 2$

$(2,0)$

Let $x = 0$.

$3(0) - 2y = 6$

$-2y = 6$

$y = -3$

$(0,-3)$

7. Let $y = 0$.

$7x + 2(0) = 10$

$7x = 10$

$x = \frac{10}{7}$ or $1\frac{3}{7}$

$\left(1\frac{3}{7}, 0\right)$

Let $x = 0$.

$7(0) + 2y = 10$

$2y = 10$

$y = 5$

$(0,5)$

8. Let $y = 0$.    Let $x = 0$.

$5x - \frac{1}{2}(0) = 2$    $5(0) - \frac{1}{2}y = 2$

$5x = 2$    $-\frac{1}{2}y = 2$

$x = \frac{2}{5}$    $y = -4$

$\left(\frac{2}{5}, 0\right)$    $(0,-4)$

9.

$(1,3); \ (-1,-1)$

10.

$(1,-3); \ (0.5,1.5)$

11.

$(0,2); \ (-1,2)$

12.

$(3,5); \ (-3,-3)$

13.

$(7,3); \ (3,1)$

14.

$(-6,4); \ (0,0)$

15. Let $y = 0$.

$6x - 3(0) = 6$

$6x = 6$

$x = 1$

$x$-intercept at $(1,0)$

Let $x = 0$.

$6(0) - 3y = 6$

$-3y = 6$

$y = -2$

$y$-intercept at $(0,-2)$

16. Let $y = 0$.

$4x + 5(0) = 20$

$4x = 20$

$x = 5$

$x$-intercept at $(5,0)$

Let $x = 0$.

$4(0) + 5y = 20$

$5y = 20$

$y = 4$

$y$-intercept $(0,4)$

17. Let $y = 0$.

$5x - 0 = -10$

$5x = -10$

$x = -2$

$x$-intercept at $(-2,0)$

Let $x = 0$.

$5(0) - y = -10$

$-y = -10$

$y = 10$

$y$-intercept at $(0,10)$

18. Let $y = 0$.

$2x + 5(0) = -10$

$2x = -10$

$x = -5$

$x$-intercept at $(-5,0)$

Let $x = 0$.

$2(0) + 5y = -10$

$5y = -10$

$y = -2$

$y$-intercept at $(0,-2)$

19. Let $y = 0$.

$7x - 2(0) = -7$

$7x = -7$

$x = -1$

$x$-intercept at $(-1,0)$

Let $x = 0$.

$7(0) - 2y = -7$

$-2y = -7$

$y = \frac{7}{2}$

$y$-intercept at $\left(0, \frac{7}{2}\right)$

20. Let $y = 0$.

$0 = 6x - 9$

$9 = 6x$

$x = \frac{9}{6} = \frac{3}{2}$

$x$-intercept at $\left(\frac{3}{2}, 0\right)$

Let $x = 0$.

$y = 6(0) - 9$

$y = -9$

$y$-intercept $(0, -9)$

21. Let $y = 0$.

$x + \frac{1}{2}(0) = 4$

$x = 4$

$x$-intercept at $(4, 0)$

Let $x = 0$.

$0 + \frac{1}{2}y = 4$

$y = 8$

$y$-intercept at $(0, 8)$

22. Let $y = 0$.

$x = 8(0) - 4$

$x = -4$

$x$-intercept at $(-4, 0)$

Let $x = 0$.

$0 = 8y - 4$

$4 = 8y$

$\frac{1}{2} = y$

$y$-intercept $\left(0, \frac{1}{2}\right)$

23. Let $y = 0$.

$\frac{2}{3}(0) = \frac{1}{2}x + 6$

$0 = \frac{1}{2}x + 6$

$-6 = \frac{1}{2}x$

$-12 = x$

$x$-intercept at $(-12, 0)$

Let $x = 0$.

$\frac{2}{3}y = \frac{1}{2}(0) + 6$

$\frac{2}{3}y = 6$

$y = 9$

$y$-intercept $(0, 9)$

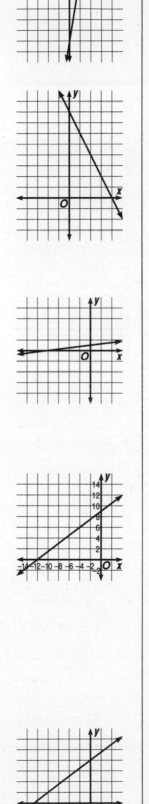

24.

25.

26.

27. $y = 4x + 6$

28. $y = 2x + 3$

29. $y = \frac{2}{3}x + \frac{7}{3}$

30.

31.

32. $y = -\frac{3}{2}x + 8$

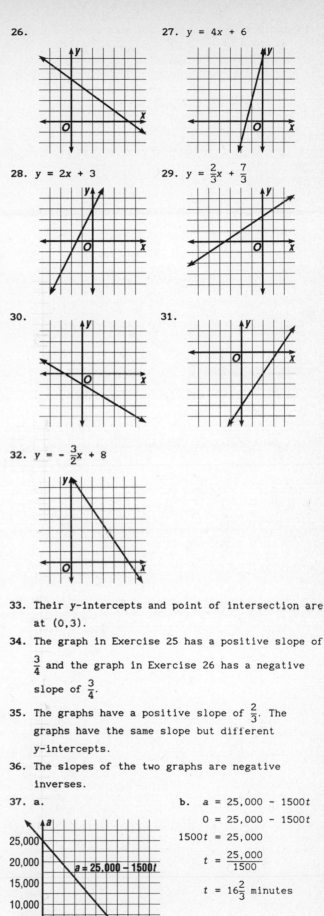

33. Their $y$-intercepts and point of intersection are at $(0, 3)$.

34. The graph in Exercise 25 has a positive slope of $\frac{3}{4}$ and the graph in Exercise 26 has a negative slope of $\frac{3}{4}$.

35. The graphs have a positive slope of $\frac{2}{3}$. The graphs have the same slope but different $y$-intercepts.

36. The slopes of the two graphs are negative inverses.

37. a.

    b. $a = 25,000 - 1500t$

    $0 = 25,000 - 1500t$

    $1500t = 25,000$

    $t = \frac{25,000}{1500}$

    $t = 16\frac{2}{3}$ minutes

$a = 25,000 - 1500t$

**38.**

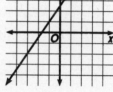

Graph showing line $150c + 300s = 300,000$

**39.** $302 = x + (x - 2)$

$302 = 2x - 2$

$304 = 2x$

$152 = x$, 152 feet

**40.** $(3y + 2)(y - 3)$

$= 3y^2 - 9y + 2y - 6$

$= 3y^2 - 7y - 6$

**41.** 2

**42.** $\dfrac{3a}{2} + \dfrac{5}{4} = \dfrac{5a}{2}$

$4\left(\dfrac{3a}{2} + \dfrac{5}{4}\right) = 4\left(\dfrac{5a}{2}\right)$

$6a + 5 = 10a$

$5 = 4a$

$\dfrac{5}{4} = a$

**43.** Add 10:

$1, 11, 21, 31, 41, 51, 61$

**44.** Let $y = 0$.

$2x + 0 = 6$

$2x = 6$

$x = 3$

$x$-intercept at $(3,0)$

Let $x = 0$.

$2(0) + y = 6$

$y = 6$

$y$-intercept at $(0,6)$

## PAGE 418  MID-CHAPTER REVIEW

**1.** $\dfrac{2 - 6}{5 - 7} = \dfrac{-4}{-2} = 2$

**2.** $\dfrac{1 - 3}{-2 - (-6)} = \dfrac{-2}{4} = -\dfrac{1}{2}$

**3.** $\dfrac{\frac{1}{2} - \frac{3}{4}}{\frac{3}{4} - \frac{1}{2}} = \dfrac{-\frac{1}{4}}{\frac{1}{4}} = -1$

**4.** $y - 2 = \dfrac{3}{4}(x - 8)$

$4(y - 2) = 3(x - 8)$

$4y - 8 = 3x - 24$

$24 - 8 = 3x - 4y$

$16 = 3x - 4y$

$3x - 4y = 16$

**5.** $y - 1 = \dfrac{3}{2}[x - (-6)]$

$2(y - 1) = 3(x + 6)$

$2y - 2 = 3x + 18$

$-2 - 18 = 3x - 2y$

$-20 = 3x - 2y$

$3x - 2y = -20$

**6.** $x = -2$

**7.** $m = \dfrac{1 - 2}{9 - 8} = \dfrac{-1}{1} = -1$

$y - 1 = -1(x - 9)$

$y - 1 = -x + 9$

$x + y = 1 + 9$

$x + y = 10$

**8.** $m = \dfrac{-4 - 5}{5 - 5}$ undefined

$x = 5$

**9.** $m = \dfrac{\frac{3}{4} - \frac{4}{5}}{\frac{1}{2} - \frac{2}{3}} = \dfrac{-\frac{1}{20}}{-\frac{1}{6}} = \dfrac{6}{20} = \dfrac{3}{10}$

$y - \dfrac{3}{4} = \dfrac{3}{10}\left(x - \dfrac{1}{2}\right)$

$10\left(y - \dfrac{3}{4}\right) = 3\left(x - \dfrac{1}{2}\right)$

$10y - \dfrac{15}{2} = 3x - \dfrac{3}{2}$

$-\dfrac{15}{2} + \dfrac{3}{2} = 3x - 10y$

$-6 = 3x - 10y$

$3x - 10y = -6$

**10.** Let $y = 0$.

$5x + 3(0) = 15$

$5x = 15$

$x = 3$

$x$-intercept at $(3,0)$

Let $x = 0$.

$5(0) + 3y = 15$

$y = 5$

$y$-intercept at $(0,5)$

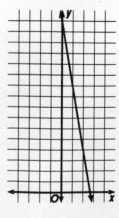

**11.** Let $y = 0$.

$3x - 2(0) = -5$

$3x = -5$

$x = -\dfrac{5}{3}$

$x$-intercept at $\left(-\dfrac{5}{3},0\right)$

Let $x = 0$.

$3(0) - 2y = -5$

$-2y = -5$

$y = \dfrac{5}{2}$

$y$-intercept at $\left(0,\dfrac{5}{2}\right)$

**12.** Let $y = 0$.

$3x + \dfrac{1}{2}(0) = 8$

$3x = 8$

$x = \dfrac{8}{3}$

$x$-intercept at $\left(\dfrac{8}{3},0\right)$

Let $x = 0$.

$3(0) + \dfrac{1}{2}y = 8$

$\dfrac{1}{2}y = 8$

$y = 16$

$y$-intercept at $(0,16)$

13. $3x + 4y = 12$

$4y = -3x + 12$

$y = -\frac{3}{4}x + 3$

slope: $-\frac{3}{4}$

y-intercept: 3

14. $10x - 14y = 21$

$-14y = -10x + 21$

$y = \frac{5}{7}x - \frac{3}{2}$

slope: $\frac{5}{7}$

y-intercept: $-\frac{3}{2}$

15. $5(x + 2) = y - 6x - 4$

$5x + 10 = y - 6x - 4$

$11x + 14 = y$

$y = 11x + 14$

slope: 11

y-intercept: 14

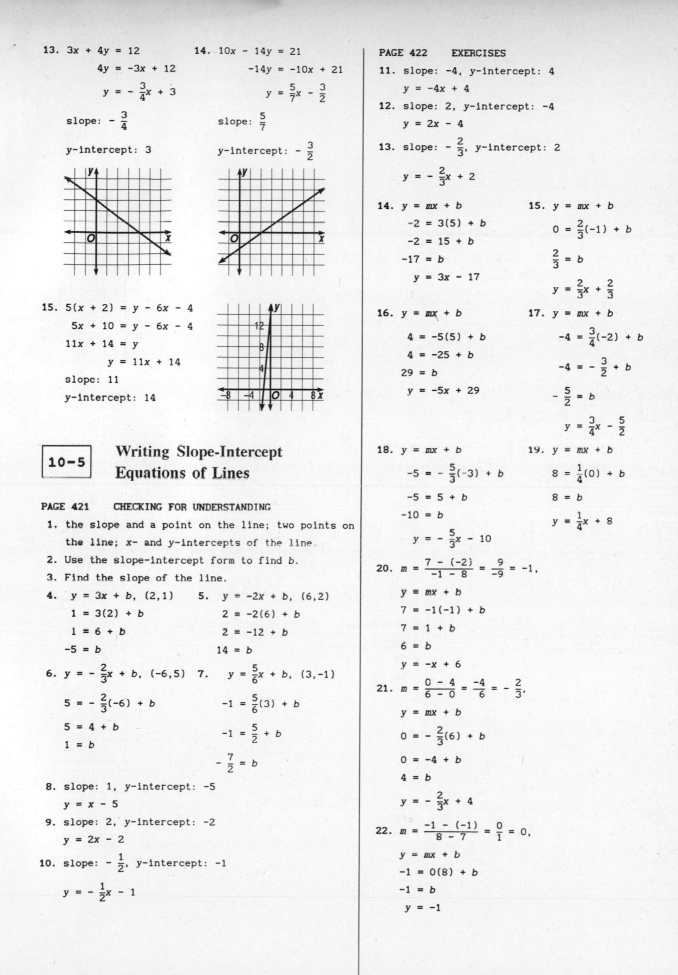

---

## 10-5 Writing Slope-Intercept Equations of Lines

### PAGE 421    CHECKING FOR UNDERSTANDING

1. the slope and a point on the line; two points on the line; x- and y-intercepts of the line.

2. Use the slope-intercept form to find $b$.

3. Find the slope of the line.

4. $y = 3x + b$, $(2,1)$

$1 = 3(2) + b$

$1 = 6 + b$

$-5 = b$

5. $y = -2x + b$, $(6,2)$

$2 = -2(6) + b$

$2 = -12 + b$

$14 = b$

6. $y = -\frac{2}{3}x + b$, $(-6,5)$

$5 = -\frac{2}{3}(-6) + b$

$5 = 4 + b$

$1 = b$

7. $y = \frac{5}{6}x + b$, $(3,-1)$

$-1 = \frac{5}{6}(3) + b$

$-1 = \frac{5}{2} + b$

$-\frac{7}{2} = b$

8. slope: 1, y-intercept: -5

$y = x - 5$

9. slope: 2, y-intercept: -2

$y = 2x - 2$

10. slope: $-\frac{1}{2}$, y-intercept: -1

$y = -\frac{1}{2}x - 1$

### PAGE 422    EXERCISES

11. slope: -4, y-intercept: 4

$y = -4x + 4$

12. slope: 2, y-intercept: -4

$y = 2x - 4$

13. slope: $-\frac{2}{3}$, y-intercept: 2

$y = -\frac{2}{3}x + 2$

14. $y = mx + b$

$-2 = 3(5) + b$

$-2 = 15 + b$

$-17 = b$

$y = 3x - 17$

15. $y = mx + b$

$0 = \frac{2}{3}(-1) + b$

$\frac{2}{3} = b$

$y = \frac{2}{3}x + \frac{2}{3}$

16. $y = mx + b$

$4 = -5(5) + b$

$4 = -25 + b$

$29 = b$

$y = -5x + 29$

17. $y = mx + b$

$-4 = \frac{3}{4}(-2) + b$

$-4 = -\frac{3}{2} + b$

$-\frac{5}{2} = b$

$y = \frac{3}{4}x - \frac{5}{2}$

18. $y = mx + b$

$-5 = -\frac{5}{3}(-3) + b$

$-5 = 5 + b$

$-10 = b$

$y = -\frac{5}{3}x - 10$

19. $y = mx + b$

$8 = \frac{1}{4}(0) + b$

$8 = b$

$y = \frac{1}{4}x + 8$

20. $m = \frac{7 - (-2)}{-1 - 8} = \frac{9}{-9} = -1,$

$y = mx + b$

$7 = -1(-1) + b$

$7 = 1 + b$

$6 = b$

$y = -x + 6$

21. $m = \frac{0 - 4}{6 - 0} = \frac{-4}{6} = -\frac{2}{3},$

$y = mx + b$

$0 = -\frac{2}{3}(6) + b$

$0 = -4 + b$

$4 = b$

$y = -\frac{2}{3}x + 4$

22. $m = \frac{-1 - (-1)}{8 - 7} = \frac{0}{1} = 0,$

$y = mx + b$

$-1 = 0(8) + b$

$-1 = b$

$y = -1$

23. $m = \dfrac{0 - 1}{1 - 0} = \dfrac{-1}{1} = -1$,    24. $m = \dfrac{7 - 6}{5 - (-1)} = \dfrac{1}{6}$,

$\quad y = mx + b$

$\quad 0 = -1(1) + b$

$\quad 0 = -1 + b$

$\quad 1 = b$,

$\quad y = -x + 1$

24. $y = mx + b$

$\quad 7 = \dfrac{1}{6}(5) + b$

$\quad 7 = \dfrac{5}{6} + b$

$\quad \dfrac{37}{6} = b$

$\quad y = \dfrac{1}{6}x + \dfrac{37}{6}$

25. $m = \dfrac{2 - (-5)}{-6 - 3} = \dfrac{7}{-9} = -\dfrac{7}{9}$,

$\quad y = mx + b$

$\quad 2 = -\dfrac{7}{9}(-6) + b$

$\quad 2 = \dfrac{14}{3} + b$

$\quad -\dfrac{8}{3} = b$

$\quad y = -\dfrac{7}{9}x - \dfrac{8}{3}$

26. $m = \dfrac{5.235 - (-1.5)}{4.67 - 0.25} = 1.524$

$\quad 5.235 = 1.524(4.67) + b$

$\quad -1.881 = b$

$\quad y = 1.524x - 1.881$

27. $m = \dfrac{7.198 - (-0.8)}{-3.2 - 12.34} = -0.515x$

$\quad 7.198 = -0.515(-3.2) + b$

$\quad 5.551 = b$

$\quad y = -0.515 + 5.551$

28. $m = \dfrac{2.63 - 12.05}{0.4 - 6.25} = 1.610$

$\quad 2.63 = 1.610(0.4) + b$

$\quad 1.986 = b$

$\quad y = 1.610x + 1.986$

29. $m = \dfrac{-4.08 - (-7.11)}{-2.1 - (-0.2)} = -1.595$

$\quad -4.08 = -1.595(-2.1) + b$

$\quad -7.429 = b$

$\quad y = -1.595x - 7.429$

30. $m = \dfrac{-0.001 - 1.33}{6.27 - 4.33} = -0.686$

$\quad -0.001 = -0.686(6.27) + b$

$\quad 4.301 = b$

$\quad y = -0.686x + 4.301$

31. $m = \dfrac{1.008 - (-11.5)}{18.2 - (-4.3)} = 0.556$

$\quad 1.008 = 0.556(18.2) + b$

$\quad -9.110 = b$

$\quad y = 0.556x - 9.110$

32. $(s, 0)$, $(0, t)$

$\quad y = mx + b$

$\quad 0 = ms + t$

$\quad -\dfrac{t}{s} = m$

$\quad y = -\dfrac{tx}{s} + t$

33. $(3, 65)$, $(6, 115)$

$\quad m = \dfrac{115 - 65}{6 - 3} = \dfrac{50}{3}$

$\quad 65 = \dfrac{50}{3}(3) + b$

$\quad 65 = 50 + b$

$\quad 15 = b$

$\quad d = \dfrac{50}{3}h + 15$

34. $x$ = distance wind carries him,

$\quad y$ = distance he jumps

$\quad m = \dfrac{6400}{580} = 11.03$

$\quad y = 11.03x + 6400$

35. $82,100,000 = 8.21 \times 10^{7}$

36. $36x^{2} - 81y^{4}$

$\quad = 9(4x^{2} - 9y^{4})$

$\quad = 9[(2x)^{2} - (3y^{2})^{2}]$

$\quad = 9(2x - 3y^{2})(2x + 3y^{2})$

37. $\dfrac{a^{2} + 3a - 10}{a^{2} + 8a + 15} \div \dfrac{a^{2} - 6a + 8}{12 + a - a^{2}}$

$\quad = \dfrac{a^{2} + 3a - 10}{a^{2} + 8a + 15} \cdot \dfrac{12 + a - a^{2}}{a^{2} - 6a + 8}$

$\quad = \dfrac{(a - 2)(a + 5)}{(a + 3)(a + 5)} \cdot \dfrac{(-1)(a - 4)(a + 3)}{(a - 4)(a + 2)}$

$\quad = -1$

38. $\{(-2, -13), (-1, -8), (0, -3), (2, 7), (5, 22)\}$

39. Let $y = 0$.

$\quad 2x + 10(0) = 5$

$\quad 2x = 5$

$\quad x = \dfrac{5}{2}$

$x$-intercept at $\left(\dfrac{5}{2}, 0\right)$

Let $x = 0$.

$\quad 2(0) + 10y = 5$

$\quad 10y = 5$

$\quad y = \dfrac{1}{2}$

$y$-intercept at $\left(0, \dfrac{1}{2}\right)$

## 10-6   Parallel and Perpendicular Lines

PAGE 425    CHECKING FOR UNDERSTANDING

1. The slopes are equal.

2. The slopes are negative reciprocals.

3. $y = c$, $c$ is a constant.

4. $x = c$, $c$ is a constant.

5. $y = 5x - 7$    6. $y = -\dfrac{3}{4}x + \dfrac{1}{2}$    7. $y = \dfrac{2}{3}x - 7$

   $5; -\dfrac{1}{5}$        $-\dfrac{3}{4}; \dfrac{4}{3}$        $\dfrac{2}{3}; -\dfrac{3}{2}$

180

8. $y = -7x + 4$   9. $x = 7$       10. $y = 4x + 2$

$-7; \frac{1}{7}$       undefined; 0       $4; -\frac{1}{4}$

11. $y = \frac{2}{3}x + \frac{5}{3}$   12. $y = -4$   13. $y = -x + \frac{4}{3}$

$\frac{2}{3}; -\frac{3}{2}$       0; undefined       $-1; 1$


**PAGE 426     EXERCISES**

14. $-1 = -\frac{3}{5}(0) + b$   15. $0 = \frac{3}{4}(0) + b$

$-1 = b$       $0 = b$

$y = -\frac{3}{5}x - 1$       $y = \frac{3}{4}x$

16. $y = -6x + 4,$   17. $y = -\frac{2}{3}x + \frac{1}{3},$

$3 = -6(-2) + b$       $2 = -\frac{2}{3}(4) + b$

$-9 = b$       $\frac{14}{3} = b$

$y = -6x - 9$       $y = -\frac{2}{3}x + \frac{14}{3}$

18. $y = \frac{5}{2}x - \frac{7}{2},$   19. $y = \frac{4}{3}x - \frac{2}{3},$

$4 = \frac{5}{2}(0) + b$       $0 = \frac{4}{3}(4) + b$

$4 = b$       $-\frac{16}{3} = b$

$y = \frac{5}{2}x + 4$       $y = \frac{4}{3}x - \frac{16}{3}$

20. $-5 = -\frac{1}{3}(2) + b$   21. $y = x$

$-\frac{13}{3} = b$       $-2 = 7 + b$

$-9 = b$

$y = -\frac{1}{3}x - \frac{13}{3}$       $y = x - 9$

22. $y = \frac{5}{3}x - \frac{7}{3}$   23. $y = -\frac{3}{8}x + \frac{1}{2}$

$-2 = -\frac{3}{5}(8) + b$       $4 = \frac{8}{3}(0) + b$

$-2 = -\frac{24}{5} + b$       $4 = b$

$\frac{14}{5} = b$       $y = \frac{8}{3}x + 4$

$y = -\frac{3}{5}x + \frac{14}{5}$

24. $y = 3x - 2$   25. $y = -3x + 7$

$-1 = -\frac{1}{3}(6) + b$       $1 = \frac{1}{3}(-3) + b$

$1 = b$       $2 = b$

$y = -\frac{1}{3}x + 1$       $y = \frac{1}{3}x + 2$

26. $y = 5x - 3$   27. $y = \frac{2}{3}x + 1$

$-1 = -\frac{1}{5}(0) + b$       $0 = -\frac{3}{2}(-3) + b$

$-1 = b$       $-\frac{9}{2} = b$

$y = -\frac{1}{5}x - 1$       $y = -\frac{3}{2}x - \frac{9}{2}$

28. $y = -\frac{5}{9}x + \frac{1}{3}$   29. $y = 2x - 7$

$0 = \frac{9}{5}(0) + b$       $-6 = -\frac{1}{2}(4) + b$

$0 = b$       $-4 = b$

$y = \frac{9}{5}x$       $y = -\frac{1}{2}x - 4$

30. Rewrite the equation in slope-intercept form.

$y = -\frac{5}{8}x + \frac{3}{8}, \; y = -\frac{5}{8}x + \frac{6}{8}$

The point in between each $y$-intercept is $\frac{4.5}{8}$.

$y = -\frac{5}{8}x + \frac{4.5}{8}$ or $5x + 8y = \frac{9}{2}$

31. Let $x$ = the price of pizza,

$y$ = the price of soda.

$52x + 28y = 518$

$28y = -52x + 518$

$y = -\frac{52}{28}x + \frac{518}{28}$

$y = -1.86x + 18.5$

$32x + 21y = 396$

$21y = -32x + 396$

$y = -\frac{32}{21}x + \frac{396}{21}$

$y = -1.52x + 18.9$

No, because the unequal slopes mean that the lines are not parallel.

32. Let $x$ = the price of lemonade,

$y$ = the price of fruit punch.

$1200x + 500y = 1650$

$500y = -1200x + 1650$

$y = -2.4x + 3.3$

$1800x + 750y = 2475$

$750y = -1800x + 2475$

$y = -2.4x + 3.3$

Yes, because each graph is on the same line.

33. $\frac{3}{4} = 75\%$

34. $(4x^3 - 3y^2)(4x^3 - 3y^2)$

$= 16x^6 - 12x^3y^2 - 12x^3y^2 + 9y^4$

$= 16x^6 - 24x^3y^2 + 9y^4$

35. $T = 5.$ $W = 4$, $E = 6$, $N = 2$ or 7, $Y = 0$, $H = 9$, $I = 3$, $R = 7$ or 2, $S = 1$, $V = 8$

36. $\dfrac{x^2 - 49}{x^2 - 2x - 35} = \dfrac{(x - 7)(x + 7)}{(x - 7)(x + 5)} = \dfrac{(x + 7)}{(x + 5)}$

37. yes

# Technology:  Graphing Linear Equations

PAGE 427     EXERCISES

1 a-e.

| Enter | Result |
|-------|--------|
| $2x + 3y = -12$ | $2x + 3y = -12$ |
| gra 2 | graphs the line |
| $2x + 3y = -6$ | $2x + 3y = -6$ |
| gra 2 | graphs the line |
| $2x + 3y = 0$ | $2x + 3y = 0$ |
| gra 2 | graphs the line |
| $2x + 3y = 6$ | $2x + 3y = 6$ |
| gra 2 | graphs the line |
| $2x + 3y = 12$ | $2x + 3y = 12$ |
| gra 2 | graphs the line |

f. As the value of $C$ increases, the slope remains the same and the $x$- and $y$-intercepts both increase.

2 a-f.

| Enter | Result |
|-------|--------|
| Clear F | removes previous graphs |
| $-4x + 3y = 12$ | $-4x + 3y = 12$ |
| gra 2 | graphs the line |
| $-2x + 3y = 12$ | $-2x + 3y = 12$ |
| gra 2 | graphs the line |
| $-x + 3y = 12$ | $-x + 3y = 12$ |
| gra 2 | graphs the line |
| $x + 3y = 12$ | $x + 3y = 12$ |
| gra 2 | graphs the line |
| $2x + 3y = 12$ | $2x + 3y = 12$ |
| gra 2 | graphs the line |
| $4x + 3y = 12$ | $4x + 3y = 12$ |
| gra 2 | graphs the line |

g. As the value of $A$ increases, the slope decreases and the $y$-intercept remains the same. The $x$-intercept decreases until $A$ changes from positive to negative. Then it changes from negative to positive and continues decreasing.

3 a-f.

| Enter | Result |
|-------|--------|
| Clear F | removes previous graph |
| $2x - 6y = 12$ | $2x - 6y = 12$ |
| gra 2 | graphs the line |
| $2x - 3y = 12$ | $2x - 3y = 12$ |
| gra 2 | graphs the line |
| $2x - y = 12$ | $2x - y = 12$ |
| gra 2 | graphs the line |
| $2x + y = 12$ | $2x + y = 12$ |
| gra 2 | graphs the line |
| $2x + 3y = 12$ | $2x + 3y = 12$ |
| gra 2 | graphs the line |
| $2x + 6y = 12$ | $2x + 6y = 12$ |
| gra 2 | graphs the line |

g. As the value of $B$ increases, the $x$-intercept remains the same. The slope increases and the $y$-intercept decreases until $B$ changes from positive to negative and continues increasing, and the $y$-intercept changes from negative to positive and continues decreasing.

## 10-7  Midpoint of a Line Segment

PAGE 429     CHECKING FOR UNDERSTANDING

1. Find the average of the coordinates of the two points.

2. Find the average of the $x$-coordinates and $y$-coordinates of the two endpoints of the line segment.

3. $\dfrac{4 + 8}{2} = \dfrac{12}{2} = 6$

4. $\dfrac{-2 + 6}{2} = \dfrac{4}{2} = 2$

5. $\dfrac{-3 + 13}{2} = \dfrac{10}{2} = 5$

6. $\dfrac{-4 + (-10)}{2} = \dfrac{-14}{2} = -7$

7. $\dfrac{-3 + 6}{2} = \dfrac{3}{2}$

8. $\dfrac{-10 + 15}{2} = \dfrac{5}{2}$

9. $\left(\dfrac{1 + 3}{2}, \dfrac{1 + 3}{2}\right) = (2,2)$

10. $\left(\dfrac{3 + 8}{2}, \dfrac{6 + (-4)}{2}\right) = \left(5\frac{1}{2}, 1\right)$

11. $\left(\dfrac{6 + 8}{2}, \dfrac{4 + 5}{2}\right) = (7, 4.5)$

12. $\left(\dfrac{-1 + (-5)}{2}, \dfrac{5 + 7}{2}\right) = (-3, 6)$

13. $\left(\dfrac{-5 + 3}{2}, \dfrac{1 + (-3)}{2}\right) = (-1, -1)$

14. $\left(\dfrac{-7 + 1}{2}, \dfrac{-4 + (-5)}{2}\right) = (-3, -4)$

15. $\left(\dfrac{-2 + (-2)}{2}, \dfrac{1 + 6}{2}\right) = (-2, 3.5)$

16. $\left(\dfrac{2 + 5}{2}, \dfrac{-4 + (-5)}{2}\right) = (3.5, -4.5)$

PAGES 430-431     EXERCISES

17. $\left(\dfrac{8 + 12}{2}, \dfrac{4 + 2}{2}\right) = (10, 3)$

18. $\left(\dfrac{9 + 17}{2}, \dfrac{5 + 3}{2}\right) = (13, 4)$

19. $\left(\dfrac{17 + 11}{2}, \dfrac{9 + (-3)}{2}\right) = (14, 3)$

20. $\left(\dfrac{19 + 11}{2}, \dfrac{-3 + 5}{2}\right) = (15, 1)$

21. $\left(\dfrac{4 + 8}{2}, \dfrac{2 + (-6)}{2}\right) = (6, -2)$

22. $\left(\dfrac{-6 + 8}{2}, \dfrac{5 + (-11)}{2}\right) = (1, -3)$

23. $\left(\dfrac{5 + 7}{2}, \dfrac{-2 + 3}{2}\right) = \left(6, \frac{1}{2}\right)$

24. $\left(\dfrac{-11 + 13}{2}, \dfrac{6 + 4}{2}\right) = (1, 5)$

25. $\left(\dfrac{9 + (-8)}{2}, \dfrac{10 + 4}{2}\right) = \left(\dfrac{1}{2}, 7\right)$

26. $\left(\dfrac{x + a}{2}, \dfrac{y + b}{2}\right)$

27. $\left(\dfrac{2x + 6x}{2}, \dfrac{3y + y}{2}\right) = (4x, 2y)$

28. $\left(\dfrac{\frac{5}{6} + \frac{1}{6}}{2}, \dfrac{\frac{1}{3} + \frac{1}{3}}{2}\right) = \left(\dfrac{1}{2}, \dfrac{1}{3}\right)$

29. $\left(\dfrac{3 + x}{2}, \dfrac{5 + y}{2}\right) = (11, 7)$

$\dfrac{3 + x}{2} = 11 \qquad \dfrac{5 + y}{2} = 7$

$3 + x = 22 \qquad 5 + y = 14$

$x = 19 \qquad\quad y = 9$

$B(19, 9)$

30. $\left(\dfrac{3 + x}{2}, \dfrac{5 + y}{2}\right) = (5, -7)$

$\dfrac{3 + x}{2} = 5 \qquad \dfrac{5 + y}{2} = -7$

$3 + x = 10 \qquad 5 + y = -14$

$x = 7 \qquad\quad y = -19$

$B(7, -19)$

31. $\left(\dfrac{5 + (-7)}{2}, \dfrac{9 + 3}{2}\right) = (-1, 6)$

$P(-1, 6)$

32. $\left(\dfrac{x + 11}{2}, \dfrac{y + (-4)}{2}\right) = (3, 8)$

$\dfrac{x + 11}{2} = 3 \qquad \dfrac{y + (-4)}{2} = 8$

$x + 11 = 6 \qquad y - 4 = 16$

$x = -5 \qquad\quad y = 20$

$A(-5, 20)$

33. $\left(\dfrac{x + 5}{2}, \dfrac{y + 3}{2}\right) = (9, 7)$

$\dfrac{x + 5}{2} = 9 \qquad\qquad \dfrac{y + 3}{2} = 7$

$x + 5 = 18 \qquad\quad y + 3 = 14$

$x = 13 \qquad\qquad y = 11$

$A(13, 11)$

34. $\left(\dfrac{11 + 5}{2}, \dfrac{-6 + (-9)}{2}\right) = \left(8, -\dfrac{15}{2}\right)$

$P\left(8, -\dfrac{15}{2}\right)$

35. $\left(\dfrac{4 + x}{2}, \dfrac{-11 + y}{2}\right) = (5, -9)$

$\dfrac{4 + x}{2} = 5 \qquad \dfrac{-11 + y}{2} = -9$

$4 + x = 10 \qquad -11 + y = -18$

$x = 6 \qquad\qquad y = -7$

$B(6, -7)$

36. $\left(\dfrac{x + (-4)}{2}, \dfrac{y + 1}{2}\right) = (3, 9)$

$\dfrac{x + (-4)}{2} = 3 \qquad \dfrac{y + 1}{2} = 9$

$x - 4 = 6 \qquad\quad y + 1 = 18$

$x = 10 \qquad\qquad y = 17$

$A(10, 17)$

37. $\left(\dfrac{4 + (-8)}{2}, \dfrac{-7 + 1}{2}\right) = (-2, -3)$

$P(-2, -3)$

38. $\left(\dfrac{7 + x}{2}, \dfrac{4 + y}{2}\right) = (9, -3)$

$\dfrac{7 + x}{2} = 9 \qquad \dfrac{4 + y}{2} = -3$

$7 + x = 18 \qquad 4 + y = -6$

$x = 11 \qquad\quad y = -10$

$B(11, -10)$

39. $\left(\dfrac{-3 + x}{2}, \dfrac{8 + y}{2}\right) = (3, -5)$

$\dfrac{-3 + x}{2} = 3 \qquad \dfrac{8 + y}{2} = -5$

$-3 + x = 6 \qquad 8 + y = -10$

$x = 9 \qquad\quad y = -18$

$B(9, -18)$

40. $\left(\dfrac{x + 5}{2}, \dfrac{y + 7}{2}\right) = (5, 6)$

$\dfrac{x + 5}{2} = 5 \qquad \dfrac{y + 7}{2} = 6$

$x + 5 = 10 \qquad y + 7 = 12$

$x = 5 \qquad\quad y = 5$

$A(5, 5)$

41. $\left(\dfrac{8 + 4}{2}, \dfrac{-2 + (-6)}{2}\right) = (6, -4)$

42. $\left(\dfrac{8 + x}{2}, \dfrac{3 + y}{2}\right) = (3, -2)$

$\dfrac{8 + x}{2} = 3 \qquad \dfrac{3 + y}{2} = -2$

$8 + x = 6 \qquad 3 + y = -4$

$x = -2 \qquad\quad y = -7$

$(2, 7)$

43. $P = A + \dfrac{1}{4}(B - A)$

$P = (8, 4) + \dfrac{1}{4}(12 - 8, 12 - 4)$

$P = (8, 4) = \dfrac{1}{4}(4, 8)$

$P = (8, 4) + (1, 2)$

$P = (9, 6)$

44. $P = A + \dfrac{1}{4}(B - A)$

$P = (-3, 9) + \dfrac{1}{4}(5 - (-3), 1 - 9)$

$P = (-3, 9) + \dfrac{1}{4}(8, -8)$

$P = (-3, 9) + (2, -2)$

$P = (-1, 7)$

45. $P = A + \dfrac{1}{4}(B - A)$

$P = (-3, 2) + \dfrac{1}{4}(5 - (-3), 4 - 2)$

$P = (-3, 2) + \dfrac{1}{4}(8, 2)$

$P = (-3, 2) + \left(2, \dfrac{1}{2}\right)$

$P = \left(-1, \dfrac{5}{2}\right)$

**46.** $P = A + \frac{1}{4}(B - A)$

$= (2, -6) + \frac{1}{4}[9 - 2, 5 - (-6)]$

$= (2, -6) + \frac{1}{4}(7, 11)$

$= (2, -6) + \left(\frac{7}{4}, \frac{11}{4}\right)$

$= \left(\frac{15}{4}, -\frac{13}{4}\right)$

**47.** The diagonals bisect each other if the midpoint of $AC$ equals the midpoint of $BD$.

midpoint$_{AC} = \left(\frac{-2 + 3}{2}, \frac{6 + 8}{2}\right)$

$= \left(\frac{1}{2}, 7\right)$

midpoint$_{BD} = \left(\frac{2 + (-1)}{2}, \frac{11 + 3}{2}\right)$

$= \left(\frac{1}{2}, 7\right)$

The midpoints are equal; therefore, the diagonals bisect each other.

**48.** midpoint$_{AC} = \left(\frac{11 + (-2)}{2}, \frac{6 + 4}{2}\right)$

$= \left(\frac{9}{2}, 5\right)$

midpoint$_{BD} = \left(\frac{1 + 3}{2}, \frac{-2 + 8}{2}\right)$

$= (2, 3)$

The midpoints are not equal; therefore, the diagonals do not bisect each other.

**49.** a. yes
b. no
c. no
d. no

**50.** Add line 75,
75 PRINT (D - B)/(C - A)

**51.** $m = \left(\frac{-6 + 7}{2}, \frac{-1 + 5}{2}\right)$
$m = \left(\frac{1}{2}, 2\right)$

**52.** $m = \left(\frac{5 + 1}{2}, \frac{-1 + (-3)}{2}\right)$
$m = (3, -2)$

**53.** $m = \left(\frac{3 + 6}{2}, \frac{3 + (-4)}{2}\right)$
$m = \left(\frac{9}{2}, -\frac{1}{2}\right)$

**54.** $m = \left(\frac{7 + 5}{2}, \frac{5 + (-1)}{2}\right)$
$m = (6, 2)$

**55.** $m = \left(\frac{1 + 7}{2}, \frac{-3 + 5}{2}\right)$
$m = (4, 1)$

**56.** $m = \left(\frac{6 + 1}{2}, \frac{-4 + (-3)}{2}\right)$
$m = \left(\frac{7}{2}, -\frac{7}{2}\right)$

**57.** $m = \left(\frac{3 + (-6)}{2}, \frac{3 + (-1)}{2}\right)$
$m = \left(-\frac{3}{2}, 1\right)$

**58.** $m = \left(\frac{7 + 3}{2}, \frac{5 + 3}{2}\right)$
$m = (5, 4)$

**59.** $3y + 7 \leq 4y + 8$
$3y - 3y + 7 \leq 4y - 3y + 8$
$7 \leq y + 8$
$7 - 8 \leq y + 8 - 8$
$-1 \leq y$
$\{y \mid y \geq -1\}$

**60.** $(7y + 9x) - (6x + 5y)$
$= (9x + 7y - 6x - 5y)$
$= (9x - 6x) + (7y - 5y)$
$= 3x + 2y$

**61.** $5x^2 + 20y^2$
$= 5(x^2 + 4y^2)$

**62.** 10 ways

**63.**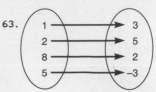

## Problem-Solving Strategy: Use a Graph

**PAGES 432-433     CHECKING FOR UNDERSTANDING**

**1.** b. circle graph
**2.** d. line graph
**3.** a. bar graph and c. comparative graph
**4.** e. pictograph
**5.** c. comparative graph
**6.** decrease
**7.** over 65

**8.** In 1960, 55% of 200 million were in the 18-64 age group.

$200,000,000 \cdot 0.55 = 110,000,000$

In 1990, 61.7% of 250 million were in the 18-64 age group.

$250,000,000 \cdot 0.617 = 154,250,000$

There were $154,250,000 - 110,000,000$ or $44,250,000$ more people in the 18-64 age group in 1990.

**PAGE 433     EXERCISES**

**9.** $A + B + D = 2400$

$A - 200 = D$

$B - 200 = A$

$B - 400 = D$

$(B - 200) + B + (B - 400) = 2400$

$3B - 600 = 2400$

$3B = 3000$

$B = 1000$

$A = 800$

$D = 600$

$C + E + F = 5400 - 2400 = 3000$

$C = \frac{1}{2}?$

$E = ?$

$F = 2 \cdot ?$

Plug in different values for "?" to find who is married to whom.

$\frac{1}{2}(800) + 600 + 2(1000) = 3000$

So Carl is married to Ana, Betty is married to Frank, Daisy is married to Ed.

**10.** 25, 39, 77

Find the number of different routes to each point on the grid and add together. There are 126 routes.

## Chapter 10    Summary and Review

PAGES 434–436    SKILLS AND CONCEPTS

1. $m = \dfrac{5 - 3}{2 - 8} = \dfrac{2}{-6} = -\dfrac{1}{3}$

2. $m = \dfrac{9 - 5}{-2 - (-2)} = \dfrac{4}{0}$, none

3. $m = \dfrac{-1 - (-5)}{9 - (-3)} = \dfrac{4}{12} = \dfrac{1}{3}$

4. $m = \dfrac{4 - 6}{-8 - (-3)} = \dfrac{-2}{-5} = \dfrac{2}{5}$

5. $m = \dfrac{-6 - (-1)}{14 - 11} = -\dfrac{5}{3}$

6. $m = \dfrac{5 - 5}{9 - (-2)} = \dfrac{0}{11} = 0$

$y - 5 = 0[x - (-2)]$

$y - 5 = 0$

$y = 5$

7. $m = \dfrac{0 - 5}{-2 - 0} = \dfrac{5}{2}$

$y - 5 = \dfrac{5}{2}(x - 0)$

$y - 5 = \dfrac{5}{2}x$

$2y - 10 = 5x$

$-5x + 2y = 10$ or

$5x - 2y = -10$

8. $m = \dfrac{-6 - 0}{0 - (-3)} = -2$

$y - 0 = -2[x - (-3)]$

$y = -2x - 6$

$2x + y = -6$

9. $m = \dfrac{2 - 2}{-7 - 4} - 0$

$y - 2 = 0(x - 4)$

$y - 2 = 0$

$y = 2$

10. $m = \dfrac{\frac{2}{7} - \frac{2}{3}}{-2 - (-2)} = \dfrac{\frac{-8}{21}}{0}$ none

$x = -2$

11. $y = \dfrac{1}{4}x + 3$

slope $= \dfrac{1}{4}$; y-intercept $= 3$

12. $8x + y = 4$

$y = -8x + 4$

slope $= -8$; y-intercept $= 4$

13. $x = 2y - 7$

$2y = x + 7$

$y = \dfrac{1}{2}x + \dfrac{7}{2}$

slope $= \dfrac{1}{2}$; y-intercept $= \dfrac{7}{2}$

14. $14x + 20y = 10$

$20y = -14x + 10$

$y = -\dfrac{7}{10}x + \dfrac{1}{2}$

slope $= -\dfrac{7}{10}$; y-intercept $= \dfrac{1}{2}$

15. $\dfrac{1}{2}x + \dfrac{1}{4}y = 3$

$\dfrac{1}{4}y = -\dfrac{1}{2}x + 3$

$y = -2x + 12$

slope $= -2$, y-intercept $= 12$

16. $3x + 4(0) = 15$          $3(0) + 4y = 15$

$3x = 15$                    $4y = 15$

$x = 5$                      $y = \dfrac{15}{4}$

x-intercept $= 5$

y-intercept $= \dfrac{15}{4}$

17. $8x + 0 = 4$          $8(0) + y = 4$

$8x = 4$                $y = 4$

$x = \dfrac{1}{2}$      y-intercept $= 4$

x-intercept $= \dfrac{1}{2}$

18. $6x + 2(0) = 3$          $6(0) + 2y = 3$

$6x = 3$                    $2y = 3$

$x = \dfrac{1}{2}$          $y = \dfrac{3}{2}$

x-intercept $= \dfrac{1}{2}$      y-intercept $= \dfrac{3}{2}$

19. $\dfrac{1}{2}x - \dfrac{3}{2}(0) = 4$          $\dfrac{1}{2}(0) - \dfrac{3}{2}y = 4$

$\dfrac{1}{2}x = 4$                    $-\dfrac{3}{2}y = 4$

$x - 8$                          $y - \dfrac{8}{3}$

x-intercept $= 8$

y-intercept $= -\dfrac{8}{3}$

20. $2.2x + 0.5(0) = 1.1$          $2.2(0) + 0.5y = 1.1$

$2.2x = 1.1$                      $0.5y = 1.1$

$x = 0.5$                          $y = \dfrac{1.1}{0.5} = 2.2$

x-intercept $= 0.5$

y-intercept $= 2.2$

21. $3x - 0 = 9$

$3x = 9$

$x = 3,$

x-intercept $= 3$

$3(0) - y = 9$

$y = 9,$

y-intercept $= 9$

22. $5x + 2(0) = 12$

$5x = 12$

$x = \dfrac{12}{5}$

x-intercept $= \dfrac{12}{5}$

$5(0) + 2y = 12$

$2y = 12$

$y = 6$

y-intercept $= 6$

185

**23.** $y = \frac{2}{3}x + 4$

slope = $\frac{2}{3}$; $y$-intercept = 4

**24.** $y = -\frac{3}{2}x - 6$

slope = $-\frac{3}{2}$;

$y$-intercept = -6

**25.** $y = mx + b$

$-2 = 4(6) + b$

$-2 = 24 + b$

$-26 = b$

$y = 4x - 26$

**26.** $m = \frac{-4 - 5}{-3 - 9} = \frac{-9}{-12} = \frac{3}{4}$

$y = mx + b$

$5 = \frac{3}{4}(9) + b$

$5 = \frac{27}{4} + b$

$-\frac{7}{4} = b$

$y = \frac{3}{4}x - \frac{7}{4}$

**27.** $y = mx + b$

$2 = m(2) + 7$

$2 = 2m + 7$

$-5 = 2m$

$-\frac{5}{2} = m$

$y = -\frac{5}{2}x + 7$

**28.** $y = -\frac{3}{5}x + 3$

**29.** $4x - y = 7$      $y = mx + b$

$y = 4x - 7$      $-1 = 4(2) + b$

$m = 4$      $-9 = b$

$y = 4x - 9$

**30.** $3x + 9y = 1$      $y = mx + b$

$9y = -3x + 1$      $0 = -\frac{1}{3}(3) + b$

$y = -\frac{1}{3}x + \frac{1}{9}$      $1 = b$

$m = -\frac{1}{3}$      $y = -\frac{1}{3}x + 1$

**31.** $2x - 7y = 1$      $y = mx + b$

$-7y = -2x + 1$      $0 = -\frac{7}{2}x\,(-4) + b$

$y = \frac{2}{7}x - \frac{1}{7}$      $-14 = b$

$m = -\frac{7}{2}$      $y = -\frac{7}{2}x - 14$

**32.** $8x - 3y = 7$      $y = mx + b$

$-3y = -8x + 7$      $5 = -\frac{3}{8}(4) + b$

$y = \frac{8}{3}x - \frac{7}{3}$      $\frac{13}{2} = b$

$m = -\frac{3}{8}$      $y = -\frac{3}{8}x + \frac{13}{2}$

**33.** $(x,y) = \left(\frac{3 + 9}{2}, \frac{5 + (-3)}{2}\right)$

$= (6,1)$

**34.** $(x,y) = \left(\frac{14 + 2}{2}, \frac{4 + 0}{2}\right)$

$= (8,2)$

**35.** $(x,y) = \left(\frac{-6 + 8}{2}, \frac{6 + (-11)}{2}\right)$

$= \left(1, -\frac{5}{2}\right)$

**36.** $(x,y) = \left(\frac{2 + 8}{2}, \frac{7 + 4}{2}\right)$

$= \left(5, \frac{11}{2}\right)$

**37.** $(x,y) = \left(\frac{2 + 4}{2}, \frac{5 + 1}{2}\right)$

$= (3,3)$

**PAGE 436      APPLICATIONS AND CONNECTIONS**

**38.** $\frac{60}{250} \leq 0.33$ is true

because the slope,

$\frac{60}{250} = 0.24$. The

hill meets the

requirement.

**39.** $y = mx + b$

Let $x$ = time and

let $y$ = distance.

$y = 45(x - 2) + 80$

$y = 45x - 10$

**40.** highest at $(6,7)$ and

lowest at $(8,4)$

$(x,y) = \left(\frac{6 + 8}{2}, \frac{7 + 4}{2}\right)$

$(x,y) = \left(7, \frac{11}{2}\right)$

Midpoint is at $\frac{11}{2}$ or $5.50.

# Chapter 10    Test

**PAGE 437**

**1.** $m = \frac{-4 - 2}{3 - 9} = \frac{-6}{-6} = 1$

**2.** $m = \frac{1 - 3}{8 - 8} = \frac{-2}{0}$ undefined

**3.** $x - 8y = 3$

$-8y = -x + 3$

$y = \frac{1}{8}x - \frac{3}{8}$

slope = $\frac{1}{8}$; $y$-intercept = $-\frac{3}{8}$

**4.** $3x - 2y = 9$

$-2y = -3x + 9$

$y = \frac{3}{2}x - \frac{9}{2}$

slope = $\frac{3}{2}$; $y$-intercept = $-\frac{9}{2}$

**5.** $\frac{1}{2}x + \frac{3}{4}y = 2$

$\frac{3}{4}y = -\frac{1}{2}x + 2$

$y = -\frac{2}{3}x + \frac{8}{3}$

slope = $-\frac{2}{3}$; $y$-intercept = $\frac{8}{3}$

**6.** $y = 7$

slope = 0;

$y$-intercept = 7

7. $m = \dfrac{-3 - 5}{8 - 2} = \dfrac{-8}{6} = -\dfrac{4}{3}$

$y - y_1 = m(x - x_1)$

$y - 5 = -\dfrac{4}{3}(x - 2)$

$3y - 15 = -4(x - 2)$

$3y - 15 = -4x + 8$

$4x + 3y = 8 + 15$

$4x + 3y = 23$

8. $m = \dfrac{-4 - (-1)}{6 - (-2)} = -\dfrac{3}{8}$

$y - y_1 = m(x - x_1)$

$y - (-1) = -\dfrac{3}{8}[x - (-2)]$

$y - 1 = -\dfrac{3}{8}(x + 2)$

$8y + 8 = -3(x + 2)$

$8y + 8 = -3x - 6$

$3x + 8y = -6 - 8$

$3x + 8y = -14$

9. $y = mx + b$

$y = 2x + 3$

$2x - y = -3$

10. $y = mx + b$

$y = mx - 4$

$-3 = m(5) - 4$

$1 = 5m$

$m = \dfrac{1}{5}$

$y = \dfrac{1}{5}x - 4$

$5y = x - 20$

$x - 5y = 20$

11. $y = mx + b$

$-2 = \dfrac{3}{4}(6) + b$

$-2 = \dfrac{9}{2} + b$

$-\dfrac{13}{2} = b$

$y = \dfrac{3}{4}x - \dfrac{13}{2}$

$4y = 3x - 26$

$3x - 4y = 26$

12. $y = mx + b$

$m = \dfrac{0 - (-2)}{0 - 4} = -\dfrac{1}{2}$

$-2 = -\dfrac{1}{2}(4) + b$

$-2 = -2 + b$

$0 = b$

$y = -\dfrac{1}{2}x$

13. $y = mx + b$

$m = \dfrac{-3 - (-5)}{8 - (-2)} = \dfrac{2}{10} = \dfrac{1}{5}$

$-5 = \dfrac{1}{5}(-2) + b$

$-5 = -\dfrac{2}{5} + b$

$-\dfrac{23}{5} = b$

$y = \dfrac{1}{5}x - \dfrac{23}{5}$

14. $y = mx + b$

$4 = m(6) - 2$

$6 = 6m$

$1 = m$

$y = x - 2$

15. $y = mx + b$

$y = -\dfrac{2}{3}x + 5$

16. $y = mx + b$

$-4 = 6(-3) + b$

$14 = b$

$y = 6x + 14$

17. $6x - y = 7$

$y = 6x - 7$

$m = 6$

$y = mx + b$

$8 = 6(-2) + b$

$20 = b$

$y = 6x + 20$

18. $3x + 7y = 4$

$7y = -3x + 4$

$y = -\dfrac{3}{7}x + \dfrac{4}{7}$

$m = -\dfrac{3}{7}$

$y = mx + b$

$-2 = -\dfrac{3}{7}(5) + b$

$\dfrac{1}{7} = b$

$y = -\dfrac{3}{7}x + \dfrac{1}{7}$

19. $5x - 3y = 9$

$-3y = -5x + 9$

$y = \dfrac{5}{3}x - 3$

$m = -\dfrac{3}{5}$

$y = mx + b$

$0 = -\dfrac{3}{5}(0) + b$

$0 = b$

$y = -\dfrac{3}{5}x$

20. $x + 3y = 7$

$3y = -x + 7$

$y = -\dfrac{1}{3}x + \dfrac{7}{3}$

$m = 3$

$y = mx + b$

$2 = 3(5) + b$

$-13 = b$

$y = 3x - 13$

21. $(x, y) = \left( \dfrac{9 + 3}{2}, \dfrac{3 + 6}{2} \right)$

$= \left( 6, \dfrac{9}{2} \right)$

22. $(x, y) = \left( \dfrac{-2 + 6}{2}, \dfrac{-7 + (-5)}{2} \right)$

$= (2, -6)$

23. $4x - 3(0) = 24$

$4x = 24$

$x = 6$

$x\text{-intercept} = 6$

$4(0) - 3y = 24$

$-3y = 24$

$y = -8$

$y\text{-intercept} = -8$

24. $2x + 7(0) = 16$

$2x = 16$

$x = 8$

$x\text{-intercept} = 8$

$2(0) + 7y = 16$

$y = \dfrac{16}{7}$

$y\text{-intercept} = \dfrac{16}{7}$

25. $m = \dfrac{14}{6} = \dfrac{7}{3}$

PAGE 437   BONUS

$(x, y) = \left( \dfrac{8 + 2}{2}, \dfrac{6 + (-2)}{2} \right)$

$(x, y) = (5, 2)$

$(5, 2)$ is the point at the center of the circle;

From the graph, other points are

$(5, 7)$, $(5, -3)$, $(2, 6)$,

$(8, 2)$, and $(9, 5)$.

# Chapter 11 Systems of Open Sentences

## Problem-Solving Strategy: Hidden Assumptions

PAGES 440-441 CHECKING FOR UNDERSTANDING

1. The problem asks what happened to the other $3.

2. The problem did not say that the total room charge plus the bellhop's tip should be equal to $65.

3. room charge - bellhop's "tip" = $60

4. Answers may vary. Sample answers:
There could be two skiers each skiing on one ski; The skier may have fallen off the skis and the skis came down the hill by themselves; One person skied down the hill twice on one ski; One "track" may be from one skier with two skis, and skiers, each on two skis, skied down the hill; Two skiers on "surf skis" came down the hill.

PAGE 441 EXERCISES

5. If you look at the 97% who do not wear one ring, half wear two rings and half wear no rings. To find the number of rings worn, double the number of students wearing two rings, or double half of the 97%. You wind up with the same number of rings as students. The other 3% wear one ring, so the total number of rings is the same as the total number of students, or 2100 rings.

6. 25 cents - 10 cents = 15 cents. Fifteen cents can be broken up into fifteen pennies, ten pennies and one nickel, five pennies and one dime, five pennies and two nickels, three nickels, or one nickel and one dime. Therefore, the quarter can be changed in 6 ways.

7. The numbers 1-9 need one number each; the numbers 10-99 need two numbers; the numbers 100-999 need three numbers each; and the numbers 1000-1037 need four numbers each. So

$$1-9 \longrightarrow 9 \text{ digits;}$$
$$10-99 \longrightarrow 90 \text{ numbers} \times 2 = 180 \text{ digits;}$$
$$100-999 \longrightarrow 900 \text{ numbers} \times 3 = 2700 \text{ digits;}$$
$$1000-1037 \longrightarrow 38 \text{ numbers} \times 4 = 152 \text{ digits;}$$
$$9 + 180 + 2700 + 152 = 3041 \text{ digits}$$

8. To find the number of rungs above the middle rung, add 3 - 5 + 7 + 6 = 11. So there are 11 rungs above the middle and also there must be 11 rungs below the middle for a total of 22 rungs. Add the middle rung to this and the ladder has 23 rungs.

PAGE 441 COOPERATIVE LEARNING ACTIVITY

Since the onion soup recipe is a divisor of the other three recipes, it will appear first in the book. The devil's food cake recipe comes next since the beef Wellington recipe is on a page five times greater than the devil's food recipe page, and the chicken salad recipe is on a page at least two times greater than the page with the beef Wellington recipe.

Next comes the beef Wellington recipe because the chicken salad recipe is on a page at least twice greater. So the onion soup recipe will appear first, then the devil's food recipe, followed by the beef Wellington recipe, and finally the chicken salad recipe.

Since page 5 is the first page with recipes, try it. It fails to work since the three other recipes will have to be multiples of 5 which means they must end in "0" or "5". This means two digits would have to repeat which cannot happen.

Next try 6. This means the onion soup recipe will appear on page 6. The devil's food cake recipe will then appear on page 12, 18, 24, or another multiple of 6. Try page 12. This means the beef Wellington recipe will appear on page 12 × 5 or 60. This cannot happen because the "6"'s repeat. Try page 18. This means the beef Wellington recipe appears on page 18 × 5 = 90. That works, and leaves numbers 3, 7, and 2 to use. This is good because the 2 and 3 are consecutive digits and the page with the chicken salad recipe is composed of consecutive digits. It must also be divisible by six, so the 2 must be the last digit. The 3 must be the first digit since recipes appear on pages 5 through 420, which leaves the second digit as 7. Therefore, the chicken salad recipe appears on page 372, which is divisible by 6.

So the recipes appear as follows: the onion soup recipe appears on page 6, the devil's food cake recipe appears on page 18, the beef Wellington recipe appears on page 90, and the chicken salad recipe appears on page 372.

**Graphing Systems of Equations**

1. parallel                    2. intersecting

3. the same $x$- and $y$-intercepts

4. Answers may vary; a typical answer is $x + y = 3$ and $x - y = 1$.

5. $(6, 3)$        6. $(-3, 3)$        7. $(1, 3)$

8. $(0, 0)$        9. $(2, 1)$        10. $(5, -5)$

11. $m = -\dfrac{A}{B} = -\dfrac{1}{1} = -1$, $b = \dfrac{C}{B} = \dfrac{6}{1} = 6$;

$m = -\dfrac{A}{B} = -\dfrac{1}{-1} = 1$, $b = \dfrac{C}{B} = \dfrac{2}{-1} = -2$;

one solution

12. $m = -\dfrac{A}{B} = -\dfrac{1}{1} = -1$, $b = \dfrac{C}{B} = \dfrac{6}{1} = 6$;

$m = -\dfrac{A}{B} = -\dfrac{3}{3} = -1$, $b = \dfrac{C}{B} = \dfrac{3}{3} = 1$;

no solution

13.      $3x - 15 = -6y$

$3x - 15 + 15 = -6y + 15$

$3x + 6y = -6y + 15 + 6y$

$3x + 6y = 15$

$x + 2y = 5$

$m = -\dfrac{A}{B} = -\dfrac{1}{2}$, $b = \dfrac{C}{B} = \dfrac{5}{2}$;

$m = -\dfrac{A}{B} = -\dfrac{3}{6} = -\dfrac{1}{2}$, $b = \dfrac{C}{B} = \dfrac{15}{6} = \dfrac{5}{2}$;

infinitely many solutions

14.      $-6x + 15 = 9y$

$-6x + 15 - 15 = 9y - 15$

$-6x - 9y = 9y - 15 - 9y$

$-6x - 9y = -15$

$6x + 9y = 15$

$2x + 3y = 5$

$m = -\dfrac{A}{B} = -\dfrac{2}{3}$, $b = \dfrac{C}{B} = \dfrac{5}{3}$;

$m = -\dfrac{A}{B} = -\dfrac{6}{9} = -\dfrac{2}{3}$, $b = \dfrac{C}{B} = \dfrac{15}{9} = \dfrac{5}{3}$;

infinitely many solutions

15.      $6x - 42 = 16y$

$6x - 42 + 42 = 16y + 42$

$6x - 16y = 16y + 42 - 16y$

$6x - 16y = 42$

$3x - 8y = 21$

$m = -\dfrac{A}{B} = -\dfrac{3}{-8} = \dfrac{3}{8}$, $b = \dfrac{C}{B} = \dfrac{4}{-8} = -\dfrac{1}{2}$;

$m = -\dfrac{A}{B} = -\dfrac{3}{-8} = \dfrac{3}{8}$, $b = \dfrac{C}{B} = \dfrac{21}{-8} = -\dfrac{21}{8}$;

no solution

16.      $y = -3x$          $6y - x = -38$

$y + 3x = -3x + 3x$     $x - 6y = 38$

$3x + y = 0$

$m = -\dfrac{A}{B} = -\dfrac{3}{1} = -3$, $b = \dfrac{C}{B} = \dfrac{0}{1} = 0$;

$m = -\dfrac{A}{B} = -\dfrac{1}{-6} = \dfrac{1}{6}$, $b = \dfrac{C}{B} = \dfrac{38}{-6} = -\dfrac{19}{3}$;

one solution

17.      $x + 3y = 12$                $x - 3y = -6$

$x - x + 3y = 12 - x$     $x - x - 3y = -6 - x$

$3y = -x + 12$                 $-3y = -x - 6$

$\dfrac{3y}{3} = \dfrac{-x}{3} + \dfrac{12}{3}$          $\dfrac{-3y}{-3} = \dfrac{-x}{-3} - \dfrac{6}{-3}$

$y = -\dfrac{1}{3}x + 4$               $y = \dfrac{1}{3}x + 2$

one solution; $(3, 3)$

18.      $x - 3y = 6$                  $x - y = 4$

$x - x - 3y = 6 - x$      $x - x - y = 4 - x$

$-3y = -x + 6$                 $-y = -x + 4$

$\dfrac{-3y}{-3} = \dfrac{-x}{-3} + \dfrac{6}{-3}$          $\dfrac{-y}{-1} = \dfrac{-x}{-1} + \dfrac{4}{-1}$

$y = \dfrac{1}{3}x - 2$                 $y = x - 4$

one solution; $(3, -1)$

19.      $x - 3y = 6$                  $x + 3y = 12$

$x - x - 3y = 6 - x$      $x - x + 3y = 12 - x$

$-3y = 6 - x$                  $3y = -x + 12$

$\dfrac{-3y}{-3} = \dfrac{6}{-3} - \dfrac{x}{-3}$          $\dfrac{3y}{3} = \dfrac{-x}{3} + \dfrac{12}{3}$

$y = \dfrac{1}{3}x - 2$                 $y = -\dfrac{1}{3}x + 4$

one solution; $(9, 1)$

20.      $x - 3y = -6$                $x - 3y = 6$

$x - x - 3y = 6 - x$      $x - x - 3y = 6 - x$

$-3y = -x - 6$                 $-3y = -x + 6$

$\dfrac{-3y}{-3} = \dfrac{-x}{-3} - \dfrac{6}{-3}$          $\dfrac{-3y}{-3} = \dfrac{-x}{-3} + \dfrac{6}{-3}$

$y = \dfrac{1}{3}x + 2$                 $y = \dfrac{1}{3}x - 2$

no solution

21.      $x + 3y = 12$                $x - y = 4$

$x - x + 3y = 12 - x$     $x - x - y = 4 - x$

$3y = -x + 12$                 $-y = -x + 4$

$\dfrac{3y}{3} = \dfrac{-x}{3} + \dfrac{12}{3}$          $\dfrac{-y}{-1} = \dfrac{-x}{-1} + \dfrac{4}{-1}$

$y = -\dfrac{1}{3}x + 4$               $y = x - 4$

one solution; $(6, 2)$

**22.**

$$x - y = 4 \qquad\qquad x - 3y = -6$$
$$x - x - y = 4 - x \qquad x - x - 3y = -6 - x$$
$$-y = -x + 4 \qquad\qquad -3y = -x - 6$$
$$\frac{-y}{-1} = \frac{-x}{-1} + \frac{4}{-1} \qquad \frac{-3y}{-3} = \frac{-x}{-3} - \frac{6}{-3}$$
$$y = x - 4 \qquad\qquad y = \frac{1}{3}x + 2$$

one solution; (9, 5)

**23.** $y = -x \qquad y = 2x$

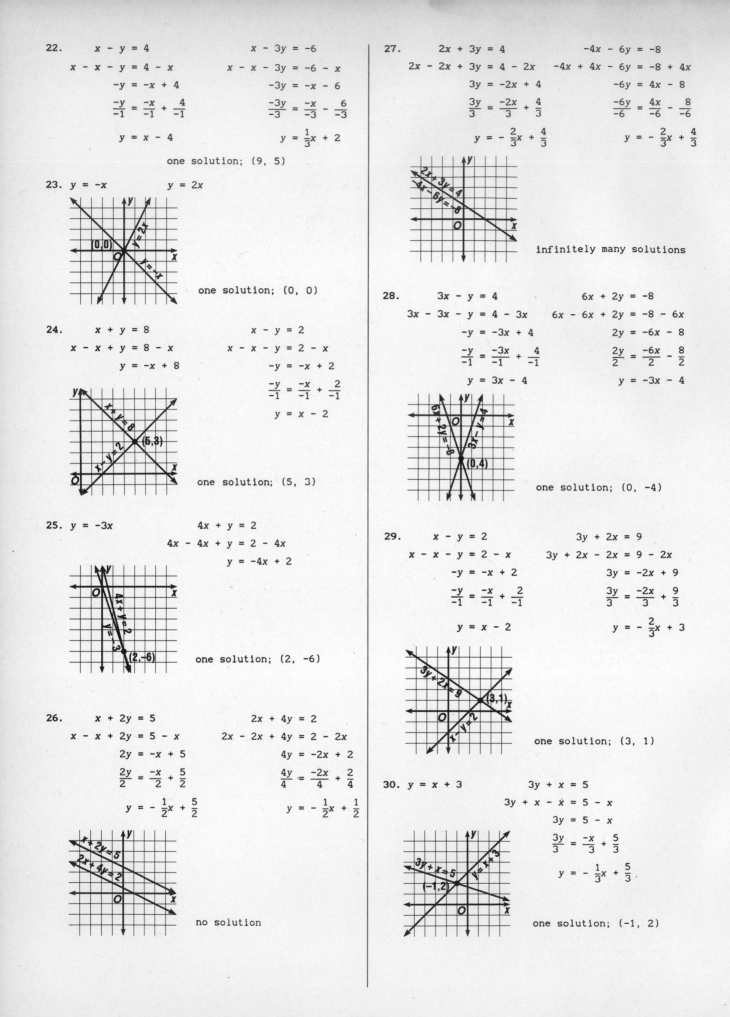

one solution; (0, 0)

**24.**

$$x + y = 8 \qquad\qquad x - y = 2$$
$$x - x + y = 8 - x \qquad x - x - y = 2 - x$$
$$y = -x + 8 \qquad\qquad -y = -x + 2$$
$$\qquad\qquad\qquad \frac{-y}{-1} = \frac{-x}{-1} + \frac{2}{-1}$$
$$\qquad\qquad\qquad y = x - 2$$

one solution; (5, 3)

**25.** $y = -3x \qquad\qquad 4x + y = 2$

$$\qquad\qquad\qquad 4x - 4x + y = 2 - 4x$$
$$\qquad\qquad\qquad y = -4x + 2$$

one solution; (2, -6)

**26.**

$$x + 2y = 5 \qquad\qquad 2x + 4y = 2$$
$$x - x + 2y = 5 - x \qquad 2x - 2x + 4y = 2 - 2x$$
$$2y = -x + 5 \qquad\qquad 4y = -2x + 2$$
$$\frac{2y}{2} = \frac{-x}{2} + \frac{5}{2} \qquad \frac{4y}{4} = \frac{-2x}{4} + \frac{2}{4}$$
$$y = -\frac{1}{2}x + \frac{5}{2} \qquad y = -\frac{1}{2}x + \frac{1}{2}$$

no solution

**27.**

$$2x + 3y = 4 \qquad\qquad -4x - 6y = -8$$
$$2x - 2x + 3y = 4 - 2x \qquad -4x + 4x - 6y = -8 + 4x$$
$$3y = -2x + 4 \qquad\qquad -6y = 4x - 8$$
$$\frac{3y}{3} = \frac{-2x}{3} + \frac{4}{3} \qquad \frac{-6y}{-6} = \frac{4x}{-6} - \frac{8}{-6}$$
$$y = -\frac{2}{3}x + \frac{4}{3} \qquad y = -\frac{2}{3}x + \frac{4}{3}$$

infinitely many solutions

**28.**

$$3x - y = 4 \qquad\qquad 6x + 2y = -8$$
$$3x - 3x - y = 4 - 3x \qquad 6x - 6x + 2y = -8 - 6x$$
$$-y = -3x + 4 \qquad\qquad 2y = -6x - 8$$
$$\frac{-y}{-1} = \frac{-3x}{-1} + \frac{4}{-1} \qquad \frac{2y}{2} = \frac{-6x}{2} - \frac{8}{2}$$
$$y = 3x - 4 \qquad\qquad y = -3x - 4$$

one solution; (0, -4)

**29.**

$$x - y = 2 \qquad\qquad 3y + 2x = 9$$
$$x - x - y = 2 - x \qquad 3y + 2x - 2x = 9 - 2x$$
$$-y = -x + 2 \qquad\qquad 3y = -2x + 9$$
$$\frac{-y}{-1} = \frac{-x}{-1} + \frac{2}{-1} \qquad \frac{3y}{3} = \frac{-2x}{3} + \frac{9}{3}$$
$$y = x - 2 \qquad\qquad y = -\frac{2}{3}x + 3$$

one solution; (3, 1)

**30.** $y = x + 3 \qquad\qquad 3y + x = 5$

$$\qquad\qquad\qquad 3y + x - x = 5 - x$$
$$\qquad\qquad\qquad 3y = 5 - x$$
$$\qquad\qquad\qquad \frac{3y}{3} = \frac{-x}{3} + \frac{5}{3}$$
$$\qquad\qquad\qquad y = -\frac{1}{3}x + \frac{5}{3}$$

one solution; (-1, 2)

**31.** $2x + 3y = -17 \qquad y = x - 4$

$2x - 2x + 3y = -17 - 2x$

$3y = -2x - 17$

$\dfrac{3y}{3} = \dfrac{-2x}{3} - \dfrac{17}{3}$

$y = -\dfrac{2}{3}x - \dfrac{17}{3}$

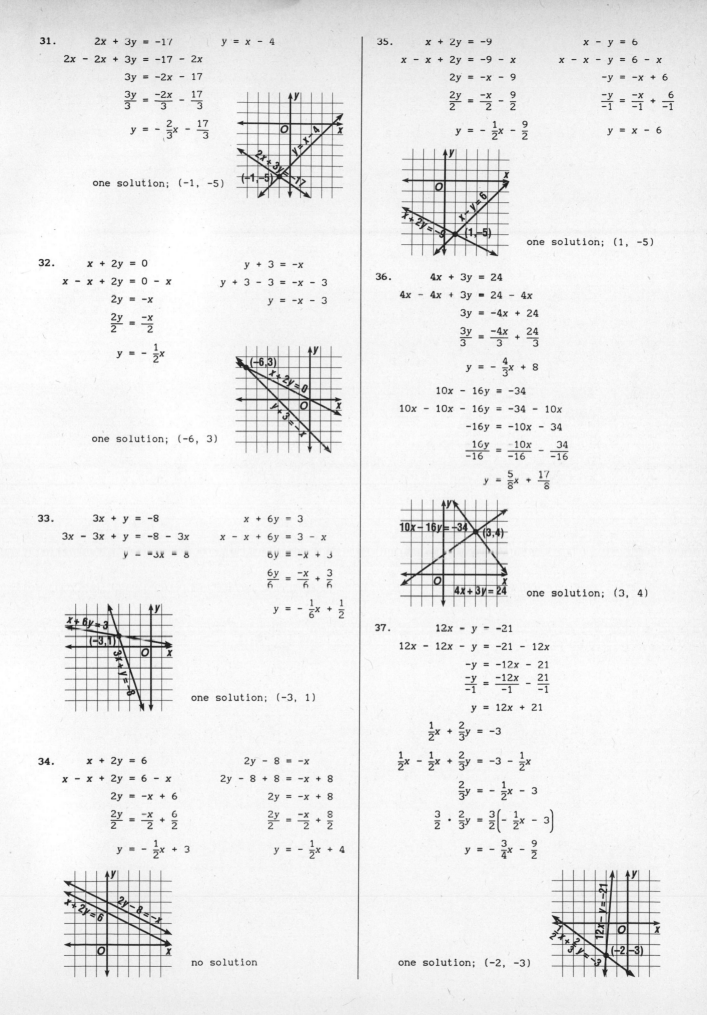

one solution; (-1, -5)

**32.** $x + 2y = 0 \qquad\qquad y + 3 = -x$

$x - x + 2y = 0 - x \qquad y + 3 - 3 = -x - 3$

$2y = -x \qquad\qquad\qquad y = -x - 3$

$\dfrac{2y}{2} = \dfrac{-x}{2}$

$y = -\dfrac{1}{2}x$

one solution; (-6, 3)

**33.** $3x + y = -8 \qquad\qquad x + 6y = 3$

$3x - 3x + y = -8 - 3x \qquad x - x + 6y = 3 - x$

$y = -3x - 8 \qquad\qquad 6y = -x + 3$

$\dfrac{6y}{6} = \dfrac{-x}{6} + \dfrac{3}{6}$

$y = -\dfrac{1}{6}x + \dfrac{1}{2}$

one solution; (-3, 1)

**34.** $x + 2y = 6 \qquad\qquad 2y - 8 = -x$

$x - x + 2y = 6 - x \qquad 2y - 8 + 8 = -x + 8$

$2y = -x + 6 \qquad\qquad 2y = -x + 8$

$\dfrac{2y}{2} = \dfrac{-x}{2} + \dfrac{6}{2} \qquad\qquad \dfrac{2y}{2} = \dfrac{-x}{2} + \dfrac{8}{2}$

$y = -\dfrac{1}{2}x + 3 \qquad\qquad y = -\dfrac{1}{2}x + 4$

no solution

**35.** $x + 2y = -9 \qquad\qquad x - y = 6$

$x - x + 2y = -9 - x \qquad x - x - y = 6 - x$

$2y = -x - 9 \qquad\qquad -y = -x + 6$

$\dfrac{2y}{2} = \dfrac{-x}{2} - \dfrac{9}{2} \qquad\qquad \dfrac{-y}{-1} = \dfrac{-x}{-1} + \dfrac{6}{-1}$

$y = -\dfrac{1}{2}x - \dfrac{9}{2} \qquad\qquad y = x - 6$

one solution; (1, -5)

**36.** $4x + 3y = 24$

$4x - 4x + 3y = 24 - 4x$

$3y = -4x + 24$

$\dfrac{3y}{3} = \dfrac{-4x}{3} + \dfrac{24}{3}$

$y = -\dfrac{4}{3}x + 8$

$10x - 16y = -34$

$10x - 10x - 16y = -34 - 10x$

$-16y = -10x - 34$

$\dfrac{16y}{-16} = \dfrac{-10x}{-16} - \dfrac{34}{-16}$

$y = \dfrac{5}{8}x + \dfrac{17}{8}$

one solution; (3, 4)

**37.** $12x - y = -21$

$12x - 12x - y = -21 - 12x$

$-y = -12x - 21$

$\dfrac{-y}{-1} = \dfrac{-12x}{-1} - \dfrac{21}{-1}$

$y = 12x + 21$

$\dfrac{1}{2}x + \dfrac{2}{3}y = -3$

$\dfrac{1}{2}x - \dfrac{1}{2}x + \dfrac{2}{3}y = -3 - \dfrac{1}{2}x$

$\dfrac{2}{3}y = -\dfrac{1}{2}x - 3$

$\dfrac{3}{2} \cdot \dfrac{2}{3}y = \dfrac{3}{2}\left(-\dfrac{1}{2}x - 3\right)$

$y = -\dfrac{3}{4}x - \dfrac{9}{2}$

one solution; (-2, -3)

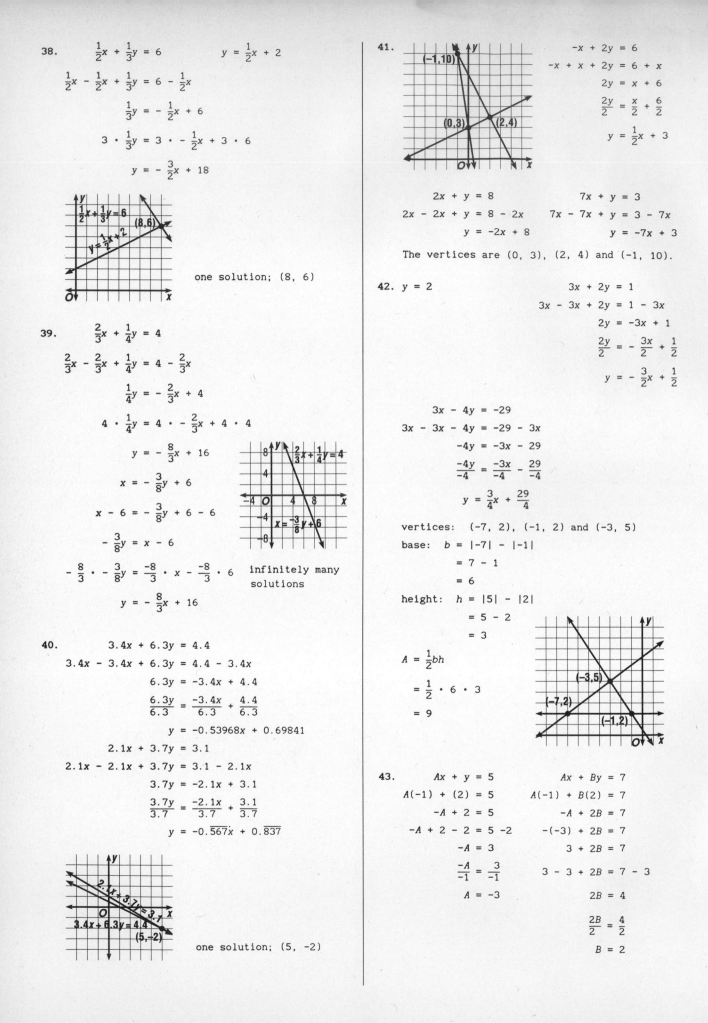

**38.**
$$\frac{1}{2}x + \frac{1}{3}y = 6 \qquad\qquad y = \frac{1}{2}x + 2$$
$$\frac{1}{2}x - \frac{1}{2}x + \frac{1}{3}y = 6 - \frac{1}{2}x$$
$$\frac{1}{3}y = -\frac{1}{2}x + 6$$
$$3 \cdot \frac{1}{3}y = 3 \cdot -\frac{1}{2}x + 3 \cdot 6$$
$$y = -\frac{3}{2}x + 18$$

one solution; (8, 6)

**39.**
$$\frac{2}{3}x + \frac{1}{4}y = 4$$
$$\frac{2}{3}x - \frac{2}{3}x + \frac{1}{4}y = 4 - \frac{2}{3}x$$
$$\frac{1}{4}y = -\frac{2}{3}x + 4$$
$$4 \cdot \frac{1}{4}y = 4 \cdot -\frac{2}{3}x + 4 \cdot 4$$
$$y = -\frac{8}{3}x + 16$$
$$x = -\frac{3}{8}y + 6$$
$$x - 6 = -\frac{3}{8}y + 6 - 6$$
$$-\frac{3}{8}y = x - 6$$
$$-\frac{8}{3} \cdot -\frac{3}{8}y = \frac{-8}{3} \cdot x - \frac{-8}{3} \cdot 6$$
$$y = -\frac{8}{3}x + 16$$

infinitely many solutions

**40.**
$$3.4x + 6.3y = 4.4$$
$$3.4x - 3.4x + 6.3y = 4.4 - 3.4x$$
$$6.3y = -3.4x + 4.4$$
$$\frac{6.3y}{6.3} = \frac{-3.4x}{6.3} + \frac{4.4}{6.3}$$
$$y = -0.53968x + 0.69841$$
$$2.1x + 3.7y = 3.1$$
$$2.1x - 2.1x + 3.7y = 3.1 - 2.1x$$
$$3.7y = -2.1x + 3.1$$
$$\frac{3.7y}{3.7} = \frac{-2.1x}{3.7} + \frac{3.1}{3.7}$$
$$y = -0.\overline{567}x + 0.\overline{837}$$

one solution; (5, -2)

**41.**
$$-x + 2y = 6$$
$$-x + x + 2y = 6 + x$$
$$2y = x + 6$$
$$\frac{2y}{2} = \frac{x}{2} + \frac{6}{2}$$
$$y = \frac{1}{2}x + 3$$

$$2x + y = 8 \qquad\qquad 7x + y = 3$$
$$2x - 2x + y = 8 - 2x \qquad 7x - 7x + y = 3 - 7x$$
$$y = -2x + 8 \qquad\qquad y = -7x + 3$$

The vertices are (0, 3), (2, 4) and (-1, 10).

**42.** $y = 2$
$$3x + 2y = 1$$
$$3x - 3x + 2y = 1 - 3x$$
$$2y = -3x + 1$$
$$\frac{2y}{2} = -\frac{3x}{2} + \frac{1}{2}$$
$$y = -\frac{3}{2}x + \frac{1}{2}$$

$$3x - 4y = -29$$
$$3x - 3x - 4y = -29 - 3x$$
$$-4y = -3x - 29$$
$$\frac{-4y}{-4} = \frac{-3x}{-4} - \frac{29}{-4}$$
$$y = \frac{3}{4}x + \frac{29}{4}$$

vertices: (-7, 2), (-1, 2) and (-3, 5)

base: $b = |-7| - |-1|$
$$= 7 - 1$$
$$= 6$$

height: $h = |5| - |2|$
$$= 5 - 2$$
$$= 3$$

$$A = \frac{1}{2}bh$$
$$= \frac{1}{2} \cdot 6 \cdot 3$$
$$= 9$$

**43.**
$$Ax + y = 5 \qquad\qquad Ax + By = 7$$
$$A(-1) + (2) = 5 \qquad A(-1) + B(2) = 7$$
$$-A + 2 = 5 \qquad\qquad -A + 2B = 7$$
$$-A + 2 - 2 = 5 - 2 \qquad -(-3) + 2B = 7$$
$$-A = 3 \qquad\qquad 3 + 2B = 7$$
$$\frac{-A}{-1} = \frac{3}{-1} \qquad\qquad 3 - 3 + 2B = 7 - 3$$
$$A = -3 \qquad\qquad 2B = 4$$
$$\frac{2B}{2} = \frac{4}{2}$$
$$B = 2$$

192

**44.**

$$P = 2\ell + 2w \qquad\qquad \ell = 2w - 1$$
$$40 = 2\ell + 2w$$
$$40 - 2\ell = 2\ell - 2\ell + 2w$$
$$40 - 40 - 2\ell = 2w - 40$$
$$-2\ell = 2w - 40$$
$$\frac{-2\ell}{-2} = \frac{2w}{-2} - \frac{40}{-2}$$
$$\ell = -w + 20$$
$$\ell = 13 \text{ m},\ w = 7 \text{ m}$$

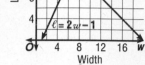

**45.** Blue Cab Co.: $y = 0.10x + 1.70$

Red Cab Co.: $y = 0.15x + 1.55$

From the graph, the rides will cost the same at 0.3 mile.

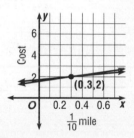

**46.** Balloon 1: $y = 15x + 10$

Balloon 2: $y = -20x + 150$

**a.** From the graph, after 4 min. the balloons will be the same height.

**b.** From the graph, both balloons will be at 70 m at the same time.

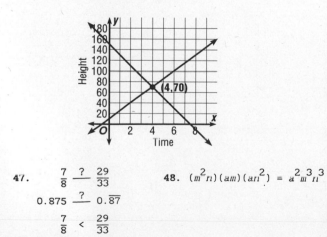

**47.**
$$\frac{7}{8} \ \overset{?}{=}\ \frac{29}{33}$$
$$0.875 \ \overset{?}{=}\ 0.\overline{87}$$
$$\frac{7}{8} < \frac{29}{33}$$

**48.** $(m^2 n)(am)(an^2) = a^2 m^3 n^3$

**49.** $x = $ rate of boat in still water

|  | $r$ | $t$ | $d$ |
|---|---|---|---|
| Upstream | $x - 5$ | $\dfrac{78}{x - 5}$ | $78$ |
| Downstream | $x + 5$ | $\dfrac{78}{x + 5}$ | $78$ |

$$\frac{78}{x - 5} + \frac{78}{x + 5} = 32$$
$$\frac{78(x + 5)}{(x - 5)(x + 5)} + \frac{78(x - 5)}{(x - 5)(x + 5)} = 32$$
$$\frac{78x + 390 + 78x - 390}{(x - 5)(x + 5)} = 32$$
$$156x = 32(x - 5)(x + 5)$$
$$156x = 32(x^2 - 25)$$
$$156x = 32x^2 - 800$$
$$0 = 32x^2 - 156x - 800$$
$$0 = 8x^2 - 39x - 200$$
$$0 = (8x + 25)(x - 8)$$
$$x - 8 = 0$$
$$x = 8$$

The rate of the boat in still water is 8 mph.

**50.** $P = (-2, 3) \qquad\qquad P = (A, B)$

$$A = (x_2, y_2) \qquad (xy) = \left(\frac{x_1 + x_2}{2},\ \frac{y_1 + y_2}{2}\right)$$

$$B = (3, 9) \qquad (-2, 3) = \left(\frac{x_1 + 3}{2},\ \frac{y_1 + 9}{2}\right)$$

$$-2 = \frac{x_1 + 3}{2} \qquad\qquad 3 = \frac{y_1 + 9}{2}$$
$$-4 = x_1 + 3 \qquad\qquad 6 = y_1 + 9$$
$$-4 - 3 = x_1 + 3 - 3 \qquad 6 - 9 = y_1 + 9 - 9$$
$$-7 = x_1 \qquad\qquad -3 = y_1$$

The other endpoint is $(-7, -3)$.

## 11-3   Substitution

**PAGE 450    CHECKING FOR UNDERSTANDING**

1. From the first equation, you know that $y$ is equal to $-5x + 1$, and $y$ must have the same value in both equations.

2. The equations are $a + b = 1000$ and $0.30a + 0.70b = 0.45(1000)$.

3. There are 9 whole numbers such that the sum of the digits are nine. They are 18, 27, 36, 45, 54, 63, 72, 81, and 90.

4. The tens digit, $t$, is the number of tens and the ones digit, $u$, is the number of ones. Any two-digit number can be written as 10 times its number of tens plus 1 times its number of ones, or $10(t) + 1u = 10t + u$.

**5.**

$$x + y = 5$$
$$x + y - y = 5 - y$$
$$x = 5 - y$$

$$x + y = 5$$
$$x - x + y = 5 - x$$
$$y = 5 - x$$

**6.**

$$2x + y = 3$$
$$2x + y - y = 3 - y$$
$$2x = 3 - y$$
$$\frac{2x}{2} = \frac{3}{2} - \frac{y}{2}$$
$$x = \frac{3}{2} - \frac{1}{2}y$$

$$2x + y = 3$$
$$2x - 2x + y = 3 - 2x$$
$$y = 3 - 2x$$

**7.**

$$2x + 3y = 6$$
$$2x + 3y - 3y = 6 - 3y$$
$$2x = 6 - 3y$$
$$\frac{2x}{2} = \frac{6}{2} - \frac{3y}{2}$$
$$x = 3 - \frac{3}{2}y$$

$$2x + 3y = 6$$
$$2x - 2x + 3y = 6 - 2x$$
$$3y = 6 - 2x$$
$$\frac{3y}{3} = \frac{6}{3} - \frac{2x}{3}$$
$$y = 2 - \frac{2}{3}x$$

**8.**

$$3y - \frac{1}{2}x = 7$$
$$3y - 3y - \frac{1}{2}x = 7 - 3y$$
$$-\frac{1}{2}x = 7 - 3y$$
$$-2 \cdot -\frac{1}{2}x = -2 \cdot 7 - (-2)3y$$
$$x = -14 + 6y$$
$$x = 6y - 14$$

$$3y - \frac{1}{2}x = 7$$
$$3y - \frac{1}{2}x + \frac{1}{2}x = 7 + \frac{1}{2}x$$
$$3y = 7 + \frac{1}{2}x$$
$$\frac{3y}{3} = \frac{7}{3} + \frac{\frac{1}{2}x}{3}$$
$$y = \frac{7}{3} + \frac{1}{6}x$$

**9.**

$$0.75x + 6 = -0.8y$$
$$0.75x + 6 - 6 = -0.8y - 6$$
$$0.75x = -0.8y - 6$$
$$\frac{0.75x}{0.75} = \frac{-0.8y}{0.75} - \frac{6}{0.75}$$
$$x = -\frac{0.8}{0.75}y - 8$$
$$x = -1.0\overline{6}y - 8$$

$$0.75x + 6 = -0.8y$$
$$-0.8y = 0.75x + 6$$
$$\frac{-0.8y}{-0.8} = \frac{0.75x}{-0.8} + \frac{6}{-0.8}$$
$$y = -\frac{0.75}{0.8}x - 7.5$$
$$y = -0.9375x - 7.5$$

**10.**

$$\frac{2}{3}x - \frac{4}{5}y = 3$$
$$\frac{2}{3}x - \frac{4}{5}y + \frac{4}{5}y = 3 + \frac{4}{5}y$$
$$\frac{2}{3}x = 3 + \frac{4}{5}y$$
$$\frac{3}{2} \cdot \frac{2}{3}x = \frac{3}{2} \cdot 3 + \frac{3}{2} \cdot \frac{4}{5}y$$
$$x = \frac{9}{2} + \frac{6}{5}y$$

$$\frac{2}{3}x - \frac{4}{5}y = 3$$
$$\frac{2}{3}x - \frac{2}{3}x - \frac{4}{5}y = 3 - \frac{2}{3}x$$
$$-\frac{4}{5}y = 3 - \frac{2}{3}x$$
$$-\frac{5}{4} \cdot -\frac{4}{5}y = -\frac{5}{4} \cdot 3 - \left(\frac{-5}{4}\right)\left(\frac{2}{3}x\right)$$
$$y = -\frac{15}{4} + \frac{5}{6}x$$
$$y = \frac{5}{6}x - \frac{15}{4}$$

**11.**

$$x + y = 7$$
$$x + (3 + 2x) = 7$$
$$3x + 3 = 7$$
$$3x + 3 - 3 = 7 - 3$$
$$3x = 4$$
$$\frac{3x}{3} = \frac{4}{3}$$
$$x = \frac{4}{3}$$

**12.**

$$2x - y = 8$$
$$2x - (7 - x) = 8$$
$$3x - 7 = 8$$
$$3x - 7 + 7 = 8 + 7$$
$$3x = 15$$
$$\frac{3x}{3} = \frac{15}{3}$$
$$x = 5$$

**13.**

$$5x = 12y$$
$$5x = 12(x)$$
$$5x = 12x$$
$$5x - 5x = 12x - 5x$$
$$0 = 7x$$
$$\frac{0}{7} = \frac{7x}{7}$$
$$0 = x$$

**14.**

$$3y = 3x + 1$$
$$3y = 3(5 - y) + 1$$
$$3y = 15 - 3y + 1$$
$$3y = 16 - 3y$$
$$3y + 3y = 16 - 3y + 3y$$
$$6y = 16$$
$$\frac{6y}{6} = \frac{16}{6}$$
$$y = \frac{8}{3}$$

**15.**

$$3x = -18 + 2y$$
$$\frac{3x}{3} = \frac{-18}{3} + \frac{2y}{3}$$
$$x = -6 + \frac{2}{3}y$$

$$x + 3y = 4$$
$$\left(-6 + \frac{2}{3}y\right) + 3y = 4$$
$$-6 + \frac{11}{3}y = 4$$
$$-6 + 6 + \frac{11}{3}y = 4 + 6$$
$$\frac{11}{3}y = 10$$
$$\frac{3}{11} \cdot \frac{11}{3}y = 10 \cdot \frac{3}{11}$$
$$y = \frac{30}{11}$$

**16.**

$$2x = 3 - y$$
$$\frac{2x}{2} = \frac{3}{2} - \frac{y}{2}$$
$$x = \frac{3}{2} - \frac{1}{2}y$$

$$2y = 12 - x$$
$$2y = 12 - \left(\frac{3}{2} - \frac{1}{2}y\right)$$
$$2y = \frac{21}{2} + \frac{1}{2}y$$
$$2y - \frac{1}{2}y = \frac{21}{2} + \frac{1}{2}y - \frac{1}{2}y$$
$$\frac{3}{2}y = \frac{21}{2}$$
$$\frac{2}{3} \cdot \frac{3}{2}y = \frac{21}{2} \cdot \frac{2}{3}$$
$$y = 7$$

**PAGES 450–451    EXERCISES**

**17.**

$$x + 2y = -21$$
$$x + 2(3x) = -21$$
$$x + 6x = -21$$
$$7x = -21$$
$$\frac{7x}{7} = \frac{-21}{7}$$
$$x = -3$$

$$y = 3x$$
$$y = 3(-3)$$
$$y = -9$$

The solution is $(-3, -9)$.

194

**18.**

$$x + 2y = 8 \qquad y = 2x$$

$$x + 2(2x) = 8 \qquad y = 2\left(\frac{8}{5}\right)$$

$$x + 4x = 8 \qquad y = \frac{16}{5}$$

$$5x = 8$$

$$\frac{5x}{5} = \frac{8}{5}$$

$$x = \frac{8}{5}$$

The solution is $\left(\frac{8}{5}, \frac{16}{5}\right)$.

**19.**

$$4x + 2y = 15 \qquad x = 2y$$

$$4(2y) + 2y = 15 \qquad x = 2\left(\frac{3}{2}\right)$$

$$8y + 2y = 15 \qquad x = 3$$

$$10y = 15$$

$$\frac{10y}{10} = \frac{15}{10}$$

$$y = \frac{3}{2}$$

The solution is $\left(3, \frac{3}{2}\right)$.

**20.**

$$3x + y = 6 \qquad y + 2 = x$$

$$3(y + 2) + y = 6 \qquad 0 + 2 = x$$

$$3y + 6 + y = 6 \qquad x = 2$$

$$4y + 6 = 6$$

$$4y + 6 - 6 = 6 - 6$$

$$4y = 0$$

$$\frac{4y}{4} = \frac{0}{4}$$

$$y = 0 \qquad \text{The solution is } (2, 0).$$

**21.**

$$-3x + y = -9$$

$$-3x + 3x + y = -9 + 3x$$

$$y = 3x - 9$$

$$2x - y = -4$$

$$2x - (3x - 9) = -4$$

$$-x + 9 = -4$$

$$-x + 9 - 9 = -4 - 9$$

$$-x = -13$$

$$\frac{-x}{-1} = \frac{-13}{-1}$$

$$x = 13$$

$$-3(13) + y = -9$$

$$-39 + y = -9$$

$$-39 + 39 + y = -9 + 39$$

$$y = 30$$

The solution is $(13, 30)$.

**22.**

$$2x + 4y = 6$$

$$2(3 - 2y) + 4y = 6$$

$$6 - 4y + 4y = 6$$

$$6 = 6$$

infinitely many solutions

**23.**

$$4x - 9y = 9$$

$$4x - 9y + 9y = 9 + 9y$$

$$4x = 9 + 9y$$

$$\frac{4x}{4} = \frac{9}{4} + \frac{9y}{4}$$

$$x = \frac{9}{4} + \frac{9}{4}y$$

$$2\left(\frac{9}{4} + \frac{9}{4}y\right) + 3y = 5$$

$$\frac{9}{2} + \frac{9}{2}y + 3y = 5$$

$$\frac{9}{2} + \frac{15}{2}y = 5$$

$$\frac{9}{2} - \frac{9}{2} + \frac{15}{2}y = 5 - \frac{9}{2}$$

$$\frac{15}{2}y = \frac{1}{2}$$

$$\frac{2}{15} \cdot \frac{15}{2}y = \frac{1}{2} \cdot \frac{2}{15}$$

$$y = \frac{1}{15}$$

$$2x + 3\left(\frac{1}{15}\right) = 5$$

$$2x + \frac{3}{15} = 5$$

$$2x + \frac{1}{5} - \frac{1}{5} = 5 - \frac{1}{5}$$

$$2x = \frac{24}{5}$$

$$\frac{2x}{2} = \frac{\frac{24}{5}}{2}$$

$$x = \frac{12}{5}$$

The solution is $\left(\frac{12}{5}, \frac{1}{15}\right)$

**24.**

$$x - 3y = 3$$

$$x - 3y + 3y = 3 + 3y$$

$$x = 3y + 3$$

$$2(3y + 3) + 9y = 11$$

$$6y + 6 + 9y = 11$$

$$15y + 6 = 11$$

$$15y + 6 - 6 = 11 - 6$$

$$15y = 5$$

$$\frac{15y}{15} = \frac{5}{15}$$

$$y = \frac{1}{3}$$

$$x - 3y = 3$$

$$x - 3\left(\frac{1}{3}\right) = 3$$

$$x - 1 = 3$$

$$x - 1 + 1 = 3 + 1$$

$$x = 4$$

The solution is $\left(4, \frac{1}{3}\right)$.

**25.**
$$9x + 6y = 14$$
$$9x - 9x + 6y = 14 - 9x$$
$$6y = -9x + 14$$
$$\frac{6y}{6} = \frac{-9x}{6} + \frac{14}{6}$$
$$y = -\frac{3}{2}x + \frac{7}{3}$$
$$3x + 2\left(-\frac{3}{2}x + \frac{7}{3}\right) = 11$$
$$3x - 3x + \frac{14}{3} = 11$$
$$\frac{14}{3} = 11$$
no solution

**26.**
$$3x + y = 2$$
$$3x - 3x + y = 2 - 3x$$
$$y = 2 - 3x$$
$$4x - 2(2 - 3x) = 1$$
$$4x - 4 + 6x = 1$$
$$10x - 4 = 1$$
$$10x - 4 + 4 = 1 + 4$$
$$10x = 5$$
$$\frac{10x}{10} = \frac{5}{10}$$
$$x = \frac{1}{2}$$
$$3x + y = 2$$
$$3\left(\frac{1}{2}\right) + y = 2$$
$$\frac{3}{2} + y = 2$$
$$\frac{3}{2} - \frac{3}{2} + y = 2 - \frac{3}{2}$$
$$y = \frac{1}{2}$$
The solution is $\left(\frac{1}{2}, \frac{1}{2}\right)$.

**27.**
$$x + 3y = y$$
$$x + 3y - 3y = y - 3y$$
$$x = -2y$$
$$3(-2y) + 5y = 2(-2y)$$
$$-6y + 5y = -4y$$
$$-y = -4y$$
$$-y + 4y = -4y + 4y$$
$$3y = 0$$
$$\frac{3y}{3} = \frac{0}{3}$$
$$y = 0$$
$$x + 3(0) = 0$$
$$x + 0 = 0$$
$$x = 0$$
The solution is (0, 0).

**28.**
$$x - 2y = 5$$
$$x - 2y + 2y = 5 + 2y$$
$$x = 2y + 5$$
$$3(2y + 5) - 5y = 8$$
$$6y + 15 - 5y = 8$$
$$y + 15 = 8$$
$$y + 15 - 15 = 8 - 15$$
$$y = -7$$
$$x - 2(-7) = 5$$
$$x + 14 = 5$$
$$x + 14 - 14 = 5 - 14$$
$$x = -9$$
The solution is (-9, -7).

**29.**
$$2x + 3 = 3y$$
$$\frac{2x}{3} + \frac{3}{3} = \frac{3y}{3}$$
$$y = \frac{2}{3}x + 1$$
$$4x - 3y = 3$$
$$4x - 3\left(\frac{2}{3}x + 1\right) = 3$$
$$4x - 2x - 3 = 3$$
$$2x - 3 = 3$$
$$2x - 3 + 3 = 3 + 3$$
$$2x = 6$$
$$\frac{2x}{2} = \frac{6}{2}$$
$$x = 3$$
$$2x + 3 = 3y$$
$$2(3) + 3 = 3y$$
$$6 + 3 = 3y$$
$$9 = 3y$$
$$\frac{9}{3} = \frac{3y}{3}$$
$$3 = y$$
The solution is (3, 3).

**30.**
$$3x - 2y = -3$$
$$3x - 2y + 2y = -3 + 2y$$
$$3x = 2y - 3$$
$$\frac{3x}{3} = \frac{2y}{3} - \frac{3}{3}$$
$$x = \frac{2}{3}y - 1$$
$$25x + 10y = 215$$
$$25\left(\frac{2}{3}y - 1\right) + 10y = 215$$
$$\frac{50}{3}y - 25 + 10y = 215$$
$$\frac{80}{3}y - 25 = 215$$
$$\frac{80}{3}y - 25 + 25 = 215 + 25$$
$$\frac{80}{3}y = 240$$
$$\frac{3}{80} \cdot \frac{80}{3}y = 240 \cdot \frac{3}{80}$$
$$y = 9$$
$$3x - 2y = -3$$
$$3x - 2(9) = -3$$
$$3x - 18 = -3$$
$$3x - 18 + 18 = -3 + 18$$
$$3x = 15$$
$$\frac{3x}{3} = \frac{15}{3}$$
$$x = 5$$
The solution is (5, 9).

**31.**
$$2x + y = 104$$
$$2x - 2x + y = 104 - 2x$$
$$y = 104 - 2x$$
$$0.5x - 2y = 17$$
$$0.5x - 2(104 - 2x) = 17$$
$$0.5x - 208 + 4x = 17$$
$$4.5x - 208 = 17$$
$$4.5x - 208 + 208 = 17 + 208$$
$$4.5x = 225$$
$$\frac{4.5x}{4.5} = \frac{225}{4.5}$$
$$x = 50$$
$$2x + y = 104$$
$$2(50) + y = 104$$
$$100 + y = 104$$
$$100 - 100 - y = 104 - 100$$
$$y = 4$$
The solution is (50, 4).

**32.**
$$3x + 2y = 18$$
$$3x - 3x + 2y = 18 - 3x$$
$$2y = 18 - 3x$$
$$\frac{2y}{2} = \frac{18}{2} - \frac{3x}{2}$$
$$y = 9 - \frac{3}{2}x$$
$$-\frac{1}{4}x - \frac{2}{3}y = -3$$
$$-\frac{1}{4}x - \frac{2}{3}\left(9 - \frac{3}{2}x\right) = -3$$
$$-\frac{1}{4}x - 6 + x = -3$$
$$\frac{3}{4}x - 6 = -3$$
$$\frac{3}{4}x - 6 + 6 = -3 + 6$$
$$\frac{3}{4}x = 3$$
$$\frac{4}{3} \cdot \frac{3}{4}x = 3 \cdot \frac{4}{3}$$
$$x = 4$$
$$3x + 2y = 18$$
$$3(4) + 2y = 18$$
$$12 + 2y = 18$$
$$12 - 12 + 2y = 18 - 12$$
$$2y = 6$$
$$\frac{2y}{2} = \frac{6}{2}$$
$$y = 3$$
The solution is (4, 3).

**33.**
$$8x + 6y = 44$$
$$8x - 8x + 6y = 44 - 8x$$
$$6y = 44 - 8x$$
$$\frac{6y}{6} = \frac{44}{6} - \frac{8x}{6}$$
$$y = \frac{22}{3} - \frac{4}{3}x$$
$$\frac{1}{4}x - 2y = -3$$
$$\frac{1}{4}x - 2\left(\frac{22}{3} - \frac{4}{3}x\right) = -3$$
$$\frac{1}{4}x - \frac{44}{3} + \frac{8}{3}x = -3$$
$$\frac{3}{12}x + \frac{32}{12}x - \frac{44}{3} = -3$$
$$\frac{35}{12}x - \frac{44}{3} + \frac{44}{3} = -3 + \frac{44}{3}$$
$$\frac{35}{12}x = \frac{35}{3}$$
$$\frac{12}{35} \cdot \frac{35}{12}x = \frac{35}{3} \cdot \frac{12}{35}$$
$$x = 4$$
$$8x + 6y = 44$$
$$8(4) + 6y = 44$$
$$32 + 6y = 44$$
$$32 - 32 + 6y = 44 - 32$$
$$6y = 12$$
$$\frac{6y}{6} = \frac{12}{6}$$
$$y = 2$$
The solution is (4, 2).

**34.**
$$0.3x + 0.2y = 0.5$$
$$0.3x - 0.3x + 0.2y = 0.5 - 0.3x$$
$$0.2y = 0.5 - 0.3x$$
$$\frac{0.2y}{0.2} = \frac{0.5}{0.2} - \frac{0.3x}{0.2}$$
$$y = 2.5 - 1.5x$$
$$0.5x - 0.3y = 0.2$$
$$0.5x - 0.3(2.5 - 1.5x) = 0.2$$
$$0.5x - 0.75 + 0.45x = 0.2$$
$$0.95x - 0.75 = 0.2$$
$$0.95x - 0.75 + 0.75 = 0.2 + 0.75$$
$$0.95x = 0.95$$
$$\frac{0.95x}{0.95} = \frac{0.95}{0.95}$$
$$x = 1$$
$$0.5x - 0.3y = 0.2$$
$$0.5(1) - 0.3y = 0.2$$
$$0.5 - 0.3y = 0.2$$
$$0.5 - 0.5 - 0.3y = 0.2 - 0.5$$
$$-0.3y = -0.3$$
$$\frac{-0.3y}{-0.3} = \frac{-0.3}{-0.3}$$
$$y = 1$$
The solution is (1, 1).

35. $t$ = tens digit
   $u$ = units digit
   $10t + u = 6u$         $t + u = 6$
    $t + u = 6$         $t - t + u = 6 - t$
                          $u = 6 - t$
      $10t + u = 6u$         $t + u = 6$
 $10t + (6 - t) = 6(6 - t)$     $2 + u = 6$
   $10t + 6 - t = 36 - 6t$     $2 - 2 + u = 6 - 2$
      $9t + 6 = 36 - 6t$          $u = 4$
  $9t + 6t + 6 = 36 - 6t + 6t$
  $15t + 6 - 6 = 36 - 6$
        $15t = 30$
       $\dfrac{15t}{15} = \dfrac{30}{15}$
          $t = 2$

  The number is 24.

36. $t$ = tens digit     $10t + u = 2 + 8(t + u)$
   $u$ = units digit        $t = 6 + u$
      $10t + u = 2 + 8t + 8u$
 $10t - 8t - 8u + u = 2 + 8t - 8t + 8u - 8u$
        $2t - 7u = 2$
    $2(6 + u) - 7u = 2$
     $12 + 2u - 7u = 2$
       $12 - 5u = 2$
  $12 - 12 - 5u = 2 - 12$
        $-5u = -10$
     $\dfrac{-5u}{-5} = \dfrac{-10}{-5}$      $t = 6 + u$
         $u = 2$       $t = 6 + 2$
                  $t = 8$

  The number is 82.

37. $t$ = tens digit      $10t + u = 7u$
   $u$ = units digit   $10t + u + 18 = 10u + t$
     $10t + u + 18 = 10u + t$
 $10t - 10t + u + 18 = 10u + t - 10t$
      $u + 18 = 10u - 9t$
   $u - 10u + 18 = 10u - 10u - 9t$
     $-9u + 18 = -9t$
   $\dfrac{-9u}{-9} + \dfrac{18}{-9} = \dfrac{-9t}{-9}$
        $u - 2 = t$
    $10t + u = 7u$
  $10t + u - 7u = 7u - 7u$
    $10t - 6u = 0$
 $10(u - 2) - 6u = 0$
  $10u - 20 - 6u = 0$     $10t + u = 7u$
    $4u - 20 = 0$     $10t + 5 = 7(5)$
 $4u - 20 + 20 = 0 + 20$   $10t + 5 - 5 = 35 - 5$
      $4u = 20$       $10t = 30$
     $\dfrac{4u}{4} = \dfrac{20}{4}$      $\dfrac{10t}{10} = \dfrac{30}{10}$
        $u = 5$         $t = 3$

  The number is 35.

38.         $x + y + z = -54$   $x = -6y$    $z = 14y$
  $(-6y) + y + (14y) = -54$   $x = -6(-6)$   $z = 14(-6)$
          $9y = -54$     $x = 36$     $z = -84$
          $\dfrac{9y}{9} = \dfrac{-54}{9}$
           $y = -6$

  The solution is $(36, -6, -84)$.

39.          $2x + 3y - z = 17$
  $(z + 2) + 3(-3z - 7) - z = 17$
    $z + 2 - 9z - 21 - z = 17$
        $-9z - 19 = 17$
   $-9z - 19 + 19 = 17 + 19$
          $-9z = 36$
        $\dfrac{-9z}{-9} = \dfrac{36}{-9}$
           $z = -4$
          $y = -3z - 7$
          $y = -3(-4) - 7$
          $y = 12 - 7$
          $y = 5$
         $2x = z + 2$
         $2x = -4 + 2$
         $2x = -2$
         $\dfrac{2x}{2} = \dfrac{-2}{2}$
          $x = -1$

  The solution is $(-1, 5, -4)$.

40.     $x + 2z = 2$        $y + 3z = 9$
  $x + 2z - 2z = 2 - 2z$    $y + 3z - 3z = 9 - 3z$
      $x = 2 - 2z$        $y = 9 - 3z$
      $12x - y + 7z = 99$
  $12(2 - 2z) - (9 - 3z) + 72 = 99$
   $24 - 24z - 9 + 3z + 7z = 99$
        $15 - 14z = 99$
     $15 - 15 - 14z = 99 - 15$
         $-14z = 84$
       $\dfrac{-14z}{-14} = \dfrac{84}{-14}$
          $z = -6$
  $x = 2 - 2z$       $y = 9 - 3z$
  $x = 2 - 2(-6)$    $y = 9 - 3(-6)$
  $x = 2 + 12$       $y = 9 + 18$
  $x = 14$         $y = 27$

  The solution is $(14, 27, -6)$.

**41.**

$$10t + u - 36 = 10u + t$$
$$10t - t + u - 36 = 10u + t - t$$
$$9t + u - u - 36 = 10u - u$$
$$9t - 36 = 9u$$
$$\frac{9t}{9} - \frac{36}{9} = \frac{9u}{9}$$
$$t - 4 = u$$

If $t = 1$, $u = -3$    no    $t = 6$, $u = 2$    yes

     $t = 2$, $u = -2$    no    $t = 7$, $u = 3$    yes

     $t = 3$, $u = -1$    no    $t = 8$, $u = 4$    yes

     $t = 4$, $u = 0$    yes    $t = 9$, $u = 5$    yes

     $t = 5$, $u = 1$    yes

$t = 1$, 2, or 3 means the number will be negative.  The integers that make the statement true are 40, 51, 62, 73, 84, 95.

**42.** $x$ = miles Eric ran      $x + y = 16$

     $y$ = miles Eric walked      $x - 1 = 2y$

$$x + y = 16$$
$$x = 16 - y$$
$$x - 1 = 2y$$
$$(16 - y) - 1 = 2y$$
$$15 - y = 2y$$
$$15 = 3y$$
$$5 = y$$
$$x + y = 16$$
$$x + 5 = 16$$
$$x = 11$$

     Eric ran 11 miles.

**43.** $x$ = money invested at 10% interest

     $y$ = money invested at 12% interest

$$x + y = 4000$$
$$0.10x + 0.12y = 460$$
$$x + y = 4000$$
$$x - x + y = 4000 - x$$
$$y = 4000 - x$$
$$0.10x + 0.12y = 460$$
$$0.10x + 0.12(4000 - x) = 460$$
$$0.10x + 480 - 0.12x = 460$$
$$-0.02x + 480 = 460$$
$$-0.02x + 480 - 480 = 460 - 480$$
$$-0.02x = -20$$
$$\frac{-0.02x}{-0.02} = \frac{-20}{-0.02}$$
$$x = 1000$$
$$x + y = 4000$$
$$1000 + y = 4000$$
$$1000 - 1000 + y = 4000 - 1000$$
$$y = 3000$$

Fina invested $1000 at 10% interest and $3000 at 12% interest.

**44.** $x$ = amount of 25% acid

     $y$ = amount of 50% acid

$$x + y = 500 \qquad\qquad x + y = 500$$
$$0.25x + 0.50y = 0.34 \cdot 500 \quad x - x + y = 500 - x$$
$$y = 500 - x$$
$$0.25x + 0.50y = 170$$
$$0.25x + 0.50(500 - x) = 170$$
$$0.25x + 250 - 0.50x = 170$$
$$-0.25x + 250 - 250 = 170 - 250$$
$$-0.25x = -80$$
$$\frac{-0.25x}{-0.25} = \frac{-80}{-0.25}$$
$$x = 320$$
$$x + y = 500$$
$$320 + y = 500$$
$$320 - 320 + y = 500 - 320$$
$$y = 180$$

MX Labs should mix 320 gallons of 25% solution and 180 gallons of 50% solution.

**45.** $x$ = tapes sold for $10

     $y$ = tapes sold for $8

$$x + y = 500$$
$$10x + 8y = 9.50 \times 500$$
$$x + y = 500$$
$$x + y - y = 500 - y$$
$$x = 500 - y$$
$$10x + 8y = 4750$$
$$10(500 - y) + 8y = 4750$$
$$5000 - 10y + 8y = 4750$$
$$5000 - 2y - 5000 = 4750 - 5000$$
$$-2y = -250$$
$$\frac{-2y}{-2} = \frac{-250}{-2}$$
$$y = 125$$

There were 125 of the $8 tapes sold.

**46.** $|13 - 2y| < 9$

$$13 - 2y < 9 \qquad\qquad\qquad 13 - 2y > -9$$
$$13 - 13 - 2y < 9 - 13 \qquad 13 - 13 - 2y > -9 - 13$$
$$-2y < -4 \qquad\qquad\qquad -2y > -22$$
$$\frac{-2y}{-2} > \frac{-4}{-2} \qquad\qquad\qquad \frac{-2y}{-2} < \frac{-22}{-2}$$
$$y > 2 \qquad\qquad\qquad\qquad y < 11$$
$$\{y \mid 2 < y < 11\}$$

**47.** $x^3 + 2x^2 - 4x - 8 = (x^3 + 2x^2) - (4x + 8)$

$$= x^2(x + 2) - 4(x + 2)$$
$$= (x^2 - 4)(x + 2)$$
$$= (x - 2)(x + 2)(x + 2)$$
$$= (x + 2)^2(x - 2)$$

**48.** $f(s) = 25 + 0.15s$

$f(s) = \$94$

$$25 + 0.15s = 94$$
$$25 - 25 + 0.15s = 94 - 25$$
$$0.15s = 69$$
$$\frac{0.15s}{0.15} = \frac{69}{0.15}$$
$$s = 460$$

Amy's total sales for the day were $460.

**49.** slope: $m = \dfrac{y_2 - y_1}{x_2 - x_1}$

$$= \frac{-2 - 1}{6 - (-5)}$$
$$= \frac{-3}{11} \text{ or } -\frac{3}{11}$$
$$y - y_1 = m(x - x_1)$$
$$y - 1 = -\frac{3}{11}[x - (-5)]$$
$$y - 1 = -\frac{3}{11}(x + 5)$$
$$11(y - 1) = -3(x + 5)$$
$$11y - 11 = -3x - 15$$
$$3x + 11y = -4$$

**50.**

$$5x - 3y = 12 \qquad\qquad 2x - 5y = 1$$
$$5x - 5x - 3y = 12 - 5x \quad 2x - 2x - 5y = 1 - 2x$$
$$-3y = 12 - 5x \qquad\qquad -5y = 1 - 2x$$
$$\frac{-3y}{-3} = \frac{12}{-3} - \frac{5x}{-3} \qquad \frac{-5y}{-5} = \frac{1}{-5} - \frac{2x}{-5}$$
$$y = \frac{5}{3}x - 4 \qquad\qquad y = \frac{2}{5}x - \frac{1}{5}$$

The solution is (3, 1).

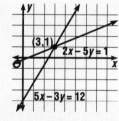

---

<table>
<tr><td>

**11-4**

</td><td>

## Elimination Using
## Addition and Subtraction

</td></tr>
</table>

**PAGES 454-455   CHECKING FOR UNDERSTANDING**

1. It is easier to solve a system of equations by elimination using subtraction when the coefficients of either the $x$-terms or the $y$-terms are the same.

2. It is easier to solve a system of equations by elimination using addition when the coefficients of either the $x$-terms or the $y$-terms are additive inverses of each other.

3. Yes, the numbers are the same if you let $y$ = the greater number and $x$ = the lesser number, but the solution is (18, 24) and not (24, 18).

4. The result when you add the two equations is $0 = 35$, which is false. The result tells you that the system has no solution.

5. subtraction

$$3a + b = 6 \qquad\qquad 3(1) + b = 6$$
$$\underline{(-)\ 4a + b = 7} \qquad\qquad 3 + b = 6$$
$$-a = -1 \qquad\qquad\qquad b = 3$$
$$a = 1$$

The solution is (1, 3).

6. neither

$$n + 2m = 3$$
$$n + 2m - 2m = 3 - 2m$$
$$n = 3 - 2m$$
$$m + 3n = 5$$
$$m + 3(3 - 2m) = 5$$
$$m + 9 - 6m = 5$$
$$-5m + 9 - 9 = 5 - 9$$
$$-5m = -4$$
$$m = \frac{4}{5}$$
$$n = 3 - 2m$$
$$n = 3 - 2\left(\frac{4}{5}\right)$$
$$n = 3 - \frac{8}{5}$$
$$n = \frac{7}{5}$$

The solution is $\left(\frac{4}{5}, \frac{7}{5}\right)$.

7. addition

$$3x + y = 12 \qquad\qquad 3x + \frac{9}{2} = 12$$
$$\underline{(+)\ -3x + 3y = 6}$$
$$4y = 18 \qquad\qquad\qquad 3x = \frac{15}{2}$$
$$y = \frac{18}{4} = \frac{9}{2} \qquad\qquad x = \frac{5}{2}$$

The solution is $\left(\frac{5}{2}, \frac{9}{2}\right)$.

8. both

$$5x + y = 9 \qquad\qquad 5x + 8 = 9$$
$$\underline{(+)\ -5x + y = 7} \qquad\qquad 5x = 1$$
$$2y = 16 \qquad\qquad\qquad x = \frac{1}{5}$$
$$y = 8$$

$$\boxed{\text{OR}}$$

$$5x + y = 9 \qquad\qquad 5\left(\frac{1}{5}\right) + y = 9$$
$$\underline{(-)\ -5x + y = 7} \qquad\qquad 1 + y = 9$$
$$10x = 2 \qquad\qquad\qquad y = 8$$
$$x = \frac{2}{10} = \frac{1}{5}$$

The solution is $\left(\frac{1}{5}, 8\right)$.

9. 
$$x + y = -3$$
$$(-)\ 2x + y = 6$$
$$-x = -9$$
$$x = 9$$

$$x + y = -3$$
$$9 + y = -3$$
$$y = -12$$

The solution is $(9, -12)$.

10. 
$$x + y = 6$$
$$(+)\ 2x - y = 6$$
$$3x = 12$$
$$x = 4$$

$$x + y = 6$$
$$4 + y = 6$$
$$y = 2$$

The solution is $(4, 2)$.

11. 
$$5x - 2y = 23$$
$$(+)\ 5x + 2y = 17$$
$$10x = 40$$
$$x = 4$$

$$5x - 2y = 23$$
$$5(4) - 2y = 23$$
$$-2y = 3$$
$$y = -\frac{3}{2}$$

The solution is $\left(4, -\frac{3}{2}\right)$.

12. $2x = 4 - 3y \rightarrow \quad 3y + 2x = 4$
$3y - x = 11 \rightarrow (-)\ 3y - x = 11$
$$3x = -7$$
$$x = -\frac{7}{3}$$

$$3y + 2x = 4$$
$$3y + 2\left(-\frac{7}{3}\right) = 4$$
$$3y - \frac{14}{3} = 4$$
$$3y = \frac{26}{3}$$
$$y = \frac{26}{9}$$

The solution is $\left(-\frac{7}{3}, \frac{26}{9}\right)$.

13. 
$$x + y = 7$$
$$(+)\ x - y = 9$$
$$2x = 16$$
$$x = 8$$

$$x + y = 7$$
$$8 + y = 7$$
$$y = -1$$

The solution is $(8, -1)$.

14. 
$$r - s = -5$$
$$(-)\ r + s = 25$$
$$-2s = -30$$
$$s = 15$$

$$r - s = -5$$
$$r - 15 = -5$$
$$r = 10$$

The solution is $(10, 15)$.

15. 
$$2x - y = 32$$
$$(+)\ 2x + y = 60$$
$$4x = 92$$
$$x = 23$$

$$2x + y = 60$$
$$2(23) + y = 60$$
$$46 + y = 60$$
$$y = 14$$

The solution is $(23, 14)$.

16. $x - y = 3 \rightarrow \quad x - y = 3$
$y + x = 3 \rightarrow (+)\ x + y = 3$
$$2x = 6$$
$$x = 3$$

$$x + y = 3$$
$$3 + y = 3$$
$$y = 0$$

The solution is $(3, 0)$.

17. $-n + m = 6 \rightarrow \quad m - n = 6$
$m + n = 5 \rightarrow (+)\ m + n = 5$
$$2m = 11$$
$$m = \frac{11}{2}$$

$$m + n = 5$$
$$\frac{11}{2} + n = 5$$
$$n = -\frac{1}{2}$$

The solution is $\left(\frac{11}{2}, -\frac{1}{2}\right)$.

18. 
$$x + y = 8$$
$$(+)\ 2x - y = 6$$
$$3x = 14$$
$$x = \frac{14}{3}$$

$$x + y = 8$$
$$\frac{14}{3} + y = 8$$
$$y = \frac{10}{3}$$

The solution is $\left(\frac{14}{3}, \frac{10}{3}\right)$.

19. 
$$x + 2y = 8$$
$$(-)\ 3x + 2y = 6$$
$$-2x = 2$$
$$x = -1$$

$$x + 2y = 8$$
$$-1 + 2y = 8$$
$$2y = 9$$
$$y = \frac{9}{2}$$

The solution is $\left(-1, \frac{9}{2}\right)$.

20. $3x + 1 = -7y \rightarrow \quad 3x + 7y = -1$
$6x + 7y = 0 \rightarrow (-)\ 6x + 7y = 0$
$$-3x = -1$$
$$x = \frac{1}{3}$$

$$3x + 7y = -1$$
$$3\left(\frac{1}{3}\right) + 7y = -1$$
$$1 + 7y = -1$$
$$7y = -2$$
$$y = -\frac{2}{7}$$

The solution is $\left(\frac{1}{3}, -\frac{2}{7}\right)$.

21. $3x = 13 - y \rightarrow \quad 3x + y = 13$
$2x - y = 2 \rightarrow (+)\ 2x - y = 2$
$$5x = 15$$
$$x = 3$$

$$3x = 13 - y$$
$$3(3) = 13 - y$$
$$9 = 13 - y$$
$$-y = -4$$
$$y = 4$$

The solution is $(3, 4)$.

22. $2x - 3y = -4 \rightarrow \quad 2x - 3y = -4$
$x = 7 - 3y \rightarrow (+)\ x + 3y = 7$
$$3x = 3$$
$$x = 1$$

$$2x - 3y = -4$$
$$2(1) - 3y = -4$$
$$2 - 3y = -4$$
$$-3y = -6$$
$$y = 2$$

The solution is $(1, 2)$.

201

23. $5s + 4t = 12 \rightarrow$ $\quad 5s + 4t = 12 \quad 5s + 4t = 12$

$3s = 4 + 4t \rightarrow$ (+) $3s - 4t = 4 \quad 5(2) + 4t = 12$

$\qquad\qquad\qquad\qquad 8s = 16 \qquad 10 + 4t = 12$

$\qquad\qquad\qquad\qquad s = 2 \qquad\qquad 4t = 2$

$\qquad\qquad\qquad\qquad\qquad\qquad\qquad t = \frac{1}{2}$

The solution is $\left(2, \frac{1}{2}\right)$

24. $12x - 9y = 114 \rightarrow \quad 12x - 9y = 114$

$7y + 12x = 82 \rightarrow$ (−) $12x + 7y = 82$

$\qquad\qquad\qquad\qquad\qquad -16y = 32$

$\qquad\qquad\qquad\qquad\qquad\quad y = -2$

$\qquad 12x - 9y = 114$

$\qquad 12x - 9(-2) = 114$

$\qquad 12x + 18 = 114$

$\qquad\quad 12x = 96$

$\qquad\qquad x = 8$

The solution is $(8, -2)$.

25. $\qquad 4x - \frac{1}{3}y = 8 \qquad\qquad 4x - \frac{1}{3}y = 8$

(+) $5x + \frac{1}{3}y = 6 \qquad 4\left(\frac{14}{9}\right) - \frac{1}{3}y = 8$

$\qquad\quad 9x = 14 \qquad\qquad \frac{56}{9} - \frac{1}{3}y = 8$

$\qquad\qquad x = \frac{14}{9} \qquad\qquad -\frac{1}{3}y = \frac{16}{9}$

$\qquad\qquad\qquad\qquad\qquad\qquad\quad y = -\frac{16}{3}$

The solution is $\left(\frac{14}{9}, -\frac{16}{3}\right)$.

26. $\qquad \frac{3}{4}x + \frac{1}{5}y = 5 \qquad\qquad \frac{3}{4}x + \frac{1}{5}y = 5$

(+) $\frac{3}{4}x - \frac{1}{5}y = -5 \qquad \frac{3}{4}(0) + \frac{1}{5}y = 5$

$\qquad\quad \frac{6}{4}x = 0 \qquad\qquad\qquad \frac{1}{5}y = 5$

$\qquad\qquad x = 0 \qquad\qquad\qquad\quad y = 25$

The solution is $(0, 25)$.

27. $\qquad \frac{2}{3}x - \frac{1}{2}y = 14 \qquad\qquad \frac{2}{3}x - \frac{1}{2}y = 14$

(−) $\frac{5}{6}x - \frac{1}{2}y = 18 \qquad \frac{2}{3}(24) - \frac{1}{2}y = 14$

$\qquad -\frac{1}{6}x = -4 \qquad\qquad 16 - \frac{1}{2}y = 14$

$\qquad\qquad x = 24 \qquad\qquad\qquad -\frac{1}{2}y = -2$

$\qquad\qquad\qquad\qquad\qquad\qquad\qquad y = 4$

The solution is $(24, 4)$.

28. $\qquad 9x + 2y = 26 \qquad\qquad 9x + 2y = 26$

(+) $1.5x - 2y = 13 \qquad\qquad 9\left(\frac{26}{7}\right) + 2y = 26$

$\qquad 10.5x = 39 \qquad\qquad\qquad \frac{234}{7} + 2y = \frac{182}{7}$

$\qquad\qquad x = \frac{39}{10.5} \qquad\qquad\qquad 2y = -\frac{52}{7}$

$\qquad\qquad\quad = \frac{390}{105} = \frac{26}{7} \qquad\qquad y = -\frac{26}{7}$

The solution is $\left(\frac{26}{7}, -\frac{26}{7}\right)$.

29. $3x + 0.2y = 7 \rightarrow \quad 3x + 0.2y = 7$

$3x = 0.4y + 4 \rightarrow$ (−) $3x - 0.4y = 4$

$\qquad\qquad\qquad\qquad\qquad 0.6y = 3$

$\qquad\qquad\qquad\qquad\qquad\quad y = 5$

$\qquad 3x + 0.2y = 7$

$\qquad 3x + 0.2(5) = 7$

$\qquad 3x + 1 = 7$

$\qquad\quad 3x = 6$

$\qquad\qquad x = 2$

The solution is $(2, 5)$.

30. $0.6m - 0.2n = 0.9 = \quad 0.6m - 0.2n = 0.9$

$0.3m = 0.9 - 0.2n =$ (+) $0.3m + 0.2n = 0.9$

$\qquad\qquad\qquad\qquad\qquad\qquad 0.9m = 1.8$

$\qquad\qquad\qquad\qquad\qquad\qquad\quad m = 2$

$\qquad 0.6m - 0.2n = 0.9$

$\qquad 0.6(2) - 0.2n = 0.9$

$\qquad 1.2 - 0.2n = 0.9$

$\qquad\qquad -0.2n = -0.3$

$\qquad\qquad\qquad n = 1.5$

The solution is $(2, 1.5)$.

31. $x$ = first number

$y$ = second number

$\qquad x + y = 64 \qquad\qquad x + y = 64$

(+) $x - y = 42 \qquad\qquad 53 + y = 64$

$\qquad\quad 2x = 106 \qquad\qquad\qquad y = 11$

$\qquad\qquad x = 53$

The numbers are 11 and 53.

32. $t$ = tens digit

$u$ = units digit

$t + u = 7 \rightarrow \qquad t + u = 7 \qquad t + u = 7$

$u = 2t + 1 \rightarrow$ (−) $-2t + u = 1 \qquad 2 + u = 7$

$\qquad\qquad\qquad\qquad\quad 3t = 6 \qquad\qquad\quad u = 5$

$\qquad\qquad\qquad\qquad\quad t = 2$

The number is 25.

33. $\qquad x - y + 2z = 8 \qquad 4x - 3z = 7$

(+) $2x + y + z = 13 \qquad 4(4) - 3z = 7$

$\qquad 3x + 3z = 21 \qquad\quad 16 - 3z = 7$

(+) $\qquad 4x - 3z = 7 \qquad\qquad -3z = -9$

$\qquad\quad 7x = 28 \qquad\qquad\qquad z = 3$

$\qquad\qquad x = 4$

$\quad x - y + 2z = 8$

$\quad 4 - y + 2(3) = 8$

$\qquad 4 - y + 6 = 8$

$\qquad\quad 10 - y = 8$

$\qquad\qquad -y = -2$

$\qquad\qquad\quad y = 2$

The solution is $(4, 2, 3)$.

**34.**

$$-3x + y - z = 6$$
$$(+)\ 3x - 2y + 2z = -9$$
$$-y + z = -3$$
$$(-)\quad -y - 3z = 1$$
$$4z = -4$$
$$z = -1$$

$$-y - 3z = 1$$
$$-y - 3(-1) = 1$$
$$-y + 3 = 1$$
$$-y = -2$$
$$y = 2$$

$$3x - 2y + 2z = -9$$
$$3x - 2(2) + 2(-1) = -9$$
$$3x - 4 - 2 = -9$$
$$3x - 6 = -9$$
$$3x = -3$$
$$x = -1$$

The solution is $(-1, 2, -1)$.

**35.**

$$5x - 2y + z = 0$$
$$(-)\ 2x - y + z = -3$$
$$3x - y = 3$$
$$(-)\quad 3x + 4y = 18$$
$$-5y = -15$$
$$y = 3$$

$$3x - y = 3$$
$$3x - 3 = 3$$
$$3x = 6$$
$$x = 2$$

$$5x - 2y + z = 0$$
$$5(2) - 2(3) + z = 0$$
$$10 - 6 + z = 0$$
$$4 + z = 0$$
$$z = -4$$

The solution is $(2, 3, -4)$.

**36.** $x$ = first number

$y$ = second number

$$\frac{x + y}{2} = 28 =$$

$$\frac{1}{2}x + \frac{1}{2}y = 28$$

$$3x = \frac{1}{2}y = (+)\ 3x - \frac{1}{2}y = 0$$

$$\frac{7}{2}x = 28$$

$$x = 8$$

$$\frac{1}{2}x + \frac{1}{2}y = 28$$

$$\frac{1}{2}(8) + \frac{1}{2}y = 28$$

$$4 + \frac{1}{2}y = 28$$

$$\frac{1}{2}y = 24$$

$$y = 48$$

The numbers are 8 and 48.

**37.**

$$Ax + By = 7$$
$$A(11) + B(-5) = 7$$
$$11A - 5B = 7$$

$$11A - 5B = 7$$
$$(-)\ 11A + 10B = 52$$
$$-15B = -45$$
$$B = 3$$

$$Ax + (1 - 2B)y = 47$$
$$A(11) + (1 - 2B)(-5) = 47$$
$$11A - 5 + 10B = 47$$
$$11A + 10B = 52$$

$$11A - 5B = 7$$
$$11A - 5(3) = 7$$
$$11A - 15 = 7$$
$$11A = 22$$
$$A = 2$$

The values are: $A = 2$ and $B = 3$.

**38.** $x$ = number of women who attended

$y$ = number of men who attended

$$x + y = 2713 \rightarrow \quad x + y = 2713 \quad x + y = 2713$$
$$x + 163 = y \rightarrow (+)\ x - y = -163 \quad 1275 + y = 2713$$
$$2x = 2550 \quad y = 1438$$
$$x = 1275$$

1275 women attended and 1438 men attended.

**39.** $x$ = Jerrod's math score

$y$ = Jerrod's verbal score

$$x + y = 1340 \rightarrow \quad x + y = 1340$$
$$x + 400 = 2y \rightarrow (-)\ x - 2y = -400$$
$$3y = 1740$$
$$y = 580$$

$$x + y = 1340$$
$$x + 580 = 1340$$
$$x = 760$$

Jerrod's score was 760 for math and 580 for verbal.

**40.** $x$ = rate of speedboat

$5x$ = rate of current

|  | $r$ | $t$ | $d$ | $r \cdot t = d$ |
|---|---|---|---|---|
| Downstream | $5x - x$ | $y$ | 48 | $4x \cdot y = 48$ |
| Upstream | $5x + x$ | $5 - y$ | 48 | $6x(5 - y) = 48$ |

$$4x \cdot y = 48 \quad 6x(5 - y) = 48 \quad\quad y = \frac{12}{x}$$

$$y = \frac{48}{4x} \quad 5 - y = \frac{48}{6x} \quad (+)\ 5 - y = \frac{8}{x}$$

$$y = \frac{12}{x} \quad 5 - y = \frac{8}{x} \quad 5 = \frac{20}{x}$$

$$5x = 20$$

$$x = 4$$

The rate of the current is 4 mph.

**41.** $y + n^3 = 2x$

**42.**

$$12m^2 + 3 = -20m$$
$$12m^2 + 20m + 3 = 0$$
$$(2m + 3)(6m + 1) = 0$$
$$2m + 3 = 0 \quad\quad 6m + 1 = 0$$
$$2m = -3 \quad\quad 6m = -1$$
$$m = -\frac{3}{2} \quad\quad m = -\frac{1}{6}$$

$$12\left(-\frac{3}{2}\right)2 + 3 \overset{?}{=} -20\left(-\frac{3}{2}\right)$$

$$12\left(\frac{9}{4}\right) + 3 \overset{?}{=} 30$$

$$27 + 3 \overset{?}{=} 30$$

$$30 = 30\ \checkmark$$

$$12\left(-\frac{1}{6}\right)2 + 3 \overset{?}{=} -20\left(-\frac{1}{6}\right)$$

$$12\left(\frac{1}{36}\right) + 3 \overset{?}{=} \frac{10}{3}$$

$$\frac{1}{3} + 3 \overset{?}{=} \frac{10}{3}$$

$$\frac{1}{3} + \frac{9}{3} \overset{?}{=} \frac{10}{3}$$

$$\frac{10}{3} = \frac{10}{3}\ \checkmark$$

**43.** $D = \{5, -3, 4, 2\}$

$R = \{1, 2, 0\}$

$I = \{(1, 5), (2, -3), (2, 4), (0, 5), (2, 2)\}$

**44.** (0, 37,000) and (140, 4500)

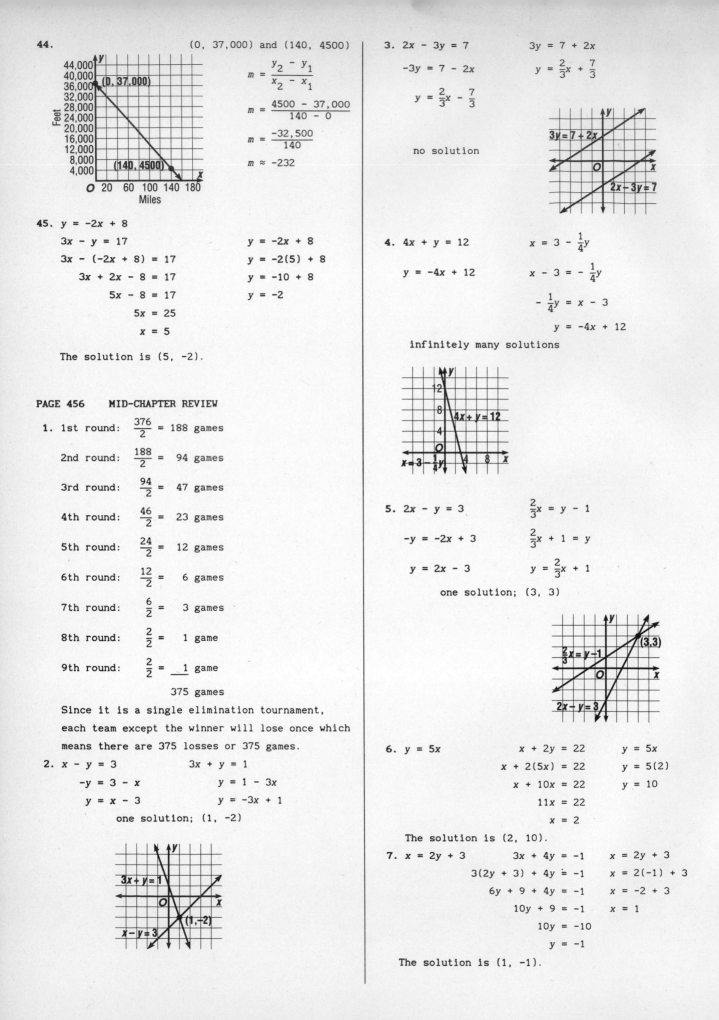

$m = \dfrac{y_2 - y_1}{x_2 - x_1}$

$m = \dfrac{4500 - 37{,}000}{140 - 0}$

$m = \dfrac{-32{,}500}{140}$

$m \approx -232$

**45.** $y = -2x + 8$

$3x - y = 17$

$3x - (-2x + 8) = 17$

$3x + 2x - 8 = 17$

$5x - 8 = 17$

$5x = 25$

$x = 5$

$y = -2x + 8$

$y = -2(5) + 8$

$y = -10 + 8$

$y = -2$

The solution is (5, -2).

**PAGE 456    MID-CHAPTER REVIEW**

**1.** 1st round: $\dfrac{376}{2} = 188$ games

2nd round: $\dfrac{188}{2} = 94$ games

3rd round: $\dfrac{94}{2} = 47$ games

4th round: $\dfrac{46}{2} = 23$ games

5th round: $\dfrac{24}{2} = 12$ games

6th round: $\dfrac{12}{2} = 6$ games

7th round: $\dfrac{6}{2} = 3$ games

8th round: $\dfrac{2}{2} = 1$ game

9th round: $\dfrac{2}{2} = \underline{1}$ game

375 games

Since it is a single elimination tournament, each team except the winner will lose once which means there are 375 losses or 375 games.

**2.** $x - y = 3$         $3x + y = 1$

$-y = 3 - x$       $y = 1 - 3x$

$y = x - 3$        $y = -3x + 1$

one solution; (1, -2)

**3.** $2x - 3y = 7$        $3y = 7 + 2x$

$-3y = 7 - 2x$       $y = \dfrac{2}{3}x + \dfrac{7}{3}$

$y = \dfrac{2}{3}x - \dfrac{7}{3}$

no solution

**4.** $4x + y = 12$        $x = 3 - \dfrac{1}{4}y$

$y = -4x + 12$       $x - 3 = -\dfrac{1}{4}y$

$-\dfrac{1}{4}y = x - 3$

$y = -4x + 12$

infinitely many solutions

**5.** $2x - y = 3$         $\dfrac{2}{3}x = y - 1$

$-y = -2x + 3$        $\dfrac{2}{3}x + 1 = y$

$y = 2x - 3$          $y = \dfrac{2}{3}x + 1$

one solution; (3, 3)

**6.** $y = 5x$        $x + 2y = 22$        $y = 5x$

$x + 2(5x) = 22$        $y = 5(2)$

$x + 10x = 22$          $y = 10$

$11x = 22$

$x = 2$

The solution is (2, 10).

**7.** $x = 2y + 3$        $3x + 4y = -1$        $x = 2y + 3$

$3(2y + 3) + 4y = -1$        $x = 2(-1) + 3$

$6y + 9 + 4y = -1$        $x = -2 + 3$

$10y + 9 = -1$        $x = 1$

$10y = -10$

$y = -1$

The solution is (1, -1).

8. $2y - x = -5$

$-x = -2y - 5$

$x = 2y + 5$

$4y - 3x = -1$

$4y - 3(2y + 5) = -1$

$4y - 6y - 15 = -1$

$-2y - 15 = -1$

$-2y = 14$

$y = -7$

$2y - x = -5$

$2(-7) - x = -5$

$-14 - x = -5$

$-x = 9$

$x = -9$

The solution is $(-9, -7)$.

9. $3x + 2y = 18$

$3x = 18 \cdot 2y$

$x = 6 - \frac{2}{3}y$

$\frac{1}{4}x + \frac{2}{3}y = 3$

$\frac{1}{4}\left(6 - \frac{2}{3}y\right) + \frac{2}{3}y = 3$

$\frac{3}{2} - \frac{1}{6}y + \frac{2}{3}y = 3$

$\frac{3}{2} + \frac{1}{2}y = 3$

$\frac{1}{2}y = \frac{3}{2}$

$y = 3$

$3x + 2y = 18$

$3x + 2(3) = 18$

$3x + 6 = 18$

$3x = 12$

$x = 4$

The solution is $(4, 3)$.

10. $x =$ Odina's speed walking

$y =$ Odina's speed on her bicycle

$x = 0.25y \qquad x + 6 = y$

$x + 6 = y \qquad 0.25y + 6 = y$

$\qquad\qquad\qquad 6 = 0.75y$

$\qquad\qquad\qquad y = 8$ mph

Odina's speed on her bicycle is 8 mph.

## 11-5  Elimination Using Multiplication

1. Yes, they are equivalent equations since
$5x - 7y = 3$ multiplied by $-3$ is $-15x + 21y = -9$.

2. You might need to multiply each equation by a different number in order to make either the $x$-term or $y$-term become additive inverses.

3. Answers may vary.  Sample answer:
$x - y = 1$ and $x + 3y = 1$

4. Multiply the first equation by $-3$.  Then add.

$x + 2y = 5 \rightarrow -3x - 6y = -15 \qquad x + 2y = 5$

$3x + y = 7 \rightarrow \underline{3x + \phantom{6}y = \phantom{-1}7} \qquad x + 2\left(\frac{8}{5}\right) = 5$

$\qquad\qquad\qquad -5y = -8 \qquad\qquad x + \frac{16}{5} = 5$

$\qquad\qquad\qquad y = \frac{8}{5} \qquad\qquad\qquad x = \frac{9}{5}$

The solution is $\left(\frac{9}{5}, \frac{8}{5}\right)$.

5. Multiply the second equation by $-4$.  Then add.

$4x + y = 8 \rightarrow 4x + \phantom{1}y = \phantom{-}8 \qquad 4x + y = 8$

$x - 7y = 2 \rightarrow \underline{-4x + 14y = -8} \qquad 4x + 0 = 8$

$\qquad\qquad\qquad 15y = 0 \qquad\qquad\quad 4x = 8$

$\qquad\qquad\qquad y = 0 \qquad\qquad\qquad x = 2$

The solution is $(2, 0)$.

6. Add.    $\quad y + x = 9 \qquad\qquad y + x = 9$

$\qquad\qquad \underline{2y - x = 1} \qquad\qquad \frac{10}{3} + x = 9$

$\qquad\qquad\quad 3y = 10 \qquad\qquad x = 9 - \frac{10}{3}$

$\qquad\qquad\quad y = \frac{10}{3} \qquad\qquad x = \frac{17}{3}$

The solution is $\left(\frac{17}{3}, \frac{10}{3}\right)$.

7. Multiply the first equation by 3 and the second equation by $-2$.  Then add.

$2x + y = 6 \rightarrow 6x + 3y = 18 \qquad 2x + y = 6$

$3x - 7y = 9 \rightarrow \underline{-6x + 14y = -18} \qquad 2x + 0 = 6$

$\qquad\qquad\qquad 17y = 0 \qquad\qquad\quad 2x = 6$

$\qquad\qquad\qquad y = 0 \qquad\qquad\qquad x = 3$

The solution is $(3, 0)$.

8. Multiply the second equation by 4.  Then add.

$x + 8y = 3 \rightarrow x + 8y = 3 \qquad x + 8y = 3$

$4x - 2y = 7 \rightarrow \underline{16x - 8y = 28} \qquad \frac{31}{17} + 8y = 3$

$\qquad\qquad\qquad 17x = 31 \qquad\qquad 8y = 3 - \frac{31}{17}$

$\qquad\qquad\qquad x = \frac{31}{17} \qquad \frac{1}{8} \cdot 8y = \frac{20}{17} \cdot \frac{1}{8}$

$\qquad\qquad\qquad\qquad\qquad\qquad y = \frac{5}{34}$

The solution is $\left(\frac{31}{17}, \frac{5}{34}\right)$.

9. Multiply the first equation by 2.  Then add.

$4x - y = 4 \rightarrow 8x - 2y = 8 \qquad 4x - y = 4$

$x + 2y = 3 \rightarrow \underline{x + 2y = 3} \qquad 4\left(\frac{11}{9}\right) - y = 4$

$\qquad\qquad\qquad 9x = 11 \qquad\qquad \frac{44}{9} - y = 4$

$\qquad\qquad\qquad x = \frac{11}{9} \qquad\qquad -y = 4 - \frac{44}{9}$

$\qquad\qquad\qquad\qquad\qquad\qquad -y = -\frac{8}{9}$

$\qquad\qquad\qquad\qquad\qquad\qquad y = \frac{8}{9}$

The solution is $\left(\frac{11}{9}, \frac{8}{9}\right)$.

**10.** Multiply the second equation by -3. Then add.

$3y - 8x = 9 \rightarrow 3y - 8x = 9$ $\qquad y - x = 2$

$y - x = 2 \rightarrow \underline{-3y + 3x = -6}$ $\qquad y - \left(-\dfrac{3}{5}\right) = 2$

$\qquad\qquad\qquad\qquad -5x = 3$ $\qquad y + \dfrac{3}{5} = 2$

$\qquad\qquad\qquad x = -\dfrac{3}{5}$ $\qquad y = 2 - \dfrac{3}{5}$

$\qquad\qquad\qquad\qquad\qquad\qquad y = \dfrac{7}{5}$

The solution is $\left(-\dfrac{3}{5}, \dfrac{7}{5}\right)$.

**11.** Multiply the first equation by 2 and the second equation by -5. Then add.

$5y - 4x = 2 \rightarrow 10y - 8x = 4$ $\qquad 10y - 8x = 4$

$2y + x = 6 \rightarrow \underline{-10y - 5x = -30}$ $\qquad 10y - 8(2) = 4$

$\qquad\qquad\qquad\qquad -13x = -26$ $\qquad 10y - 16 = 4$

$\qquad\qquad\qquad\qquad\quad x = 2$ $\qquad 10y = 20$

$\qquad\qquad\qquad\qquad\qquad\qquad y = 2$

The solution is (2, 2).

**PAGES 460-461    EXERCISES**

**12.** $x - 5y = 0 \rightarrow -2x + 10y = 0$ $\qquad x - 5y = 0$

$2x - 3y = 7 \rightarrow \underline{2x - 3y = 7}$ $\qquad x - 5(1) = 0$

$\qquad\qquad\qquad\qquad 7y = 7$ $\qquad x - 5 = 0$

$\qquad\qquad\qquad\qquad y = 1$ $\qquad\qquad x = 5$

The solution is (5, 1).

**13.** $x + 4y = 30 \rightarrow x + 4y = 30$ $\qquad x + 4y = 30$

$2x - y = -6 \rightarrow \underline{8x - 4y = -24}$ $\qquad \dfrac{2}{3} + 4y = 30$

$\qquad\qquad\qquad\qquad 9x = 6$ $\qquad 4y = 30 - \dfrac{2}{3}$

$\qquad x = \dfrac{6}{9} = \dfrac{2}{3}$ $\quad \dfrac{1}{4} \cdot 4y = \dfrac{88}{3} \cdot \dfrac{1}{4}$

$\qquad\qquad\qquad\qquad\qquad\qquad y = \dfrac{22}{3}$

The solution is $\left(\dfrac{2}{3}, \dfrac{22}{3}\right)$.

**14.** $9x + 8y = 7 \rightarrow -18x - 16y = -14$

$18x - 15y = 14 \rightarrow \underline{18x - 15y = 14}$

$\qquad\qquad\qquad\qquad -31y = 0$

$\qquad\qquad\qquad\qquad y = 0$

$9x + 8y = 7$

$9x + 8(0) = 7$

$\qquad 9x = 7$

$\qquad x = \dfrac{7}{9}$

The solution is $\left(\dfrac{7}{9}, 0\right)$.

**15.** $-5x + 8y = 21 \rightarrow -10x + 16y = 42$

$10x + 3y = 15 \rightarrow \underline{10x + 3y = 15}$

$\qquad\qquad\qquad\qquad\qquad 19y = 57$

$\qquad\qquad\qquad\qquad\qquad y = \dfrac{57}{19}$

$\qquad\qquad\qquad\qquad\qquad y = 3$

$-5x + 8y = 21$

$-5x + 8(3) = 21$

$-5x + 24 = 21$

$\qquad -5x = 21 - 24$

$\qquad -5x = -3$

$\qquad x = \dfrac{-3}{-5} = \dfrac{3}{5}$

The solution is $\left(\dfrac{3}{5}, 3\right)$.

**16.** $5x + 3y = 12 \rightarrow 25x + 15y = 60$

$4x - 5y = 17 \rightarrow \underline{12x - 15y = 51}$

$\qquad\qquad\qquad\qquad\qquad 37x = 111$

$\qquad\qquad\qquad\qquad\qquad x = \dfrac{111}{37}$

$\qquad\qquad\qquad\qquad\qquad x = 3$

$5x + 3y = 12$

$5(3) + 3y = 12$

$15 + 3y = 12$

$\qquad 3y = 12 - 15$

$\qquad 3y = -3$

$\qquad y = -1$

The solution is (3, -1).

**17.** $4x + 3y = 19 \rightarrow 16x + 12y = 76$ $\qquad 4x + 3y = 19$

$3x - 4y = 8 \rightarrow \underline{9x - 12y = 24}$ $\qquad 4(4) + 3y = 19$

$\qquad\qquad\qquad\qquad 25x = 100$ $\qquad 16 + 3y = 19$

$\qquad\qquad\qquad\qquad x = 4$ $\qquad\qquad 3y = 3$

$\qquad\qquad\qquad\qquad\qquad\qquad\qquad y = 1$

The solution is (4, 1).

**18.** $7x + 2y = 3(x + 16)$ $\qquad x + 16 = 5y + 3x$

$7x + 2y = 3x + 48$ $\qquad 2x + 5y = 16$

$4x + 2y = 48$

$2x + y = 24$

$2x + y = 24 \rightarrow 2x + y = 24$ $\qquad 2x + y = 24$

$2x + 5y = 16 \rightarrow \underline{-2x - 5y = -16}$ $\qquad 2x - 2 = 24$

$\qquad\qquad\qquad\qquad -4y = 8$ $\qquad 2x = 26$

$\qquad\qquad\qquad\qquad y = -2$ $\qquad x = 13$

The solution is (13, -2).

**19.** $2x - y = 36 \rightarrow 2x - y = 36$ $\qquad 2x - y = 36$

$3x - 0.5y = 26 \rightarrow \underline{-6x + y = -52}$ $\qquad 2(4) - y = 36$

$\qquad\qquad\qquad\qquad -4x = -16$ $\qquad 8 - y = 36$

$\qquad\qquad\qquad\qquad x = 4$ $\qquad -y = 28$

$\qquad\qquad\qquad\qquad\qquad\qquad y = -28$

The solution is (4, -28).

**20.** $x - 0.5y = 1 \rightarrow 2x - y = 2$ $\qquad x - 0.5y = 1$

$0.4x + y = -2 \rightarrow \underline{0.4x + y = -2}$ $\qquad 0 - 0.5y = 1$

$\qquad\qquad\qquad\qquad 2.4x = 0$ $\qquad -0.5y = 1$

$\qquad\qquad\qquad\qquad x = 0$ $\qquad y = -2$

The solution is (0, -2).

21. $\frac{1}{3}x - y = -1 \rightarrow \quad \frac{1}{3}x - y = -1 \qquad\qquad \frac{1}{3}x - y = -1$

$\frac{1}{5}x - \frac{2}{5}y = -1 \rightarrow -\frac{1}{2}x + y = \frac{5}{2} \qquad \frac{1}{3}(-9) - y = -1$

$\qquad\qquad\qquad\qquad -\frac{1}{6}x = \frac{3}{2} \qquad\qquad -3 - y = -1$

$\qquad\qquad\qquad\qquad\qquad x = -9 \qquad\qquad\qquad -y = 2$

$\qquad\qquad\qquad\qquad\qquad\qquad\qquad\qquad\qquad y = -2$

The solution is $(-9, -2)$.

22. $\frac{1}{2}x - \frac{2}{3}y = \frac{7}{3} \quad \rightarrow -\frac{3}{2}x + 2y = -7$

$\frac{3}{2}x + 2y = -25 \rightarrow \quad \frac{3}{2}x + 2y = -25$

$\qquad\qquad\qquad\qquad\qquad 4y = -32$

$\qquad\qquad\qquad\qquad\qquad\quad y = -8$

$\qquad\quad \frac{3}{2}x + 2y = -25$

$\qquad\quad \frac{3}{2}x + 2(-8) = -25$

$\qquad\quad \frac{3}{2}x - 16 = -25$

$\qquad\quad \frac{2}{3} \cdot \frac{3}{2}x = -9 \cdot \frac{2}{3}$

$\qquad\qquad\qquad x = -6$

The solution is $(-6, -8)$.

23. $\frac{2x + y}{3} = 15 \rightarrow \frac{2}{3}x + \frac{1}{3}y = 15 \rightarrow 2x + y = 45$

$\frac{3x - y}{5} = 1 \quad \rightarrow \frac{3}{5}x - \frac{1}{5}y = 1 \rightarrow 3x - y = 5$

$\qquad\qquad\qquad\qquad\qquad\qquad\qquad\qquad 5x = 50$

$\qquad\qquad\qquad\qquad\qquad\qquad\qquad\qquad\quad x = 10$

$\qquad 2x + y = 45$

$\qquad 2(10) + y = 45$

$\qquad 20 + y = 45$

$\qquad\qquad\quad y = 25$

The solution is $(10, 25)$.

24. $\qquad x + y = 600 \rightarrow -0.08x - 0.08y = -48$

$0.06x + 0.08y = 46 \quad \rightarrow \quad 0.06x + 0.08y = 46$

$\qquad\qquad\qquad\qquad\qquad\qquad -0.02x = -2$

$\qquad\qquad\qquad\qquad\qquad\qquad\qquad x = \frac{-2}{-0.02}$

$\qquad\qquad\qquad\qquad\qquad\qquad\qquad\quad = 100$

$\qquad x + y = 600$

$\qquad 100 + y = 600$

$\qquad\qquad\quad y = 500$

The solution is $(100, 500)$.

25. $\qquad x + y = 20 \rightarrow -0.4x - 0.4y = -8$

$0.4x + 0.15y = 4 \quad \rightarrow \quad 0.4x + 0.15y = 4$

$\qquad\qquad\qquad\qquad\qquad\qquad -0.25y = -4$

$\qquad\qquad\qquad\qquad\qquad\qquad\qquad\quad y = 16$

$\qquad x + y = 20$

$\qquad x + 16 = 20$

$\qquad\qquad x = 4$

The solution is $(4, 16)$.

26. $\quad 0.25x + y = 3.5 \rightarrow -0.5x - 2y = -7$

$0.5x - 0.25y = 1 \quad \rightarrow \quad 0.5x - 0.25y = 1$

$\qquad\qquad\qquad\qquad\qquad\qquad -2.25y = -6$

$\qquad\qquad\qquad\qquad\qquad\qquad y = \frac{-6}{-2.25} = \frac{8}{3}$

$\quad 0.25x + y = 3.5$

$\quad 0.25x + \frac{8}{3} = 3.5$

$\qquad 0.25x = \frac{2.5}{3}$

$\qquad\qquad x = \frac{10}{3}$

The solution is $\left(\frac{10}{3}, \frac{8}{3}\right)$.

27. $t$ = tens digit

$u$ = units digit

$10t + u$ = original number

$10u + t$ = new number

$t + u = 7 \qquad\qquad 10u + t = 4(10t + u) - 3$

$\qquad\qquad\qquad\qquad 10u + t = 40t + 4u - 3$

$\qquad\qquad\qquad\qquad\quad 6u + t = 40t - 3$

$\qquad\qquad\qquad\qquad\quad 6u - 39t = -3$

$\qquad\qquad\qquad\qquad\quad 2u - 13t = -1$

$\quad u + t = 7 \quad \rightarrow -2u - 2t = -14$

$2u - 13t = -1 \rightarrow \quad 2u - 13t = -1$

$\qquad\qquad\qquad\qquad\qquad -15t = -15$

$\qquad\qquad\qquad\qquad\qquad\quad t = 1$

$\quad u + t = 7$

$\quad u + 1 = 7$

$\qquad\quad u = 6$

The number is 16.

28. $t$ = tens digit

$u$ = units digit

$10t + u$ = original number

$10u + t$ = new number

$\quad 4t = u \qquad (10t + u) + (10u + t) = 110$

$4t - u = 0 \qquad\qquad\qquad 11t + 11u = 110$

$\quad 4t - u = 0 \quad \rightarrow 44t - 11u = 0$

$11t + 11u = 110 \rightarrow \quad 11t + 11u = 110$

$\qquad\qquad\qquad\qquad\qquad 55t = 110$

$\qquad\qquad\qquad\qquad\qquad\quad t = 2$

$\quad 4t - u = 0$

$\quad 4(2) - u = 0$

$\qquad 8 - u = 0$

$\qquad\quad -u = -8$

$\qquad\qquad u = 8$

The number is 28.

**29.**

$$\frac{2}{x+7} - \frac{1}{y-3} = 0$$

$$\frac{2(y-3)}{(x+7)(y-3)} - \frac{1(x+7)}{(y-3)(x+7)} = 0$$

$$\frac{2y-6-x-7}{(x+7)(y-3)} = 0$$

$$2y - 6 - x - 7 = 0$$

$$2y - x - 13 = 0$$

$$2y - x = 13$$

$$\frac{1}{x-5} - \frac{3}{y+6} = 0$$

$$\frac{1(y+6)}{(x-5)(y+6)} - \frac{3(x-5)}{(x-5)(y+6)} = 0$$

$$\frac{y+6-3x+15}{(x-5)(y+6)} = 0$$

$$y - 3x + 21 = 0$$

$$y - 3x = -21$$

| | | |
|---|---|---|
| $2y - x = 13 \rightarrow$ | $2y - x = 13$ | $2y - x = 13$ |
| $y - 3x = -21 \rightarrow$ | $\underline{-2y + 6x = 42}$ | $2y - 11 = 13$ |
| | $5x = 55$ | $2y = 24$ |
| | $x = 11$ | $y = 12$ |

The solution is $(11, 12)$.

**30.**

| | | |
|---|---|---|
| $\frac{1}{x} + \frac{1}{y} = 7 \rightarrow$ | $-\frac{2}{x} - \frac{2}{y} = -14$ | $\frac{1}{x} + \frac{1}{y} = 7$ |
| $\frac{2}{x} + \frac{3}{y} = 16 \rightarrow$ | $\underline{\frac{2}{x} + \frac{3}{y} = 16}$ | $\frac{1}{x} + \frac{1}{\frac{1}{2}} = 7$ |
| | $\frac{1}{y} = 2$ | $\frac{1}{x} + 2 = 7$ |
| | $1 = 2y$ | $\frac{1}{x} = 5$ |
| | $y = \frac{1}{2}$ | $1 = 5x$ |
| | | $x = \frac{1}{5}$ |

The solution is $\left(\frac{1}{5}, \frac{1}{2}\right)$.

**31.**

| | |
|---|---|
| $\frac{1}{x+y} = 2$ | $\frac{1}{x-y} = \frac{1}{y}$ |
| $1 = 2(x+y)$ | $y = 1(x-y)$ |
| $2x + 2y = 1$ | $x - y = y$ |
| | $x - 2y = 0$ |
| $2x + 2y = 1$ | $x - 2y = 0$ |
| $\underline{x - 2y = 0}$ | $\frac{1}{3} - 2y = 0$ |
| $3x = 1$ | $-2y = -\frac{1}{3}$ |
| $x = \frac{1}{3}$ | $y = \frac{1}{6}$ |

The solution is $\left(\frac{1}{3}, \frac{1}{6}\right)$.

**32.** When using either method, if you ever reach an equation such as $0 = 3$, which is always false, then the system is inconsistent. If you ever reach an equation such as $0 = 0$, which is always true, then the system is consistent and dependent.

**33.** $x$ = rate of riverboat in still water
$y$ = rate of current

| | $r$ | $t$ | $d$ | $r \cdot t = d$ |
|---|---|---|---|---|
| Downstream | $x + y$ | $2$ | $48$ | $2x - 2y = 48$ |
| Upstream | $x - y$ | $2\frac{2}{3}$ | $48$ | $\frac{8}{3}x + \frac{8}{3}y = 48$ |

| | | |
|---|---|---|
| $2x + 2y = 48 \rightarrow$ | $\frac{8}{3}x + \frac{8}{3}y = 64$ | $2x + 2y = 48$ |
| $\frac{8}{3}x - \frac{8}{3}y = 48 \rightarrow$ | $\underline{\frac{8}{3}x - \frac{8}{3}y = 48}$ | $2(21) + 2y = 48$ |
| | $\frac{16}{3}x = 112$ | $42 + 2y = 48$ |
| | $\frac{3}{16} \cdot \frac{16}{3}x = 112 \cdot \frac{3}{16}$ | $2y = 6$ |
| | $x = 21$ | $y = 3$ |

**a.** The rate of the boat in still water is 21 mph.

**b.** The rate of the current is 3 mph.

**34.** $x$ = price of hot dogs
$y$ = price of soda

$$6x + 4y = 6.70 \rightarrow 12x + 8y = 13.40$$

$$4x + 3y = 4.65 \rightarrow \underline{-12x - 9y = -13.95}$$

$$-y = -0.55$$

$$y = 0.55$$

$$6x + 4y = 6.70$$

$$6x + 4(0.55) = 6.70$$

$$6x + 2.20 = 6.70$$

$$6x = 4.50$$

$$x = 0.75$$

**a.** The price of a hot dog is $0.75.

**b.** The price of a soda is $0.55.

**35.** $x$ = rate of plane in still air
$y$ = rate of wind

| | $r$ | $t$ | $d$ | $r \cdot t = d$ |
|---|---|---|---|---|
| Downwind | $x + 2y$ | $4$ | $2100$ | $4x + 8y = 2100$ |
| Upwind | $x - y$ | $4\frac{2}{3}$ | $2100$ | $\frac{14}{3}x - \frac{14}{3}y = 2100$ |

| | |
|---|---|
| $4x + 8y = 2100$ | $\frac{14}{3}x - \frac{14}{3} = 2100$ |
| $x + 2y = 525$ | $14x - 14y = 6300$ |
| $x + 2y = 525 \rightarrow$ | $7x + 14y = 3675$ |
| $14x - 14y = 6300 \rightarrow$ | $\underline{14x - 14y = 6300}$ |
| | $21x = 9975$ |
| | $x = 475$ |

The rate of the plane in still air is 475 mph.

36. $x$ = cost of a 1-night stay

 $y$ = cost per meal

 $2x + 3y = 195 \rightarrow 6x + 9y = 585$

 $3x + 5y = 300 \rightarrow \underline{-6x - 10y = -600}$

 $\phantom{3x + 5y = 300 \rightarrow} -y = -15$

 $\phantom{3x + 5y = 300 \rightarrow} y = 15$

 $2x + 3y = 195$

 $2x + 3(15) = 195$

 $2x + 45 = 195$

 $2x = 150$

 $x = 75$

 a. The cost of a 1-night stay is $75.

 b. The cost for a meal is $15.

37. a. $A = 5$, $B = 5$, $C = 16$, $D = 2$, $E = 2$, $F = 5$

 line 30: $A*E - B*D = 5*2 - 5*2$

 $= 10 - 10$

 $= 0$

 line 80: $C*E - B*F = 16*2 - 5*5$

 $= 32 - 25$

 $= 7$

 $A*F - C*D = 5*5 - 16*2$

 $= 25 - 32$

 $= 7$

 line 90: NO SOLUTION

 b. $A = 7$, $B = -3$, $C = 5$, $D = 14$, $E = -6$, $F = 10$

 line 30: $A*E - B*D = 7*(-6) - (-3)*14$

 $= -42 + 42$

 $= 0$

 line 80: $C*E - D*F = 5*(-6) - (-3)*10$

 $= -30 + 30$

 $= 0$

 line 110: INFINITE NUMBER OF SOLUTIONS

 c. $A = 1$, $B = -2$, $C = 5$, $D = 3$, $E = -5$, $F = 8$

 line 30: $A*E - B*D = 1*(-5) - (-2)*3$

 $= -5 - (-6)$

 $= 1$

 line 40:

 $X = (C*E - B*F)/(A*E - B*D)$

 $= (5*(-5) - (-2)*8)/(1*(-5) - (-2)*3)$

 $= (-25 + 16)/(-5 + 6)$

 $= -9/1$

 $= 9$

 line 50:

 $Y = (A*F - C*D)/(A*E - B*D)$

 $= (1*8 - 5*3)/(1*(-5) - (-2)*3)$

 $= (8 - 15)/(-5 + 6)$

 $= -7/1$

 $= -7$

 line 60: $(-9, -7)$ is a solution.

d. $A = 6$, $B = 3$, $C = 0$, $D = 4$, $E = 2$, $F = 0$

 line 30: $A*E - B*D = 6*2 - 3*4$

 $= 12 - 12$

 $= 0$

 line 80: $C*E - B*F = 0*2 - 3*0$

 $= 0 - 0$

 $= 0$

 line 110: INFINITE NUMBER OF SOLUTIONS

38. $\frac{1}{3}a + 3 = \frac{1}{2}a$ $\qquad$ $\frac{1}{3}a + 3 \stackrel{?}{=} \frac{1}{2}a$

 $\frac{1}{3}a - \frac{1}{3}a + 3 = \frac{1}{2}a - \frac{1}{3}a$ $\qquad$ $\frac{1}{3}(18) + 3 \stackrel{?}{=} \frac{1}{2}(18)$

 $3 = \frac{3}{6}a - \frac{2}{6}a$ $\qquad$ $6 + 3 \stackrel{?}{=} 9$

 $3 = \frac{1}{6}a$ $\qquad$ $9 = 9$ ✓

 $6 \cdot 3 = \frac{1}{6}a \cdot 6$

 $18 = a$

39.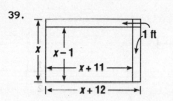

 $x(x + 12) - (x - 1)(x + 11) = 55$

 $x^2 + 12x - (x^2 + 10x - 11) = 55$

 $x^2 + 12x - x^2 - 10x + 11 = 55$

 $2x + 11 = 55$

 $2x = 44$

 $x = 22$

 $x + 12 = 34$

The original dimensions were 34 ft by 22 ft.

40. $\dfrac{\dfrac{m + 4}{m^2 + 4m + 4}}{\dfrac{m^2 - 16}{4m + 8}} = \dfrac{\dfrac{m + 4}{(m + 2)(m + 2)}}{\dfrac{(m - 4)(m + 4)}{4(m - 2)}} =$

 $\dfrac{m + 4}{(m + 2)(m + 2)} \cdot \dfrac{4(m + 2)}{(m - 4)(m + 4)} = \dfrac{1}{m + 2} \cdot \dfrac{4}{m - 4}$

 $= \dfrac{4}{(m + 2)(m - 4)}$

41. $x - 2y = 12$ $\qquad$ $x - 2y = 12$

 $\underline{-3x + 2y = 16}$ $\qquad$ $-14 - 2y = 12$

 $-2x = 28$ $\qquad$ $-2y = 26$

 $x = -14$ $\qquad$ $y = -13$

The solution is $(-14, -13)$.

209

# Technology: Solving Systems of Equations

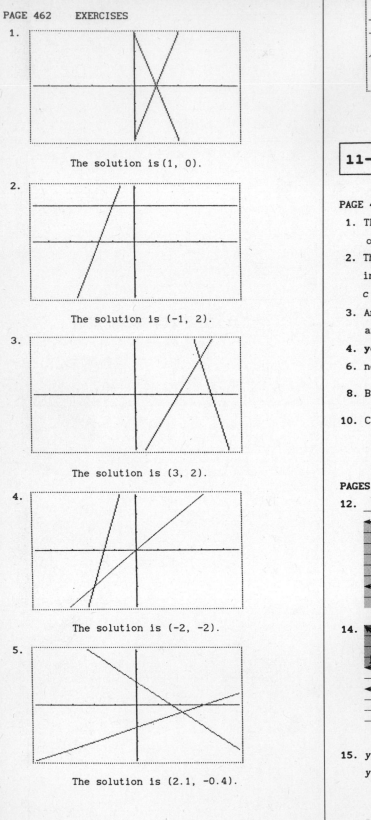

**1.**

The solution is (1, 0).

**2.**

The solution is (-1, 2).

**3.**

The solution is (3, 2).

**4.**

The solution is (-2, -2).

**5.**

The solution is (2.1, -0.4).

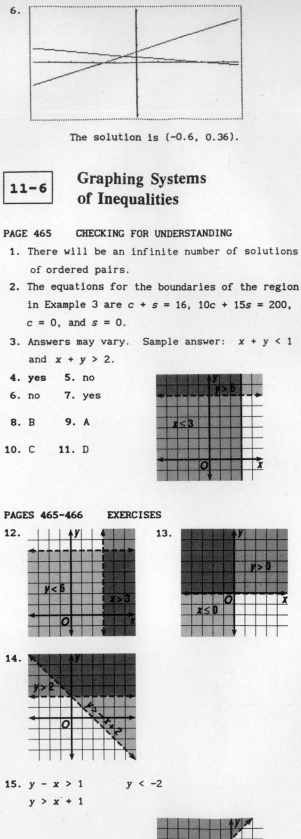

**6.**

The solution is (-0.6, 0.36).

## 11-6  Graphing Systems of Inequalities

**PAGE 465    CHECKING FOR UNDERSTANDING**

1. There will be an infinite number of solutions of ordered pairs.

2. The equations for the boundaries of the region in Example 3 are $c + s = 16$, $10c + 15s = 200$, $c = 0$, and $s = 0$.

3. Answers may vary. Sample answer: $x + y < 1$ and $x + y > 2$.

4. yes    5. no

6. no    7. yes

8. B    9. A

10. C    11. D

**PAGES 465-466    EXERCISES**

12.

13.

14.

15. $y - x > 1$    $y < -2$
    $y > x + 1$

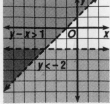

16. $x \leq 2$ $y - 3 \geq 5$
$y \geq 8$

17. $x \geq 1$ $y + x \leq 3$
$y \leq -x + 3$

18. $|y| < x$
$y < x$ $y > -x$

19. $|x| \geq y$
$x \geq y$ $x \leq -y$
$y \leq x$ $-y \geq x$
$y \leq -x$

20.

21.

22. $y \geq 3x$ $3y \leq 5x$
$y \leq \frac{5}{3}x$

23.

24. $y - x < 1$ $y - x > 3$
$y < x + 1$ $y > x + 3$

25. $2y + x < 4$
$2y < -x + 4$
$y < -\frac{1}{2}x + 2$

$3x - y > 6$
$-y > -3x + 6$
$y < 3x - 6$

26. $y + 2 < x$
$y < x - 2$

$2y - 3 > 2x$
$2y > 2x + 3$
$y > x + \frac{3}{2}$

27. $x + 2y \leq 7$
$2y \leq -x + 7$
$y \leq -\frac{1}{2}x + \frac{7}{2}$

$3x - 4y < 1$
$-4y < -3x + 1$
$y > \frac{3}{4}x - \frac{1}{4}$

28. $|y| + 1 < x$
$|y| < x - 1$
$y < x - 1$

$y > -x + 1$

29. $|y| > x + 3$
$y > x + 3$

$y < -x - 3$

30. $|y - 4| > x$
$y - 4 > x$
$y > x + 4$

$y - 4 < -x$
$y < -x + 4$

31. $|2y + 4| \leq x$

$2y + 4 \leq x$

$2y \leq x - 4$

$y \leq \frac{1}{2}x - 2$

$2y + 4 \geq -x$

$2y \geq -x - 4$

$y \geq -\frac{1}{2}x - 2$

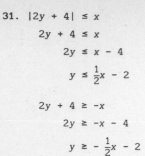

32. No, the point of intersection will not be part of the solution set because it will not satisfy the equation $y < -x$.

33. Yes, the point of intersection will be part of the solution set because it will satisfy both equations.

34. No, the point of intersection will not be part of the solution set because it will not satisfy the equation $2x - y < 5$.

For problems 35-42, answers may vary. Sample answers are given.

35. $x > 1$

$y > -2$

36. $y \geq 0$    $y < -\frac{1}{2}x + 2$

$y + \frac{1}{2}x < 2$

$2y + x < 4$

37. $y \geq -x$    $y < -x + 3$

$y < 3 - x$

38. $y \geq x - 3$    $y \leq -x - 3$

$x + y \leq -3$

39. $y < x + 3$    $y < -x + 3$

$y < 3 - x$

40. $5y - 1 \geq x$    $y < 2x + 2$

41. $x \geq 0$    $y \geq 0$    $y \leq -\frac{1}{2}x + 3$

$y + \frac{1}{2}x \leq 3$

$x + 2y \leq 6$

42. $y \leq x + 3$    $y \geq \frac{2}{7}x - \frac{4}{7}$    $y \leq -\frac{3}{2}x + 3$

$7y \geq 2x - 4$    $y + \frac{3}{2}x \leq 3$

$7y - 2x \geq -4$    $3x + 2y \leq 6$

$2x - 7y \leq 4$

43. $x - y \leq 3$    $x + y \leq 1$    $y \geq 0$

$-y \leq -x + 3$    $y \leq -x + 1$

$y \geq x - 3$

44. $x + 4y < 4$      $5x - 8y < -8$

$4y < -x + 4$      $-8y < -5x - 8$

$y < -\frac{1}{4}x + 1$      $y > \frac{5}{8}x + 1$

$3x - 2y \geq -16$

$-2y \geq -3x - 16$

$y \leq \frac{3}{2}x + 8$

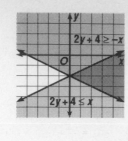

45. $x < 3$      $5y > x$

$y > \frac{1}{5}x$

$x + 3y < 9$

$3y < -x + 9$

$y < -\frac{1}{3}x + 3$

$2x - y < -9$

$-y < -2x - 9$

$y > 2x + 9$

46. line 1: $y \geq x - 2$

line 2: $y \geq -x - 2$

line 3: $y \leq x + 2$

line 4: $y \leq -x + 2$

Line 1 and line 4 can be rewritten as

$|y| \leq -x + 2$.

Line 2 and line 3 can be rewritten as

$|y| \leq x + 2$.

If we solve these two inequalities for $x$ we

obtain $-x \geq |y| - 2$    and $x \geq |y| - 2$.

$x \leq -|y| + 2$

Looking closer at these two inequalities, we

see that they can be rewritten as

$|x| \leq -|y| + 2$.

We can rewrite this as $|x| + |y| \leq 2$.

47. $c$ = pounds of cashews

$p$ = pounds of peanuts

Since $c$ and $p$ both represent nuts, they cannot be negative numbers. Thus, $c \geq 0$ and $p \geq 0$. Also, $3p + 5c \leq 24$ and $c + p \geq 5$, where $c \geq 0$ and $p \geq 0$.

Answers may vary. Possible answers:

1 pound of cashews, 6 pounds of peanuts;

3 pounds of cashews, 3 pounds of peanuts;

4 pounds of cashews, 1 pound of peanuts.

48. $x$ = \$2 student tickets sold

$y$ = \$3 tickets sold

Since $x$ and $y$ represent tickets, they cannot be negative numbers. Therefore, $x \geq 0$ and $y \geq 0$.

The debate team needs to earn at least \$500, so $2x + 3y \geq 500$, where $x \geq 0$ and $y \geq 0$.

The debate team can only sell 200 tickets, so $x + y \leq 200$ where $x \geq 0$ and $y \geq 0$.

Graphing the four inequalities, we get:

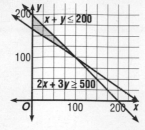

Answers may vary. Possible answers:

25 student tickets and 175 others;

50 student tickets and 140 others;

100 student tickets and 100 others.

49. $x$ = gallons of light shade of green

$y$ = gallons of dark shade of green

Since $x$ and $y$ represent gallons of dye they cannot be negative numbers. So $x \geq 0$ and $y \geq 0$.

To mix the light shade of green, you need to watch how many units of yellow dye you mix since you will run out of yellow before you run out of blue. Thus the equation $4x + y \leq 32$ where $x \geq 0$ and $y \geq 0$.

To mix the dark shade of green, you need to watch how many units of blue dye you mix since you will run out of blue before you run out of yellow. Thus the equation $x + 6y \leq 54$ where $x \geq 0$ and $y \geq 0$.

Graphing these equations, we get:

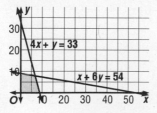

Answers may vary. Possible answers:

2 light gallons and 8 dark gallons;

6 light gallons and 8 dark gallons;

7 light gallons and 4 dark gallons.

50. $125 - 37.50 = \$87.50$

$$\frac{37.50}{125} = \frac{r}{100}$$

$$125r = 3750$$

$$\frac{125r}{125} = \frac{3750}{125}$$

$$r = 30$$

The rate of discount is 30%.

51. $-16 + 9x^2 = (4 + 3x)(-4 + 3x)$

52. 
$$\frac{x}{x^2 + 2x + 1} + \frac{1}{x + 1} = \frac{x}{(x + 1)(x + 1)} + \frac{1}{x + 1}$$

$$= \frac{x}{(x + 1)(x + 1)} + \frac{x + 1}{(x + 1)(x + 1)}$$

$$= \frac{2x + 1}{(x + 1)(x + 1)}$$

$$= \frac{2x + 1}{(x + 1)^2}$$

53. $4y = 3 + 2x$

a.) $4y = 3 + 2(-2)$
$4y = 3 + (-4)$
$4y = -1$
$y = -\frac{1}{4}$

b.) $4y = 3 + 2(-1)$
$4y = 3 + (-2)$
$4y = 1$
$y = \frac{1}{4}$

c.) $4y = 3 + 2(0)$
$4y = 3 + 0$
$4y = 3$
$y = \frac{3}{4}$

d.) $4y = 3 + 2(1)$
$4y = 3 + 2$
$4y = 5$
$y = \frac{5}{4}$

e.) $4y = 3 + 2(3)$
$4y = 3 + 6$
$4y = 9$
$y = \frac{9}{4}$

The solution set is $\left\{\left(-2, -\frac{1}{4}\right), \left(-1, \frac{1}{4}\right), \left(0, \frac{3}{4}\right), \left(1, \frac{5}{4}\right), \left(3, \frac{9}{4}\right)\right\}$.

54. $m = \frac{y_2 - y_1}{x_2 - x_1}$    $y - y_1 = m((x - x_1)$

$= \frac{-5 - 3}{6 - (-4)}$    $y - 3 = -\frac{4}{5}[x - (-4)]$

$= \frac{-8}{10}$    $y - 3 = -\frac{4}{5}(x + 4)$

$= -\frac{4}{5}$    $y - 3 = -\frac{4}{5}x - \frac{16}{5}$

$y = -\frac{4}{5}x - \frac{16}{5} + \frac{15}{5}$

$y = -\frac{4}{5}x - \frac{1}{5}$

55. $x$ = number of small peaches sold

$y$ = number of large peaches sold

$\quad x + y = 30 \quad \longrightarrow \quad -0.20x - 0.20y = -6$

$0.20x + 0.35y = 7.50 \longrightarrow \quad \underline{0.20x + 0.35y = 7.50}$

$\qquad\qquad\qquad\qquad\qquad\qquad 0.15y = 1.5$

$\qquad\qquad\qquad\qquad\qquad\qquad\qquad y = 10$

$\qquad\qquad\qquad\qquad\qquad\qquad x + y = 30$

$\qquad\qquad\qquad\qquad\qquad\qquad x + 10 = 30$

$\qquad\qquad\qquad\qquad\qquad\qquad\qquad x = 20$

Joey sold 20 small peaches and 10 large peaches.

# Chapter 11    Summary and Review

PAGES 468-470    SKILLS AND CONCEPTS

1. $x + y = 6$          $x - y = 2$
    $y = -x + 6$        $-y = -x + 2$
                      $y = x - 2$

The solution is (4, 2).

2. $y = 2x - 7$       $x + y = 11$
                  $y = -x + 11$

The solution is (6, 5).

3. $5x - 3y = 11$      $2x + 3y = -25$
   $-3y = -5x + 11$     $3y = -2x - 25$
     $y = \frac{5}{3}x - \frac{11}{3}$      $y = -\frac{2}{3}x - \frac{25}{3}$

The solution is (-2, -7).

4. $x - y = 9$         $x + y = 11$
   $-y = -x + 9$       $y = -x + 11$
    $y = x - 9$

one solution; (10, 1)

5. $9x + 2 = 3y$       $y - 3x = 8$
   $3y = 9x + 2$       $y = 3x + 8$
    $y = 3x + \frac{2}{3}$

no solution

6. $2x - 3y = 4$      $6y = 4x - 8$
   $-3y = -2x + 4$    $y = \frac{2}{3}x - \frac{4}{3}$
    $y = \frac{2}{3}x - \frac{4}{3}$

infinitely many solutions

7. $3x - y = 8$
   $-y = -3x + 8$
    $y = 3x - 8$

   $3x = 4 - y$
   $4 - y = 3x$
   $-y = 3x - 4$
    $y = -3x + 4$

one solution; (2, -2)

8. $x = 2y$       $x + y = 6$       $x = 2y$
          $(2y) + y = 6$        $= 2(2)$
             $3y = 6$           $= 4$
              $y = 2$

The solution is (4, 2).

9. $2m + n = 1$         $m - n = 8$
    $n = 1 - 2m$     $m - (1 - 2m) = 8$
               $m - 1 + 2m = 8$
                  $3m - 1 = 8$
                    $3m = 9$
                     $m = 3$

$n = 1 - 2m$
  $= 1 - 2(3)$
  $= 1 - 6$
  $= -5$

The solution is (3, -5).

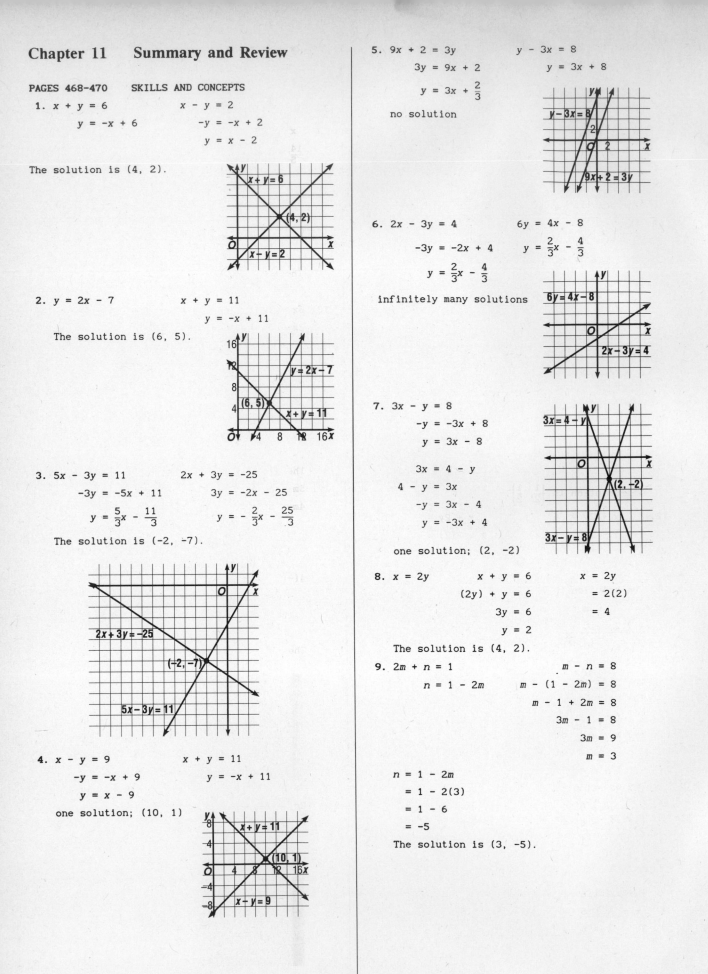

214

10. $3a + b = 2$        $3a - 2b = -4$

   $b = 2 - 3a$      $3a - 2(2 - 3a) = -4$

                $3a - 4 + 6a = -4$

                      $9a = 0$

                       $a = 0$

   $b = 2 - 3a$

   $\ = 2 - 3(0)$

   $\ = 2 - 0$

   $\ = 2$

   The solution is $(0, 2)$.

11. $3x - y = 1$          $2x + 4y = 3$

    $-y = 1 - 3x$      $2x + 4(3x - 1) = 3$

    $y = 3x - 1$      $2x + 12x - 4 = 3$

                    $14x = 7$

                    $x = \dfrac{7}{14}$

                    $x = \dfrac{1}{2}$

   $y = 3x - 1$

   $\ = 3\left(\dfrac{1}{2}\right) - 1$

   $\ = \dfrac{3}{2} - 1$

   $\ = \dfrac{3}{2} - \dfrac{2}{2}$

   $\ = \dfrac{1}{2}$

   The solution is $\left(\dfrac{1}{2}, \dfrac{1}{2}\right)$.

12.    $x + 2y = 6$        $x + 2y = 6$

   $(-)\ x - 3y = -4$      $x + 2(2) = 6$

       $5y = 10$        $x + 4 = 6$

        $y = 2$          $x = 2$

   The solution is $(2, 2)$.

13.   $2m - n = 5$        $2m - n = 5$

   $(+)\ 2m + n = 3$      $2(2) - n = 5$

      $4m = 8$        $4 - n = 5$

       $m = 2$          $-n = 1$

                     $n = -1$

   The solution is $(2, -1)$.

14.   $3x - y = 11$        $x + y = 5$

   $(+)\ x + y = 5$      $4 + y = 5$

      $4x = 16$          $y = 1$

       $x = 4$

   The solution is $(4, 1)$.

15.    $2s + 6r = 32$        $2s + 6r = 32$

   $(-)\ -9s + 6r = 21$      $2(1) + 6r = 32$

       $11s = 11$        $2 + 6r = 32$

        $s = 1$          $6r = 30$

                      $r = 5$

   The solution is $(5, 1)$.

16. $x - 2y = 5 \rightarrow$     $3x - 6y = 15$       $x - 2y = 5$

   $3x - 5y = 8 \rightarrow$  $(-)\ 3x - 5y = 8$      $x - 2(-7) = 5$

                    $-y = 7$        $x + 14 = 5$

                     $y = -7$          $x = -9$

   The solution is $(-9, -7)$.

17. $2x + 3y = 8 \rightarrow$      $2x + 3y = 8$

   $x - y = 2 \rightarrow$  $(+)\ 3x - 3y = 6$

                    $5x = 14$

                     $x = \dfrac{14}{5}$

   $x - y = 2$

   $\dfrac{14}{5} - y = 2$

   $-y = 2 - \dfrac{14}{5}$

   $-y = -\dfrac{4}{5}$

   $y = \dfrac{4}{5}$

   The solution is $\left(\dfrac{14}{5}, \dfrac{4}{5}\right)$.

18. $6x + 7y = 5 \rightarrow$      $6x + 7y = 5$

   $2x - 3y = 7 \rightarrow$  $(+)\ -6x + 9y = -21$

                    $16y = -16$

                     $y = -1$

   $2x - 3y = 7$

   $2x - 3(-1) = 7$

   $2x + 3 = 7$

   $2x = 4$

   $x = 2$

   The solution is $(2, -1)$.

19. $5m + 2n = -8 \rightarrow$      $15m + 6n = -24$

   $4m + 3n = 2 \rightarrow$  $(+)\ -8m - 6n = -4$

                    $7m = -28$

                     $m = -4$

   $4m + 3n = 2$

   $4(-4) + 3n = 2$

   $-16 + 3n = 2$

   $3n = 18$

   $n = 6$

   The solution is $(-4, 6)$.

20.

21. $2r + s < 9$        $r + 11s < -6$

    $s < 9 - 2r$        $11s < -r - 6$

                    $s < -\dfrac{1}{11}r - \dfrac{6}{11}$

**22.** $|x + 2| \geq y$

$y \leq x + 2$

$y \geq -x - 2$

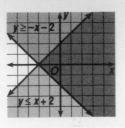

PAGE 470     APPLICATIONS AND CONNECTIONS

**23.**

A hidden assumption may be that the line segments cannot be longer than the length of a row or column of dots.

**24.** $t$ = tens digit

$u$ = units digit

$10t + u = 7u$      $10t + u + 18 = 10u + t$      $t = \frac{3}{5}u$

$10t = 6u$           $9t - 9u = -18$              $t = \frac{3}{5}(5)$

$5t = 3u$            $9\left(\frac{3}{5}u\right) - 9u = -18$       $t = 3$

$t = \frac{3}{5}u$   $\frac{27}{5}u - 9u = -18$

$-\frac{18}{5}u = -18$

$u = 5$

The number is 35.

**25.** $\ell$ = length

$w$ = width

$\ell - w = 7 \rightarrow \quad 2\ell - 2w = 14 \qquad \ell - w = 7$

$2\ell + 2w = 50 \rightarrow \underline{(+)\ 2\ell + 2w = 50} \qquad 16 - w = 7$

$4\ell = 64 \qquad\qquad -w = -9$

$\ell = 16 \qquad\qquad w = 9$

The rectangle is 16 cm by 9 cm.

**26.** $x$ = rate of train #1

$y$ = rate of train #2

|         | $r$ | $t$ | $d$ |
|---------|-----|-----|-----|
| Train 1 | $x$ | 5   | $5x$ |
| Train 2 | $y$ | 5   | $5y$ |

$x = y - 6 \qquad\quad 5x + 5y = 450 \qquad x = y - 6$

$\qquad\qquad\quad 5(y - 6) + 5y = 450 \qquad = 48 - 6$

$\qquad\qquad\quad 5y - 30 + 5y = 450 \qquad = 42$

$\qquad\qquad\qquad 10y - 30 = 450$

$\qquad\qquad\qquad\quad 10y = 480$

$\qquad\qquad\qquad\qquad y = 48$

One train travels at the rate of 42 mph and the other travels at the rate of 48 mph.

**27.** $x$ = price of shirt

$y$ = price of tie

$5x + 3y = 102 \qquad\qquad 5x + 3y = 102$

$\underline{(-)\ 8x + 3y = 147} \qquad\quad 5(15) + 3y = 102$

$\quad -3x = -45 \qquad\qquad\quad 75 + 3y = 102$

$\qquad x = 15 \qquad\qquad\qquad\quad 3y = 27$

$\qquad\qquad\qquad\qquad\qquad\qquad y = 9$

The price of a shirt is \$15 and the price of a tie is \$9.

**28.** $x$ = amount invested at 6%

$y$ = amount invested at 8%

$\qquad x + y = 10{,}000 \rightarrow -0.06x - 0.06y = -600$

$0.06x + 0.08y = 760 \rightarrow \underline{\ 0.06x + 0.08y = \ 760\ }$

$\qquad\qquad\qquad\qquad\qquad\qquad 0.02y = 160$

$\qquad\qquad\qquad\qquad\qquad\qquad\quad y = 8000$

$x + y = 10{,}000$

$x + 8000 = 10{,}000$

$x = 2000$

Jodi invested \$2000 at 6% interest and \$8000 at 8% interest.

**29.** $x$ = rate of boat in still water

$y$ = rate of the current

|            | $r$     | $t$ | $d$ |
|------------|---------|-----|-----|
| Upstream   | $x - y$ | 4   | 60  |
| Downstream | $x + y$ | 3   | 60  |

$\qquad\qquad 4(x - y) = 60$

$\qquad\qquad 3(x + y) = 60$

$4x - 4y = 60 \rightarrow x - y = 15 \qquad x + y = 20$

$3x + 3y = 60 \rightarrow \underline{x + y = 20} \qquad \frac{35}{2} + y = 20$

$\qquad\qquad\qquad 2x = 35 \qquad\qquad y = 20 - \frac{35}{2}$

$\qquad\qquad\qquad\quad x = \frac{35}{2} \qquad\qquad y = \frac{5}{2}$

The rate of the boat in still water is $\frac{35}{2}$ mph, and the rate of the current is $\frac{5}{2}$ mph.

# Chapter 11     Test

PAGE 471

**1.**

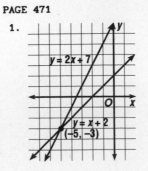

The solution is $(-5, -3)$.

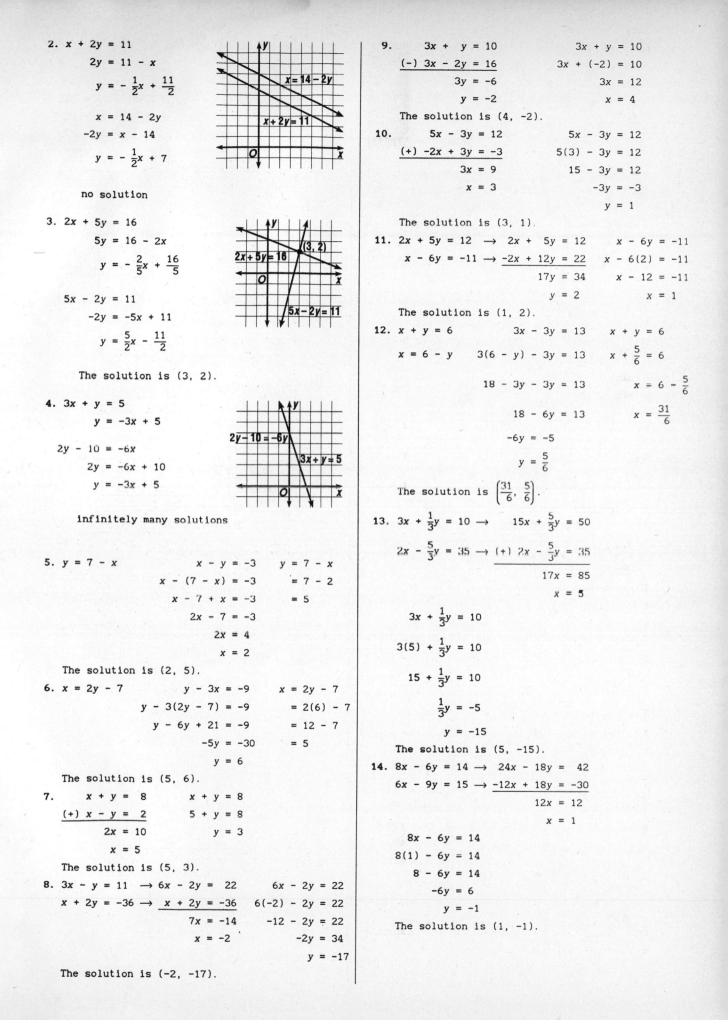

2. $x + 2y = 11$

$2y = 11 - x$

$y = -\frac{1}{2}x + \frac{11}{2}$

$x = 14 - 2y$

$-2y = x - 14$

$y = -\frac{1}{2}x + 7$

no solution

3. $2x + 5y = 16$

$5y = 16 - 2x$

$y = -\frac{2}{5}x + \frac{16}{5}$

$5x - 2y = 11$

$-2y = -5x + 11$

$y = \frac{5}{2}x - \frac{11}{2}$

The solution is (3, 2).

4. $3x + y = 5$

$y = -3x + 5$

$2y - 10 = -6x$

$2y = -6x + 10$

$y = -3x + 5$

infinitely many solutions

5. $y = 7 - x$

$x - y = -3$     $y = 7 - x$

$x - (7 - x) = -3$     $= 7 - 2$

$x - 7 + x = -3$     $= 5$

$2x - 7 = -3$

$2x = 4$

$x = 2$

The solution is (2, 5).

6. $x = 2y - 7$

$y - 3x = -9$     $x = 2y - 7$

$y - 3(2y - 7) = -9$     $= 2(6) - 7$

$y - 6y + 21 = -9$     $= 12 - 7$

$-5y = -30$     $= 5$

$y = 6$

The solution is (5, 6).

7.    $x + y = 8$     $x + y = 8$

(+) $\underline{x - y = 2}$     $5 + y = 8$

$2x = 10$     $y = 3$

$x = 5$

The solution is (5, 3).

8. $3x - y = 11 \rightarrow 6x - 2y = 22$     $6x - 2y = 22$

$x + 2y = -36 \rightarrow \underline{x + 2y = -36}$     $6(-2) - 2y = 22$

$7x = -14$     $-12 - 2y = 22$

$x = -2$     $-2y = 34$

    $y = -17$

The solution is (-2, -17).

9.    $3x + y = 10$     $3x + y = 10$

(−) $\underline{3x - 2y = 16}$     $3x + (-2) = 10$

$3y = -6$     $3x = 12$

$y = -2$     $x = 4$

The solution is (4, -2).

10.    $5x - 3y = 12$     $5x - 3y = 12$

(+) $\underline{-2x + 3y = -3}$     $5(3) - 3y = 12$

$3x = 9$     $15 - 3y = 12$

$x = 3$     $-3y = -3$

    $y = 1$

The solution is (3, 1).

11. $2x + 5y = 12 \rightarrow 2x + 5y = 12$     $x - 6y = -11$

$x - 6y = -11 \rightarrow \underline{-2x + 12y = 22}$     $x - 6(2) = -11$

$17y = 34$     $x - 12 = -11$

$y = 2$     $x = 1$

The solution is (1, 2).

12. $x + y = 6$     $3x - 3y = 13$     $x + y = 6$

$x = 6 - y$     $3(6 - y) - 3y = 13$     $x + \frac{5}{6} = 6$

    $18 - 3y - 3y = 13$     $x = 6 - \frac{5}{6}$

    $18 - 6y = 13$     $x = \frac{31}{6}$

    $-6y = -5$

    $y = \frac{5}{6}$

The solution is $\left(\frac{31}{6}, \frac{5}{6}\right)$.

13. $3x + \frac{1}{3}y = 10 \rightarrow 15x + \frac{5}{3}y = 50$

$2x - \frac{5}{3}y = 35 \rightarrow$ (+) $\underline{2x - \frac{5}{3}y = 35}$

    $17x = 85$

    $x = 5$

$3x + \frac{1}{3}y = 10$

$3(5) + \frac{1}{3}y = 10$

$15 + \frac{1}{3}y = 10$

$\frac{1}{3}y = -5$

$y = -15$

The solution is (5, -15).

14. $8x - 6y = 14 \rightarrow 24x - 18y = 42$

$6x - 9y = 15 \rightarrow \underline{-12x + 18y = -30}$

    $12x = 12$

    $x = 1$

$8x - 6y = 14$

$8(1) - 6y = 14$

$8 - 6y = 14$

$-6y = 6$

$y = -1$

The solution is (1, -1).

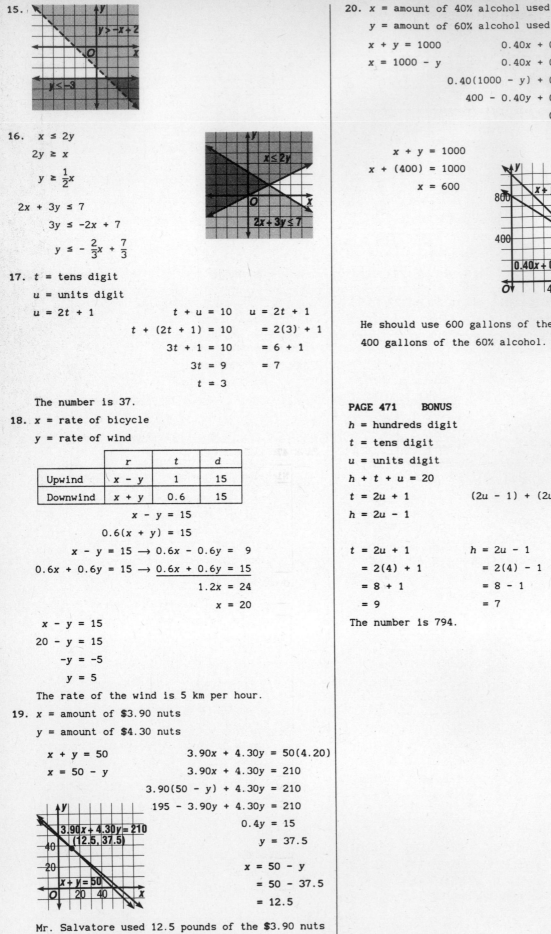

15.

$y > -x + 2$

$y < -3$

16. $x \le 2y$

$2y \ge x$

$y \ge \frac{1}{2}x$

$2x + 3y \le 7$

$3y \le -2x + 7$

$y \le -\frac{2}{3}x + \frac{7}{3}$

$x \le 2y$

$2x + 3y \le 7$

17. $t$ = tens digit

$u$ = units digit

$u = 2t + 1$

| | |
|---|---|
| $t + u = 10$ | $u = 2t + 1$ |
| $t + (2t + 1) = 10$ | $= 2(3) + 1$ |
| $3t + 1 = 10$ | $= 6 + 1$ |
| $3t = 9$ | $= 7$ |
| $t = 3$ | |

The number is 37.

18. $x$ = rate of bicycle

$y$ = rate of wind

| | $r$ | $t$ | $d$ |
|---|---|---|---|
| Upwind | $x - y$ | 1 | 15 |
| Downwind | $x + y$ | 0.6 | 15 |

$x - y = 15$

$0.6(x + y) = 15$

$x - y = 15 \rightarrow 0.6x - 0.6y = 9$

$0.6x + 0.6y = 15 \rightarrow \underline{0.6x + 0.6y = 15}$

$1.2x = 24$

$x = 20$

$x - y = 15$

$20 - y = 15$

$-y = -5$

$y = 5$

The rate of the wind is 5 km per hour.

19. $x$ = amount of \$3.90 nuts

$y$ = amount of \$4.30 nuts

$x + y = 50$          $3.90x + 4.30y = 50(4.20)$

$x = 50 - y$          $3.90x + 4.30y = 210$

$3.90(50 - y) + 4.30y = 210$

$195 - 3.90y + 4.30y = 210$

$0.4y = 15$

$y = 37.5$

$x = 50 - y$

$= 50 - 37.5$

$= 12.5$

Mr. Salvatore used 12.5 pounds of the \$3.90 nuts and 37.5 pounds of the \$4.30 nuts.

20. $x$ = amount of 40% alcohol used

$y$ = amount of 60% alcohol used

$x + y = 1000$          $0.40x + 0.60y = 0.48(1000)$

$x = 1000 - y$          $0.40x + 0.60y = 480$

$0.40(1000 - y) + 0.60y = 480$

$400 - 0.40y + 0.60y = 480$

$0.20y = 80$

$y = 400$

$x + y = 1000$

$x + (400) = 1000$

$x = 600$

He should use 600 gallons of the 40% alcohol and 400 gallons of the 60% alcohol.

**PAGE 471    BONUS**

$h$ = hundreds digit

$t$ = tens digit

$u$ = units digit

$h + t + u = 20$          $h + t + u = 20$

$t = 2u + 1$          $(2u - 1) + (2u + 1) + u = 20$

$h = 2u - 1$          $5u = 20$

$u = 4$

| | |
|---|---|
| $t = 2u + 1$ | $h = 2u - 1$ |
| $= 2(4) + 1$ | $= 2(4) - 1$ |
| $= 8 + 1$ | $= 8 - 1$ |
| $= 9$ | $= 7$ |

The number is 794.

218

# Chapter 12  Radical Expressions

## 12-1  Problem-Solving Strategy: Use a Table

1. 
| April | | June | |
|---|---|---|---|
| Rinehart | 287 | Alvarez | 286 |
| Alvarez | -223 | Rinehart | -268 |
| Difference | 64 | Difference | 18 |

| August | | October | |
|---|---|---|---|
| Lewis | 387 | Lewis | 399 |
| Alvarez | -294 | Alvarez | -347 |
| Difference | 93 | Difference | 52 |

The greatest difference was in August.

2. Look for a pattern; list possibilities; guess and check.

3. a. Boston
   b. March
   c. 8.86 in., July, Mobile
   d.

| January | | February | |
|---|---|---|---|
| Mobile | 4.71 | Mobile | 4.76 |
| Albuquerque | -0.30 | Albuquerque | -0.39 |
| Difference | 4.41 | Difference | 4.37 |

| March | | April | |
|---|---|---|---|
| Mobile | 7.07 | Mobile | 5.59 |
| Albuquerque | -0.47 | Albuquerque | -0.48 |
| Difference | 6.60 | Difference | 5.11 |

| May | | June | |
|---|---|---|---|
| Houston | 5.10 | Mobile | 6.09 |
| San Francisco | -0.41 | San Francisco | -0.13 |
| Difference | 4.69 | Difference | 5.96 |

| July | | August | |
|---|---|---|---|
| Mobile | 8.86 | Mobile | 6.93 |
| San Francisco | -0.01 | San Francisco | -0.03 |
| Difference | 8.85 | Difference | 6.90 |

| September | | October | |
|---|---|---|---|
| Mobile | 6.59 | Houston | 4.05 |
| San Francisco | -0.16 | Albuquerque | -0.79 |
| Difference | 6.43 | Difference | 3.26 |

| November | | December | |
|---|---|---|---|
| Boston | 4.51 | Mobile | 5.92 |
| Albuquerque | -0.29 | Albuquerque | -0.52 |
| Difference | 4.22 | Difference | 5.40 |

3.26 in., October

4. a.

| Age at First Inauguration | Number of Times | Age at First Inauguration | Number of Times |
|---|---|---|---|
| 42 | 1 | 56 | 3 |
| 43 | 1 | 57 | 4 |
| 44 | 0 | 58 | 1 |
| 45 | 0 | 59 | 0 |
| 46 | 2 | 60 | 1 |
| 47 | 1 | 61 | 3 |
| 48 | 1 | 62 | 1 |
| 49 | 2 | 63 | 0 |
| 50 | 2 | 64 | 1 |
| 51 | 4 | 65 | 1 |
| 52 | 2 | 66 | 0 |
| 53 | 0 | 67 | 0 |
| 54 | 4 | 68 | 1 |
| 55 | 4 | 69 | 1 |

b. 21
c. 69 - 42 = 27 years
d. 51, 54, 55, 57
e. 10

5.

| Nickels | Dimes | Quarters | Nickels | Dimes | Quarters |
|---|---|---|---|---|---|
| 0 | 0 | 2 | 2 | 4 | 0 |
| 1 | 2 | 1 | 4 | 3 | 0 |
| 3 | 1 | 1 | 6 | 2 | 0 |
| 5 | 0 | 1 | 8 | 1 | 0 |
| 0 | 5 | 0 | 10 | 0 | 0 |

10 different combinations

6.

| A | B | C | D | F |
|---|---|---|---|---|
| 3 | 0 | 0 | 1 | 1 |
| 2 | 1 | 1 | 0 | 1 |
| 2 | 1 | 0 | 2 | 0 |
| 2 | 0 | 2 | 1 | 0 |
| 1 | 3 | 0 | 0 | 1 |
| 1 | 2 | 1 | 1 | 0 |
| 1 | 1 | 3 | 0 | 0 |
| 0 | 4 | 0 | 1 | 0 |
| 0 | 3 | 2 | 0 | 0 |

AAADF, AABCF, AABDD, AACCD, ABBBF, ABBCD, ABCCC, BBBBD, BBBCC

7. 3, for the units digit of $7^3$

8.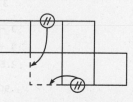

219

9. $43^2 = 1849$

   $1885 - 1849 = 36$

   $36 + 43 = 79$ years old

10. $5 + 4 + 3 + 2 + 1 = 15$ games

PAGE 476    COOPERATIVE LEARNING ACTIVITY

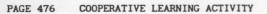

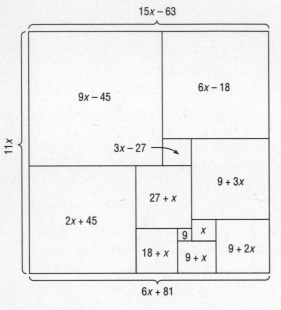

176 cm by 177 cm

## 12-2   Square Roots

PAGE 479    CHECKING FOR UNDERSTANDING

1. 25, 5

2. because $2(2) = 4$ and $(-2)(-2) = 4$

3. The result is the positive number entered; taking the square root and squaring are inverse operations.

4. Error message is given; the square root of a negative number is not a real number.

5. 144   6. 400   7. 0.09   8. $\frac{16}{49}$   9. $\frac{121}{16}$   10. 11

11. -9   12. $\pm\frac{9}{8}$   13. 0.04   14. 9.22   15. -12.21

16. ±14.35   17. 7.77

PAGES 479-481    EXERCISES

18. $\sqrt{169} = 13$

19. $256 = 2^8$

    $= (2^4)^2$

    $= (16)^2$

    $\sqrt{256} = 16$

20. $\sqrt{\frac{81}{121}} = \frac{9}{11}$

21. $\frac{36}{196}$

    $= \frac{(6)^2}{(2)^2(7)^2}$

    $= \left(\frac{6}{14}\right)^2$

    $\sqrt{\frac{36}{196}} = \sqrt{\left(\frac{6}{14}\right)^2} = \frac{6}{14} = \frac{3}{7}$

22. $\frac{400}{225}$

    $= \frac{20^2}{15^2}$

    $\sqrt{\frac{400}{225}} = \sqrt{\left(\frac{20}{15}\right)^2} = \frac{20}{15} = \frac{4}{3}$

23. $\sqrt{0.0025} = 0.05$       24. $\sqrt{0.0289} = 0.17$

25. $\sqrt{3.24} = 1.8$   26. ±12   27. -10   28. 23

29. $484 = 2 \cdot 2 \cdot 11 \cdot 11$

    $= 2^2 \cdot 11^2$

    $= 22^2$

    $\sqrt{484} = 22$

30. $676 = 2 \cdot 2 \cdot 13 \cdot 13$

    $= 2^2 \cdot 13^2$

    $= 26^2$

    $-\sqrt{676} = -26$

31. ±31

32. $1764 = 2 \cdot 2 \cdot 3 \cdot 3 \cdot 7 \cdot 7$

    $= 2^2 \cdot 3^2 \cdot 7^2$

    $= 42^2$

    $\pm\sqrt{1764} = \pm42$

33. $2025 = 3 \cdot 3 \cdot 3 \cdot 3 \cdot 5 \cdot 5$

    $= 3^2 \cdot 3^2 \cdot 5^2$

    $= 45^2$

    $\sqrt{2025} = 45$

34. $729 = 3 \cdot 3 \cdot 3 \cdot 3 \cdot 3 \cdot 3$

    $= 3^2 \cdot 3^2 \cdot 3^2$

    $= 27^2$

    $\sqrt{0.0729} = 0.27$

35. $1024 = 2 \cdot 2 \cdot 2 \cdot 2 \cdot 2 \cdot 2 \cdot 2 \cdot 2 \cdot 2 \cdot 2$

    $= 2^2 \cdot 2^2 \cdot 2^2 \cdot 2^2 \cdot 2^2$

    $= 32^2$

    $-\sqrt{10.24} = -3.2$

36. $-\sqrt{\frac{169}{121}}$

    $= -\sqrt{\left(\frac{13}{11}\right)^2}$

    $= -\frac{13}{11}$

37. $1521 = 3 \cdot 3 \cdot 13 \cdot 13$

$\quad\quad = 3^2 \cdot 13^2$

$\quad\quad = 39^2$

$\pm\sqrt{\dfrac{144}{1521}} = \pm\sqrt{\left(\dfrac{12}{39}\right)^2} = \pm\dfrac{12}{39}$

38. $10.756$   39. $-13.251$   40. $\pm12.454$   41. $23.052$

42. $-0.781$   43. $1.521$   44. $0.068$   45. $\pm0.097$

46. $\sqrt{32.49 \text{ ft}^2} \approx 5.70 \text{ ft}$

47. $\sqrt{129 \text{ in.}^2} \approx 11.36 \text{ in.}$

48. $\sqrt{1400 \text{ cm}^2} \approx 37.42 \text{ cm}$

49. $\sqrt{9} = 3$   50. $\sqrt{25} = 5$   51. $\sqrt{\sqrt{16}} = \sqrt{4} = 2$

52. $V = \ell \cdot w \cdot h = 100$

$\quad h = \ell \cdot w$

$\quad \ell \cdot w \cdot \ell \cdot w = 100$

$\quad (\ell w)^2 = 100$

$\quad \ell w = 10$

$\quad h = 10$

$\quad \ell = w = \sqrt{10} \approx 3.16$

Dimensions are 3.16 cm by 3.16 cm by 10 cm.

53. The absolute value of the number appears; calculators provide the principal square root.

54. $s = \sqrt{24 \cdot 150}$

$\quad s = \sqrt{3600}$

$\quad s = 60$ miles per hour

55. $17 = \dfrac{v^2}{20}$

$\quad v^2 = 340$

$\quad v = \sqrt{340}$

$\quad v = 18.4$ meters per second

56. $1200 = I^2 \cdot 5$

$\quad I^2 = 240$

$\quad I = \sqrt{240}$

$\quad I = 15.5$ amperes

57. $0.2x = 8$

$\quad x = \dfrac{8}{0.2}$

$\quad x = 40$

58. $5a^2(4c^2 + 12c + 9)$

$\quad = 5a^2(2c + 3)^2$

59. Let $w$ = speed of wind

|  | $d$ | $r$ | $t$ |
|---|---|---|---|
| With Wind | 2413 | $600 + w$ | $\dfrac{2413}{600 + w}$ |
| Against Wind | 2147 | $600 - w$ | $\dfrac{2147}{600 - w}$ |

$\dfrac{2413}{600 + w} = \dfrac{2147}{600 - w}$

$2413(600 - w) = 2147(600 + w)$

$1{,}447{,}800 - 2413w = 1{,}288{,}200 + 2147w$

$4560w = 159{,}600$

$w = 35$ mph

60.

61. slope $= \dfrac{4 - 3}{-2 - 6} = -\dfrac{1}{8}$

$y - 3 = -\dfrac{1}{8}(x - 6)$

$y - 3 = -\dfrac{1}{8}x + \dfrac{3}{4}$

$y = -\dfrac{1}{8}x + 3\dfrac{3}{4}$

$y = -\dfrac{1}{8}x + \dfrac{15}{4}$

62.

| 12-3 | The Pythagorean Theorem |
|---|---|

PAGES 484-485   CHECKING FOR UNDERSTANDING

1. hypotenuse

2. The sum of the squares of the measures of the two legs of a right triangle equals the square of the measure of the hypotenuse.

3. If the square of the length of the longest side equals the sum of the squares of the lengths of the other sides, then the triangle is a right triangle.

4. $9 + 16 \overset{?}{=} 25$

$\quad 25 = 25$

$\quad$ true

5. $81 + 100 \overset{?}{=} 121$

$\quad 181 \neq 121$

$\quad$ false

6. $36 + 64 \overset{?}{=} 81$

$\quad 100 \neq 81$

$\quad$ false

7. $36 + 64 = c^2$

$\quad 100 = c^2$

$\quad c = \sqrt{100}$

$\quad c = 10$

8. $25 + 144 = c^2$

$\quad 169 = c^2$

$\quad c = \sqrt{169}$

$\quad c = 13$

9. $a^2 + 225 = 289$

$\quad a^2 = 64$

$\quad a = \sqrt{64}$

$\quad a = 8$

10. $a^2 + 576 = 625$

$\quad a^2 = 49$

$\quad a = \sqrt{49}$

$\quad a = 7$

11. $144 + b^2 = 400$

$\quad b^2 = 256$

$\quad b = \sqrt{256}$

$\quad b = 16$

12. $100 + b^2 = 676$

$\quad b^2 = 576$

$\quad b = \sqrt{576}$

$\quad b = 24$

13. $9^2 + 12^2 = c^2$

$\quad 81 + 144 = c^2$

$\quad c^2 = 225$

$\quad c = \sqrt{225}$

$\quad c = 15$

**14.** $(\sqrt{7})^2 + (\sqrt{9})^2 = c^2$

$7 + 9 = c^2$

$c^2 = 16$

$c = \sqrt{16}$

$c = 4$

**15.** $a^2 + (\sqrt{30})^2 = (\sqrt{34})^2$

$a^2 + 30 = 34$

$a^2 = 4$

$a = \sqrt{4}$

$a = 2$

**16.** $(\sqrt{11})^2 + b^2 = (\sqrt{47})^2$

$11 + b^2 = 47$

$b^2 = 36$

$b = \sqrt{36}$

$b = 6$

**PAGES 485-486     EXERCISES**

**17.** $16^2 + 30^2 = c^2$

$256 + 900 = c^2$

$c^2 = 1156$

$c = \sqrt{1156}$

$c = 34$

**18.** $11^2 + b^2 = 61^2$

$121 + b^2 = 3721$

$b^2 = 3600$

$b = \sqrt{3600}$

$b = 60$

**19.** $a^2 + 21^2 = 29^2$

$a^2 + 441 = 841$

$a^2 = 400$

$a = \sqrt{400}$

$a = 20$

**20.** $(\sqrt{13})^2 + 6^2 = c^2$

$13 + 36 = c^2$

$c^2 = 49$

$c = \sqrt{49}$

$c = 7$

**21.** $(\sqrt{11})^2 + b^2 = 6^2$

$11 + b^2 = 36$

$b^2 = 25$

$b = \sqrt{25}$

$b = 5$

**22.** $a^2 + 13^2 = (\sqrt{233})^2$

$a^2 + 169 = 233$

$a^2 = 64$

$a = \sqrt{64}$

$a = 8$

**23.** $6^2 + 3^2 = c^2$

$36 + 9 = c^2$

$c^2 = 45$

$c = \sqrt{45}$

$c \approx 6.71$

**24.** $4^2 + (\sqrt{11})^2 = c^2$

$16 + 11 = c^2$

$c^2 = 27$

$c = \sqrt{27}$

$c \approx 5.20$

**25.** $15^2 + b^2 = (\sqrt{253})^2$

$225 + b^2 = 253$

$b^2 = 28$

$b = \sqrt{28}$

$b \approx 5.29$

**26.** $a^2 + (\sqrt{77})^2 = 12^2$

$a^2 + 77 = 144$

$a^2 = 67$

$a = \sqrt{67}$

$a \approx 8.19$

**27.** $a^2 + 10^2 = 11^2$

$a^2 + 100 = 121$

$a^2 = 21$

$a = \sqrt{21}$

$a \approx 4.58$

**28.** $12^2 + b^2 = 17^2$

$144 + b^2 = 289$

$b^2 = 145$

$b = \sqrt{145}$

$b \approx 12.04$

**29.** $9^2 + 16^2 \overset{?}{=} 20^2$

$81 + 256 \overset{?}{=} 400$

$337 \neq 400$

no

**30.** $9^2 + 40^2 \overset{?}{=} 41^2$

$81 + 1600 \overset{?}{=} 1681$

$1681 = 1681$

yes

**31.** $45^2 + 60^2 \overset{?}{=} 75^2$

$2025 + 3600 \overset{?}{=} 5625$

$5625 = 5625$

yes

**32.** $12^2 + 11^2 \overset{?}{=} 15^2$

$144 + 121 \overset{?}{=} 225$

$265 \neq 225$

no

**33.** $18^2 + (\sqrt{24})^2 \overset{?}{=} 30^2$

$324 + 24 \overset{?}{=} 900$

$348 \neq 900$

no

**34.** $15^2 + (\sqrt{31})^2 \overset{?}{=} 16^2$

$225 + 31 \overset{?}{=} 256$

$256 = 256$

yes

**35.** Let $x$ = length of side of square.

$x^2 = 98$

$x = \sqrt{98}$

Let $d$ = diagonal of square.

$(\sqrt{98})^2 + (\sqrt{98})^2 = d^2$

$98 + 98 = d^2$

$d^2 = 196$

$d = 14$ cm

**36.** $d^2 = 5^2 + 5^2 + 5^2$

$d^2 = 25 + 25 + 25$

$d^2 = 75$

$d = \sqrt{75}$

$d \approx 8.66$ in.

**37.** Let $\ell$ = length, $\dfrac{\ell + 2}{2}$ = width.

$\dfrac{\ell + 2}{2} \cdot \ell = 40$

$\ell^2 + 2\ell - 80 = 0$

$(\ell + 10)(\ell - 8) = 0$

$\ell = 8$

width $= \dfrac{\ell + 2}{2} = \dfrac{8 + 2}{2} = \dfrac{10}{2} = 5$

$5^2 + 8^2 = d^2$

$25 + 64 = d^2$

$d^2 = 89$

$d = \sqrt{89}$

$d \approx 9.43$ m

**38.** rectangle

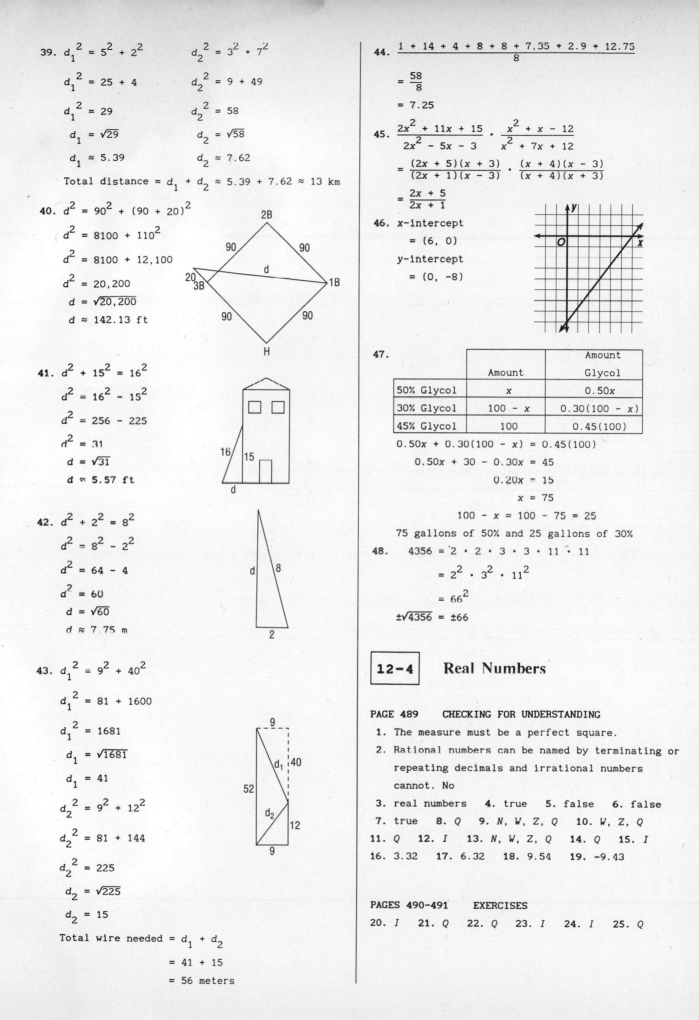

39. 
$$d_1{}^2 = 5^2 + 2^2 \qquad d_2{}^2 = 3^2 + 7^2$$
$$d_1{}^2 = 25 + 4 \qquad d_2{}^2 = 9 + 49$$
$$d_1{}^2 = 29 \qquad d_2{}^2 = 58$$
$$d_1 = \sqrt{29} \qquad d_2 = \sqrt{58}$$
$$d_1 \approx 5.39 \qquad d_2 \approx 7.62$$
Total distance = $d_1 + d_2 \approx 5.39 + 7.62 \approx 13$ km

40. 
$$d^2 = 90^2 + (90 + 20)^2$$
$$d^2 = 8100 + 110^2$$
$$d^2 = 8100 + 12{,}100$$
$$d^2 = 20{,}200$$
$$d = \sqrt{20{,}200}$$
$$d \approx 142.13 \text{ ft}$$

41. 
$$d^2 + 15^2 = 16^2$$
$$d^2 = 16^2 - 15^2$$
$$d^2 = 256 - 225$$
$$d^2 = 31$$
$$d = \sqrt{31}$$
$$d \approx 5.57 \text{ ft}$$

42. 
$$d^2 + 2^2 = 8^2$$
$$d^2 = 8^2 - 2^2$$
$$d^2 = 64 - 4$$
$$d^2 = 60$$
$$d = \sqrt{60}$$
$$d \approx 7.75 \text{ m}$$

43. 
$$d_1{}^2 = 9^2 + 40^2$$
$$d_1{}^2 = 81 + 1600$$
$$d_1{}^2 = 1681$$
$$d_1 = \sqrt{1681}$$
$$d_1 = 41$$
$$d_2{}^2 = 9^2 + 12^2$$
$$d_2{}^2 = 81 + 144$$
$$d_2{}^2 = 225$$
$$d_2 = \sqrt{225}$$
$$d_2 = 15$$
Total wire needed = $d_1 + d_2$
$$= 41 + 15$$
$$= 56 \text{ meters}$$

44. 
$$\frac{1 + 14 + 4 + 8 + 8 + 7.35 + 2.9 + 12.75}{8}$$
$$= \frac{58}{8}$$
$$= 7.25$$

45. 
$$\frac{2x^2 + 11x + 15}{2x^2 - 5x - 3} \cdot \frac{x^2 + x - 12}{x^2 + 7x + 12}$$
$$= \frac{(2x + 5)(x + 3)}{(2x + 1)(x - 3)} \cdot \frac{(x + 4)(x - 3)}{(x + 4)(x + 3)}$$
$$= \frac{2x + 5}{2x + 1}$$

46. x-intercept
= (6, 0)
y-intercept
= (0, -8)

47.

| | Amount | Amount Glycol |
|---|---|---|
| 50% Glycol | $x$ | $0.50x$ |
| 30% Glycol | $100 - x$ | $0.30(100 - x)$ |
| 45% Glycol | 100 | $0.45(100)$ |

$$0.50x + 0.30(100 - x) = 0.45(100)$$
$$0.50x + 30 - 0.30x = 45$$
$$0.20x = 15$$
$$x = 75$$
$$100 - x = 100 - 75 = 25$$
75 gallons of 50% and 25 gallons of 30%

48. 
$$4356 = 2 \cdot 2 \cdot 3 \cdot 3 \cdot 11 \cdot 11$$
$$= 2^2 \cdot 3^2 \cdot 11^2$$
$$= 66^2$$
$$\pm\sqrt{4356} = \pm 66$$

## 12-4  Real Numbers

PAGE 489    CHECKING FOR UNDERSTANDING
1. The measure must be a perfect square.
2. Rational numbers can be named by terminating or repeating decimals and irrational numbers cannot. No
3. real numbers    4. true    5. false    6. false
7. true    8. $Q$    9. $N, W, Z, Q$    10. $W, Z, Q$
11. $Q$    12. $I$    13. $N, W, Z, Q$    14. $Q$    15. $I$
16. 3.32    17. 6.32    18. 9.54    19. -9.43

PAGES 490-491    EXERCISES
20. $I$    21. $Q$    22. $Q$    23. $I$    24. $I$    25. $Q$

26. $\sqrt{7} \approx 2.65$

```
        √7
←+++++•++→
 -2  0  2  4
```

27. $\sqrt{20} \approx 4.47$

```
            √20
←+++++++•+→
 -2  0  2  4
```

28. $-\sqrt{50} \approx -7.07$

```
  -√50
←++•+++++→
 -8  -6  -4  -2
```

29. $-\sqrt{66} \approx -8.12$

```
 -√66
←+•+++++++→
 -8  -6  -4  -2
```

30. $\sqrt{84} \approx 9.17$

```
           √84
←++++++++•+→
  4   6   8   10
```

31. $-\sqrt{31} \approx -5.57$

```
-√31
←+•+++++++→
 -6  -4  -2  0
```

32. $-\sqrt{98} \approx -9.90$

```
 -√98
←+•+++++++→
 -10  -8  -6  -4
```

33. $\sqrt{107} \approx 10.34$

```
              √107
←+++++++++•→
  4   6   8   10
```

34. $I$; 80, 81    35. $Q$; 95

36. $I$; 61, 62    37. $I$; 86, 87

38. $\ell^2 + 8^2 = 16^2$

$\ell^2 = 16^2 - 8^2$

$\ell^2 = 256 - 64$

$\ell^2 = 192$

$\ell = \sqrt{192}$

$\ell \approx 13.86$ cm

Area $\approx (13.86)(8)$

$\approx 110.88$ cm$^2$

39. $\ell^2 + 18^2 = 27^2$

$\ell^2 = 27^2 - 18^2$

$\ell^2 = 729 - 324$

$\ell^2 = 405$

$\ell = \sqrt{405}$

$\ell \approx 20.12$

Area $\approx (20.12)(18)$

$\approx 362.16$ ft$^2$

40. $\sqrt{549} \approx 23.43$

The length of a side of the new square = 24 in.

Area of new square = $(24$ in.$)^2 = 576$ in$^2$.

Increase = $576 - 549 = 27$ in$^2$.

41. Let $w$ = width;

$3w$ = length.

$3w \cdot w = 186$

$3w^2 = 186$

$w^2 = 62$

$w = \sqrt{62}$

$w \approx 7.9$ ft

$3w \approx 3(7.9) \approx 23.7$ ft

Dimensions are 7.9 ft by 23.7 ft.

42. Let $x$ = length of side of square.

$x^2 + x^2 = 6^2$

$2x^2 = 36$

$x^2 = 18$

$x = \sqrt{18}$

$x \approx 4.24$ cm

Perimeter = $4x$

$\approx 4(4.24)$

$\approx 17$ cm

43. Area of circle = $\pi r^2$

$= (3.14)(3)^2$

$= 28.3$ cm$^2$

Area of square $\approx (4.24)^2$

$\approx 18.0$ cm$^2$

Shaded area = $28.3 - 18.0$

$\approx 10.3$ cm$^2$

44. $\sqrt{10}$, $\sqrt{11}$, $\sqrt{12}$, $\sqrt{13}$, $\sqrt{14}$, $\sqrt{15}$

45. $\sqrt{28}$, $\sqrt{29}$, $\sqrt{30}$

46. $V_1 = \sqrt{(4.6)(1200)}$

$= \sqrt{5520}$

$\approx 74.30$ volts

$V_2 = \sqrt{(4.6)(1500)}$

$= \sqrt{6900}$

$\approx 83.07$ volts

$V_3 = \sqrt{(5.2)(1200)}$

$= \sqrt{6240}$

$\approx 78.99$ volts

$V_4 = \sqrt{(5.2)(1500)}$

$= \sqrt{7800}$

$\approx 88.32$ volts

5.2 ohms and 1200 watts or 4.6 ohms and 1500 watts

47. $t = \sqrt{\dfrac{(12)^3}{216}}$

$t = \sqrt{8}$

$t \approx 2.83$ hrs $\approx 2$ hrs 50 min

No, since the rain will end at about 12:50 A.M.

48. $9x^2 - 0.25$

49. $F = \dfrac{GMn}{d^2}$

$Fd^2 = GMn$

$d^2 = \dfrac{GMn}{F}$

$d = \pm\sqrt{\dfrac{GMn}{F}}$

50. $y = \dfrac{7}{3}x - \dfrac{10}{3}$

$m = \dfrac{7}{3}$, $b = -\dfrac{10}{3}$

**51.**
$$3x + 4y = 7$$
$$\underline{3x - 4y = 8}$$
$$6x = 15$$
$$x = \frac{15}{6} = \frac{5}{2}$$
$$3\left(\frac{5}{2}\right) - 4y = 8$$
$$-4y = \frac{1}{2}$$
$$y = -\frac{1}{8}$$
$$\left(\frac{5}{2}, -\frac{1}{8}\right)$$

**52.**
$$d^2 = 14^2 + 10^2$$
$$d^2 = 196 + 100$$
$$d^2 = 296$$
$$d = \sqrt{296}$$
$$d \approx 17.2 \text{ m}$$

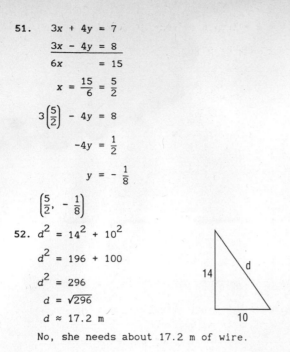

No, she needs about 17.2 m of wire.

**PAGE 491    MID-CHAPTER REVIEW**

**1.**

| Temp. in Degrees F | Number of Days | Temp. in Degrees F | Number of Days |
|---|---|---|---|
| 0 | 1 | 16 | 4 |
| 1 | 0 | 17 | 2 |
| 2 | 1 | 18 | 2 |
| 3 | 0 | 19 | 0 |
| 4 | 1 | 20 | 0 |
| 5 | 3 | 21 | 0 |
| 6 | 1 | 22 | 1 |
| 7 | 0 | 23 | 2 |
| 8 | 1 | 24 | 1 |
| 9 | 0 | 25 | 1 |
| 10 | 0 | 26 | 1 |
| 11 | 0 | 27 | 2 |
| 12 | 2 | 28 | 0 |
| 13 | 0 | 29 | 3 |
| 14 | 0 | 30 | 1 |
| 15 | 0 | | |

**2.** $16\,°F$          **3.** 10 days

**4.**
$$441 = 3 \cdot 3 \cdot 7 \cdot 7$$
$$= 3^2 \cdot 7^2 = 21^2$$
$$-\sqrt{441} = -\sqrt{21^2} = -21$$

**5.** $\sqrt{10.89} = 3.3$          **6.** $\pm\sqrt{0.0841} = \pm0.29$

**7.**
$$576 = 2 \cdot 2 \cdot 12 \cdot 12 = 2^2 \cdot 12^2 = 24^2$$
$$729 = 3 \cdot 3 \cdot 9 \cdot 9 = 3^2 \cdot 9^2 = 27^2$$
$$\sqrt{\frac{576}{729}} = \sqrt{\frac{24^2}{27^2}} = \frac{24}{27} = \frac{8}{9}$$

**8.**
$$21^2 + 28^2 = c^2$$
$$441 + 784 = c^2$$
$$c^2 = 1225$$
$$c = \sqrt{1225}$$
$$c = 35$$

**9.**
$$(0.5)^2 + b^2 = (1.3)^2$$
$$0.25 + b^2 = 1.69$$
$$b^2 = 1.44$$
$$b = \sqrt{1.44}$$
$$b = 1.2$$

**10.**
$$a^2 + (\sqrt{17})^2 = 9^2$$
$$a^2 + 17 = 81$$
$$a^2 = 64$$
$$a = \sqrt{64}$$
$$a = 8$$

**11.**
$$24^2 + 30^2 \overset{?}{=} 36^2$$
$$576 + 900 \overset{?}{=} 1296$$
$$1476 \neq 1296$$
no

---

## 12-5   Simplifying Square Roots

**PAGE 495    CHECKING FOR UNDERSTANDING**

**1.** The square root of the product of two or more positive numbers is equal to the product of their square roots.

**2.** to ensure non-negative results

**3.** Multiply the numerator and denominator of a fraction by the same number so that a radical is not left in the denominator.

**4.** $5 + 9\sqrt{2}$

**5.** $\sqrt{2 \cdot 2 \cdot 5}$
$$= \sqrt{2^2} \cdot \sqrt{5}$$
$$= 2\sqrt{5}$$

**6.** $\sqrt{2 \cdot 3 \cdot 3}$
$$= \sqrt{2} \cdot \sqrt{3^2}$$
$$= 3\sqrt{2}$$

**7.** $\sqrt{2 \cdot 2 \cdot 2 \cdot 2 \cdot 3}$
$$= \sqrt{2^2} \cdot \sqrt{2^2} \cdot \sqrt{3}$$
$$= 2 \cdot 2\sqrt{3}$$
$$= 4\sqrt{3}$$

**8.** $\dfrac{\sqrt{6 \cdot 7}}{\sqrt{6}}$
$$= \frac{\sqrt{6} \cdot \sqrt{7}}{\sqrt{6}}$$
$$= \sqrt{7}$$

**9.** $\dfrac{\sqrt{2 \cdot 2 \cdot 5}}{\sqrt{5}}$
$$= \frac{\sqrt{2^2} \cdot \sqrt{5}}{\sqrt{5}}$$
$$= 2$$

**10.** $3 - \sqrt{2}$
$$(3 + \sqrt{2})(3 - \sqrt{2})$$
$$= 9 - 2$$
$$= 7$$

**11.** $\sqrt{5} + 7$
$$(\sqrt{5} - 7)(\sqrt{5} + 7)$$
$$= 5 - 49$$
$$= -44$$

**12.** $\sqrt{3} + \sqrt{7}$
$$(\sqrt{3} - \sqrt{7})(\sqrt{3} + \sqrt{7})$$
$$= 3 - 7$$
$$= -4$$

**13.** $2\sqrt{8} - 3\sqrt{5}$
$$(2\sqrt{8} + 3\sqrt{5})(2\sqrt{8} - 3\sqrt{5})$$
$$= (4 \cdot 8) - (9 \cdot 5)$$
$$= 32 - 45$$
$$= -13$$

**14.** $\dfrac{\sqrt{5}}{\sqrt{5}}$

**15.** $\dfrac{2\sqrt{3}}{\sqrt{8}} = \dfrac{2\sqrt{3}}{2\sqrt{2}} = \dfrac{\sqrt{3}}{\sqrt{2}}$ so, $\dfrac{\sqrt{2}}{\sqrt{2}}$

16. $\dfrac{\sqrt{8}}{\sqrt{7}}$ so, $\dfrac{\sqrt{7}}{\sqrt{7}}$

17. $\dfrac{4 + \sqrt{3}}{4 + \sqrt{3}}$

PAGES 495–496    EXERCISES

18. $\sqrt{3 \cdot 5 \cdot 5}$

$= \sqrt{3} \cdot \sqrt{5^2}$

$= 5\sqrt{3}$

19. $\sqrt{3 \cdot 3 \cdot 5}$

$= \sqrt{3^2} \cdot \sqrt{5}$

$= 3\sqrt{5}$

20. $\sqrt{2 \cdot 2 \cdot 2 \cdot 2 \cdot 5}$

$= \sqrt{2^2} \cdot \sqrt{2^2} \cdot \sqrt{5}$

$= 2 \cdot 2 \cdot \sqrt{5}$

$= 4\sqrt{5}$

21. $\sqrt{2 \cdot 2 \cdot 2 \cdot 3 \cdot 3}$

$= \sqrt{2} \cdot \sqrt{2^2} \cdot \sqrt{3^2}$

$= 2 \cdot 3 \cdot \sqrt{2}$

$= 6\sqrt{2}$

22. $\sqrt{2 \cdot 7 \cdot 7}$

$= \sqrt{2} \cdot \sqrt{7^2}$

$= 7\sqrt{2}$

23. $\sqrt{2 \cdot 2 \cdot 2 \cdot 5 \cdot 7}$

$= \sqrt{2^2} \cdot \sqrt{2} \cdot \sqrt{5} \cdot \sqrt{7}$

$= 2\sqrt{2 \cdot 5 \cdot 7}$

$= 2\sqrt{70}$

24. $\sqrt{2 \cdot 2 \cdot 5 \cdot 5 \cdot 5}$

$= \sqrt{2^2} \cdot \sqrt{5^2} \cdot \sqrt{5}$

$= 2 \cdot 5 \cdot \sqrt{5}$

$= 10\sqrt{5}$

25. $\sqrt{2 \cdot 2 \cdot 2 \cdot 5 \cdot 5 \cdot 5}$

$= \sqrt{2^2} \cdot \sqrt{2} \cdot \sqrt{5^2} \cdot \sqrt{5}$

$= 2 \cdot 5 \cdot \sqrt{2} \cdot \sqrt{5}$

$= 10\sqrt{2 \cdot 5}$

$= 10\sqrt{10}$

26. $\dfrac{\sqrt{7}}{\sqrt{3}} \cdot \dfrac{\sqrt{3}}{\sqrt{3}}$

$= \dfrac{\sqrt{7 \cdot 3}}{3}$

$= \dfrac{\sqrt{21}}{3}$

27. $\dfrac{\sqrt{5}}{\sqrt{2 \cdot 5}}$

$= \dfrac{\sqrt{5}}{\sqrt{2} \cdot \sqrt{5}}$

$= \dfrac{1}{\sqrt{2}} \cdot \dfrac{\sqrt{2}}{\sqrt{2}}$

$= \dfrac{\sqrt{2}}{2}$

28. $\dfrac{\sqrt{3}}{\sqrt{7}} \cdot \dfrac{\sqrt{7}}{\sqrt{7}}$

$= \dfrac{\sqrt{3 \cdot 7}}{7}$

$= \dfrac{\sqrt{21}}{7}$

29. $\dfrac{\sqrt{11}}{\sqrt{2 \cdot 2 \cdot 2 \cdot 2 \cdot 2}}$

$= \dfrac{\sqrt{11}}{\sqrt{2^2} \cdot \sqrt{2^2} \cdot \sqrt{2}}$

$= \dfrac{\sqrt{11}}{2 \cdot 2 \cdot \sqrt{2}}$

$= \dfrac{\sqrt{11}}{4\sqrt{2}} \cdot \dfrac{\sqrt{2}}{\sqrt{2}}$

$= \dfrac{\sqrt{11 \cdot 2}}{4 \cdot 2}$

$= \dfrac{\sqrt{22}}{8}$

30. $\sqrt{2 \cdot 5} \cdot \sqrt{2 \cdot 3 \cdot 5}$

$= \sqrt{2 \cdot 2 \cdot 3 \cdot 5 \cdot 5}$

$= \sqrt{2^2} \cdot \sqrt{5^2} \cdot \sqrt{3}$

$= 2 \cdot 5 \cdot \sqrt{3}$

$= 10\sqrt{3}$

31. $2\sqrt{5 \cdot 5}$

$= 2\sqrt{5^2}$

$= 2 \cdot 5$

$= 10$

32. $5\sqrt{2 \cdot 5} \cdot 3 \cdot \sqrt{2 \cdot 5}$

$= 15\sqrt{2 \cdot 2 \cdot 5 \cdot 5}$

$= 15\sqrt{2^2} \cdot \sqrt{5^2}$

$= 15 \cdot 2 \cdot 5$

$= 150$

33. $7 \cdot \sqrt{2 \cdot 3 \cdot 5} \cdot 2 \cdot \sqrt{2 \cdot 3}$

$= 14\sqrt{2 \cdot 2 \cdot 3 \cdot 3 \cdot 5}$

$= 14 \cdot \sqrt{2^2} \cdot \sqrt{3^2} \cdot \sqrt{5}$

$= 14 \cdot 2 \cdot 3 \cdot \sqrt{5}$

$= 84\sqrt{5}$

34. $\dfrac{\sqrt{2}}{\sqrt{3}} \cdot \dfrac{\sqrt{5}}{\sqrt{2}}$

$= \dfrac{\sqrt{5}}{\sqrt{3}} \cdot \dfrac{\sqrt{3}}{\sqrt{3}}$

$= \dfrac{\sqrt{3 \cdot 5}}{3}$

$= \dfrac{\sqrt{15}}{3}$

35. $\dfrac{\sqrt{1}}{\sqrt{6}} \cdot \dfrac{\sqrt{6}}{\sqrt{11}}$

$= \dfrac{1}{\sqrt{11}} \cdot \dfrac{\sqrt{11}}{\sqrt{11}}$

$= \dfrac{\sqrt{11}}{11}$

36. $\sqrt{32} \cdot \sqrt{x^2}$

$= |x| \cdot \sqrt{2 \cdot 2 \cdot 2 \cdot 2 \cdot 2}$

$= |x| \cdot \sqrt{2^2} \cdot \sqrt{2^2} \cdot \sqrt{2}$

$= 2 \cdot 2 \cdot |x| \cdot \sqrt{2}$

$= 4|x|\sqrt{2}$

37. $\sqrt{40} \cdot \sqrt{b^2} \cdot \sqrt{b^2}$

$= b \cdot b \cdot \sqrt{2 \cdot 2 \cdot 2 \cdot 5}$

$= b^2 \cdot \sqrt{2^2} \cdot \sqrt{2} \cdot \sqrt{5}$

$= 2b^2\sqrt{10}$

38. $\sqrt{a^2} \cdot \sqrt{b^2} \cdot \sqrt{2 \cdot 3 \cdot 3 \cdot 3}$

$= |a| \cdot |b| \cdot \sqrt{2} \cdot \sqrt{3} \cdot \sqrt{3^2}$

$= 3|ab|\sqrt{6}$

39. $\sqrt{x^2} \cdot \sqrt{y^2} \cdot \sqrt{y} \cdot \sqrt{2 \cdot 2 \cdot 2 \cdot 2 \cdot 5}$

$= |x| \cdot y \cdot \sqrt{y} \cdot \sqrt{2^2} \cdot \sqrt{2^2} \cdot \sqrt{5}$

$= 2 \cdot 2 \cdot |x| \cdot y \cdot \sqrt{5y}$

$= 4|x|y\sqrt{5y}$

40. $\sqrt{m^2} \cdot \sqrt{y^2} \cdot \sqrt{y^2} \cdot \sqrt{2 \cdot 2 \cdot 3 \cdot 5}$

$= |m| \cdot y \cdot y \cdot \sqrt{2^2} \cdot \sqrt{3} \cdot \sqrt{5}$

$= 2|m|y^2\sqrt{15}$

41. $\sqrt{x^2} \cdot \sqrt{x^2} \cdot \sqrt{x} \cdot \sqrt{y^2} \cdot \sqrt{y^2} \cdot \sqrt{y^2} \cdot \sqrt{y}$
$\cdot \sqrt{3 \cdot 7 \cdot 7}$

$= x \cdot x \cdot y \cdot y \cdot y \cdot \sqrt{x} \cdot \sqrt{y} \cdot \sqrt{3} \cdot \sqrt{7^2}$

$= 7x^2y^3\sqrt{3xy}$

42. $\dfrac{\sqrt{b}}{\sqrt{6}} \cdot \dfrac{\sqrt{6}}{\sqrt{6}}$

$= \dfrac{\sqrt{6b}}{6}$

43. $\dfrac{\sqrt{27}}{\sqrt{r^2}}$

$= \dfrac{\sqrt{3 \cdot 3 \cdot 3}}{|r|}$

$= \dfrac{\sqrt{3^2} \cdot \sqrt{3}}{|r|} = \dfrac{3\sqrt{3}}{|r|}$

**44.**

$$\frac{\sqrt{5} \cdot \sqrt{n^2} \cdot \sqrt{n^2} \cdot \sqrt{n}}{\sqrt{4} \cdot \sqrt{m^2} \cdot \sqrt{m^2} \cdot \sqrt{m}}$$

$$= \frac{n \cdot n \cdot \sqrt{5n}}{2 \cdot |m| \cdot |m| \cdot \sqrt{m}}$$

$$= \frac{n^2\sqrt{5n}}{2|m^2|\sqrt{m}} \cdot \frac{\sqrt{m}}{\sqrt{m}}$$

$$= \frac{n^2\sqrt{5mn}}{2|m^2|\sqrt{m^2}}$$

$$= \frac{n^2\sqrt{5mn}}{2|m^3|}$$

**45.**

$$\frac{\sqrt{3} \cdot \sqrt{3} \cdot \sqrt{x^2} \cdot \sqrt{x^2} \cdot \sqrt{x} \cdot \sqrt{y}}{\sqrt{3} \cdot \sqrt{4} \cdot \sqrt{x^2} \cdot \sqrt{y^2} \cdot \sqrt{y^2} \cdot \sqrt{y^2}}$$

$$= \frac{|x| \cdot |x| \cdot \sqrt{3xy}}{2 \cdot |x| \cdot |y| \cdot |y| \cdot |y|}$$

$$= \frac{|x|\sqrt{3xy}}{2|y^3|}$$

**46.**

$$\frac{1}{6 + \sqrt{3}} \cdot \frac{6 - \sqrt{3}}{6 - \sqrt{3}}$$

$$= \frac{6 - \sqrt{3}}{36 - 3}$$

$$= \frac{6 - \sqrt{3}}{33}$$

**47.**

$$\frac{10}{\sqrt{5} - 9} \cdot \frac{\sqrt{5} + 9}{\sqrt{5} + 9}$$

$$= \frac{10\sqrt{5} + 90}{5 - 81}$$

$$= \frac{10\sqrt{5} + 90}{-76}$$

$$= \frac{5\sqrt{5} + 45}{-38}$$

**48.**

$$\frac{12}{\sqrt{6} - \sqrt{5}} \cdot \frac{\sqrt{6} + \sqrt{5}}{\sqrt{6} + \sqrt{5}}$$

$$= \frac{12(\sqrt{6} + \sqrt{5})}{6 - 5}$$

$$= 12\sqrt{6} + 12\sqrt{5}$$

**49.**

$$\frac{9b}{6 + \sqrt{b}} \cdot \frac{6 - \sqrt{b}}{6 - \sqrt{b}}$$

$$= \frac{9b(6 - \sqrt{b})}{36 - b}$$

$$= \frac{54b - 9b\sqrt{b}}{36 - b}$$

**50.**

$$\frac{2\sqrt{5}}{-4 + \sqrt{8}} \cdot \frac{-4 - \sqrt{8}}{-4 - \sqrt{8}}$$

$$= \frac{-8\sqrt{5} - 2\sqrt{40}}{16 - 8}$$

$$= \frac{-8\sqrt{5} - 2\sqrt{4}\sqrt{10}}{8}$$

$$= \frac{-8\sqrt{5} - 4\sqrt{10}}{8}$$

$$= \frac{-2\sqrt{5} - \sqrt{10}}{2}$$

**51.**

$$\frac{2\sqrt{7}}{3\sqrt{5} + 5\sqrt{3}} \cdot \frac{3\sqrt{5} - 5\sqrt{3}}{3\sqrt{5} - 5\sqrt{3}}$$

$$= \frac{6\sqrt{35} - 10\sqrt{21}}{45 - 75}$$

$$= \frac{6\sqrt{35} - 10\sqrt{21}}{-30}$$

$$= \frac{3\sqrt{35} - 5\sqrt{21}}{-15}$$

**52.**

$$\frac{3\sqrt{2} - \sqrt{7}}{2\sqrt{3} - 5\sqrt{2}} \cdot \frac{2\sqrt{3} + 5\sqrt{2}}{2\sqrt{3} + 5\sqrt{2}}$$

$$= \frac{6\sqrt{6} + 15\sqrt{2}^2 - 2\sqrt{21} - 5\sqrt{14}}{12 - 50}$$

$$= \frac{6\sqrt{6} - 2\sqrt{21} - 5\sqrt{14} + 30}{-38}$$

**53.**

$$\frac{\sqrt{a} - \sqrt{b}}{\sqrt{a} + \sqrt{b}} \cdot \frac{\sqrt{a} - \sqrt{b}}{\sqrt{a} - \sqrt{b}}$$

$$= \frac{a - 2\sqrt{ab} + b}{a - b}$$

**54.** length = $\sqrt{48s^3}$

$$= \sqrt{4} \cdot \sqrt{4} \cdot \sqrt{3} \cdot \sqrt{s^2} \cdot \sqrt{s}$$

$$= 2 \cdot 2 \cdot s \cdot \sqrt{3s}$$

$$= 4s\sqrt{3s} \text{ ft}$$

$$(4s\sqrt{3s})^2 + (4s\sqrt{3s})^2 = d^2$$

$$16s^2 \cdot 3s + 16s^2 \cdot 3s = d^2$$

$$96s^3 = d^2$$

$$d = \sqrt{96s^3}$$

$$d = \sqrt{4} \cdot \sqrt{4} \cdot \sqrt{6} \cdot \sqrt{s^2} \cdot \sqrt{s}$$

$$= 2 \cdot 2 \cdot s \cdot \sqrt{6s}$$

$$= 4s\sqrt{6s} \text{ ft}$$

**55.** No; square roots of negative numbers are not defined in the set of real numbers.

**56.** $P = 2(3.14)\sqrt{\dfrac{2}{32}}$

$$= \frac{6.28\sqrt{2}}{\sqrt{32}}$$

$$= \frac{6.28\sqrt{2}}{\sqrt{2}\sqrt{4}\sqrt{4}}$$

$$= \frac{6.28}{2 \cdot 2}$$

$$= \frac{6.28}{4}$$

$$= 1.57 \text{ sec}$$

$$\frac{60 \text{ sec}}{1.57 \text{ sec}} = 38 \text{ ticks}$$

**57.**

|       | $d$(miles) | $r$(mph) | $t$(hrs) |
|-------|------------|----------|----------|
| West  | $d_1$      | $s$      | 2        |
| North | $d_2$      | $2s$     | 3        |

**a.** $d_{total}^2 = d_1^2 + d_2^2$

$$d_{total}^2 = (2s)^2 + (6s)^2$$

$$d_{total}^2 = 4s^2 + 36s^2$$

$$d_{total}^2 = 40s^2$$

$$d_{total} = \sqrt{40s^2}$$

$$d_{total} = \sqrt{4} \cdot \sqrt{10} \cdot \sqrt{s^2} = 2s\sqrt{10} \text{ miles}$$

**b.** $s = 5$ mph

$$d_{total} = 2 \cdot 5\sqrt{10}$$

$$\approx 31.62 \text{ miles}$$

**58.** $(a + b)^2 = a^2b^2$       **59.** $(2r + s)(6r - 11s)$

**60.** yes

$\{(4, 5), (1, 6), (3, -2), (3, 0)\}$ ← inverse

no

**61.** $\frac{1}{2}d = \sqrt{(11 - 3)^2 + (-4 - 8)^2}$

$= \sqrt{8^2 + (-12)^2}$

$= \sqrt{64 + 144}$

$= \sqrt{208}$

$\frac{1}{2}d = \sqrt{(-5 - 3)^2 + (20 - 8)^2}$

$= \sqrt{(-8)^2 + (12)^2}$

$= \sqrt{64 + 144}$

$= \sqrt{208}$

So, the point is (20, -5).

**62.**

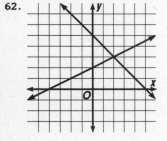

(2, 3)

**63.** $I^2 = \frac{P}{R}$

$I^2 = \frac{1500}{4.5}$

$I = \sqrt{\frac{1500}{4.5}}$

$I \approx 18.26$ amperes

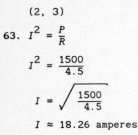

## 12-6 Adding and Subtracting Radical Expressions

**PAGE 499   CHECKING FOR UNDERSTANDING**

1. distributive property
2. to determine if there are any like radicands
3. Use the calculator to evaluate each expression and check that each gives the same decimal approximation.
4. $5\sqrt{3}$ and $3\sqrt{3}$    5. $4\sqrt{2}$ and $7\sqrt{2}$    6. $2\sqrt{10}$ and $-5\sqrt{10}$

**7.** $5\sqrt{14} = 5\sqrt{7} \cdot \sqrt{2}$       **8.** $3\sqrt{20} = 3\sqrt{4} \cdot \sqrt{5}$

$2\sqrt{28} = 2 \cdot \sqrt{4} \cdot \sqrt{7}$           $= 3 \cdot 2 \cdot \sqrt{5}$

$= 2 \cdot 2 \cdot \sqrt{7}$           $= 6\sqrt{5}$

$= 4\sqrt{7}$           $5\sqrt{6} = 5\sqrt{2} \cdot \sqrt{3}$

$-3\sqrt{7}$ and $2\sqrt{28}$           $3\sqrt{20}$ and $3\sqrt{5}$

**9.** $\sqrt{18} = \sqrt{2} \cdot \sqrt{9} = 3\sqrt{2}$

$\sqrt{24} = \sqrt{2} \cdot \sqrt{3} \cdot \sqrt{4} = 2\sqrt{3} \cdot \sqrt{2}$

$\sqrt{12} = \sqrt{3} \cdot \sqrt{4} = 2\sqrt{3}$

$\sqrt{28} = \sqrt{4} \cdot \sqrt{7} = 2\sqrt{7}$

**10.** $3\sqrt{32} = 3\sqrt{2} \cdot \sqrt{4} \cdot \sqrt{4} = 3 \cdot 2 \cdot 2 \cdot \sqrt{2} = 12\sqrt{2}$

$2\sqrt{48} = 2 \cdot \sqrt{3} \cdot \sqrt{4} \cdot \sqrt{4} = 2 \cdot 2 \cdot 2 \cdot \sqrt{3} = 8\sqrt{3}$

$\sqrt{50} = \sqrt{2} \cdot \sqrt{25} = 5\sqrt{2}$

$7\sqrt{200} = 7 \cdot \sqrt{2} \cdot \sqrt{100} = 7 \cdot 10\sqrt{2} = 70\sqrt{2}$

$3\sqrt{32}$, $\sqrt{50}$, and $7\sqrt{200}$

**11.** $(8 + 3)\sqrt{6}$          **12.** $(4 - 7)\sqrt{3}$

$= 11\sqrt{6}$           $= -3\sqrt{3}$

**13.** in simplest form

**14.** $(25 + 1)\sqrt{13}$    **15.** $(18 + 3)\sqrt{2x}$    **16.** $(3 - 5)\sqrt{5m}$

$= 26\sqrt{13}$           $= 21\sqrt{2x}$           $= -2\sqrt{5m}$

**PAGES 499-500    EXERCISES**

**17.** $(4 + 7 - 2)\sqrt{3}$          **18.** $(2 - 6 - 3)\sqrt{11}$

$= 9\sqrt{3}$           $= -7\sqrt{11}$

$\approx 15.59$           $\approx -23.22$

**19.** $(5 + 3 - 18)\sqrt{5}$

$= -10\sqrt{5}$

$\approx -22.36$

**20.** $\sqrt{6} + 2\sqrt{2} + \sqrt{10}$ (in simplest form)

$\approx 8.44$

**21.** $(8 + 5)\sqrt{3} + (3 - 2)\sqrt{2}$

$= 13\sqrt{3} + \sqrt{2}$

$\approx 23.93$

**22.** $4\sqrt{6} - 6\sqrt{2} + (1 + 4)\sqrt{7}$

$= 4\sqrt{6} - 6\sqrt{2} + 5\sqrt{7}$

$\approx 14.54$

**23.** $2\sqrt{3} + \sqrt{4} \cdot \sqrt{3}$          **24.** $3\sqrt{7} - 2\sqrt{4} \cdot \sqrt{7}$

$= 2\sqrt{3} + 2\sqrt{3}$           $= 3\sqrt{7} - 2 \cdot 2\sqrt{7}$

$= (2 + 2)\sqrt{3}$           $= 3\sqrt{7} - 4\sqrt{7}$

$= 4\sqrt{3}$           $= (3 - 4)\sqrt{7}$

$\approx 6.93$           $= -\sqrt{7}$

$\approx -2.65$

**25.** $2\sqrt{25} \cdot \sqrt{2} - 3\sqrt{16} \cdot \sqrt{2}$

$= 2 \cdot 5\sqrt{2} - 3 \cdot 4\sqrt{2}$

$= 10\sqrt{2} - 12\sqrt{2}$

$= (10 - 12)\sqrt{2}$

$= -2\sqrt{2}$

$\approx -2.83$

**26.** $3\sqrt{9} \cdot \sqrt{3} + 5\sqrt{3} \cdot \sqrt{16}$

$= 3 \cdot 3\sqrt{3} + 5 \cdot 4\sqrt{3}$

$= 9\sqrt{3} + 20\sqrt{3}$

$= 29\sqrt{3}$

$\approx 50.23$

**27.** $\sqrt{2} \cdot \sqrt{9} + \sqrt{3} \cdot \sqrt{36} + \sqrt{2} \cdot \sqrt{25}$

$= 3\sqrt{2} + 6\sqrt{3} + 5\sqrt{2}$

$= (3 + 5)\sqrt{2} + 6\sqrt{3}$

$= 8\sqrt{2} + 6\sqrt{3}$

$\approx 21.71$

28. $2 \cdot \sqrt{4} \cdot \sqrt{5} - 3\sqrt{4} \cdot \sqrt{6} - \sqrt{5} \cdot \sqrt{36}$

$= 2 \cdot 2\sqrt{5} - 3 \cdot 2\sqrt{6} - 6\sqrt{5}$

$= 4\sqrt{5} - 6\sqrt{6} - 6\sqrt{5}$

$= (4 - 6)\sqrt{5} - 6\sqrt{6}$

$= -2\sqrt{5} - 6\sqrt{6}$

$\approx -19.17$

29. $\sqrt{7} + \dfrac{1}{\sqrt{7}} \cdot \dfrac{\sqrt{7}}{\sqrt{7}}$

$= \sqrt{7} + \dfrac{\sqrt{7}}{7}$

$= \dfrac{7\sqrt{7}}{7} + \dfrac{\sqrt{7}}{7}$

$= \dfrac{8}{7}\sqrt{7}$

$\approx 3.02$

30. $\sqrt{10} - \dfrac{\sqrt{2}}{\sqrt{5}} \cdot \dfrac{\sqrt{5}}{\sqrt{5}}$

$= \sqrt{10} - \dfrac{\sqrt{10}}{5}$

$= \dfrac{5\sqrt{10}}{5} - \dfrac{\sqrt{10}}{5}$

$= \dfrac{(5 - 1)\sqrt{10}}{5}$

$= \dfrac{4}{5}\sqrt{10}$

$\approx 2.53$

31. $3\sqrt{3} - \sqrt{9} \cdot \sqrt{5} + \dfrac{3}{\sqrt{3}}$

$= 3\sqrt{3} - 3\sqrt{5} + \dfrac{3}{\sqrt{3}} \cdot \dfrac{\sqrt{3}}{\sqrt{3}}$

$= 3\sqrt{3} - 3\sqrt{5} + \dfrac{3\sqrt{3}}{3}$

$= \dfrac{3 \cdot 3\sqrt{3}}{3} - 3\sqrt{5} + \dfrac{3\sqrt{3}}{3}$

$= \dfrac{(9 + 3)\sqrt{3}}{3} - 3\sqrt{5}$

$= \dfrac{12\sqrt{3}}{3} - 3\sqrt{5}$

$= 4\sqrt{3} - 3\sqrt{5}$

$\approx 0.22$

32. $\dfrac{6\sqrt{7}}{2} + 3\sqrt{4} \cdot \sqrt{7} - \dfrac{10}{\sqrt{7}} \cdot \dfrac{\sqrt{7}}{\sqrt{7}}$

$= 3\sqrt{7} + 3 \cdot 2\sqrt{7} - \dfrac{10\sqrt{7}}{7}$

$= \dfrac{3 \cdot 7\sqrt{7}}{7} + \dfrac{6 \cdot 7 \cdot \sqrt{7}}{7} - \dfrac{10\sqrt{7}}{7}$

$= \dfrac{(21 + 42 - 10)\sqrt{7}}{7}$

$= \dfrac{53\sqrt{7}}{7}$

$\approx 20.03$

33. $P = 2\sqrt{7} + 2(\sqrt{7} + \sqrt{14})$

$= 2\sqrt{7} + 2\sqrt{7} + 2\sqrt{14}$

$= (2 + 2)\sqrt{7} + 2\sqrt{14}$

$= 4\sqrt{7} + 2\sqrt{14}$

$A = \sqrt{7}(\sqrt{14} + \sqrt{7})$

$= \sqrt{98} + 7$

$= \sqrt{2} \cdot \sqrt{49} + 7$

$= 7\sqrt{2} + 7$

34. $P = 2\sqrt{3} + 2(4\sqrt{7} - 2\sqrt{12})$

$= 2\sqrt{3} + 8\sqrt{7} - 4\sqrt{12}$

$= 2\sqrt{3} + 8\sqrt{7} - 4 \cdot \sqrt{4} \cdot \sqrt{3}$

$= 2\sqrt{3} + 8\sqrt{7} - 4 \cdot 2\sqrt{3}$

$= (2 - 8)\sqrt{3} + 8\sqrt{7}$

$= -6\sqrt{3} + 8\sqrt{7}$

$A = \sqrt{3}(4\sqrt{7} - 2\sqrt{12})$

$= 4\sqrt{21} - 2\sqrt{36}$

$= 4\sqrt{21} - 2 \cdot 6$

$= 4\sqrt{21} - 12$

35. $P = 2(\sqrt{8} + \sqrt{27}) + 2(\sqrt{3} - \sqrt{2})$

$= 2\sqrt{8} + 2\sqrt{27} + 2\sqrt{3} - 2\sqrt{2}$

$= 2\sqrt{4}\sqrt{2} + 2\sqrt{9}\sqrt{3} + 2\sqrt{3} - 2\sqrt{2}$

$= 2 \cdot 2\sqrt{2} + 2 \cdot 3\sqrt{3} + 2\sqrt{3} - 2\sqrt{2}$

$= (4 - 2)\sqrt{2} + (6 + 2)\sqrt{3}$

$= 2\sqrt{2} + 8\sqrt{3}$

$A = (\sqrt{8} + \sqrt{27})(\sqrt{3} - \sqrt{2})$

$= \sqrt{24} - \sqrt{16} + \sqrt{81} - \sqrt{54}$

$= \sqrt{4} \cdot \sqrt{6} - 4 + 9 - \sqrt{9} \cdot \sqrt{6}$

$= 2\sqrt{6} + 5 - 3\sqrt{6}$

$= 5 + (2 - 3)\sqrt{6}$

$= 5 - \sqrt{6}$

36. $\sqrt{70} - \sqrt{28} + \sqrt{175} - \sqrt{70}$

$= -\sqrt{4} \cdot \sqrt{7} + \sqrt{25} \cdot \sqrt{7}$

$= -2\sqrt{7} + 5\sqrt{7}$

$= (-2 + 5)\sqrt{7}$

$= 3\sqrt{7}$

37. $6\sqrt{30} - 4\sqrt{20} + 9\sqrt{45} - 6\sqrt{30}$

$= -4\sqrt{4} \cdot \sqrt{5} + 9 \cdot \sqrt{9} \cdot \sqrt{5}$

$= -4 \cdot 2\sqrt{5} + 9 \cdot 3 \cdot \sqrt{5}$

$= -8\sqrt{5} + 27\sqrt{5}$

$= (-8 + 27)\sqrt{5}$

$= 19\sqrt{5}$

38. $\sqrt{144} + \sqrt{12} + \sqrt{192} + \sqrt{16}$

$= 12 + \sqrt{4} \cdot \sqrt{3} + \sqrt{4} \cdot \sqrt{16} \cdot \sqrt{3} + 4$

$= 16 + 2\sqrt{3} + 2 \cdot 4\sqrt{3}$

$= 16 + (2 + 8)\sqrt{3}$

$= 16 + 10\sqrt{3}$

39. $6\sqrt{50} + 10\sqrt{20} - 9\sqrt{5} - 15\sqrt{2}$

$= 6\sqrt{25} \cdot \sqrt{2} + 10\sqrt{4} \cdot \sqrt{5} - 9\sqrt{5} - 15\sqrt{2}$

$= 6 \cdot 5\sqrt{2} + 10 \cdot 2\sqrt{5} - 9\sqrt{5} - 15\sqrt{2}$

$= 30\sqrt{2} + 20\sqrt{5} - 9\sqrt{5} - 15\sqrt{2}$

$= (30 - 15)\sqrt{2} + (20 - 9)\sqrt{5}$

$= 15\sqrt{2} + 11\sqrt{5}$

40. No; for example $-\sqrt{2} + \sqrt{2} = 0$.

41. Yes, if $a$ and $b$ are nonnegative and at least one of them equals 0.

42. Length of side $= \sqrt{44}$

$= \sqrt{4} \cdot \sqrt{11}$

$= 2\sqrt{11}$

$\approx 6.63$ ft.

Perimeter $\approx 4(6.63)$

$= 26.52$ ft

Akikta must purchase 27 ft of wood.

43. $10^2 + a^2 = (18 - a)^2$

$100 + a^2 = 324 - 36a + a^2$

$36a = 224$

$a \approx 6.22$ ft

44. $5(2n + 1) \geq 7(n + 4)$

$10n + 5 \geq 7n + 28$

$3n \geq 23$

$n \geq \dfrac{23}{3}$

45. $\dfrac{(k + 3)(k - 1)(k - 1)(k + 1)}{(k + 1)(k + 5)(k + 3)3}$

$= \dfrac{(k - 1)^2}{3(k + 5)}$

$= \dfrac{k^2 - 2k + 1}{3k + 15}$

46.

| $x$ | 110 | 175 | 200 |
|---|---|---|---|
| $y$ | 42.20 | 56.50 | 62.00 |

$y = 18 + 0.22x$; $0.22 per mile

47. $y = -4x - 3$

48. $1944 = 2 \cdot 2 \cdot 2 \cdot 3 \cdot 81$

$= 2^2 \cdot 2 \cdot 3 \cdot 81$

$\sqrt{1944} = \sqrt{2^2} \cdot \sqrt{2} \cdot \sqrt{3} \cdot \sqrt{81}$

$= 2 \cdot \sqrt{6} \cdot 9$

$= 18\sqrt{6}$

## 12-7 Radical Equations

**PAGE 503    CHECKING FOR UNDERSTANDING**

1. Isolate the radical.

2. false

3. $\sqrt{x} = -1$; $\sqrt{2x} + 4 = 2$

   Answers may vary.

4. $\pm\sqrt{5x}$

5. $(\sqrt{x})^2 = 5^2$

   $x = 25$

6. $(\sqrt{y + 1})^2 = 3^2$

   $y + 1 = 9$

7. $11^2 = (\sqrt{2a - 5})^2$

   $121 = 2a - 5$

8. $(\sqrt{y})^2 = 3^2$

   $y = 9$

9. no real solution

10. $(-\sqrt{a})^2 = (-8)^2$

    $a = 64$

11. $(\sqrt{5x})^2 = 5^2$

    $5x = 25$

    $x = 5$

12. $(\sqrt{-3a})^2 = 6^2$

    $-3a = 36$

    $a = -12$

13. $(\sqrt{x - 3})^2 = 6^2$

    $x - 3 = 36$

    $x = 39$

14. $\pm\sqrt{4 \cdot 9}$

    $= \pm\sqrt{36}$

    $= \pm 6$

15. $\pm\sqrt{5 \cdot 20}$

    $= \pm\sqrt{100}$

    $= \pm 10$

16. $\pm\sqrt{7 \cdot 10}$

    $= \pm\sqrt{70}$

17. $\pm\sqrt{4 \cdot 8}$

    $= \pm\sqrt{32}$

    $= \pm\sqrt{2} \cdot \sqrt{16}$

    $= \pm 4\sqrt{2}$

18. $(\sqrt{r})^2 = (3\sqrt{5})^2$

    $r = 9 \cdot 5$

    $r = 45$

19. $(4\sqrt{7})^2 = (\sqrt{-m})^2$

    $-m = 16 \cdot 7$

    $m = -112$

20. $\sqrt{b} = 5$

    $(\sqrt{b})^2 = 5^2$

    $b = 25$

21. $\sqrt{2d} = -1$

    no real solution

22. $\sqrt{3x} = 4$

    $(\sqrt{3x})^2 = 4^2$

    $3x = 16$

    $x = \dfrac{16}{3}$

23. $3\sqrt{m} = 11$

    $(3\sqrt{m})^2 = 11^2$

    $9m = 121$

    $m = \dfrac{121}{9}$

24. $(\sqrt{4x + 1})^2 = 3^2$

    $4x + 1 = 9$

    $4x = 8$

    $x = 2$

25. $\sqrt{8s + 1} = 5$

    $(\sqrt{8s + 1})^2 = 5^2$

    $8s + 1 = 25$

    $8s = 24$

    $s = 3$

26. $\sqrt{3b - 5} = -4$

    no real solution

27. $\dfrac{\sqrt{x}}{\sqrt{4}} = 6$

    $\dfrac{\sqrt{x}}{2} = 6$

    $\sqrt{x} = 12$

    $(\sqrt{x})^2 = 12^2$

    $x = 144$

28. $\sqrt{\dfrac{5k}{7}} = 10$

    $\left(\sqrt{\dfrac{5k}{7}}\right)^2 = 10^2$

    $\dfrac{5k}{7} = 100$

    $5k = 700$

    $k = 140$

29. $5\sqrt{\dfrac{4a}{3}} = 2$

    $\left(5\sqrt{\dfrac{4a}{3}}\right)^2 = 2^2$

    $25\left(\dfrac{4a}{3}\right) = 4$

    $100a = 12$

    $a = \dfrac{12}{100} = \dfrac{3}{25}$

30. $(4\sqrt{3m^2 - 15})^2 = 4^2$

    $16(3m^2 - 15) = 16$

        $3m^2 - 15 = 1$

            $3m^2 = 16$

             $m^2 = \dfrac{16}{3}$

              $m = \pm\sqrt{\dfrac{16}{3}}$

                $= \pm\dfrac{\sqrt{16}}{\sqrt{3}}$

                $= \pm\dfrac{4}{\sqrt{3}} \cdot \dfrac{\sqrt{3}}{\sqrt{3}}$

                $= \pm\dfrac{4\sqrt{3}}{3}$

31. $(\sqrt{2z^2 - 121})^2 = z^2$

    $2z^2 - 121 = z^2$

           $z^2 = 121$

            $z = \sqrt{121}$

            $z = 11$

32. $(\sqrt{5x^2 - 7})^2 = (2x)^2$

    $5x^2 - 7 = 4x^2$

           $x^2 = 7$

            $x = \sqrt{7}$

33. $(\sqrt{x + 2})^2 = (x - 4)^2$

    $x + 2 = x^2 - 8x + 16$

    $x^2 - 9x + 14 = 0$

    $(x - 7)(x - 2) = 0$

           $x = 7$

34. $(\sqrt{1 - 2x})^2 = (1 + x)^2$

    $1 - 2x = x^2 + 2x + 1$

    $x^2 + 4x = 0$

    $x(x + 4) = 0$

          $x = 0$

35. $\sqrt{x - 2} = x - 4$

    $(\sqrt{x - 2})^2 = (x - 4)^2$

        $x - 2 = x^2 - 8x + 16$

    $x^2 - 9x + 18 = 0$

    $(x - 3)(x - 6) = 0$

           $x = 6$

36. $\pm\sqrt{4x} = 26$

    $(\pm\sqrt{4x})^2 = 26^2$

      $4x = 676$

       $x = 169$

37. $\pm\sqrt{x(x + 2)} = \sqrt{24}$

    $[\pm\sqrt{x(x + 2)}]^2 = (\sqrt{24})^2$

        $x(x + 2) = 24$

         $x^2 + 2x = 24$

    $x^2 + 2x - 24 = 0$

    $(x + 6)(x - 4) = 0$

        $x = -6,\ 4$

    $-6$ and $-4$ or $4$ and $6$

38. $\pm\sqrt{x(3x - 11)} = 12$

    $[\pm\sqrt{x(3x - 11)}]^2 = 12^2$

        $x(3x - 11) = 144$

    $3x^2 - 11x - 144 = 0$

    $(3x + 16)(x - 9) = 0$

        $x = -\dfrac{16}{3},\ 9$

    $-\dfrac{16}{3}$ and $-27$ or $9$ and $16$

39. $(\sqrt{x + 16})^2 = (\sqrt{x} + 4)^2$

    $x + 16 = x + 8\sqrt{x} + 16$

    $8\sqrt{x} = 0$

    $(\sqrt{x})^2 = (0)^2$

      $x = 0$

40. $(6 - \sqrt{x})^2 = (\sqrt{x - 12})^2$

    $36 - 12\sqrt{x} + x = x - 12$

    $12\sqrt{x} = 48$

    $\sqrt{x} = 4$

    $(\sqrt{x})^2 = 4^2$

      $x = 16$

41. $(\sqrt{x + 5})^2 = (5 + \sqrt{x})^2$

    $x + 5 = 25 + 10\sqrt{x} + x$

    $10\sqrt{x} = -20$

    $\sqrt{x} = -2$

    no real solution

42. $3\sqrt{x} - 5\sqrt{y} = 9$

    $\underline{2\sqrt{x} + 5\sqrt{y} = 6}$

    $5\sqrt{x} \qquad = 15$

        $\sqrt{x} = 3$

       $(\sqrt{x})^2 = 3^2$

           $x = 9$

    $3\sqrt{9} - 5\sqrt{y} = 9$

    $3 \cdot 3 - 5\sqrt{y} = 9$

    $9 - 5\sqrt{y} = 9$

    $-5\sqrt{y} = 0$

      $\sqrt{y} = 0$

        $y = 0$

    $(9,\ 0)$

43. $-4\sqrt{a} + 6\sqrt{b} = 3$

    $\underline{6\sqrt{a} - 6\sqrt{b} = -2}$

    $2\sqrt{a} \qquad = 1$

        $\sqrt{a} = \dfrac{1}{2}$

       $(\sqrt{a})^2 = \left(\dfrac{1}{2}\right)^2$

           $a = \dfrac{1}{4}$

    $-4\sqrt{\dfrac{1}{4}} + 6\sqrt{b} = 3$

    $-4 \cdot \dfrac{1}{2} + 6\sqrt{b} = 3$

    $-2 + 6\sqrt{b} = 3$

    $6\sqrt{b} = 5$

    $\sqrt{b} = \dfrac{5}{6}$

    $(\sqrt{b})^2 = \left(\dfrac{5}{6}\right)^2$

       $b = \dfrac{25}{36}$

    $\left(\dfrac{1}{4},\ \dfrac{25}{36}\right)$

**44.**
$$\sqrt{4n} - 5\sqrt{n} = -6$$
$$\sqrt{4} \cdot \sqrt{n} - 5\sqrt{n} = -6$$
$$2\sqrt{n} - 5\sqrt{n} = -6$$
$$-3\sqrt{n} = -6$$
$$\sqrt{n} = 2$$
$$(\sqrt{n})^2 = 2^2$$
$$n = 4$$
$$m = 4n = 4 \cdot 4 = 16$$
$$(16, 4)$$

**45.**
$$\sqrt{a + b} = 5$$
$$\sqrt{ab} = 12$$
$$(\sqrt{ab})^2 = 12^2$$
$$ab = 144$$
$$a = \frac{144}{b}$$
$$\sqrt{\frac{144}{b} + b} = 5$$
$$\left(\sqrt{\frac{144}{b} + b}\right)^2 = 5^2$$
$$\frac{144}{b} + b = 25$$
$$144 + b^2 = 25b$$
$$b^2 - 25b + 144 = 0$$
$$(b - 16)(b - 9) = 0$$
$$b = 16, 9$$
$$a = 9, 16$$
9 and 16

**46.**
$$315 = 3.5\sqrt{h}$$
$$\sqrt{h} = 90$$
$$(\sqrt{h})^2 = 90^2$$
$$h = 8100 \text{ m}$$
$$= 8.1 \text{ km}$$

**47.**
$$3 = \sqrt{\frac{2(7.2)}{g}}$$
$$3 = \frac{\sqrt{14.4}}{\sqrt{g}}$$
$$3\sqrt{g} = \sqrt{14.4}$$
$$\sqrt{g} = \frac{\sqrt{14.4}}{3}$$
$$(\sqrt{g})^2 = \left(\frac{\sqrt{14.4}}{3}\right)^2$$
$$g = 1.6 \text{ m/s}^2$$

**48.** Let $x$ = distance traveled due east.
$$(60 - x)^2 + 10^2 = (66 - x)^2$$
$$3600 - 120x + x^2 + 100 = 4356 - 132x + x^2$$
$$12x = 656$$
$$x = 54\frac{2}{3} \text{ miles}$$

**49.**
$$11t - 10 = 56$$
$$11t = 66$$
$$t = 6$$

**50.** original area = $10 \cdot 15 = 150 \text{ ft}^2$
$$(10 + 2x)(15 + 2x) = 2 \cdot 150$$
$$150 + 50x + 4x^2 = 300$$
$$4x^2 + 50x - 150 = 0$$
$$2x^2 + 25x - 75 = 0$$
$$(2x - 5)(x + 15) = 0$$
$$2x - 5 = 0$$
$$2x = 5$$
$$x = 2\frac{1}{2} \text{ ft}$$

**51.** $\left\{(-4, 7), \left(-2, \frac{23}{5}\right), \left(0, \frac{11}{5}\right), (1, 1), \left(5, -\frac{19}{5}\right)\right\}$

**52.** $\dfrac{4 - (-r)}{r - 3} = 2r$
$$4 + r = 2r(r - 3)$$
$$4 + r = 2r^2 - 6r$$
$$2r^2 - 7r - 4 = 0$$
$$(2r + 1)(r - 4) = 0$$
$$2r + 1 = 0, \quad r - 4 = 0$$
$$2r = -1 \qquad r = 4$$
$$r = -\frac{1}{2}$$
$$\left\{4, -\frac{1}{2}\right\}$$

**53.**
$$2x + 3(-2x + 10) = 6$$
$$2x - 6x + 30 = 6$$
$$-4x = -24$$
$$x = 6$$
$$y = -2(6) + 10$$
$$y = -12 + 10$$
$$y = -2$$
$$(6, -2)$$

**54.** $P = \sqrt{363} + \sqrt{27} + 2\sqrt{108}$
$$= \sqrt{3} \cdot \sqrt{121} + \sqrt{3} \cdot \sqrt{9} + 2 \cdot \sqrt{3} \cdot \sqrt{36}$$
$$= 11\sqrt{3} + 3\sqrt{3} + 2 \cdot 6\sqrt{3}$$
$$= 11\sqrt{3} + 3\sqrt{3} + 12\sqrt{3}$$
$$= (11 + 3 + 12)\sqrt{3}$$
$$= 26\sqrt{3}$$
$$\approx 45.03$$

# Technology: Solving Radical Equations

1. $&x + 4 = 1$         $\sqrt{x} + 4 = 1$

   sto $a$

   sub 4         $\sqrt{x} + 4 - 4 = 1 - 4$

   simp                 $\sqrt{x} = -3$

   rai 2             $(\sqrt{x})^2 = (-3)^2$

   simp                 $x = 9$

   Check:  $a$         $\sqrt{x} + 4 = 1$

   subs 9 $x$     $\sqrt{9} + 4 = 1$

   simp         $7 \neq 1$     no solution

2. $3 + &(2x) = 7$         $3 + \sqrt{2x} = 7$

   sto $a$

   sub 3         $3 + \sqrt{2x} - 3 = 7 - 3$

   simp                 $\sqrt{2x} = 4$

   rai 2             $(\sqrt{2x})^2 = 4^2$

   simp                 $2x = 16$

   div 2                 $\dfrac{2x}{2} = \dfrac{16}{2}$

   simp                 $x = 8$

   Check:  $a$         $3 + \sqrt{2x} = 7$

   subs 8 $x$     $3 + \sqrt{2 \cdot 8} = 7$

   simp             $7 = 7$

   The solution is 8.

3. $&(3x - 8) = 5$         $\sqrt{3x - 8} = 5$

   sto $a$

   rai 2             $(\sqrt{3x - 8})^2 = 5^2$

   simp                 $3x - 8 = 25$

   add 8         $3x - 8 + 8 = 25 + 8$

   simp                 $3x = 33$

   div 3                 $\dfrac{3x}{3} = \dfrac{33}{3}$

   simp                 $x = 11$

   Check:  $a$         $\sqrt{3x - 8} = 5$

   subs 11 $x$     $\sqrt{3 \cdot 11 - 8} = 5$

   simp             $5 = 5$

   The solution is 11.

4. $x - &(x + 1) = 1$     $x - \sqrt{x + 1} = 1$

   sto $a$

   add $&(x + 1)$     $x - \sqrt{x + 1} + \sqrt{x + 1} = 1 + \sqrt{x + 1}$

   simp             $x = \sqrt{x + 1} + 1$

   sub 1         $x - 1 = \sqrt{x + 1} + 1 - 1$

   simp             $x - 1 = \sqrt{x + 1}$

   rai 2             $(x - 1)^2 = (\sqrt{x + 1})^2$

   simp             $x^2 - 2x + 1 = x + 1$

   sub $(x + 1)$     $x^2 - 2x + 1 - (x + 1) = x + 1$
                                     $- (x + 1)$

   simp             $x^2 - 3x = 0$

   fac             $x(x - 3) = 0$

   By inspection, the solutions are $x = 0$ or $x = 3$.

   Check:  $a$         $x - \sqrt{x + 1} = 1$

   subs 0 $x$     $0 - \sqrt{0 + 1} = 1$

   simp                 $-1 \neq 1$

   $a$         $x - \sqrt{x + 1} = 1$

   subs 3 $x$     $3 - \sqrt{3 + 1} = 1$

   simp             $1 = 1$

   The only solution is 3.

5. $&(6 - x) = 4 - x$     $\sqrt{6 - x} = 4 - x$

   sto $a$

   rai 2             $(\sqrt{6 - x})^2 = (4 - x)^2$

   simp         $-x + 6 = x^2 - 8x + 16$

   sub $(-x + 6)$     $-x + 6 - (-x + 6) = x^2 - 8x + 16$
                                     $- (-x + 6)$

   simp         $0 = x^2 - 7x + 10$

   fac         $0 = (x - 2)(x - 5)$

   By inspection, the solutions are $x = 2$ or $x = 5$.

   Check:  $a$         $\sqrt{6 - x} = 4 - x$

   subs 2 $x$     $\sqrt{6 - 2} = 4 - 2$

   simp             $2 = 2$

   $a$         $\sqrt{6 - x} = 4 - x$

   subs 5 $x$     $\sqrt{6 - 5} = 4 - 5$

   simp             $1 \neq -1$

   The only solution is 2.

6. $&(2x + 6) = &(3x - 9)$     $\sqrt{2x + 6} = \sqrt{3x - 9}$

   sto $a$

   rai 2             $(\sqrt{2x + 6})^2 = (\sqrt{3x - 9})^2$

   simp             $2x + 6 = 3x - 9$

   sub 2x         $2x + 6 - 2x = 3x - 9 - 2x$

   simp                 $6 = x - 9$

   add 9         $6 + 9 = x - 9 + 9$

   simp                 $15 = x$

   Check:  $a$         $\sqrt{2x + 6} = \sqrt{3x - 9}$

   subs 15 $x$     $\sqrt{2 \cdot 15 + 6} = \sqrt{3 \cdot 15 - 9}$

   simp             $6 = 6$

   The solution is 15.

233

# The Distance Formula

1. Apply the Pythagorean Theorem to the right triangle with vertices $(x_1, y_1)$, $(x_2, y_1)$, and $(x_2, y_2)$, where $d$, the distance between $(x_1, y_1)$ and $(x_2, y_2)$ is the measure of the hypotenuse.

2. No, you can use 18 for $x_2$ as long as you use 8 for $y_2$, 5 for $x_1$, and 7 for $y_1$.

3. The distance between them is the absolute value of the difference of their $x$-coordinates, $|10 - 2|$ or 8 units.

4. The distance between them is the absolute value of the difference of their $y$-coordinates, $|5 - (-2)|$ or 7 units.

5. $d = \sqrt{(6 - 3)^2 + (8 - 4)^2}$
   $= \sqrt{3^2 + 4^2}$
   $= \sqrt{9 + 16}$
   $= \sqrt{25}$
   $= 5$

6. $d = \sqrt{(17 - 2)^2 + [4 - (-4)]^2}$
   $= \sqrt{15^2 + 8^2}$
   $= \sqrt{225 + 64}$
   $= \sqrt{289}$
   $= 17$

7. $d = \sqrt{(-5 - 7)^2 + (-2 - 3)^2}$
   $= \sqrt{(-12)^2 + (-5)^2}$
   $= \sqrt{144 + 25}$
   $= \sqrt{169}$
   $= 13$

8. $d = \sqrt{(7 - (-1))^2 + (11 - 5)^2}$
   $= \sqrt{8^2 + 6^2}$
   $= \sqrt{64 + 36}$
   $= \sqrt{100}$
   $= 10$

9. $d = \sqrt{(-1 - 2)^2 + (5 - 2)^2}$
   $= \sqrt{(-3)^2 + 3^2}$
   $= \sqrt{9 + 9}$
   $= \sqrt{18}$
   $= \sqrt{2} \cdot \sqrt{9}$
   $= 3\sqrt{2}$
   $\approx 4.24$

10. $d = \sqrt{[-8 - (-4)]^2 + [-3 - (-8)]^2}$
    $= \sqrt{(-4)^2 + 5^2}$
    $= \sqrt{16 + 25}$
    $= \sqrt{41}$
    $\approx 6.40$

11. $d = \sqrt{(8 - 4)^2 + (-3 - 5)^2}$
    $= \sqrt{4^2 + (-8)^2}$
    $= \sqrt{16 + 64}$
    $= \sqrt{80}$
    $= \sqrt{16} \cdot \sqrt{5} = 4\sqrt{5} \approx 8.94$

12. $d = \sqrt{(-4 - 7)^2 + (10 - 2)^2}$
    $= \sqrt{(-11)^2 + 8^2}$
    $= \sqrt{121 + 64}$
    $= \sqrt{185}$
    $\approx 13.60$

13. $d = \sqrt{[-6 - (-2)]^2 + (3 - 9)^2}$
    $= \sqrt{(-4)^2 + (-6)^2}$
    $= \sqrt{16 + 36}$
    $= \sqrt{52}$
    $= \sqrt{4} \cdot \sqrt{13}$
    $= 2\sqrt{13}$
    $\approx 7.21$

14. $d = \sqrt{\left(-\dfrac{2}{3} - 2\right)^2 + (6 - 4)^2}$
    $= \sqrt{\left(-\dfrac{8}{3}\right)^2 + 2^2}$
    $= \sqrt{\dfrac{64}{9} + 4}$
    $= \sqrt{\dfrac{64 + 36}{9}}$
    $= \sqrt{\dfrac{100}{9}}$
    $= \dfrac{10}{3}$
    $\approx 3.33$

15. $d = \sqrt{\left[\dfrac{3}{7} - \left(-\dfrac{2}{7}\right)\right]^2 + (5 - 6)^2}$
    $= \sqrt{\left(\dfrac{5}{7}\right)^2 + (-1)^2}$
    $= \sqrt{\dfrac{25}{49} + 1}$
    $= \sqrt{\dfrac{25 + 49}{49}}$
    $= \sqrt{\dfrac{74}{49}}$
    $= \dfrac{\sqrt{74}}{7}$
    $\approx 1.23$

**16.** $d = \sqrt{\left(-\frac{1}{2} - (-1)\right)^2 + \left(2 - \frac{4}{5}\right)^2}$

$\phantom{d} = \sqrt{\left(\frac{1}{2}\right)^2 + \left(\frac{6}{5}\right)^2}$

$\phantom{d} = \sqrt{\frac{1}{4} + \frac{36}{25}}$

$\phantom{d} = \sqrt{\frac{25 + 144}{100}}$

$\phantom{d} = \sqrt{\frac{169}{100}}$

$\phantom{d} = \frac{13}{10}$

$\phantom{d} = \approx 1.3$

**17.** $d = \sqrt{(3 - 9)^2 + (4\sqrt{5} - 2\sqrt{5})^2}$

$\phantom{d} = \sqrt{(-6)^2 + (2\sqrt{5})^2}$

$\phantom{d} = \sqrt{36 + 20}$

$\phantom{d} = \sqrt{56}$

$\phantom{d} = \sqrt{4} \cdot \sqrt{14}$

$\phantom{d} = 2\sqrt{14}$

$\phantom{d} \approx 7.48$

**18.** $d = \sqrt{(9 - 7)^2 + (5\sqrt{2} - 3\sqrt{2})^2}$

$\phantom{d} = \sqrt{2^2 + (2\sqrt{2})^2}$

$\phantom{d} = \sqrt{4 + 8}$

$\phantom{d} = \sqrt{12}$

$\phantom{d} = \sqrt{4} \cdot \sqrt{3}$

$\phantom{d} = 2\sqrt{3}$

$\phantom{d} \approx 3.46$

**19.** $5 = \sqrt{(3 - 7)^2 + (a - 4)^2}$

$5 = \sqrt{(-4)^2 + (a^2 - 8a + 16)}$

$5 = \sqrt{16 + a^2 - 8a + 16}$

$5 = \sqrt{a^2 - 8a + 32}$

$5^2 = \left(\sqrt{a^2 - 8a + 32}\right)^2$

$25 = a^2 - 8a + 32$

$a^2 - 8a + 7 = 0$

$(a - 7)(a - 1) = 0$

$a = 7 \text{ or } 1$

**20.** $17 = \sqrt{(2 - a)^2 + [5 - (-3)]^2}$

$17 = \sqrt{4 - 4a + a^2 + 8^2}$

$17 = \sqrt{a^2 - 4a + 4 + 64}$

$17 = \sqrt{a^2 - 4a + 68}$

$17^2 = \left(\sqrt{a^2 - 4a + 68}\right)^2$

$289 = a^2 - 4a + 68$

$a^2 - 4a - 221 = 0$

$(a + 13)(a - 17) = 0$

$a = 17 \text{ or } -13$

**21.** $\sqrt{29} = \sqrt{(3 - 5)^2 + (-7 - a)^2}$

$\sqrt{29} = \sqrt{(-2)^2 + 49 + 14a + a^2}$

$\sqrt{29} = \sqrt{a^2 + 14a + 49 + 4}$

$\sqrt{29} = \sqrt{a^2 + 14a + 53}$

$(\sqrt{29})^2 = \left(\sqrt{a^2 + 14a + 53}\right)^2$

$29 = a^2 + 14a + 53$

$a^2 + 14a + 24 = 0$

$(a + 2)(a + 12) = 0$

$a = -2 \text{ or } -12$

**22.** $\sqrt{130} = \sqrt{[a - (-2)]^2 + (-5 - 4)^2}$

$\sqrt{130} = \sqrt{a^2 + 4a + 4 + (-9)^2}$

$\sqrt{130} = \sqrt{a^2 + 4a + 4 + 81}$

$\sqrt{130} = \sqrt{a^2 + 4a + 85}$

$(\sqrt{130})^2 = \left(\sqrt{a^2 + 4a + 85}\right)^2$

$130 = a^2 + 4a + 85$

$a^2 + 4a - 45 = 0$

$(a - 5)(a + 9) = 0$

$a = 5 \text{ or } -9$

**23.** $d_1 = \sqrt{(4 - 0)^2 + (7 - 0)^2}$

$\phantom{d_1} = \sqrt{4^2 + 7^2}$

$\phantom{d_1} = \sqrt{16 + 49}$

$\phantom{d_1} = \sqrt{65}$

$d_2 = \sqrt{(4 - 0)^2 + (1 - 7)^2}$

$\phantom{d_2} = \sqrt{4^2 + (-6)^2}$

$\phantom{d_2} = \sqrt{16 + 36}$

$\phantom{d_2} = \sqrt{52}$

$\sqrt{65} \neq \sqrt{52}$

no

**24.** $d_1 = \sqrt{(8 - 1)^2 + (2 - 1)^2}$

$\phantom{d_1} = \sqrt{7^2 + 1^2}$

$\phantom{d_1} = \sqrt{49 + 1}$

$\phantom{d_1} = \sqrt{50}$

$\phantom{d_1} = \sqrt{2} \cdot \sqrt{25}$

$\phantom{d_1} = 5\sqrt{2}$

$d_2 = \sqrt{(4 - 9)^2 + (0 - 5)^2}$

$\phantom{d_2} = \sqrt{(-5)^2 + (-5)^2}$

$\phantom{d_2} = \sqrt{25 + 25}$

$\phantom{d_2} = \sqrt{50}$

$\phantom{d_2} = \sqrt{2} \cdot \sqrt{25}$

$\phantom{d_2} = 5\sqrt{2}$

$5\sqrt{2} = 5\sqrt{2}$

yes

25. $d_{AB} = \sqrt{[2 - (-1)]^2 + (-2 - 2)^2}$

$\quad = \sqrt{3^2 + (-4)^2}$

$\quad = \sqrt{9 + 16}$

$\quad = \sqrt{25}$

$\quad = 5$

$d_{BC} = \sqrt{(14 - 2)^2 + [-6 - (-2)]^2}$

$\quad = \sqrt{12^2 + (-4)^2}$

$\quad = \sqrt{144 + 16}$

$\quad = \sqrt{160}$

$\quad = \sqrt{16} \cdot \sqrt{10}$

$\quad = 4\sqrt{10}$

$d_{CA} = \sqrt{[14 - (-1)]^2 + (-6 - 2)^2}$

$\quad = \sqrt{15^2 + (-8)^2}$

$\quad = \sqrt{225 + 64}$

$\quad = \sqrt{289}$

$\quad = 17$

$P = d_{AB} + d_{BC} + d_{CA}$

$\quad = 5 + 4\sqrt{10} + 17$

$\quad = 22 + 4\sqrt{10}$

$\quad \approx 34.65$ units

26. $d = \sqrt{(-\sqrt{8} - \sqrt{3})^2 + (\sqrt{3} - \sqrt{8})^2}$

$\quad = \sqrt{8 + 2\sqrt{24} + 3 + 3 - 2\sqrt{24} + 8}$

$\quad = \sqrt{22}$

27. $d = \sqrt{(6\sqrt{3} - \sqrt{10})^2 + [2\sqrt{5} - (-3\sqrt{6})]^2}$

$\quad = \sqrt{36 \cdot 3 - 12\sqrt{30} + 10 + 4 \cdot 5 + 12\sqrt{30} + 9 \cdot 6}$

$\quad = \sqrt{108 + 10 + 20 + 54}$

$\quad = \sqrt{192}$

$\quad = \sqrt{3} \cdot \sqrt{64}$

$\quad = 8\sqrt{3}$

28. $5 = \sqrt{(-2a - 5)^2 + (3 - a)^2}$

$5 = \sqrt{4a^2 + 20a + 25 + 9 - 6a + a^2}$

$5 = \sqrt{5a^2 + 14a + 34}$

$5^2 = \left(\sqrt{5a^2 + 14a + 34}\right)^2$

$25 = 5a^2 + 14a + 34$

$5a^2 + 14a + 9 = 0$

$(5a + 9)(a + 1) = 0$

$5a + 9 = 0, \qquad a + 1 = 0$

$\quad 5a = -9 \qquad\qquad a = -1$

$\qquad a = -\dfrac{9}{5}$

$\qquad -1$ or $-\dfrac{9}{5}$

29. $d_1 = \sqrt{[7 - (-2)]^2 + (-3 - 3)^2}$

$\quad = \sqrt{9^2 + (-6)^2}$

$\quad = \sqrt{81 + 36}$

$\quad = \sqrt{117}$

$\quad = \sqrt{9} \cdot \sqrt{13}$

$\quad = 3\sqrt{13}$

$d_2 = \sqrt{(3 - 7)^2 + [-9 - (-3)]^2}$

$\quad = \sqrt{(-4)^2 + (-6)^2}$

$\quad = \sqrt{16 + 36}$

$\quad = \sqrt{52}$

$\quad = \sqrt{4} \cdot \sqrt{13}$

$\quad = 2\sqrt{13}$

$d_3 = \sqrt{[3 - (-2)]^2 + (-9 - 3)^2}$

$\quad = \sqrt{5^2 + (-12)^2}$

$\quad = \sqrt{25 + 144}$

$\quad = \sqrt{169}$

$\quad = 13$

$(3\sqrt{13})^2 + (2\sqrt{13})^2 \stackrel{?}{=} 13^2$

$9 \cdot 13 + 4 \cdot 13 \stackrel{?}{=} 169$

$117 + 52 \stackrel{?}{=} 169$

$169 = 169$

Therefore, it is a right triangle.

30. $d_1 = \sqrt{[5 - (-12)]^2 + (4 - 0)^2}$

$\quad = \sqrt{17^2 + 4^2}$

$\quad = \sqrt{289 + 16}$

$\quad = \sqrt{305}$

$\quad \approx 17.46$ miles

$d_2 = \sqrt{[2 - (-12)]^2 + (-5 - 0)^2}$

$\quad = \sqrt{14^2 + (-5)^2}$

$\quad = \sqrt{196 + 25}$

$\quad = \sqrt{221}$

$\quad \approx 14.87$ miles

$d_3 = \sqrt{[0 - (-12)]^2 + (0 - 0)^2}$

$\quad = \sqrt{12^2}$

$\quad = 12$ miles

$d_1 + d_2 + d_3 \approx 17.46 + 14.87 + 12$

$\qquad \approx 44.33$ miles

31. $d = \sqrt{(9213 - 5622)^2 + (7878 - 1583)^2}$

$\quad = \sqrt{(3591)^2 + (6295)^2}$

$\quad = \sqrt{12,895,281 + 39,627,025}$

$\quad = \sqrt{52,522,306}$

$\quad \approx 7247.23$ units

Distance in miles $= 7247.23(0.316)$

$\qquad \approx 2290$ miles

**32. a.** 10

**b.** $\approx 16.55$

**c.** $\approx 3.07$

**33.** $\dfrac{(2m + 1)(2m - 4)}{(2m - 4)(m - 2)}$

$= \dfrac{2m + 1}{m - 2}$

**34.** $f[g(-2)] = 3[(-2)^2 - (-2)] - 5$

$\qquad\qquad = 3(4 + 2) - 5$

$\qquad\qquad = 3 \cdot 6 - 5$

$\qquad\qquad = 18 - 5$

$\qquad\qquad = 13$

**35.** $4x - 3y = 23$

**36.**

|  | $d$(miles) | $r$(mph) | $t$(hrs) |
|---|---|---|---|
| With Wind | 300 | 450 | $\frac{2}{3}$ |
| Against Wind | 300 | 400 | $\frac{3}{4}$ |

speed of wind $= \dfrac{450 - 400}{2}$

$\qquad\qquad\quad = 25$ mph

air speed of plane $= 400 + 25$

$\qquad\qquad\qquad\quad = 425$ mph

$\qquad\qquad\qquad$ or $450 - 25$

$\qquad\qquad\qquad\quad = 425$ mph

**37.** $\left(\sqrt{x^2 + 3}\right)^2 = (3 - x)^2$

$\qquad x^2 + 3 = 9 - 6x + x^2$

$\qquad\qquad 6x = 6$

$\qquad\qquad\ x = 1$

# Chapter 12    Summary and Review

PAGES 510–512    SKILLS AND CONCEPTS

**1.** 13

**2.** $784 = 2 \cdot 2 \cdot 14 \cdot 14$

$\qquad\quad = 2^2 \cdot 14^2$

$-\sqrt{784} = -\sqrt{2^2} \cdot \sqrt{14^2}$

$-\sqrt{784} = -2 \cdot 14$

$-\sqrt{784} = -28$

**3.** $-0.17$

**4.** $\pm \sqrt{\dfrac{14^2}{15^2}}$

$= \pm \dfrac{14}{15}$

**5.** $-7.85$    **6.** $13.84$    **7.** $\pm 4.8$    **8.** $\pm 3.17$

**9.** $30^2 + 16^2 = c^2$

$900 + 256 = c^2$

$\qquad\quad c^2 = 1156$

$\qquad\quad\ c = \sqrt{1156}$

$\qquad\quad\ c = 34$

**10.** $6^2 + 10^2 = c^2$

$36 + 100 = c^2$

$\qquad\quad c^2 = 136$

$\qquad\quad\ c = \sqrt{136}$

$\qquad\quad\ c \approx 11.66$

**11.** $10^2 + b^2 = 15^2$

$100 + b^2 = 225$

$\qquad\ b^2 = 125$

$\qquad\ b = \sqrt{125}$

$\qquad\ b \approx 11.18$

**12.** $20^2 + 21^2 \overset{?}{=} 29^2$

$400 + 441 \overset{?}{=} 841$

$\qquad\qquad 841 = 841$

$\qquad$ yes

**13.** irrational    **14.** rational

**15.** rational    **16.** irrational

**17.** $\sqrt{6} \cdot \sqrt{6} \cdot \sqrt{3}$

$= \sqrt{6^2} \cdot \sqrt{3}$

$= 6\sqrt{3}$

**18.** $\sqrt{2 \cdot 2 \cdot 2 \cdot 2 \cdot 3 \cdot 3 \cdot 5}$

$= \sqrt{2^2} \cdot \sqrt{2^2} \cdot \sqrt{3^2} \cdot \sqrt{5}$

$= 2 \cdot 2 \cdot 3 \cdot \sqrt{5}$

$= 12\sqrt{5}$

**19.** $2\sqrt{6} - \sqrt{4} \cdot \sqrt{4} \cdot \sqrt{3}$

$= 2\sqrt{6} - 2 \cdot 2 \cdot \sqrt{3}$

$= 2\sqrt{6} - 4\sqrt{3}$

**20.** $\dfrac{\sqrt{5}}{\sqrt{55}} \cdot \dfrac{\sqrt{55}}{\sqrt{55}}$

$= \dfrac{\sqrt{5^2} \cdot \sqrt{11}}{55}$

$= \dfrac{5\sqrt{11}}{55}$

$= \dfrac{\sqrt{11}}{11}$

**21.** $\dfrac{\sqrt{20}}{\sqrt{7}} \cdot \dfrac{\sqrt{7}}{\sqrt{7}}$

$= \dfrac{\sqrt{4} \cdot \sqrt{5} \cdot \sqrt{7}}{7}$

$= \dfrac{2\sqrt{35}}{7}$

**22.** $\dfrac{9}{3 + \sqrt{2}} \cdot \dfrac{3 - \sqrt{2}}{3 - \sqrt{2}}$

$= \dfrac{9(3 - \sqrt{2})}{9 - 2}$

$= \dfrac{27 - 9\sqrt{2}}{7}$

**23.** $\sqrt{6} \cdot \sqrt{4} \cdot \sqrt{4} \cdot \sqrt{x^2} \cdot \sqrt{x^2}$

$= 2 \cdot 2 \cdot x \cdot x \cdot \sqrt{6}$

$= 4x^2\sqrt{6}$

**24.** $\sqrt{4} \cdot \sqrt{11} \cdot \sqrt{a^2} \cdot \sqrt{b^4} \cdot \sqrt{b}$

$= 2 \cdot |a| \cdot b^2 \cdot \sqrt{11b}$

$= 2|a|b^2\sqrt{11b}$

**25.** $\dfrac{\sqrt{4} \cdot \sqrt{15}}{\sqrt{y^2}}$

$= \dfrac{2\sqrt{15}}{|y|}$

**26.** $\dfrac{\sqrt{3} \cdot \sqrt{a} \cdot \sqrt{a^2} \cdot \sqrt{b^4}}{\sqrt{2} \cdot \sqrt{4} \cdot \sqrt{a} \cdot \sqrt{b^{10}}}$

$= \dfrac{a|b^2|\sqrt{3}}{2|b^5|\sqrt{2}} \cdot \dfrac{\sqrt{2}}{\sqrt{2}}$

$= \dfrac{a\sqrt{3} \cdot \sqrt{2}}{2 \cdot 2 \cdot |b^3|}$

$= \dfrac{a\sqrt{6}}{4|b^3|}$

**27.** $(2 + 3)\sqrt{13} + (8 - 3)\sqrt{15}$

$= 5\sqrt{13} + 5\sqrt{15}$

$\approx 37.39$

28. $4 \cdot \sqrt{3} \cdot \sqrt{9} + 6 \cdot \sqrt{3} \cdot \sqrt{16}$

$= 4 \cdot 3\sqrt{3} + 6 \cdot 4\sqrt{3}$

$= 12\sqrt{3} + 24\sqrt{3}$

$= (12 + 24)\sqrt{3}$

$= 36\sqrt{3}$

$\approx 62.35$

29. $5 \cdot \sqrt{2} \cdot \sqrt{9} - 3 \cdot \sqrt{16} \cdot \sqrt{7} - 3\sqrt{2} \cdot \sqrt{49}$

$= 5 \cdot 3\sqrt{2} - 3 \cdot 4\sqrt{7} - 3 \cdot 7\sqrt{2}$

$= 15\sqrt{2} - 12\sqrt{7} - 21\sqrt{2}$

$= (15 - 21)\sqrt{2} - 12\sqrt{7}$

$= -6\sqrt{2} - 12\sqrt{7}$

$\approx -40.23$

30. $\sqrt{8} + \dfrac{1}{\sqrt{8}} \cdot \dfrac{\sqrt{8}}{\sqrt{8}}$

$= \sqrt{8} + \dfrac{\sqrt{8}}{8}$

$= \dfrac{9\sqrt{8}}{8}$

$= \dfrac{9\sqrt{2} \cdot \sqrt{4}}{8}$

$= \dfrac{9 \cdot 2\sqrt{2}}{8}$

$= \dfrac{9\sqrt{2}}{4}$

$\approx 3.18$

31. $(\sqrt{3x})^2 = 6^2$

$3x = 36$

$x = 12$

32. $(\sqrt{7x - 1})^2 = 5^2$

$7x - 1 = 25$

$7x = 26$

$x = \dfrac{26}{7}$

33. $\sqrt{\dfrac{4a}{3}} = 2$

$\left(\sqrt{\dfrac{4a}{3}}\right)^2 = 2^2$

$\dfrac{4a}{3} = 4$

$4a = 12$

$a = 3$

34. $(\sqrt{x + 4})^2 = (x - 8)^2$

$x + 4 = x^2 - 16x + 64$

$x^2 - 17x + 60 = 0$

$(x - 12)(x - 5) = 0$

$x = 12$

35. $d = \sqrt{[13 - (-2)]^2 + (1 - 9)^2}$

$= \sqrt{15^2 + (-8)^2}$

$= \sqrt{225 + 64}$

$= \sqrt{289}$

$= 17$

36. $d = \sqrt{(-9 - 2)^2 + (7 - 4)^2}$

$= \sqrt{(-11)^2 + 3^2}$

$= \sqrt{121 + 9}$

$= \sqrt{130}$

$\approx 11.40$

37. $\sqrt{170} = \sqrt{[-3 - (-2)]^2 + (a - 5)^2}$

$\sqrt{170} = \sqrt{(-1)^2 + a^2 - 10a + 25}$

$\sqrt{170} = \sqrt{1 + a^2 - 10a + 25}$

$\sqrt{170} = \sqrt{a^2 - 10a + 26}$

$(\sqrt{170})^2 = \left(\sqrt{a^2 - 10a + 26}\right)^2$

$170 = a^2 - 10a + 26$

$a^2 - 10a - 144 = 0$

$(a + 8)(a - 18) = 0$

$a = 18 \text{ or } -8$

PAGE 512    APPLICATIONS AND CONNECTIONS

38. 4 times    39. 1985, 1990    40. $\sqrt{108} \approx 10.39$

41. $d = \sqrt{(6 - 0)^2 + (1.1 - 0)^2}$

$= \sqrt{6^2 + (1.1)^2}$

$= \sqrt{36 + 1.21}$

$= \sqrt{37.21}$

$= 6.1 \text{ cm}$

42. $\pm\sqrt{x(2x + 3)} = 18$

$(\pm\sqrt{x(2x + 3)})^2 = 18^2$

$x(2x + 3) = 324$

$2x^2 + 3x - 324 = 0$

$(2x + 27)(x - 12) = 0$

$2x + 27 = 0, \qquad x - 12 = 0$

$2x = -27 \qquad\qquad x = 12$

$x = -\dfrac{27}{2}$

12 and 27 or $-\dfrac{27}{2}$ and $-24$

43. $d_{AB} = \sqrt{(4 - 0)^2 + (-3 - 0)^2}$

$= \sqrt{4^2 + (-3)^2}$

$= \sqrt{16 + 9}$

$= \sqrt{25}$

$= 5$

$d_{BC} = \sqrt{(8 - 4)^2 + [6 - (-3)]^2}$

$= \sqrt{4^2 + 9^2}$

$= \sqrt{16 + 81}$

$= \sqrt{97}$

$\approx 9.85$

$d_{CA} = \sqrt{(8 - 0)^2 + (6 - 0)^2}$

$= \sqrt{8^2 + 6^2}$

$= \sqrt{64 + 36}$

$= \sqrt{100}$

$= 10$

$P = d_{AB} + d_{BC} + d_{CA} \approx 5 + 10 + 9.85$

$= 24.85 \text{ units}$

44. $x^2 + 12^2 = (18 - x)^2$

$x^2 + 144 = 324 - 36x + x^2$

$36x = 180$

$x = 5 \text{ ft}$

45. $55 = \sqrt{15d}$

$55^2 = (\sqrt{15d})^2$

$3025 = 15d$

$d \approx 201.7 \text{ ft}$

No, it should skid about 201.7 ft.

# Chapter 12    Test

1. bananas    2. 1975    3. They weigh less.

4. N, W, Z, Q    5. I    6. Q    7. Q

8. $8^2 + 10^2 = c^2$              9. $12^2 + b^2 = 20^2$

$64 + 100 = c^2$              $144 + b^2 = 400$

$c^2 = 164$              $b^2 = 256$

$c = \sqrt{164}$              $b = \sqrt{256}$

$c = \sqrt{4} \cdot \sqrt{41}$              $b = 16$

$c = 2\sqrt{41}$

$c \approx 12.81$

10. $b^2 + b^2 = 12^2$

$2b^2 = 144$

$b^2 = 72$

$b = \sqrt{72}$

$b = \sqrt{36} \cdot \sqrt{2}$

$b = 6\sqrt{2}$

$b \approx 8.49$

11. $\sqrt{4} \cdot \sqrt{10}$              12. $\sqrt{2} \cdot \sqrt{36} \cdot \sqrt{3} \cdot \sqrt{16}$

$= 2\sqrt{10}$              $= 6 \cdot 4 \cdot \sqrt{6}$

$\approx 6.32$              $= 24\sqrt{6}$

$\approx 58.79$

13. $\sqrt{6} \cdot \sqrt{9} \cdot \sqrt{x^4} \cdot \sqrt{y}$

$= 3x^2\sqrt{6y}$

$\approx 7.35x^2\sqrt{y}$

14. $\sqrt{9} \cdot \sqrt{5} \cdot \sqrt{x} \cdot \sqrt{y^2} \cdot \sqrt{y}$

$= 3|y|\sqrt{5xy}$

15. $\dfrac{\sqrt{2} \cdot \sqrt{16}}{\sqrt{25}}$              16. $\dfrac{\sqrt{3} \cdot \sqrt{x^2}}{2\sqrt{n^2} \cdot \sqrt{n}}$

$= \dfrac{4\sqrt{2}}{5}$              $= \dfrac{|x|\sqrt{3}}{2n\sqrt{n}} \cdot \dfrac{\sqrt{n}}{\sqrt{n}}$

$\approx 1.13$              $= \dfrac{|x|\sqrt{3n}}{2n^2}$

$\approx \dfrac{0.87|x|\sqrt{n}}{n^2}$

17. $\dfrac{7}{7 + \sqrt{5}} \cdot \dfrac{7 - \sqrt{5}}{7 - \sqrt{5}}$

$= \dfrac{7(7 - \sqrt{5})}{49 - 5}$

$= \dfrac{49 - 7\sqrt{5}}{44}$

$\approx 0.76$

18. $3 \cdot \sqrt{25} \cdot \sqrt{2} - 2\sqrt{4} \cdot \sqrt{2}$

$= 3 \cdot 5\sqrt{2} - 2 \cdot 2\sqrt{2}$

$= 15\sqrt{2} - 4\sqrt{2}$

$= (15 - 4)\sqrt{2}$

$= 11\sqrt{2}$

$\approx 15.56$

19. $\sqrt{6} + \dfrac{\sqrt{2}}{\sqrt{3}} \cdot \dfrac{\sqrt{3}}{\sqrt{3}}$

$= \sqrt{6} + \dfrac{\sqrt{6}}{3}$

$= \dfrac{3\sqrt{6} + \sqrt{6}}{3}$

$= \dfrac{4\sqrt{6}}{3}$

$\approx 3.27$

20. $2 \cdot \sqrt{3} \cdot \sqrt{9} + \sqrt{7} \cdot \sqrt{9} - 4\sqrt{3}$

$= 2 \cdot 3\sqrt{3} + 3\sqrt{7} - 4\sqrt{3}$

$= 6\sqrt{3} + 3\sqrt{7} - 4\sqrt{3}$

$= (6 - 4)\sqrt{3} + 3\sqrt{7}$

$= 2\sqrt{3} + 3\sqrt{7}$

$\approx 11.40$

21. $16 - 5$

$= 11$

22. $\sqrt{2} \cdot \sqrt{18} + \sqrt{2} \cdot 4\sqrt{3}$

$= \sqrt{2} \cdot \sqrt{2} \cdot \sqrt{9} + 4\sqrt{6}$

$= 2 \cdot 3 + 4\sqrt{6}$

$= 6 + 4\sqrt{6}$

$\approx 15.80$

23. $\sqrt{t} = -2$

no real solution

24. $\left(\sqrt{5x^2 - 9}\right)^2 = (2x)^2$

$5x^2 - 9 = 4x^2$

$x^2 = 9$

$x = \sqrt{9}$

$x = 3$

25. $(\sqrt{4x + 1})^2 = 5^2$

$4x + 1 = 25$

$4x = 24$

$x = 6$

26. $(\sqrt{4x - 3})^2 = (6 - x)^2$

$4x - 3 = 36 - 12x + x^2$

$x^2 - 16x + 39 = 0$

$(x - 3)(x - 13) = 0$

$x = 3$

27. $d = \sqrt{(-2 - 7)^2 + (4 - 4)^2}$

$\quad = \sqrt{(-9)^2}$

$\quad = \sqrt{81}$

$\quad = 9$

28. $d = \sqrt{(-3 - 2)^2 + [3 - (-9)]^2}$

$\quad = \sqrt{(-5)^2 + 12^2}$

$\quad = \sqrt{25 + 144}$

$\quad = \sqrt{169}$

$\quad = 13$

29. $d = \sqrt{(-5 - 1)^2 + [1 - (-1)]^2}$

$\quad = \sqrt{(-6)^2 + 2^2}$

$\quad = \sqrt{36 + 4}$

$\quad = \sqrt{40}$

$\quad = \sqrt{4} \cdot \sqrt{10}$

$\quad = 2\sqrt{10}$

$\quad \approx 6.32$

30. $P = 2\sqrt{6} + 2(2\sqrt{32} - 3\sqrt{6})$

$\quad = 2\sqrt{6} + 4\sqrt{32} - 6\sqrt{6}$

$\quad = 4\sqrt{2} \cdot \sqrt{16} - 4\sqrt{6}$

$\quad = 4 \cdot 4\sqrt{2} - 4\sqrt{6}$

$\quad = 16\sqrt{2} - 4\sqrt{6}$

$A = \sqrt{6}(2\sqrt{32} - 3\sqrt{6})$

$\quad = 2\sqrt{64} \cdot \sqrt{3} - 3 \cdot 6$

$\quad = 2 \cdot 8\sqrt{3} - 18$

$\quad = 16\sqrt{3} - 18$

31. $5 = \sqrt{(a - 1)^2 + (5 - 8)^2}$

$5 = \sqrt{a^2 - 2a + 1 + (-3)^2}$

$5 = \sqrt{a^2 - 2a + 1 + 9}$

$5 = \sqrt{a^2 - 2a + 10}$

$5^2 = \left(\sqrt{a^2 - 2a + 10}\right)^2$

$25 = a^2 - 2a + 10$

$a^2 - 2a - 15 = 0$

$(a + 3)(a - 5) = 0$

$a = -3 \text{ or } 5$

32. Let $w$ = width;

$\quad 4w$ = length.

$w(4w) = 224$

$4w^2 = 224$

$w^2 = 56$

$w = \sqrt{56}$

$w = \sqrt{4} \cdot \sqrt{14}$

$w = 2\sqrt{14} \approx 7.48$

$4w = 4 \cdot 2\sqrt{14}$

$\quad\;\; = 8\sqrt{14} \approx 29.93$

Dimensions are approximately
7.48 cm by 29.93 cm.

33. $10^2 + x^2 = 12^2$

$100 + x^2 = 144$

$x^2 = 44$

$x = \sqrt{44}$

$x = \sqrt{4} \cdot \sqrt{11}$

$x = 2\sqrt{11} \text{ ft}$

$x \approx 6.63 \text{ ft}$

**PAGE 513    BONUS**

$\left(\sqrt{2a^2}\right)^2 + a^2 = 96^2$

$2a^2 + a^2 = 96^2$

$3a^2 = 9216$

$a^2 = 3072$

$a = \sqrt{3072}$

$a = \sqrt{16} \cdot \sqrt{16} \cdot \sqrt{4} \cdot \sqrt{3}$

$a = 4 \cdot 4 \cdot 2 \cdot \sqrt{3}$

$a = 32\sqrt{3}$

Volume $= a^3 = 98,304\sqrt{3}$

$\approx 170,267.52 \text{ cm}^3$

# Chapter 12    College Entrance Exam Preview

**PAGES 514–515**

1. B

$\quad$ slope $= \dfrac{5 - 2}{-1 - (-3)} = \dfrac{3}{2}$

2. C

3. C

$\quad 6^2 + \left(\dfrac{x}{2}\right)^2 = x^2$

$\quad 36 + \dfrac{x^2}{4} = x^2$

$\quad 144 + x^2 = 4x^2$

$\quad 3x^2 = 144$

$\quad x^2 = 48$

$\quad x = \sqrt{48}$

$\quad x = \sqrt{3} \cdot \sqrt{16}$

$\quad x = 4\sqrt{3}$

Area of triangle $= \dfrac{1}{2}b \cdot h$

$\quad = \dfrac{1}{2}(4\sqrt{3}) \cdot 6$

$\quad = 12\sqrt{3}$

**4.** D

If the rectangle is 217 ft by 31 ft, then the perimeter is $2(217) + 2(31)$

$$= 434 + 62$$
$$= 496 \text{ ft}$$

and area of each square $= 31^2 = 961 \text{ ft}^2$.

**5.** D

$2 \cdot 34 + 2 \cdot 46$

$= 68 + 92$

$= 160 \text{ ft}$

$= \dfrac{160}{3} \text{ yds}$

$= 53\dfrac{1}{3} \text{ yds}$

**6.** B

**7.** A

$4\left(\dfrac{3}{5}x + 1\right)$

$= \dfrac{12}{5}x + 4$

$= \dfrac{12x}{5} + 4 \cdot \dfrac{5}{5}$

$= \dfrac{12x + 20}{5}$

**8.** C

$y = mx + b$

$y = 4x + 2$

**9.** C

$\pi\left(\dfrac{b}{2}\right)^2 - \pi\left(\dfrac{c}{2}\right)^2$

$= \dfrac{\pi b^2}{4} - \dfrac{\pi c^2}{4}$

$= \dfrac{1}{4}\pi(b^2 - c^2)$

**10.** D

$\dfrac{\pi(8^2)}{\pi(10^2)} = 64\%$

Decrease $= 100\% - 64\%$

$= 36\%$

**11.** B

Area of square $= 4 \cdot 4 = 16$

Area of triangle $= \dfrac{1}{4} \cdot 16 = 4$

$\dfrac{1}{2}b \cdot h = 4$

$\dfrac{1}{2}x \cdot x = 4$

$\dfrac{1}{2}x^2 = 4$

$x^2 = 8$

$x = \sqrt{8}$

$x = \sqrt{4} \cdot \sqrt{2}$

$x = 2\sqrt{2}$

**12.** A

$m = \dfrac{7 - (-5)}{-4 - 2}$

$= \dfrac{12}{-6}$

$= -2$

**13.** D

$3x + 4(0) = 12$

$3x = 12$

$x = 4$

$(4, 0)$

**14.** A

$A = \dfrac{1}{2}b \cdot h$

$= \dfrac{1}{2}\left(\dfrac{3}{2}\right)(3)$

$= \dfrac{9}{4}$

**15.** A

**16.** B

$\dfrac{\pi r^2}{2\pi r} = \dfrac{r}{2}$

**17.** D

$m = \dfrac{2}{3}$

perpendicular slope $= -\dfrac{3}{2}$

**18.** A

$$\left.\begin{array}{l} x - 2y = 6 \\ 3x + y = 4 \end{array}\right\}$$

$$\begin{array}{l} x - 2y = 6 \\ \underline{6x + 2y = 8} \\ 7x \quad\quad = 14 \\ \quad\quad x = 2 \end{array}$$

$x - 2y = 6$

$2 - 2y = 6$

$y = -2$

The lines intersect at $(2, -2)$.

# Chapter 13   Quadratics

 **13-1**   Graphing Quadratic Functions

1. parabola   2. maximum, minimum   3. symmetric

4. negative   5. up   6. down   7. down   8. up

9. $y = x^2 + x + 3$

$x = -\dfrac{b}{2a} = -\dfrac{1}{2}$

10. $y = -x^2 + 4x + 5$

$x = -\dfrac{b}{2a} = -\dfrac{4}{-2} = 2$

11. $y = 3x^2 + 6x + 16$

$x = -\dfrac{b}{2a} = -\dfrac{6}{6} = -1$

12. $y = x^2 + 6x + 8$

$x = -\dfrac{b}{2a} = -\dfrac{6}{2} = -3$

$y = (-3)^2 + 6(-3) + 8$

$y = 9 - 18 + 8$

$y = -1$

vertex $(-3, -1)$

13. $y = -x^2 + 3x$

$x = -\dfrac{b}{2a} = -\dfrac{3}{2(-1)} = \dfrac{3}{2}$

$y = -\left(\dfrac{3}{2}\right)^2 + 3\left(\dfrac{3}{2}\right)$

$y = -\dfrac{9}{4} + \dfrac{9}{2}$

$y = \dfrac{9}{4}$

vertex $\left(\dfrac{3}{2}, \dfrac{9}{4}\right)$

14. $y = 5x^2 - 20x + 37$

$x = -\dfrac{b}{2a} = -\dfrac{-20}{2(5)} = 2$

$y = 5(2^2) - 20(2) + 37$

$y = 20 - 40 + 37$

$y = 17$

vertex $(2, 17)$

15. $y = -x^2 + 5x + 6$

$x = -\dfrac{b}{2a} = -\dfrac{5}{-2} = \dfrac{5}{2}$

$y = -x^2 + 5x + 6$

$y = -\left(\dfrac{5}{2}\right)^2 + 5\left(\dfrac{5}{2}\right) + 6$

$y = -\dfrac{25}{4} + \dfrac{25}{2} + 6$

$y = \dfrac{49}{4}$

vertex $\left(\dfrac{5}{2}, \dfrac{49}{4}\right)$

16. $y = x^2 - 4x + 13$

$x = -\dfrac{b}{2a} = -\dfrac{-4}{2} = 2$

$y = x^2 - 4x + 13$

$y = 2^2 - 4(2) + 13$

$y = 4 - 8 + 13$

$y = 9$

vertex $(2, 9)$

17. $y = x^2 + 2x$

$x = -\dfrac{b}{2a} = -\dfrac{2}{2} = -1$

$y = x^2 + 2x$

$y = (-1)^2 + 2(-1)$

$y = 1 - 2$

$y = -1$

vertex $(-1, -1)$

18. $y = -3x^2 + 4$

$x = -\dfrac{b}{2a} = -\dfrac{0}{-6} = 0$

$y = -3x^2 + 4$

$y = -3(0)^2 + 4$

$y = 4$

vertex $(0, 4)$

19. $y = 3x^2 + 24x + 80$

$x = -\dfrac{b}{2a} = -\dfrac{24}{6} = -4$

$y = 3x^2 + 24x + 80$

$y = 3(-4)^2 + 24(-4) + 80$

$y = 48 - 96 + 80$

$y = 32$

vertex $(-4, 32)$

20. $y = -4x^2 + 8x + 13$

$x = -\dfrac{b}{2a} = -\dfrac{8}{-8} = 1$

$y = -4x^2 + 8x + 13$

$y = -4(1)^2 + 8(1) + 13$

$y = -4 + 8 + 13$

$y = 17$

vertex $(1, 17)$

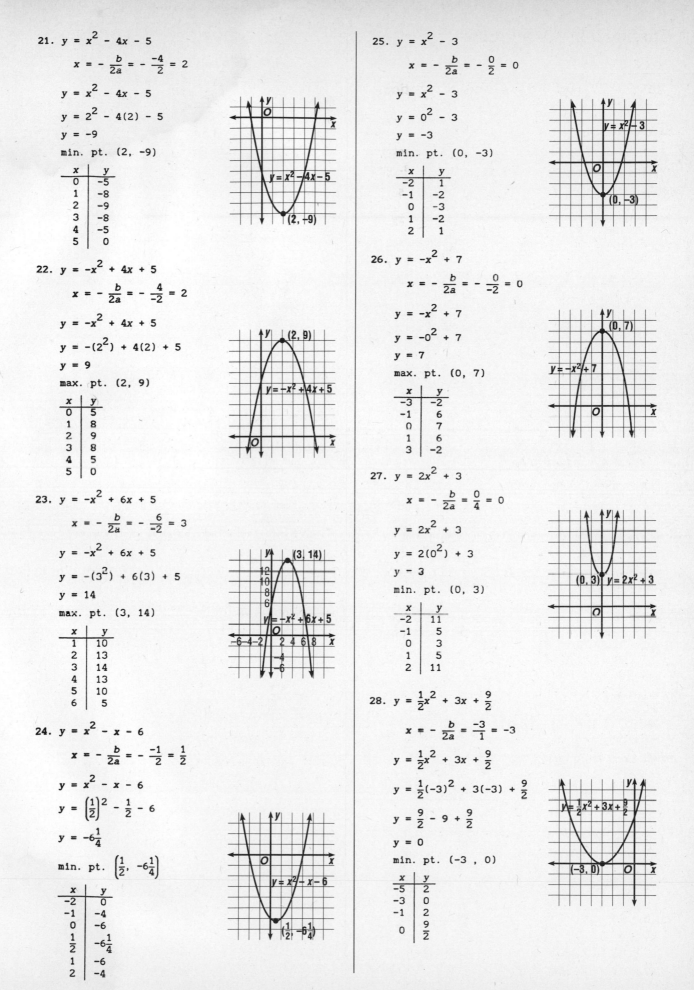

21. $y = x^2 - 4x - 5$

$x = -\frac{b}{2a} = -\frac{-4}{2} = 2$

$y = x^2 - 4x - 5$

$y = 2^2 - 4(2) - 5$

$y = -9$

min. pt. (2, -9)

| x | y |
|---|---|
| 0 | -5 |
| 1 | -8 |
| 2 | -9 |
| 3 | -8 |
| 4 | -5 |
| 5 | 0 |

22. $y = -x^2 + 4x + 5$

$x = -\frac{b}{2a} = -\frac{4}{-2} = 2$

$y = -x^2 + 4x + 5$

$y = -(2^2) + 4(2) + 5$

$y = 9$

max. pt. (2, 9)

| x | y |
|---|---|
| 0 | 5 |
| 1 | 8 |
| 2 | 9 |
| 3 | 8 |
| 4 | 5 |
| 5 | 0 |

23. $y = -x^2 + 6x + 5$

$x = -\frac{b}{2a} = -\frac{6}{-2} = 3$

$y = -x^2 + 6x + 5$

$y = -(3^2) + 6(3) + 5$

$y = 14$

max. pt. (3, 14)

| x | y |
|---|---|
| 1 | 10 |
| 2 | 13 |
| 3 | 14 |
| 4 | 13 |
| 5 | 10 |
| 6 | 5 |

24. $y = x^2 - x - 6$

$x = -\frac{b}{2a} = -\frac{-1}{2} = \frac{1}{2}$

$y = x^2 - x - 6$

$y = \left(\frac{1}{2}\right)^2 - \frac{1}{2} - 6$

$y = -6\frac{1}{4}$

min. pt. $\left(\frac{1}{2}, -6\frac{1}{4}\right)$

| x | y |
|---|---|
| -2 | 0 |
| -1 | -4 |
| 0 | -6 |
| $\frac{1}{2}$ | $-6\frac{1}{4}$ |
| 1 | -6 |
| 2 | -4 |

25. $y = x^2 - 3$

$x = -\frac{b}{2a} = -\frac{0}{2} = 0$

$y = x^2 - 3$

$y = 0^2 - 3$

$y = -3$

min. pt. (0, -3)

| x | y |
|---|---|
| -2 | 1 |
| -1 | -2 |
| 0 | -3 |
| 1 | -2 |
| 2 | 1 |

26. $y = -x^2 + 7$

$x = -\frac{b}{2a} = -\frac{0}{-2} = 0$

$y = -x^2 + 7$

$y = -0^2 + 7$

$y = 7$

max. pt. (0, 7)

| x | y |
|---|---|
| -3 | -2 |
| -1 | 6 |
| 0 | 7 |
| 1 | 6 |
| 3 | -2 |

27. $y = 2x^2 + 3$

$x = -\frac{b}{2a} = \frac{0}{4} = 0$

$y = 2x^2 + 3$

$y = 2(0^2) + 3$

$y - 3$

min. pt. (0, 3)

| x | y |
|---|---|
| -2 | 11 |
| -1 | 5 |
| 0 | 3 |
| 1 | 5 |
| 2 | 11 |

28. $y = \frac{1}{2}x^2 + 3x + \frac{9}{2}$

$x = -\frac{b}{2a} = \frac{-3}{1} = -3$

$y = \frac{1}{2}x^2 + 3x + \frac{9}{2}$

$y = \frac{1}{2}(-3)^2 + 3(-3) + \frac{9}{2}$

$y = \frac{9}{2} - 9 + \frac{9}{2}$

$y = 0$

min. pt. (-3, 0)

| x | y |
|---|---|
| -5 | 2 |
| -3 | 0 |
| -1 | 2 |
| 0 | $\frac{9}{2}$ |

29. $y = \frac{1}{4}x^2 - 4x + \frac{15}{4}$

$x = -\frac{b}{2a} = -\frac{-4}{\frac{1}{2}} = 8$

$y = \frac{1}{4}x^2 - 4x + \frac{15}{4}$

$y = \frac{1}{4}(64) - 4(8) + \frac{15}{4}$

$y = 16 - 32 + \frac{15}{4}$

$y = -12\frac{1}{4}$

min. pt. $\left(8, -12\frac{1}{4}\right)$

| x | y |
|---|---|
| 0 | $3\frac{3}{4}$ |
| 1 | 0 |
| 2 | $-3\frac{1}{4}$ |
| 8 | $-12\frac{1}{4}$ |
| 14 | $-3\frac{1}{4}$ |
| 15 | 0 |

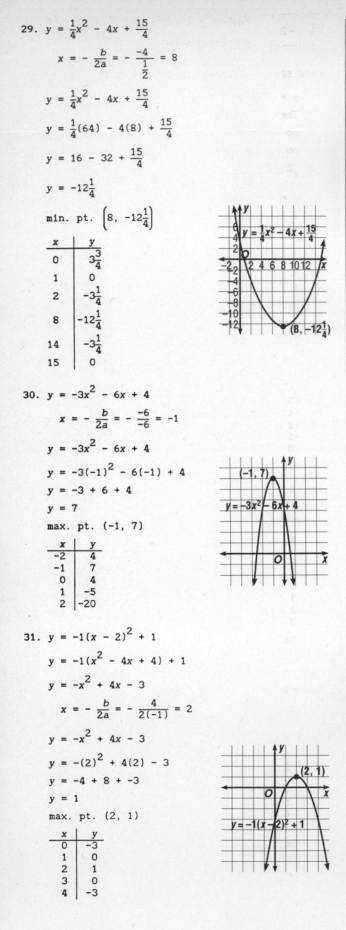

30. $y = -3x^2 - 6x + 4$

$x = -\frac{b}{2a} = -\frac{-6}{-6} = -1$

$y = -3x^2 - 6x + 4$

$y = -3(-1)^2 - 6(-1) + 4$

$y = -3 + 6 + 4$

$y = 7$

max. pt. (-1, 7)

| x | y |
|---|---|
| -2 | 4 |
| -1 | 7 |
| 0 | 4 |
| 1 | -5 |
| 2 | -20 |

31. $y = -1(x - 2)^2 + 1$

$y = -1(x^2 - 4x + 4) + 1$

$y = -x^2 + 4x - 3$

$x = -\frac{b}{2a} = -\frac{4}{2(-1)} = 2$

$y = -x^2 + 4x - 3$

$y = -(2)^2 + 4(2) - 3$

$y = -4 + 8 + -3$

$y = 1$

max. pt. (2, 1)

| x | y |
|---|---|
| 0 | -3 |
| 1 | 0 |
| 2 | 1 |
| 3 | 0 |
| 4 | -3 |

32. $y = 3(x + 1)^2 - 20$

$y = 3(x^2 + 2x + 1) - 20$

$y = 3x^2 + 6x - 17$

$x = -\frac{b}{2a} = -\frac{6}{2(3)} = -1$

$y = 3x^2 + 6x - 17$

$y = 3(-1)^2 + 6(-1) - 17$

$y = 3 + -6 - 17$

$y = -20$

min. pt. (-1, -20)

| x | y |
|---|---|
| -3 | -8 |
| -2 | -17 |
| -1 | -20 |
| 0 | -17 |
| 1 | -8 |

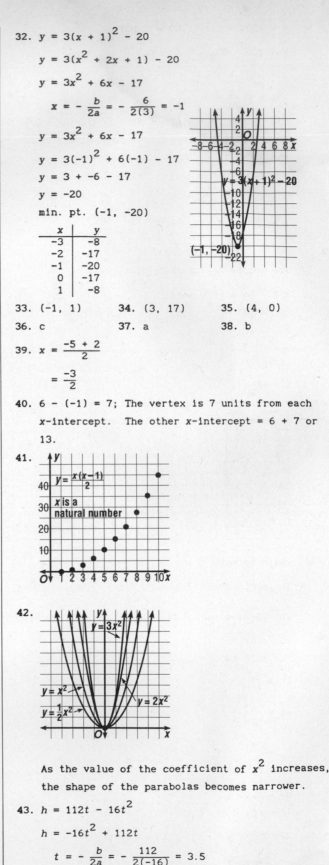

33. (-1, 1)    34. (3, 17)    35. (4, 0)

36. c          37. a          38. b

39. $x = \frac{-5 + 2}{2}$

$= \frac{-3}{2}$

40. $6 - (-1) = 7$; The vertex is 7 units from each $x$-intercept. The other $x$-intercept $= 6 + 7$ or 13.

41. 

As the value of the coefficient of $x^2$ increases, the shape of the parabolas becomes narrower.

43. $h = 112t - 16t^2$

$h = -16t^2 + 112t$

$t = -\frac{b}{2a} = -\frac{112}{2(-16)} = 3.5$

$h = -16(3.5)^2 + 112(3.5)$

$h = 196$

The maximum height is 196 ft.

**44.** $y = (900 - 60x)(1.00 + 0.10x)$

$y = 900 + 90x - 60x - 6x^2$

$y = -6x^2 + 30x + 900$

$x = -\dfrac{b}{2a} = -\dfrac{30}{2(-6)} = 2.5$

The income is maximized when owners make 2.5 $0.10 price increases. Thus the ticket price should be $1.00 + 2.5(0.10) = \$1.25$.

**45.** $y = (20{,}000 + 1000x)(9.50 - 0.25x)$

$y = 190{,}000 - 5000x + 9500x - 250x^2$

$y = -250x^2 + 4500x + 190{,}000$

$x = -\dfrac{b}{2a} = -\dfrac{4500}{2(-250)} = 9$

The income is maximized in 9 weeks.

**46.** $400 + 9x = 12(x + 25)$

$400 + 9x = 12x + 300$

$100 = 3x$

$33.\overline{3} = x$

$400 + 9(33.\overline{3}) = 700$

The sofa cost $700.

**47.**

**48.** $-5x + 6y = 12$

The slope is $-\dfrac{A}{B} = -\dfrac{-5}{6} = \dfrac{5}{6}$.

The lines of the form $y = \dfrac{5}{6}x + b$ are parallel to $-5x + 6y = 12$.

Use this point $(-2, -2)$ to solve for $b$.

$-2 = \dfrac{5}{6}(-2) + b$

$-2 = -\dfrac{5}{3} + b$

$b = -\dfrac{1}{3}$

$y = \dfrac{5}{6}x - \dfrac{1}{3}$

$6y = 5x - 2$

$-5x + 6y = -2$ is parallel to $-5x + 6y = 12$.

**49.** Add $2x + \phantom{3}y = 5$

$\underline{-2x + 3y = 7}$

$4y = 12$

$y = 3$

$2x + 3 = 5$

$2x = 2$

$x = 1$

**50.** $3^2 + y^2 = 5^2$

$9 + y^2 = 25$

$y^2 = 16$

$y = \pm 4$

$a = 1 - 4 = -3$ and

$a = 1 + 4 = 5$

---

## 13-2 Solving Quadratic Equations by Graphing

**1.** $y = x^2 - 5x + 6$

**2.** They are the $x$-intercepts of the graph.

**3.** no       **4.** -1, 1       **5.** 0, 2

**6.** no real roots       **7.** 2

**8.** $x^2 - x - 12 = 0$

$y = x^2 - x - 12$

| x | y |
|----|-----|
| -4 | 8 |
| -3 | 0 |
| 0 | -12 |
| 1 | -12 |
| 3 | -6 |
| 4 | 0 |

Roots are -3, 4.

**9.** $x^2 + 7x + 12 = 0$

$y = x^2 + 7x + 12$

| x | y |
|----|----|
| -6 | 6 |
| -5 | 2 |
| -4 | 0 |
| -2 | 2 |
| -1 | 6 |
| 0 | 12 |

Roots are -3, -4.

**10.** $x^2 - 9 = 0$

$y = x^2 - 9$

| x | y |
|----|----|
| -3 | 0 |
| -2 | -5 |
| -1 | -8 |
| 0 | -9 |
| 1 | -8 |
| 2 | -5 |
| 3 | 0 |

Roots are -3, 3

**11.** $x^2 - 10x = -21$

$y = x^2 - 10x + 21$

| x | y |
|---|----|
| 2 | 5 |
| 3 | 0 |
| 4 | -3 |
| 5 | -4 |
| 6 | -3 |
| 7 | 0 |

Roots are 3, 7.

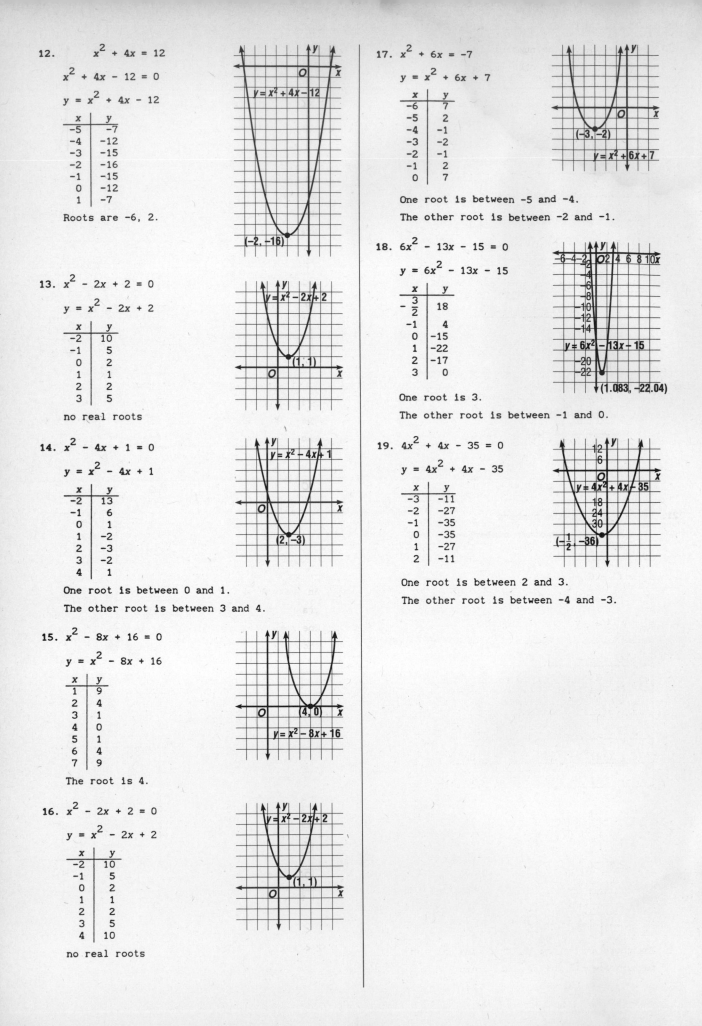

12.　　$x^2 + 4x = 12$

$x^2 + 4x - 12 = 0$

$y = x^2 + 4x - 12$

| x | y |
|---|---|
| -5 | -7 |
| -4 | -12 |
| -3 | -15 |
| -2 | -16 |
| -1 | -15 |
| 0 | -12 |
| 1 | -7 |

Roots are -6, 2.

13. $x^2 - 2x + 2 = 0$

$y = x^2 - 2x + 2$

| x | y |
|---|---|
| -2 | 10 |
| -1 | 5 |
| 0 | 2 |
| 1 | 1 |
| 2 | 2 |
| 3 | 5 |

no real roots

14. $x^2 - 4x + 1 = 0$

$y = x^2 - 4x + 1$

| x | y |
|---|---|
| -2 | 13 |
| -1 | 6 |
| 0 | 1 |
| 1 | -2 |
| 2 | -3 |
| 3 | -2 |
| 4 | 1 |

One root is between 0 and 1.

The other root is between 3 and 4.

15. $x^2 - 8x + 16 = 0$

$y = x^2 - 8x + 16$

| x | y |
|---|---|
| 1 | 9 |
| 2 | 4 |
| 3 | 1 |
| 4 | 0 |
| 5 | 1 |
| 6 | 4 |
| 7 | 9 |

The root is 4.

16. $x^2 - 2x + 2 = 0$

$y = x^2 - 2x + 2$

| x | y |
|---|---|
| -2 | 10 |
| -1 | 5 |
| 0 | 2 |
| 1 | 1 |
| 2 | 2 |
| 3 | 5 |
| 4 | 10 |

no real roots

17. $x^2 + 6x = -7$

$y = x^2 + 6x + 7$

| x | y |
|---|---|
| -6 | 7 |
| -5 | 2 |
| -4 | -1 |
| -3 | -2 |
| -2 | -1 |
| -1 | 2 |
| 0 | 7 |

One root is between -5 and -4.

The other root is between -2 and -1.

18. $6x^2 - 13x - 15 = 0$

$y = 6x^2 - 13x - 15$

| x | y |
|---|---|
| $-\frac{3}{2}$ | 18 |
| -1 | 4 |
| 0 | -15 |
| 1 | -22 |
| 2 | -17 |
| 3 | 0 |

One root is 3.

The other root is between -1 and 0.

19. $4x^2 + 4x - 35 = 0$

$y = 4x^2 + 4x - 35$

| x | y |
|---|---|
| -3 | -11 |
| -2 | -27 |
| -1 | -35 |
| 0 | -35 |
| 1 | -27 |
| 2 | -11 |

One root is between 2 and 3.

The other root is between -4 and -3.

20. Let $x$ = one of the numbers.

Then $18 - x$ is the other number.

$$x(18 - x) = 81$$
$$18x - x^2 = 81$$
$$x^2 - 18x + 81 = 0$$
$$x = -\frac{-18}{2} = 9$$

| $x$ | $x^2 - 18x + 81$ | $y$ |
|---|---|---|
| 7 | $7^2 - 18(7) + 81$ | 4 |
| 8 | $8^2 - 18(8) + 81$ | 1 |
| 9 | $9^2 - 18(9) + 81$ | 0 |
| 10 | $10^2 - 18(10) + 81$ | 1 |
| 11 | $11^2 - 18(11) + 81$ | 4 |

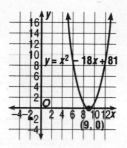

The roots are 9 and 9.

21. Let $x$ = one of the numbers.

Then $x - 6$ is the other number.

$$x(x - 6) = 91$$
$$x^2 - 6x = 91$$
$$x^2 - 6x - 91 = 0$$
$$x = -\frac{-6}{2} = 3$$

| $x$ | $x^2 - 6x - 91$ | $y$ |
|---|---|---|
| 15 | $15^2 - 6(15) - 91$ | 44 |
| 13 | $13^2 - 6(13) - 91$ | 0 |
| 3 | $3^2 - 6(3) - 91$ | -100 |
| -4 | $(-4)^2 - 6(-4) - 91$ | -83 |
| -6 | $(-6)^2 - 6(-6) - 91$ | -19 |

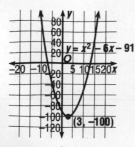

The roots are -7 and 13. Thus, the pairs of numbers are -13 and -7, and 13 and 7.

22. c          23. b          24. a

25.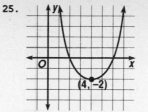

26.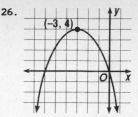

27. An infinite number of graphs can be drawn. One possible graph is shown.

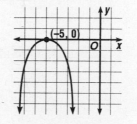

28. An infinite number of graphs can be drawn. One possible graph is shown.

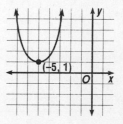

29. An infinite number of graphs can be drawn. One possible graph is shown.

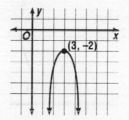

30. An infinite number of graphs can be drawn. One possible graph is shown.

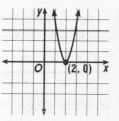

31. An infinite number of graphs can be drawn. One possible graph is shown.

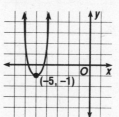

32. An infinite number of graphs can be drawn. One possible graph is shown.

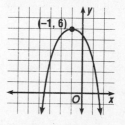

33.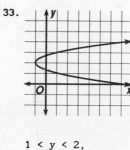

$1 < y < 2,$
$2 < y < 3$

34.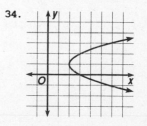

no $y$-intercept

35.

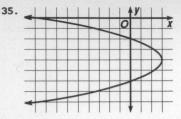

-2, -6

36. The value of the function changes from negative when $x = 1$ to positive when $x = 2$. To do this, the value of the function would have to be 0 for some value of $x$ between 1 and 2. Thus, this value of $x$ represents the $x$-intercept of the function and would therefore be a root of the related equation.

37. $h = -x^2 + 2x + 10$

She enters the water at $h = 0$.

| $x$ | $-x^2 + 2x + 10$ | $h$ |
|---|---|---|
| 3 | $-3^2 + 2(3) + 10$ | 7 |
| 4 | $-4^2 + 2(4) + 10$ | 2 |
| 5 | $-5^2 + 2(5) + 10$ | -5 |
| 6 | $-6^2 + 2(6) + 10$ | -14 |

$h$ equals zero when $x$ is between 4 and 5 meters.

38. $h = 84t - 16t^2$

a. $84t - 16t^2 = 80$

$16t^2 - 84t + 80 = 0$

| $t$ | $16t^2 - 84t + 80$ | $h$ |
|---|---|---|
| 1 | $16(1)^2 - 84(1) + 80$ | 12 |
| 2 | $16(2)^2 - 84(2) + 80$ | -24 |
| 3 | $16(3)^2 - 84(3) + 80$ | -28 |
| 4 | $16(4)^2 - 84(4) + 80$ | 0 |
| 5 | $16(5)^2 - 84(5) + 80$ | 60 |

Each time the ball passes 80 ft, $h$ changes in sign. So $t = 4$ for the second time through 80 ft.

b. $84t - 16t^2 = 0$

$(84 - 16t)t = 0$

$t = 0$ or $t = 5.25$ seconds

5.25 seconds when the ball hits the ground.

c. $h = 84t - 16t^2$

maximum height at $\frac{1}{2}(5.25)$

$h = 84(2.625) - 16(2.625)^2$

$h = 110.25$ ft

39. $\dfrac{(2b - 4) + (b + 5) + (3b + 8)}{3} = \dfrac{6b + 9}{3}$

$= 2b + 3$

40.

| $x$ | -2 | -1 | 0 | 1 | 2 |
|---|---|---|---|---|---|
| $y$ | 0 | -3 | -4 | -3 | 0 |

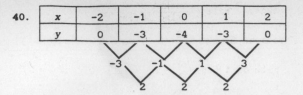

Two levels indicate a square. Try $y = x^2$.

This relation is not quite right. $y = x^2 - 4$.

41. $2x - 3y = 13$

$y = \frac{2}{3}x - \frac{13}{3}$

Let $y = 0$          Let $x = 0$

$0 = \frac{2}{3}x - \frac{13}{3}$     $y = \frac{2}{3}(0) - \frac{13}{3}$

$\frac{13}{3} = \frac{2}{3}x$          $y = -\frac{13}{3}$

$\frac{13}{2} = x$

slope: $\frac{2}{3}$; $x$-intercept: $\frac{13}{2}$; $y$-intercept: $-\frac{13}{3}$

42. $\sqrt{720} = \sqrt{10 \cdot 72}$

$= \sqrt{2 \cdot 5 \cdot 8 \cdot 9} = \sqrt{5 \cdot 2 \cdot 2 \cdot 2 \cdot 2 \cdot 3 \cdot 3}$

$= 3 \cdot 2 \cdot 2\sqrt{5} = 12\sqrt{5}$

43. $2x + y = 120$

$y = 120 - 2x$

$A = xy = x(120 - 2x)$

$= 120x - 2x^2$

| $x$ | $120x - 2x^2$ | $A$ |
|---|---|---|
| 10 | $120(10) - 2(10)^2$ | 1000 |
| 20 | $120(20) - 2(20)^2$ | 1600 |
| 30 | $120(30) - 2(30)^2$ | 1800 |
| 40 | $120(40) - 2(40)^2$ | 1600 |

1800 m$^2$ is the maximum area.

## 13-3  Problem-Solving Strategy: Identify Subgoals

PAGE 528    CHECKING FOR UNDERSTANDING

1. produce part of the solution or make the problem easier to solve

2. guess and check, look for a pattern, make a table, solve a simpler problem

3. step 1:   rate = $\dfrac{\text{amount of food}}{\text{time needed}}$

    rate of 2 dogs = $\dfrac{3}{1}$      rate of $x$ dogs = $\dfrac{90}{6}$

    rate of 1 dog = $\dfrac{3}{1} \div 2$     rate of 1 dog = $\dfrac{90}{6} \div x$

                 $= \dfrac{3}{2}$                  $= \dfrac{90}{6x}$

    step 2:     $\dfrac{3}{2} = \dfrac{90}{6x}$

                $3(6x) = 2(90)$

                   $18x = 180$

                     $x = 10$

Therefore, 10 dogs can eat 90 pounds of dog food in 6 weeks.

    step 3:   Check solution. There are 5 times as many dogs eating 6 times as long. Hence, there should be 5 · 6 or 30 times as many pounds eaten. Since 3 · 30 = 90, the solution checks.

4. Unit fractions less than $\dfrac{1}{6}$:   $\dfrac{1}{7}$, $\dfrac{1}{8}$, $\dfrac{1}{9}$, ...

Suppose one fraction in the pair is $\dfrac{1}{7}$,

$\dfrac{1}{6} - \dfrac{1}{7} = \dfrac{1}{42}$. The pair $\dfrac{1}{7}$ and $\dfrac{1}{42}$ is one solution.

Suppose one fraction in the pair is $\dfrac{1}{8}$,

$\dfrac{1}{6} - \dfrac{1}{8} = \dfrac{1}{24}$. The pair $\dfrac{1}{8}$ and $\dfrac{1}{24}$ is another solution. Other fractions in the pair:

$\dfrac{1}{6} - \dfrac{1}{9} = \dfrac{1}{18}$, $\dfrac{1}{9}$ and $\dfrac{1}{18}$ is a pair.

$\dfrac{1}{6} - \dfrac{1}{10} = \dfrac{1}{15}$, $\dfrac{1}{10}$ and $\dfrac{1}{15}$ is a pair.

$\dfrac{1}{6} - \dfrac{1}{11} = \dfrac{5}{66}$, $\dfrac{5}{66}$ is not a unit fraction.

$\dfrac{1}{6} - \dfrac{1}{12} = \dfrac{1}{12}$, $\dfrac{1}{12}$ and $\dfrac{1}{12}$ is a pair.

5 pairs exist since any other pairs must have one fraction greater than $\dfrac{1}{12}$ and one less than $\dfrac{1}{12}$.

5. First digit is 1:   1 + 0 + 9; 1 + 1 + 8; 1 + 2 + 7; 1 + 3 + 6; 1 + 4 + 5; 1 + 5 + 4; 1 + 6 + 3; 1 + 7 + 2; 1 + 8 + 1; 1 + 9 + 0
First digit is 0:   0 + 1 + 9; 0 + 2 + 8; 0 + 3 + 7; 0 + 4 + 6; 0 + 5 + 5; 0 + 6 + 4; 0 + 7 + 3; 0 + 8 + 2; 0 + 9 + 1
A total of 19 numbers

6. Numbers between 10 and 100: any repeated number, such as 11, 22,... Nine of these numbers exist.
Numbers between 100 and 200: any number that begins and ends with 1, such as 101, 111, 121,... Ten of these numbers exist.
It is the same for numbers beginning with 2, 3, 4, 5, 6, 7, 8, and 9.   8 · 10 of these numbers exist.
Adding up all the possibilities, there are 9 + 10 + (8 · 10) or 99 numbers that are palindromes exist.

PAGE 529     EXERCISES

7. Since 3 is smallest number of points, 1 and 2 points cannot be scored.   3 + 1, 3 + 2, 7 + 1, and 7 + 3 + 1 points cannot be scored.
The scores impossible to score are 1, 2, 4, 5, 8, and 11.

8.

|  | Apples | Pears | Peaches | Berries |
|---|---|---|---|---|
| Mr. Apple | X | X | X |  |
| Mr. Pear | X | X |  | X |
| Miss Peach |  | X | X | X |
| Mrs. Berry | X |  | X | X |

Mr. Apple is eating berries; Mr. Pear is eating peaches; Miss Peach is eating apples; Mrs. Berry is eating pears.

9. Each of the 4 co-captains must shake hands with each of the 3 opposing co-captains.   4 · 3 = 12 handshakes.
All 7 co-captains shake hands with the referee. 7 handshakes.
Total number of handshakes is 12 + 7 or 19.

10. The next symbol is 88 since each symbol is the mirror image of 1, 2, 3, 4, ...

11. If 102 games, Babe Ruth averages $\dfrac{714}{22 \cdot 102}$ homeruns per game.

If 162 games per season, $\dfrac{714}{x \cdot 162} = \dfrac{714}{22 \cdot 102}$

                $x = \dfrac{714}{22 \cdot 102} \cdot \dfrac{162}{714}$

                $x = 13.8$

So during the 13th season, Babe Ruth would have hit his 714th home run.

12. Let $J$ = Jim's age and $B$ = the brother's age.

$J - (B - J) - (B - J) = 3J - 2B$

$B = 17(3J - 2B)$

$B = 51J - 34B$

$35B = 51J$

Jim is 51 years old and his brother is 35.

5 rectangles and 50 triangles

## Technology:   Solving Quadratic Equations

PAGE 530      EXERCISES

1. 3 units above

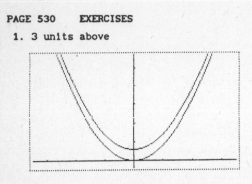

2. 10 units to the right

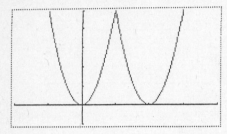

3. wider

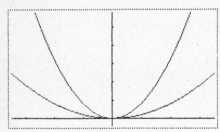

4. 4 units to the left,
   8 units below

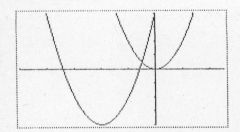

---

$\boxed{13\text{-}4}$  **Solving Quadratic Equations by Completing the Square**

PAGE 534     CHECKING FOR UNDERSTANDING

1. $\sqrt{x^2} = |x|$

2. step 1:  Find one-half of $b$;

   step 2:  Square the result of step 1;

   step 3:  Add the result of step 2 to $x^2 + bx$.

3. Divide each side by 3.

4. completing the square

5. $b^2 + 4b + 3$

   $\left(\frac{4}{2}\right)^2 \neq 3$

   no

6. $m^2 - 10m + 25$

   $\left(-\frac{10}{2}\right)^2 = 25$

   yes

7. $r^2 - 8r - 16$

   $\left(-\frac{8}{2}\right)^2 \neq -16$

   no

8. $d^2 + 11d + 121$

   $\left(\frac{11}{2}\right)^2 \neq 121$

   no

9. $h^2 - 13h + \frac{169}{4}$

   $\left(-\frac{13}{2}\right)^2 = \frac{169}{4}$

   yes

10. $4x^2 + 12x + 9$

    $x^2 + 3x + \frac{9}{4}$

    $\left(\frac{3}{2}\right)^2 = \frac{9}{4}$

    yes

11. $x^2 + 8x + c$

    $\left(\frac{8}{2}\right)^2 = c$

    $16 = c$

12. $a^2 - 6a + c$

    $\left(-\frac{6}{2}\right)^2 = c$

    $9 = c$

13. $m^2 + 7m + c$

    $\left(\frac{7}{2}\right)^2 = c$

    $\frac{49}{4} = c$

14. $y^2 + 4y + 3 = 0$

    $y^2 + 4y = -3$

    $y^2 + 4y + 4 = -3 + 4$

    $(y + 2)^2 = 1$

    $y + 2 = \pm 1$

    $y = -2 \pm 1$

    $y = -1 \quad y = -3$

15. $n^2 - 8n + 7 = 0$

    $n^2 - 8n = -7$

    $n^2 - 8n + 16 = -7 + 16$

    $(n - 4)^2 = 9$

    $n - 4 = \pm 3$

    $n = 4 \pm 3$

    $n = 7 \quad n = 1$

16.   $t^2 - 4t = 21$

      $t^2 - 4t = 21$

    $t^2 - 4t + 4 = 21 + 4$

      $(t - 2)^2 = 25$

      $t - 2 = \pm 5$

      $t = 2 \pm 5$

    $t = 7 \quad t = -3$

17. $x^2 - 7x + c$

$\left(-\dfrac{7}{2}\right)^2 = c$

$\dfrac{49}{4} = c$

18. $a^2 + 5a + c$

$\left(\dfrac{5}{2}\right)^2 = c$

$\dfrac{25}{4} = c$

19. $9x^2 - 18x + c$

$x^2 - 2x + \dfrac{c}{9}$

$\left(-\dfrac{2}{2}\right)^2 = \dfrac{c}{9}$

$1 = \dfrac{c}{9}$

$9 = c$

20. $r^2 + 14r - 10 = 5$

$r^2 + 14r + 49 = 15 + 49$

$(r + 7)^2 = 64$

$r + 7 = \pm 8$

$r = -7 \pm 8$

$r = 1 \qquad r = -15$

21. $y^2 + 7y + 10 = -2$

$y^2 + 7y + \dfrac{49}{4} = -12 + \dfrac{49}{4}$

$\left(y + \dfrac{7}{2}\right)^2 = \dfrac{1}{4}$

$y + \dfrac{7}{2} = \pm \dfrac{1}{2}$

$y = -\dfrac{7}{2} \pm \dfrac{1}{2}$

$y = -3 \qquad y = -4$

22. $x^2 - 5x + 2 = -2$

$x^2 - 5x + \dfrac{25}{4} = -4 + \dfrac{25}{4}$

$\left(x - \dfrac{5}{2}\right)^2 = \dfrac{9}{4}$

$x - \dfrac{5}{2} = \pm \dfrac{3}{2}$

$x = \dfrac{5}{2} \pm \dfrac{3}{2}$

$x = 4 \qquad x = 1$

23. $4x^2 - 20x + 25 = 0$

$x^2 - 5x + \dfrac{25}{4} = -\dfrac{25}{4} + \dfrac{25}{4}$

$\left(x - \dfrac{5}{2}\right)^2 = 0$

$x - \dfrac{5}{2} = 0$

$x = \dfrac{5}{2}$

24. $z^2 - 4z = 2$

$z^2 - 4z + 4 = 2 + 4$

$(z - 2)^2 = 6$

$z - 2 = \pm\sqrt{6}$

$z = 2 \pm \sqrt{6}$

$z = 2 + \sqrt{6} \approx 4.45$

$z = 2 - \sqrt{6} \approx -0.45$

25. $b^2 + 4 = 6b$

$b^2 - 6b + 4 = 0$

$b^2 - 6b + 9 = -4 + 9$

$(b - 3)^2 = 5$

$b - 3 = \pm\sqrt{5}$

$b = 3 \pm \sqrt{5}$

$b = 3 + \sqrt{5} \approx 5.24$

$b = 3 - \sqrt{5} \approx 0.76$

26. $y^2 - 8y = 4$

$y^2 - 8y + 16 = 4 + 16$

$(y - 4)^2 = 20$

$y - 4 = \pm\sqrt{20}$

$y = 4 \pm 2\sqrt{5}$

$y = 4 + 2\sqrt{5} \approx 8.47$

$y = 4 - 2\sqrt{5} \approx -0.47$

27. $x^2 - 10x = 23$

$x^2 - 10x + 25 = 23 + 25$

$(x - 5)^2 = 48$

$x - 5 = \pm\sqrt{48}$

$x = 5 \pm 4\sqrt{3}$

$x = 5 + 4\sqrt{3} \approx 11.93$

$x = 5 - 4\sqrt{3} \approx -1.93$

28. $2d^2 + 3d - 20 = 0$

$d^2 + \dfrac{3}{2}d + \dfrac{9}{16} = 10 + \dfrac{9}{16}$

$\left(d + \dfrac{3}{4}\right)^2 = \dfrac{169}{16}$

$d + \dfrac{3}{4} = \pm \dfrac{13}{4}$

$d = -\dfrac{3}{4} \pm \dfrac{13}{4}$

$d = \dfrac{5}{2} \qquad d = -4$

29. $a^2 - \dfrac{7}{2}a + \dfrac{3}{2} = 0$

$a^2 - \dfrac{7}{2}a + \dfrac{49}{16} = -\dfrac{3}{2} + \dfrac{49}{16}$

$\left(a - \dfrac{7}{4}\right)^2 = \dfrac{25}{16}$

$a - \dfrac{7}{4} = \pm \dfrac{5}{4}$

$a = \dfrac{7}{4} \pm \dfrac{5}{4}$

$a = 3 \qquad a = \dfrac{1}{2}$

30. $\dfrac{1}{2}q^2 - \dfrac{5}{4}q - 3 = 0$

$q^2 - \dfrac{5}{2}q = 6$

$q^2 - \dfrac{5}{2}q + \dfrac{25}{16} = 6 + \dfrac{25}{16}$

$\left(q - \dfrac{5}{4}\right)^2 = \dfrac{121}{16}$

$q - \dfrac{5}{4} = \pm \dfrac{11}{4}$

$q = \dfrac{5}{4} \pm \dfrac{11}{4}$

$q = 4 \qquad q = -\dfrac{3}{2}$

31. $0.3x^2 + 0.1x = 0.2$

$$x^2 + \frac{0.1}{0.3}x = \frac{0.2}{0.3}$$

$$x^2 + \frac{1}{3}x = \frac{2}{3}$$

$$x^2 + \frac{1}{3}x + \frac{1}{36} = \frac{2}{3} + \frac{1}{36}$$

$$\left(x + \frac{1}{6}\right)^2 = \frac{25}{36}$$

$$x + \frac{1}{6} = \pm\frac{5}{6}$$

$$x = -\frac{1}{6} \pm \frac{5}{6}$$

$$x = \frac{2}{3} \qquad x = -1$$

32. $r^2 + 0.25r = 0.5$

$$r^2 + 0.25r + 0.015625 = 0.5 + 0.015625$$

$$(r + 0.125)^2 \approx 0.516$$

$$r + 0.125 \approx \pm\sqrt{0.516}$$

$$r \approx -0.125 \pm \sqrt{0.516}$$

$$r = -0.125 + \sqrt{0.516} \approx 0.59$$

$$r = -0.125 - \sqrt{0.516} \approx -0.84$$

33. $2x^2 - 5x + 1 = 0$

$$x^2 - \frac{5}{2}x + \frac{1}{2} = 0$$

$$x^2 - \frac{5}{2}x = -\frac{1}{2}$$

$$x^2 - \frac{5}{2}x + \frac{25}{16} = -\frac{1}{2} + \frac{25}{16}$$

$$\left(x - \frac{5}{4}\right)^2 = \frac{17}{16}$$

$$x - \frac{5}{4} = \pm\frac{\sqrt{17}}{4}$$

$$x = \frac{5}{4} \pm \frac{\sqrt{17}}{4}$$

$$x = \frac{5 \pm \sqrt{17}}{4}$$

34. $3x^2 - 7x - 3 = 0$

$$x^2 - \frac{7}{3} - 1 = 0$$

$$x^2 - \frac{7}{3}x = 1$$

$$x^2 - \frac{7}{3}x + \frac{49}{36} = 1 + \frac{49}{36}$$

$$\left(x - \frac{7}{6}\right)^2 = \frac{85}{36}$$

$$x - \frac{7}{6} = \frac{\pm\sqrt{85}}{6}$$

$$x = \frac{7}{6} \pm \frac{\sqrt{85}}{6}$$

$$x = \frac{7 \pm \sqrt{85}}{6}$$

35. $2x + 2y = 37$

$$x = \frac{37 - 2y}{2}$$

$$xy = 78$$

$$\left(\frac{37 - 2y}{2}\right)y = 78$$

$$\frac{37}{2}y - y^2 = 78$$

$$y^2 - \frac{37}{2}y = -78$$

$$y^2 - \frac{37}{2}y + \left(\frac{37}{4}\right)^2 = -78 + \left(\frac{37}{4}\right)^2$$

$$\left(y - \frac{37}{4}\right)^2 = -78 + \left(\frac{37}{4}\right)^2$$

$$\left(y - \frac{37}{4}\right)^2 = \frac{121}{16}$$

$$y - \frac{37}{4} = \pm\frac{11}{4}$$

$$y = \frac{37}{4} \pm \frac{11}{4}$$

$$y = 12 \qquad y = 6.5$$

36. $x^2 + cx + 64$

$$\frac{c}{2} = \sqrt{64}$$

$$c = 2 \cdot (\pm 8)$$

$$c = \pm 16$$

$$c = 16 \qquad c = -16$$

37. $4x^2 + cx + 225$

$$x^2 + \frac{c}{4}x + \frac{225}{4}$$

$$\frac{c}{2 \cdot 4} = \sqrt{\frac{225}{4}}$$

$$\frac{c}{8} = \pm\frac{15}{2}$$

$$c = 8 \cdot \left(\pm\frac{15}{2}\right)$$

$$c = \pm 60$$

$$c = 60 \qquad c = -60$$

38. $cx^2 + 28x + 49$

$$x^2 + \frac{28}{c}x + \frac{49}{c}$$

$$\frac{28}{2c} = \sqrt{\frac{49}{c}}$$

$$\left(\frac{14}{c}\right)^2 = \frac{49}{c}$$

$$\frac{196}{c^2} = \frac{49}{c}$$

$$196 = \frac{49}{c} \cdot c^2$$

$$196 = 49c$$

$$c = 4$$

39. $cx^2 - 18x + 36$

$$x^2 - \frac{18}{c}x + \frac{36}{c}$$

$$-\frac{18}{2c} = \sqrt{\frac{36}{c}}$$

$$\left(-\frac{9}{c}\right)^2 = \frac{36}{c}$$

$$\frac{81}{c^2} = \frac{36}{c}$$

$$81 = \frac{36}{c} \cdot c^2$$

$$81 = 36c$$

$$c = \frac{9}{4}$$

40. $x^2 + 4x + c = 0$

$$x^2 + 4x + 4 = 4 - c$$

$$(x + 2)^2 = 4 - c$$

$$x + 2 = \pm\sqrt{4 - c}$$

$$x = -2 \pm \sqrt{4 - c}$$

41. $ax^2 + bx + c = 0$

$$x^2 + \frac{b}{a}x = -\frac{c}{a}$$

$$x^2 + \frac{b}{a}x + \frac{b^2}{4a^2} = \frac{b^2}{4a^2} - \frac{c}{a}$$

$$x^2 + \frac{b}{a}x + \frac{b^2}{4a^2} = \frac{b^2}{4a^2} - \frac{4ac}{4a^2}$$

$$\left(x + \frac{b}{2a}\right)^2 = \frac{b^2 - 4ac}{4a^2}$$

$$x + \frac{b}{2a} = \frac{\sqrt{b^2 - 4ac}}{\sqrt{4a^2}}$$

$$x = \frac{-b}{2a} \pm \frac{\sqrt{b^2 - 4ac}}{2a}$$

$$x = \frac{-b \pm \sqrt{b^2 - 4ac}}{2a}$$

42. $x^2 + 4bx + b^2 = 0$

$$x^2 + 4bx = -b^2$$

$$x^2 + 4bx + 4b^2 = -b^2 + 4b^2$$

$$(x^2 + 2b)^2 = 3b$$

$$x + 2b = \pm b\sqrt{3}$$

$$x = -2b \pm b\sqrt{3}$$

$$x = b(-2 \pm \sqrt{3})$$

43. $y = x^2 - 4x + 7$

$$y = x^2 - 4x + \left(\frac{4}{2}\right)^2 + 7 - \left(\frac{4}{2}\right)^2$$

$$y = x^2 - 4x + (2)^2 + 3$$

$$y = (x - 2)^2 + 3$$

$h = 2, \ k = 3$

| x | y |
|---|---|
| 0 | 7 |
| 1 | 4 |
| 2 | 3 |
| 3 | 4 |
| 4 | 7 |

$y = (x - 2)^2 + 3$
$(2, 3)$

$(h, \ k) = (2, \ 3)$

$(h, \ k)$ is the vertex of the graph.

44. $A = (12 + x)(8 + x) = 2(12)(8)$

$$x^2 + 20x + 96 = 192$$

$$x^2 + 20x - 96 = 0$$

$$(x - 4)(x + 24) = 0$$

$x = 4, \ x = -24$

The length and width should be increased by 4 meters.

45. $(12 - 2x)(12 - x) = 54$

$$2x^2 - 36x + 144 = 54$$

$$x^2 - 18x + 18 = 0$$

$$(x - 3)(x - 6) = 0$$

$x = 3, \ x = 6$

$12 - 2(3) = 6$

$12 - 2(6) = 0$     So width cannot be 6 meters.

$12 - 3 = 9$

The photo is 9 in. by 6 in.

46. $x^2 + (x + 10)^2 = 71^2$

$$x^2 + x^2 + 20x + 100 = 5041$$

$$2x^2 + 20x + 100 = 5041$$

$$x^2 + 10x + 50 = 2520.5$$

$$x^2 + 10x = 2470.5$$

$$x^2 + 10x + \left(\frac{10}{2}\right)^2 = 2470.5 + \left(\frac{10}{2}\right)^2$$

$$(x + 5)^2 = 2445.5$$

$$x + 5 = \pm\sqrt{2445.5}$$

$$x = -5 \pm \sqrt{2445.5}$$

$$x = -5 \pm 49.45$$

$$x \approx 45 \text{ or } -55$$

$x = 45, \ x + 10 = 55$

47. $150 - 11 - 6x = 0$

$$139 - 6x = 0$$

$$6x = 139$$

$$x = 23.1667 \approx 23$$

$23 \times 100 = 2300$ cards

48. $y = 2x + 1$

$$3(x + y) + 4 = 10x + y$$

$$3x + 3y + 4 = 10x + y$$

$$2y = 7x - 4$$

$$2(2x + 1) = 7x - 4$$

$$4x + 2 = 7x - 4$$

$$6 = 3x$$

$x = 2 \qquad y = 5$

The number is 52.

49. $5\sqrt{72} + 2\sqrt{20} - 3\sqrt{5} = 5 \cdot 6\sqrt{2} + 2 \cdot 2\sqrt{5} - 3\sqrt{5}$

$$= 30\sqrt{2} + 4\sqrt{5} - 3\sqrt{5}$$

$$= 30\sqrt{2} + \sqrt{5}$$

50. $4x^2 - 12x + 3 = 0$

Axis of Sym: $x = -\dfrac{b}{2a} = 1.5$

$y = 4(1.5)^2 - 12(1.5) + 3 = -6$

vertex $(1.5, -6)$

| $x$ | $4x^2 - 12x + 3$ | $y$ |
|---|---|---|
| 0 | $4(0)^2 - 12(0) + 3$ | 3 |
| 1 | $4(1)^2 - 12(1) + 3$ | -5 |
| 2 | $4(2)^2 - 12(2) + 3$ | -5 |
| 3 | $4(3)^2 - 12(3) + 3$ | 3 |

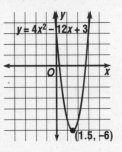

The roots are between 0 and 1 and between 2 and 3.

51. numbers < 100  19, 28, 37, 46, 55, 64, 73, 82, 91

A total of 9 numbers

Each time you add 1 to the hundreds place, the total number of the tens and ones drop by one, so for $100 \le x \le 200$, the ten's digit + one's digit = 9. For $200 \le x \le 300$, the ten's digit + one's digit = 8. So there are 63 whole numbers.

## 13-5  Solving Quadratic Equations Using the Quadratic Formula

PAGES 538-539  CHECKING FOR UNDERSTANDING

1. completing the square  2. $a \ne 0$  3. false

4. $\dfrac{-b + \sqrt{b^2 - 4ac}}{2a}$, $\dfrac{-b - \sqrt{b^2 - 4ac}}{2a}$

5. $a = 1$; $b = 7$; $c = 6$  6. $a = 2$; $b = -1$; $c = -15$

7. $a = 2$; $b = 7$; $c = 3$  8. $a = 2$; $b = 0$; $c = -98$

9. $a = 4$; $b = 8$; $c = 0$  10. $a = 3$; $b = 11$; $c = -4$

11. $x^2 + 5x - 6 = 0$

$b^2 - 4ac = 5^2 - 4(1)(-6)$

$= 25 + 24$

$= 49$

12. $y^2 - 7y - 8 = 0$

$b^2 - 4ac = (-7)^2 - 4(1)(-8)$

$= 49 + 32$

$= 81$

13. $m^2 - 2m - 35 = 0$

$b^2 - 4ac = (-2)^2 - 4(1)(-35)$

$= 4 + 140$

$= 144$

14. $4n^2 - 20n = 0$

$b^2 - 4ac = (-20)^2 - 4(4)(0)$

$= 400$

15. $5t^2 - 125 = 0$

$b^2 - 4ac = 0^2 - 4(5)(-125)$

$= 2500$

16. $3x^2 + 14x - 5 = 0$

$b^2 - 4ac = (14)^2 - 4(3)(-5)$

$= 196 + 60$

$= 256$

17. $m^2 + 4m + 2 = 0$

$m = \dfrac{-b \pm \sqrt{b^2 - 4ac}}{2a}$

$m = \dfrac{-4 \pm \sqrt{4^2 - 4(1)(2)}}{2 \cdot 1}$

$m = \dfrac{-4 \pm \sqrt{8}}{2}$

$m = \dfrac{-4 \pm 2\sqrt{2}}{2}$

$m = -2 \pm \sqrt{2}$; $-0.56$, $-3.41$

18. $-4x^2 + 8x = -3$

$-4x^2 + 8x + 3 = 0$

$x = \dfrac{-8 \pm \sqrt{8^2 - 4(-4)(3)}}{2(-4)}$

$x = \dfrac{-8 \pm \sqrt{112}}{-8}$

$x = \dfrac{-8 \pm 4\sqrt{7}}{-8} = \dfrac{2 \pm \sqrt{7}}{2}$

19. $3k^2 + 2 = -8k$

$3k^2 + 8k + 2 = 0$

$k = \dfrac{-8 \pm \sqrt{8^2 - 4(3)(2)}}{2(3)}$

$k = \dfrac{-8 \pm \sqrt{40}}{6}$

$k = \dfrac{-4 \pm \sqrt{10}}{3}$

20. $x^2 + 7x + 6 = 0$

$$x = \frac{-b \pm \sqrt{b^2 - 4ac}}{2a}$$

$$x = \frac{-7 \pm \sqrt{49 - 4(1)(6)}}{2 \cdot 1}$$

$$x = \frac{-7 \pm \sqrt{25}}{2}$$

$$x = \frac{-7 \pm 5}{2}$$

$$x = -1 \qquad x = -6$$

21. $r^2 + 10r + 9 = 0$

$$r = \frac{-10 \pm \sqrt{10^2 - 4(1)(9)}}{2(1)}$$

$$r = \frac{-10 \pm \sqrt{64}}{2}$$

$$r = \frac{-10 \pm 8}{2}$$

$$r = -1 \qquad r = -9$$

22. $-a^2 + 5a - 6 = 0$

$$a^2 - 5a + 6 = 0$$

$$a = \frac{5 \pm \sqrt{(-5)^2 - 4(1)(6)}}{2(1)}$$

$$a = \frac{5 \pm \sqrt{1}}{2}$$

$$a = \frac{5 \pm 1}{2}$$

$$a = 3 \qquad a = 2$$

23. $y^2 - 25 = 0$

$$y = \frac{0 \pm \sqrt{0 - 4(1)(-25)}}{2(1)}$$

$$y = \frac{\pm\sqrt{100}}{2}$$

$$y = \frac{\pm 10}{2}$$

$$y = 5 \qquad y = -5$$

24. $-2x^2 + 8x + 3 = 3$

$$-2x^2 + 8x = 0$$

$$x = \frac{-8 \pm \sqrt{8^2 - 4(-2)(0)}}{2(-2)}$$

$$x = \frac{-8 \pm \sqrt{64}}{-4}$$

$$x = \frac{-8 \pm 8}{-4}$$

$$x = 0 \qquad x = 4$$

25. $2r^2 + r - 15 = 0$

$$r = \frac{-1 \pm \sqrt{1^2 - 4(2)(-15)}}{2 \cdot 2}$$

$$r = \frac{-1 \pm \sqrt{121}}{4}$$

$$r = \frac{-1 \pm 11}{4}$$

$$r = \frac{5}{2} \qquad r = -3$$

26. $3n^2 - 2n = 1$

$$3n^2 - 2n - 1 = 0$$

$$n = \frac{2 \pm \sqrt{(-2)^2 - 4(3)(-1)}}{2(3)}$$

$$n = \frac{2 \pm \sqrt{16}}{6}$$

$$n = \frac{2 \pm 4}{6}$$

$$n = 1 \qquad n = -\frac{1}{3}$$

27. $2y^2 + 3 = -7y$

$$2y^2 + 7y + 3 = 0$$

$$y = \frac{-7 \pm \sqrt{7^2 - 4(2)(3)}}{2(2)}$$

$$y = \frac{-7 \pm \sqrt{25}}{4}$$

$$y = \frac{-7 \pm 5}{4}$$

$$y = -\frac{1}{2} \qquad y = -3$$

28. $8t^2 + 10t + 3 = 0$

$$t = \frac{-10t \pm \sqrt{10^2 - 4(8)(3)}}{2 \cdot 8}$$

$$t = \frac{-10 \pm \sqrt{4}}{16}$$

$$t = \frac{-10 \pm 2}{16}$$

$$t = -\frac{1}{2} \qquad t = -\frac{3}{4}$$

29. $z^2 - 13z - 32 = 0$

$$z = \frac{13 \pm \sqrt{(-13)^2 - 4(1)(-32)}}{2(1)}$$

$$z = \frac{13 \pm 3\sqrt{33}}{2}$$

$$z \approx 15.12 \qquad z \approx -2.12$$

30. $y^2 - \frac{3}{5}y + \frac{2}{25} = 0$

$$y = \frac{\frac{3}{5} \pm \sqrt{\left(\frac{3}{5}\right)^2 - 4(1)\left(\frac{2}{25}\right)}}{2 \cdot 1}$$

$$y = \frac{\frac{3}{5} \pm \sqrt{\frac{1}{25}}}{2} = \frac{\frac{3}{5} \pm \frac{1}{5}}{2}$$

$$y = \frac{2}{5} \qquad y = \frac{1}{5}$$

31. $3x^2 - \frac{5}{4}x - \frac{1}{2} = 0$

$$x = \frac{\frac{5}{4} \pm \sqrt{\left(-\frac{5}{4}\right)^2 - 4(3)\left(-\frac{1}{2}\right)}}{2 \cdot 3}$$

$$x = \frac{\frac{5}{4} \pm \sqrt{\frac{121}{16}}}{6} = \frac{\frac{5}{4} \pm \frac{11}{4}}{6}$$

$$x = \frac{2}{3} \qquad x = -\frac{1}{4}$$

32. $24x^2 - 2x - 15 = 0$

$$x = \frac{2 \pm \sqrt{(-2)^2 - 4(24)(-15)}}{2(24)}$$

$$x = \frac{2 \pm \sqrt{1444}}{48}$$

$$x = \frac{2 \pm 38}{48}$$

$$x = \frac{5}{6} \qquad x = -\frac{3}{4}$$

33. $21x^2 + 5x - 6 = 0$

$$x = \frac{-5 \pm \sqrt{5^2 - 4(21)(-6)}}{2(21)}$$

$$x = \frac{-5 \pm \sqrt{529}}{42}$$

$$x = \frac{-5 \pm 23}{42}$$

$$x = -\frac{2}{3} \qquad x = \frac{3}{7}$$

34. $2x^2 - 0.7x - 0.3 = 0$

$$x = \frac{0.7 \pm \sqrt{(-0.7)^2 - 4(2)(-0.3)}}{2(2)}$$

$$x = \frac{0.7 \pm \sqrt{2.89}}{4}$$

$$x = \frac{0.7 \pm 1.7}{4}$$

$$x = 0.6 \qquad x = -0.25$$

35. $-r^2 - 6r + 3 = 0$

$$r = \frac{6 \pm \sqrt{(-6)^2 - 4(-1)(3)}}{2(-1)}$$

$$r = \frac{6 \pm \sqrt{48}}{-2}$$

$$r = \frac{6 \pm 4\sqrt{3}}{-2}$$

$$r = -3 \pm 2\sqrt{3}$$

$$r \approx 0.46 \qquad r \approx -6.46$$

36. $4b^2 + 20b + 23 = 0$

$$b = \frac{-20 \pm \sqrt{(20)^2 - 4(4)(23)}}{2(4)}$$

$$b = \frac{-20 \pm \sqrt{32}}{8} =$$

$$b = \frac{-20 \pm 4\sqrt{2}}{8}$$

$$b = \frac{-5 \pm \sqrt{2}}{2}$$

$$b \approx -1.79 \qquad b \approx -3.21$$

37. $-4y^2 + 16y + 13 = 0$

$$y = \frac{-16 \pm \sqrt{(16)^2 - 4(-4)(13)}}{2(-4)}$$

$$y = \frac{-16 \pm \sqrt{464}}{-8}$$

$$y = \frac{-16 \pm 4\sqrt{29}}{-8}$$

$$y = \frac{4 \pm \sqrt{29}}{2}$$

$$y \approx 4.69 \qquad y \approx -0.69$$

38. $y = x^2 - 6x + 1$

$$x = \frac{6 \pm \sqrt{(-6)^2 - 4(1)(1)}}{2(1)}$$

$$x = \frac{6 \pm \sqrt{32}}{2}$$

$$x \approx 5.8 \qquad x \approx 0.2$$

39. $y = 4x^2 + 8x - 1$

$$x = \frac{-8 \pm \sqrt{8^2 - 4(4)(-1)}}{2(4)}$$

$$x = \frac{-8 \pm \sqrt{80}}{8}$$

$$x \approx -2.1 \qquad x \approx 0.1$$

40. $y = 2x^2 - x - 2$

$$x = \frac{1 \pm \sqrt{(-1)^2 - 4(2)(-2)}}{2(2)}$$

$$x = \frac{1 \pm \sqrt{17}}{4}$$

$$x \approx 1.3 \qquad x \approx -0.8$$

41. $y = 3x^2 - 5x + 1$

$$x = \frac{5 \pm \sqrt{(-5)^2 - 4(3)(1)}}{2(3)}$$

$$x = \frac{5 \pm \sqrt{13}}{6}$$

$$x \approx 1.4 \qquad x \approx 0.2$$

42. $y = 3.2x^2 - 5.6x - 7.1$

$$x = \frac{5.6 \pm \sqrt{(-5.6)^2 - 4(3.2)(-7.1)}}{2(3.2)}$$

$$x = \frac{5.6 \pm \sqrt{122.24}}{6.4}$$

$$x \approx -0.8 \qquad x \approx 2.6$$

43. $y = 1.9x^2 + 6.5x + 2.7$

$$x = \frac{-6.5 \pm \sqrt{(6.5)^2 - 4(1.9)(2.7)}}{2(1.9)}$$

$$x = \frac{-6.5 \pm \sqrt{21.73}}{3.8}$$

$$x \approx -0.5 \qquad x \approx -2.9$$

44. $(x - (-1 + \sqrt{3}))(x - (-1 - \sqrt{3}))$

$$= x^2 - (-1 - \sqrt{3})x - (-1 + \sqrt{3})x + (1 - 3)$$

$$= x^2 + 2x - 2$$

$$x^2 + 2x - 2 = 0$$

45. $\left(x - \left(\frac{-3 + \sqrt{5}}{2}\right)\right)\left(x - \left(\frac{-3 - \sqrt{5}}{2}\right)\right)$

$$= x^2 - \left(\frac{-3 - \sqrt{5}}{2}\right)x - \left(\frac{-3 + \sqrt{5}}{2}\right)x + \left(\frac{9 - 5}{4}\right)$$

$$= x^2 + 3x + 1$$

$$x^2 + 3x + 1 = 0$$

46. $\left(x - \left(\frac{1 + \sqrt{33}}{4}\right)\right)\left(x - \left(\frac{1 - \sqrt{33}}{4}\right)\right)$

$$= x^2 - \left(\frac{1 - \sqrt{33}}{4}\right)x - \left(\frac{1 + \sqrt{33}}{4}\right)x + \left(\frac{1 - 33}{16}\right)$$

$$= x^2 - \frac{1}{2}x - 2$$

$$2x^2 - x - 4 = 0$$

**47.** $\left(x - \left(\dfrac{4 + \sqrt{7}}{3}\right)\right)\left(x - \left(\dfrac{4 - \sqrt{7}}{3}\right)\right)$

$= x^2 - \left(\dfrac{4 - \sqrt{7}}{3}\right)x - \left(\dfrac{4 + \sqrt{7}}{3}\right)x + \left(\dfrac{16 - 7}{9}\right)$

$= x^2 - \dfrac{8}{3}x + 1$

$3x^2 - 8x + 3 = 0$

**48.** It is a perfect square.  **49.** It is equal to 0.

**50.** $H = -4.9t^2 + vt + h$

a. $-4.9t^2 + 15t + 10 = 25$

$-4.9t^2 + 15t - 15 = 0$

$t = \dfrac{-15 \pm \sqrt{15^2 - 4(-4.9)(-15)}}{2(-4.9)}$

$t = \dfrac{-15 \pm \sqrt{-69}}{-9.8}$

It will never reach 25 m.

b. $-4.9t^2 + 15t + 10 = 10$

$(-4.9t + 15)t = 0$

$t = \dfrac{-15}{-4.9} \approx 3.1$ sec

c. $-4.9t^2 + 15t + 10 = 0$

$t = \dfrac{-15 \pm \sqrt{15^2 - 4(-4.9)(10)}}{2(-4.9)}$

$t = 1.53 \pm 2.09$

$t = 3.62 \qquad t = -0.56$

$t = 3.6$ sec

**51.** $100[(1 + r)^2 + (1 + r) + 1] = T$

$(r^2 + 2r + 1 + r + 1 + 1)100 = 325$

$100r^2 + 300r + 300 = 325$

$100r^2 + 300r - 25 = 0$

$r = \dfrac{-300 \pm \sqrt{(-300)^2 - 4(100)(-25)}}{2(100)}$

$r = -1.5 \pm 1.5811$

$r = 0.081 \qquad r = -3.0811$

The rate is 8.1%.

**52.** $\dfrac{3}{4}a^2 + 5ab + \dfrac{1}{2}a^2 = \left(\dfrac{3}{4} + \dfrac{1}{2}\right)a^2 + 5ab$

$= \dfrac{5}{4}a^2 + 5ab$

**53.** $\dfrac{a^2}{a^2 - b^2} + \dfrac{a}{(a - b)^2}$

$= \dfrac{a^2}{(a - b)(a + b)} + \dfrac{a}{(a - b)(a - b)}$

$= \dfrac{a^2(a - b) + a(a + b)}{(a - b)^2(a + b)}$

$= \dfrac{a^3 - a^2b + a^2 + ab}{(a - b)^2(a + b)}$

**54.**

$\dfrac{5}{2}x + \dfrac{2}{3}y = 1$

**55.** $(4, -1), (2, 5)$

$m = \dfrac{-1 - 5}{4 - 2} = \dfrac{-6}{2} = -3$

$y - y_1 = m(x - x_1)$

$y - (-1) = -3(x - 4)$

$y + 1 = -3(x - 4)$

$y + 1 = -3x + 12$

$3x + y = 12 - 1$

$3x + y = 11$

**56.** $16t^2 = d$

$16(t + 1)^2 = d + 112$

$16(t^2 + 2t + 1) = 16t^2 + 112$

$16t^2 + 32t + 16 - 16t^2 - 112 = 0$

$32t - 96 = 0$

$t = \dfrac{96}{32} = 3$ seconds

Lu-Chan's stone drops in $3 + 1$ or 4 seconds.

**57.** $2x^2 - 6x - 5 = 0$

$x^2 - 3x - \dfrac{5}{2} = 0$

$x^2 - 3x = \dfrac{5}{2}$

$x^2 - 3x + \left(\dfrac{3}{2}\right)^2 = \dfrac{5}{2} + \left(\dfrac{3}{2}\right)^2$

$\left(x - \dfrac{3}{2}\right)^2 = \dfrac{19}{4}$

$x - \dfrac{3}{2} = \pm\dfrac{\sqrt{19}}{2}$

$x = \dfrac{3}{2} \pm \dfrac{\sqrt{19}}{2} = \dfrac{3 \pm \sqrt{19}}{2}$

**PAGE 540    MID-CHAPTER REVIEW**

**1.** $y = x^2 - x - 12$

$x = -\dfrac{b}{2a} = -\dfrac{(-1)}{2(1)} = \dfrac{1}{2}$

$y = \left(\dfrac{1}{2}\right)^2 - \dfrac{1}{2} - 12$

$y = \dfrac{1}{4} - \dfrac{1}{2} - 12$

$y = -\dfrac{49}{4}$

vertex $\left(\dfrac{1}{2}, -\dfrac{49}{4}\right)$

257

2. $y = -2x^2 - 9$

$x = -\dfrac{b}{2a} = -\dfrac{0}{2(-2)} = 0$

$y = -2(0)^2 - 9$

$y = -9$

vertex $(0, -9)$

3. $y = -3x^2 - 6x + 5$

$x = -\dfrac{b}{2a} = -\dfrac{(-6)}{2(-3)} = -1$

$y = -3(-1)^2 - 6(-1) + 5$

$y = -3 + 6 + 5$

$y = 8$

vertex $(-1, 8)$

4. $x^2 + 6x + 10 = 0$

$y = x^2 + 6x + 10$

| x | y |
|----|----|
| -5 | 5 |
| -3 | 1 |
| -1 | 5 |
| 0 | 10 |

no real roots

5. $x^2 - 2x - 1 = 0$

$y = x^2 - 2x - 1$

| x | y |
|----|----|
| -2 | 7 |
| -1 | 2 |
| 0 | -1 |
| 1 | -2 |
| 2 | -1 |
| 3 | 2 |
| 4 | 7 |

One root is between -1 and 0.

The other root is between 2 and 3.

6. $x^2 - 5x - 6 = 0$

$y = x^2 - 5x - 6$

| x | y |
|----|----|
| -2 | 8 |
| -1 | 0 |
| 0 | -6 |
| 2 | 12 |
| 3 | 12 |
| 5 | -6 |
| 6 | 0 |

Roots are -1, 6.

7. $x^2 - 6x + 7 = 0$

$x^2 - 6x = -7$

$x^2 - 6x + \left(\dfrac{6}{2}\right)^2 = -7 + \left(\dfrac{6}{2}\right)^2$

$(x - 3)^2 = 2$

$x - 3 = \pm\sqrt{2}$

$x = 3 \pm \sqrt{2}$

8. $2b^2 - b - 7 = 14$

$b^2 - \dfrac{1}{2}b - \dfrac{7}{2} = 7$

$b^2 - \dfrac{1}{2}b = \dfrac{21}{2}$

$b^2 - \dfrac{1}{2}b + \left(\dfrac{1}{4}\right)^2 = \dfrac{21}{2} + \left(\dfrac{1}{4}\right)^2$

$\left(b - \dfrac{1}{4}\right)^2 = \dfrac{169}{16}$

$b - \dfrac{1}{4} = \pm\dfrac{13}{4}$

$b = \dfrac{1}{4} \pm \dfrac{13}{4}$

$b = \dfrac{7}{2} \qquad b = -3$

9. $y^2 + 8y + 15 = 0$

$y = \dfrac{-8 \pm \sqrt{8^2 - 4(1)(15)}}{2(1)}$

$y = \dfrac{-8 \pm \sqrt{4}}{2}$

$y = \dfrac{-8 \pm 2}{2}$

$y = -3 \qquad y = -5$

10. $p^2 + 5p + 3 = 0$

$p = \dfrac{-5 \pm \sqrt{25 - 4(1)(3)}}{2(1)}$

$p = \dfrac{-5 \pm \sqrt{13}}{2}$

$p \approx -0.70 \qquad p \approx -4.30$

11. 4 houses in 5 days by 3 painters

5 · 3 days for 1 painter to paint 4 houses

3.75 days/house for 1 painter

$\dfrac{3.75 \times 18 \text{ houses}}{5 \text{ painters}} = 13.5 \text{ days}$

## 13-6  Using the Discriminant

PAGE 544    CHECKING FOR UNDERSTANDING

1. $b^2 - 4ac$

2. greater than zero

3. vertex

4. is not

5. $x^2 + 3x - 4 = 0$

$b^2 - 4ac = 9 - 4(1)(-4)$

$\qquad\qquad = 9 + 16 = 25$

2 real roots

6. $m^2 + 5m - 6 = 0$

$b^2 - 4ac = 25 - 4(1)(-6)$

$\qquad\qquad = 25 + 24 = 49$

2 real roots

7. $s^2 + 8s + 16 = 0$

$b^2 - 4ac = 64 - 4(1)(16)$

$\qquad\qquad = 64 - 64 = 0$

1 real root

258

8. $2z^2 + 7z + 50 = 0$

$b^2 - 4ac = 49 - 4(2)(50)$

$\quad\quad\quad = 49 - 400 = -351$

no real roots

9. $3x^2 + x + 1 = 0$

$b^2 - 4ac = 1 - 4(3)(1)$

$\quad\quad\quad = 1 - 12 = -11$

no real roots

10. $2a^2 - 2a - 1 = 0$

$b^2 - 4ac = 4 - 4(2)(-1)$

$\quad\quad\quad = 4 + 8 = 12$

2 real roots

**PAGES 544-545    EXERCISES**

11. $y^2 + 3y + 1 = 0$

$b^2 - 4ac = 9 - 4(1)(1)$

$\quad\quad\quad = 9 - 4 = 5$

2 real roots

12. $x^2 - 1.2x = 0$

$b^2 - 4ac = 1.44 - 4(1)(6)$

$\quad\quad\quad = 1.44 - 0 = 1.44$

2 real roots

13. $\quad\quad 4a^2 + 10a = -6.25$

$4a^2 + 10a + 6.25 = 0$

$b^2 - 4ac = 100 - 4(4)(6.25)$

$\quad\quad\quad = 100 - 100 = 0$

1 real root

14. $\frac{4}{3}n^2 + 4n + 3 = 0$

$b^2 - 4ac = 16 - 4\left(\frac{4}{3}\right)(3)$

$\quad\quad\quad = 16 - 16 = 0$

1 real root

15. $\frac{3}{2}m^2 + m = -\frac{7}{2}$

$b^2 - 4ac = 1 - 4\left(\frac{3}{2}\right)\left(\frac{7}{2}\right)$

$\quad\quad\quad = 1 - 21 = -20$

no real roots

16. $2r^2 = \frac{1}{2}r - \frac{2}{3}$

$2r^2 - \frac{1}{2}r + \frac{2}{3} = 0$

$b^2 - 4ac = \left(-\frac{1}{2}\right)^2 - 4(2)\left(\frac{2}{3}\right)$

$\quad\quad\quad = \frac{1}{4} - \frac{16}{3} = -\frac{61}{12}$

no real roots

17. $y^2 - 4y + 1 = 0$

$b^2 - 4ac = 16 - 4 = 12$

2 real roots

$y = \dfrac{4 \pm \sqrt{12}}{2}$

$y = \dfrac{4 \pm 2\sqrt{3}}{2} = 2 \pm \sqrt{3}$

$y = 3.73 \quad\quad y = 0.27$

18. $k^2 + 6k + 10 = 0$

$b^2 - 4ac = 36 - 40 = -4$

no real roots

19. $r^2 + 4r - 12 = 0$

$b^2 - 4ac = 16 + 48 = 64$

2 real roots

$\quad\quad r^2 + 4r - 12 = 0$

$(r + 6)(r - 2) = 0$

$r + 6 = 0 \quad\quad r - 2 = 0$

$\quad\quad r = -6 \quad\quad\quad r = 2$

20. $h^2 - 16h + 64 = 0$

$b^2 - 4ac = 256 - 256 = 0$

one real root

$\quad\quad h^2 - 16h + 64 = 0$

$(h - 8)(h - 8) = 0$

$\quad\quad\quad\quad h - 8 = 0$

$\quad\quad\quad\quad\quad h = 8$

21. $2x^2 + 3x + 1 = 0$

$b^2 - 4ac = 9 - 8 = 1$

2 real roots

$\quad\quad 2x^2 + 3x + 1 = 0$

$(2x + 1)(x + 1) = 0$

$2x + 1 = 0 \text{ or } x + 1 = 0$

$\quad\quad 2x = -1 \quad\quad\quad x = -1$

$\quad\quad\quad x = -\frac{1}{2}$

22. $3y^2 + y - 1 = 0$

$b^2 - 4ac = 1 + 12 = 13$

2 real roots

$y = \dfrac{-1 \pm \sqrt{13}}{6}$

$y = 0.43 \quad\quad y = -0.77$

23. $\quad\quad 6r^2 - 5r = 7$

$6r^2 - 5r - 7 = 0$

$b^2 - 4ac = (-5)^2 - 4(6)(-7) = 193$

2 real roots

$r = \dfrac{5 \pm \sqrt{193}}{2(6)}$

$r = 1.57 \quad\quad r = -0.74$

**24.**

$8p^2 + 1 = -7p$

$8p^2 + 7p + 1 = 0$

$b^2 - 4ac = 49 - 32 = 17$

2 real roots

$p = \dfrac{-7 \pm \sqrt{17}}{16}$

$p \approx -0.18 \qquad p \approx -0.70$

**25.** $9y^2 = 6y - 1$

$9y^2 - 6y + 1 = 0$

$b^2 - 4ac = 36 - 36 = 0$

one real root

$9y^2 - 6y + 1 = 0$

$(3y - 1)(3y - 1) = 0$

$3y - 1 = 0$

$3y = 1$

$y = \dfrac{1}{3}$

**26.**

$0.3a^2 + 0.8a = -0.4$

$0.3a^2 + 0.8a + 0.4 = 0$

$b^2 - 4ac = (0.8)^2 - 4(0.3)(0.4) = 0.16$

2 real roots

$a = \dfrac{-0.8 \pm \sqrt{0.16}}{2(0.6)}$

$a = \dfrac{-0.8 \pm 0.4}{1.2}$

$a = -2.00 \qquad a = -0.67$

**27.**

$x^2 - \dfrac{5}{3}x = -\dfrac{2}{3}$

$x^2 - \dfrac{5}{3}x + \dfrac{2}{3} = 0$

$3x^2 - 5x + 2 = 0$

$b^2 - 4ac = 25 - 24 = 1$

2 real roots

$3x^2 - 5x + 2 = 0$

$(3x - 2)(x - 1) = 0$

$3x - 2 = 0$ or $x - 1 = 0$

$x = \dfrac{2}{3} \qquad x = 1$

**28.** $\dfrac{1}{3}x^2 + 13\dfrac{1}{3} = 4x$

$\dfrac{1}{3}x^2 - 4x + 13\dfrac{1}{3} = 0$

$x^2 - 12x + 40 = 0$

$b^2 - 4ac = 144 - 160 = -16$

no real roots

**29.** $5c^2 - 7c = 1$

$5c^2 - 7c - 1 = 0$

$b^2 - 4ac = 49 + 20 = 69$

2 real roots

$c = \dfrac{7 \pm \sqrt{69}}{10}$

$c \approx 1.53 \qquad c \approx -0.13$

**30.** $15a^2 + 2a + 16 = 0$

$b^2 - 4ac = 4 - 960 = -956$

no real roots

**31.** $11z^2 = z + 3$

$11z^2 - z - 3 = 0$

$b^2 - 4ac = 1 + 132 = 133$

2 real roots

$z = \dfrac{1 \pm \sqrt{133}}{22}$

$z = 0.57 \qquad z = -0.48$

**32.** $y = x^2 + 5x + 3$

$b^2 - 4ac = 25 - 4(1)(3) = 13$

2 $x$-intercepts

**33.** $y = x^2 + 4x + 7$

$b^2 - 4ac = 16 - 4(1)(7) = -16$

0 $x$-intercepts

**34.** $y = 7x^2 - 3x - 1$

$b^2 - 4ac = 9 - 4(7)(-1) = 37$

2 $x$-intercepts

**35.** $y = 0.6x^2 + x - 1.8$

$b^2 - 4ac = 1 - 4(0.6)(-1.8) = 5.32$

2 $x$-intercepts

**36.** $y = \dfrac{3}{2}x^2 + 2x + \dfrac{5}{4}$

$b^2 - 4ac = 4 - 4\left(\dfrac{3}{2}\right)\left(\dfrac{5}{4}\right) = -\dfrac{7}{2}$

0 $x$-intercepts

**37.** $y = 4x^2 - \dfrac{4}{3}x + \dfrac{1}{9}$

$b^2 - 4ac = \dfrac{16}{9} - 4(4)\left(\dfrac{1}{9}\right) = 0$

1 $x$-intercept

38. $2l + 2w = 56$

$2l = 56 - 2w$

$l = \dfrac{56 - 2w}{2}$

$l = 28 - w$

$lw = 200$

$(28 - w)w = 200$

$28w - w^2 = 200$

$w^2 - 28w + 200 = 0$

$b^2 - 4ac = (-28)^2 - 4(1)(200) = -16$

This rectangle cannot exist.

39. $x^2 + kx + 36 = 0$

$b^2 - 4ac = k^2 - 4(1)(36)$

$= k^2 - 144$

$k^2 - 144 = 0$

$k^2 = 144$

$k = \pm 12$

$k = 12, \ k = -12$

40. $x^2 + 8x + k = 0$

$b^2 - 4ac = 64 - 4(1)(k)$

$= 64 - 4k$

$64 - 4k > 0$

$64 > 4k$

$16 > k$

41. $kx^2 + 5x = 1$

$kx^2 + 5x - 1 = 0$

$b^2 - 4ac = 25 - 4(k)(-1)$

$25 + 4k < 0$

$4k < -25$

$k < -\dfrac{25}{4}$

42. $ax^2 + bx + c = 0$

If $ac < 0$, then $b^2 - 4ac = b^2 + 4ac$.

$b^2 + 4ac > 0$ so there will always be 2 real

roots.

43. a.  $h = -16t^2 + 2320t + 125$

$84225 = -16t^2 + 2320t + 125$

$16t^2 - 2320t + 84100 = 0$

$t = \dfrac{2320 \pm \sqrt{(-2320)^2 - 4(16)(84100)}}{2(16)}$

$t = \dfrac{2320 \pm \sqrt{0}}{2(16)}$

$t = 72.5$ seconds

b. yes

44. $50(1.15) = 57.50$

$(1.15 + 0.05x)(50 - 2x) = 65$

$-0.1x^2 + 0.2x - 7.5 = 0$

$x = \dfrac{-0.2 \pm \sqrt{(0.2)^2 - 4(-0.1)(-7.5)}}{(2)(-0.1)}$

$x = \dfrac{1 \pm \sqrt{-1.76}}{-0.2}$

$\sqrt{-1.76}$ is not a real number,

so this cannot be done.

45. a. none      46. Let $x =$ cost before taxes.

b. $-\dfrac{1}{2}$          $19.61 - 0.06x = x$

c. $-1, \dfrac{5}{7}$              $19.61 = 1.06x$

d. 10, 1                $x = 18.5$

e. none          The price before taxes was

f. 0.6          $18.50.

47. The inverse is $\{(3, -1), (0, -1), (-1, 2)\}$.

This relation is a function because each element

of the domain is paired with exactly one element

of the range.

48. Let $h =$ the number of hours for the repair job;

$c =$ the total charge.

$c = 34h + 15$

49.

$x + 2y \geq -21$

$y < 3x$

50. $\sqrt{59.29} = 7.7$

51. $2l + 2w = 8$          $w^2 - 4w + 2 = 0$

$2l = 8 - 2w$          $w^2 - 4w = -2$

$l = \dfrac{8 - 2w}{2}$      $w^2 - 4w + \left(\dfrac{-4}{2}\right)^2 = -2 + \left(\dfrac{-4}{2}\right)^2$

$l = 4 - w$          $(w - 2)^2 = 2$

$lw = 2$          $w - 2 = \pm\sqrt{2}$

$(4 - w)w = 2$          $w = 2 \pm \sqrt{2}$

$4w - w^2 = 2$          $w = 3.4$

$w^2 - 4w + 2 = 0$          $wl = 2$

$(3.4)l = 2$

$l = 0.6$

The rectangle is 3.4 m by 0.6 m.

| 13-7 | **Application:** **Solving Quadratic Equations** |
|---|---|

1. graphing, factoring, completing the square, and using the quadratic formula

2. graphing

3.
$$\ell wh = V$$
$$(x - 2)(x - 2)1 = 441$$
$$x^2 - 4x + 4 = 441$$
$$x^2 - 4x - 437 = 0$$
$$x = \frac{4 \pm \sqrt{(-4)^2 - 4(1)(-437)}}{2(1)}$$
$$x = \frac{4 \pm \sqrt{16 + 1748}}{2}$$
$$x = \frac{4 \pm \sqrt{1764}}{2}$$
$$x = \frac{4 + 42}{2} = 23 \qquad x = \frac{4 - 42}{2} = -19$$

The dimensions of the original piece would be 23 cm by 23 cm.

4. factoring    5. factoring or quadratic formula

6. quadratic formula or completing the square

7. quadratic formula

8. factoring or quadratic formula

9. quadratic formula or completing the square

10.
$$x^2 - 8x - 20 = 0$$
$$x^2 - 8x + \left(\frac{8}{2}\right)^2 = 20 + \left(\frac{8}{2}\right)^2$$
$$x^2 - 8x + 16 = 36$$
$$(x - 4)^2 = 36$$
$$x - 4 = \pm\sqrt{36}$$
$$x = 4 \pm 6$$
$$x = 10 \qquad x = -2$$

11. $y^2 + 10y - 2 = 0$
$$y = \frac{-10 \pm \sqrt{100 - 4(1)(-2)}}{2 \cdot 1}$$
$$y = \frac{-10 \pm \sqrt{108}}{2}$$
$$y = \frac{-10 \pm 6\sqrt{3}}{2}$$
$$y = -5 \pm 3\sqrt{3}$$
$$y \approx 0.20 \qquad y \approx -10.20$$

12.
$$r^2 + 13r = -42$$
$$r^2 + 13r + 42 = 0$$
$$(r + 6)(r + 7) = 0$$
$$r + 6 = 0 \text{ or } r + 7 = 0$$
$$r = -6 \qquad r = -7$$

13. $3x^2 - 7x - 6 = 0$
$$x = \frac{7 \pm \sqrt{49 - 4(3)(6)}}{2 \cdot 3}$$
$$x = \frac{7 \pm \sqrt{121}}{6}$$
$$x = \frac{7 \pm 11}{6}$$
$$x = 3 \qquad x = -\frac{2}{3}$$

14. $2a^2 + 4a + 1 = 0$
$$a = \frac{-4 \pm \sqrt{16 - 4(2)(1)}}{2 \cdot 2}$$
$$a = \frac{-4 \pm \sqrt{8}}{4}$$
$$a = \frac{-4 \pm 2\sqrt{2}}{4}$$
$$a = \frac{-2 \pm \sqrt{2}}{2}$$
$$t \approx -0.29 \qquad t \approx -1.71$$

15.
$$3z^2 - 7z = 3$$
$$3z^2 - 7z - 3 = 0$$
$$z = \frac{7 \pm \sqrt{49 - 4(3)(-3)}}{2 \cdot 3}$$
$$z = \frac{7 \pm \sqrt{85}}{6}$$
$$z \approx 2.70 \qquad z \approx -0.37$$

16. $3h^2 - 5h - 2 = 0$
$$h = \frac{5 \pm \sqrt{25 - 4(3)(-2)}}{2 \cdot 3}$$
$$h = \frac{5 \pm \sqrt{49}}{6}$$
$$h = \frac{5 \pm 7}{6}$$
$$h = 2 \qquad h = -\frac{1}{3}$$

17. $2k^2 + k - 5 = 0$
$$k = \frac{-1 \pm \sqrt{1 - 4(2)(-5)}}{2 \cdot 2}$$
$$k = \frac{-1 \pm \sqrt{41}}{4}$$
$$k \approx 1.35 \qquad k \approx -1.85$$

18. $2y^2 - 4y + 3 = 0$
$$y = \frac{4 \pm \sqrt{16 - 4(2)(3)}}{2(2)}$$
$$y = \frac{4 \pm \sqrt{-8}}{4}$$
no real roots

19.
$$3z^2 = 5z - 1$$
$$3z^2 - 5z + 1 = 0$$
$$z = \frac{5 \pm \sqrt{25 - 4(3)(1)}}{2 \cdot 3}$$
$$z = \frac{5 \pm \sqrt{13}}{6}$$
$$z \approx 1.43 \qquad z \approx 0.23$$

20. $2m^2 + 4m = 5$

$2m^2 + 4m - 5 = 0$

$m = \dfrac{-4 \pm \sqrt{16 - 4(2)(-5)}}{2(2)}$

$m = \dfrac{-4 \pm \sqrt{56}}{4}$

$m = \dfrac{-2 \pm \sqrt{14}}{2}$

$m = 0.87 \qquad m = -2.87$

21. $\qquad x^2 - 1.1x = 0.6$

$x^2 - 1.1x - 0.6 = 0$

$10x^2 - 11x - 6 = 0$

$x = \dfrac{11 \pm \sqrt{121 - 4(10)(-6)}}{2 \cdot 10}$

$x = \dfrac{11 \pm \sqrt{361}}{20}$

$x = \dfrac{11 \pm 19}{20}$

$x = \dfrac{3}{2} \qquad x = -\dfrac{2}{5}$

22. $x^2 - \dfrac{17}{20}x + \dfrac{3}{20} = 0$

$20x^2 - 17x + 3 = 0$

$x = \dfrac{17 \pm \sqrt{289 - 4(20)(3)}}{2 \cdot 20}$

$x = \dfrac{17 \pm \sqrt{49}}{40}$

$x = \dfrac{17 \pm 7}{40}$

$x = \dfrac{3}{5} \qquad x = \dfrac{1}{4}$

23. $\qquad \dfrac{1}{4}y^2 = y + \dfrac{1}{2}$

$\dfrac{1}{4}y^2 - y - \dfrac{1}{2} = 0$

$y^2 - 4y - 2 = 0$

$y^2 - 4y + \left(\dfrac{4}{2}\right)^2 = 2 + \left(\dfrac{4}{2}\right)^2$

$(y - 2)^2 = 6$

$y - 2 = \pm\sqrt{6}$

$y = 2 \pm \sqrt{6}$

$y = 4.45 \qquad y = -0.45$

24. $\quad 0.7a^2 - 2.8a = 7$

$7a^2 - 28a = 70$

$7a^2 - 28a - 70 = 0$

$a = \dfrac{28 \pm \sqrt{784 - 4(7)(-70)}}{2 \cdot 7}$

$a = \dfrac{28 \pm \sqrt{2744}}{14}$

$a = \dfrac{28 \pm 14\sqrt{14}}{14}$

$a = 2 \pm \sqrt{14}$

$a \approx 5.74 \qquad a \approx -1.74$

25. Let $x$ = one integer.

$12 - x$ = other integer

$x^2 - (12 - x)^2 = 24$

$x^2 - 144 + 24x - x^2 = 24$

$-144 + 24x = 24$

$24x = 168$

$x = 7$

$12 - 7 = 5$

The integers are 5 and 7.

26. Let $x$ = the number.

$x + \dfrac{1}{x} = \dfrac{10}{3}$

$x^2 + 1 = \dfrac{10}{3}x$

$x^2 - \dfrac{10}{3}x + 1 = 0$

$3x^2 - 10x + 3 = 0$

$x = \dfrac{10 \pm \sqrt{100 - 4(3)(3)}}{2(3)}$

$x = \dfrac{10 \pm \sqrt{64}}{6}$

$x = \dfrac{10 \pm 8}{6}$

$x = 3 \qquad x = \dfrac{1}{3}$

27. Let $w$ = width in inches.

$2w$ = length in inches

$5(w - 10)(2w - 10) = 1760$

$5(2w^2 - 30w + 100) = 1760$

$2w^2 - 30w + 100 = 352$

$2w^2 - 30w - 252 = 0$

$w^2 - 15w - 126 = 0$

$(w - 21)(w + 6) = 0$

$w - 21 = 0 \;\text{ or }\; w + 6 = 0$

$w = 21 \qquad w = -6$

-6 is not reasonable.

The width is 21 inches;

the length is 42 inches.

28. Let $x$ = the width of walk in meters.

$(20 + 2x)(15 + 2x) - 15(20) = 74$

$300 + 70x + 4x^2 - 300 = 74$

$4x^2 + 70x - 74 = 0$

$2x^2 + 35x - 37 = 0$

$(2x + 37)(x - 1) = 0$

$2x + 37 = 0 \;\text{ or }\; x - 1 = 0$

$2x = -37 \qquad x = 1$

$x = \dfrac{-37}{2}$ (not reasonable)

The width of the walk can be 1 meter.

29. a. $h = vt - 16t^2$

$84 = 100t - 16t^2$

$16t^2 - 100t + 84 = 0$

$t = \dfrac{100 \pm \sqrt{10000 - 4(16)(84)}}{2(16)}$

$t = \dfrac{100 \pm \sqrt{4624}}{32}$

$t = \dfrac{100 \pm 68}{32}$

$t = 5.25 \qquad t = 1$

5.25 seconds and 1 second

   b. $h = vt - 16t^2$

$0 = 100t - 16t^2$

$16t^2 - 100t = 0$

$4t(4t - 25) = 0$

$t = 0$ or $4t - 25 = 0$

$\qquad\qquad\quad 4t = 25$

$\qquad\qquad\quad\; t = 6.25$

6.25 seconds

30. Let $x$ = the width.

frame $= (x + 10)(x + 10)$

$\dfrac{2}{3}(x + 10)(x + 10) = x^2$

$\dfrac{2}{3}(x^2 + 20x + 100) = x^2$

$2x^2 + 40x + 200 = 3x^2$

$x^2 - 40x - 200 = 0$

$x = \dfrac{40 \pm \sqrt{1600 - 4(1)(-200)}}{2 \cdot 1}$

$x = \dfrac{40 \pm \sqrt{2400}}{2} \approx \dfrac{40 \pm 48.99}{2}$

$x \approx 44.49$

$x + 10 = 54.49$

The frame is about 54.5 cm by 54.5 cm.

31. After Lisa mows one-third, there is two-thirds of the lawn left for Nicole and Amber to mow.

$\dfrac{2}{3}(100 \times 120) = 8000 \text{ ft}^2$

$(100 - 2x)(120 - 2x) = 8000$

$4x^2 - 440x + 12000 = 8000$

$x^2 - 110x + 3000 = 2000$

$x^2 - 110x = -1000$

$x^2 - 110x + \left(\dfrac{110}{2}\right)^2 = -1000 + \left(\dfrac{110}{2}\right)^2$

$(x - 55)^2 = 2025$

$x - 55 = \pm\sqrt{2025}$

$x = 55 \pm 45$

Lisa cuts a uniform strip of 10 ft. The dimensions of the lawn still to be mowed are $[100 - 2(10)]$ by $[120 - 2(10)]$ or 80 ft by 100 ft.

32. Without adding the student, the equation representing the problem would be $x \cdot \dfrac{68}{x} = 68$.

Add 1 student and decrease the price by 0.25:

$(x + 1)\left(\dfrac{68}{x} - 0.25\right) = 68$

$68 - 0.25x + \dfrac{68}{x} - 0.25 = 68$

$68x - 0.25x^2 + 68 - 0.25x = 68x$

$0.25x^2 + 0.25x - 68 = 0$

$x^2 + x - 272 = 0$

$x = \dfrac{1 \pm \sqrt{1 - 4(1)(-272)}}{2(1)}$

$x = \dfrac{1 \pm \sqrt{1089}}{2}$

$x = \dfrac{1 \pm 33}{2}$

$x = 17 \qquad x = -16$

There are $17 - 1$ or 16 students in the club.

33. Let $x$ = the positive number.

$\dfrac{1}{x} = \dfrac{x}{1 - x}$

$1 \cdot (1 - x) = x \cdot x$

$1 - x = x^2$

$x^2 + x - 1 = 0$

$x = \dfrac{-1 \pm \sqrt{1 - 4(1)(-1)}}{2(1)}$

$x = \dfrac{-1 \pm \sqrt{5}}{2}$

$x = \dfrac{-1 + \sqrt{5}}{2}$ since $x$ is a positive number.

$x \approx 0.618$

34. $A = s^2$

$\quad = 4x^2 - 28x + 49$

$\quad = (2x - 7)^2$

$s = 2x - 7$

$P = 4s$

$60 = 4(2x - 7)$

$60 = 8x - 28$

$88 = 8x$

$11 = x$

**35.** Let $t$ = time to fill tank. In $t$ hours, Pipe $A$ can fill $\frac{1}{4} \cdot t$ or $\frac{t}{4}$ of the tank. In $t - 1$ hours, Pipe $B$ can fill $\frac{1}{8}(t - 1)$ or $\frac{t - 1}{8}$ of the tank.

|  | $r$ | $t$ | $w$ |
|---|---|---|---|
| Pipe $A$ | $\frac{1}{4}$ | $t$ | $\frac{t}{4}$ |
| Pipe $B$ | $\frac{1}{8}$ | $t - 1$ | $\frac{t - 1}{8}$ |

$$\frac{t}{4} + \frac{t - 1}{8} = 1$$
$$4t + 2(t - 1) = 16$$
$$6t - 2 = 16$$
$$6t = 18$$
$$t = 3$$

Pipe $B$ will run for $3 - 1$ or 2 hours.

**36.** $2x - 3y = 8 \qquad\qquad x = \frac{3}{2}y + 4$

$2x = 3y + 8 \qquad\qquad = \frac{3}{2}(4) + 4$

$x = \frac{3}{2}y + 4 \qquad\qquad = 10$

$5\left(\frac{3}{2}y + 4\right) + 6y = 74 \qquad (10, 4)$

$\frac{15}{2}y + 20 + 6y = 74$

$15y + 40 + 12y = 148$

$27y = 108$

$y = 4$

**37.** $c^2 = a^2 + b^2$

$(2.0)^2 \overset{?}{=} (0.9)^2 + (1.6)^2$

$4 \overset{?}{=} 0.81 + 2.56$

$4 \neq 3.37 \qquad$ It is not a right triangle.

**38.** $\qquad\qquad 5b^2 = 1 + 6b$

$5b^2 - 6b - 1 = 0$

$b^2 - 4ac = (-6)^2 - 4(5)(-1)$

$\qquad\qquad = 36 + 20$

$\qquad\qquad = 56$

Since $b^2 - 4ac > 0$, $5b^2 = 1 + 6b$ has two real distinct roots.

## 13-8 The Sum and Product of Roots

PAGE 552    CHECKING FOR UNDERSTANDING

1. It is the opposite of the sum of the roots.

2. It is the product of the roots.

3. $(x - r)(x - s) = 0$

4. product: 5 $\qquad\qquad$ 5. product: $-2$

   sum: 6 $\qquad\qquad\qquad$ sum: $-1$

6. product: $-2$ $\qquad\qquad$ 7. product: $\frac{13}{6}$

   sum: $\frac{3}{4}$ $\qquad\qquad\qquad$ sum: $-\frac{5}{2}$

8. $(-6 + 3) = -3$, $-6(3) = -18$, yes

9. $2 + 3 = 5$, $2(3) = 6$, no

10. $-1 + 7 = 6$, $-1(7) = -7$, no

11. $\frac{-1}{3} + \frac{1}{2} = \frac{1}{6}$, $-\frac{1}{3}\left(\frac{1}{2}\right) = -\frac{1}{6}$, yes

12. $1 + \sqrt{7} + 1 - \sqrt{7} = 2$,

    $(1 + \sqrt{7})(1 - \sqrt{7}) = 1 - 7 = -6$, yes

13. $4 + \sqrt{3} + 4 - \sqrt{3} = 8$,

    $(4 + \sqrt{3})(4 - \sqrt{3}) = 16 - 3 = 13$, no

14. $-(5 + 2) = -7$ $\qquad$ 15. $-(1 + (-6)) = 5$

    $5(2) = 10 \qquad\qquad\qquad 1(-6) = -6$

    $x^2 - 7x + 10 = 0 \qquad x^2 + 5x - 6 = 0$

16. $-\left(\frac{2}{3} + 7\right) = -\frac{23}{3}$ $\quad$ 17. $-(0.3 + (-0.6)) = 0.3$

    $\frac{2}{3}(7) = \frac{14}{3} \qquad\qquad\qquad 0.3(-0.6) = -0.18$

    $x^2 - \frac{23}{3}x + \frac{14}{3} = 0 \quad x^2 + 0.3x - 0.18 = 0$

    $3x^2 - 23x + 14 = 0$

PAGES 552-553    EXERCISES

| | Sum | Product |
|---|---|---|
| 18. | $-15$ | $54$ |
| 19. | $5$ | $-24$ |
| 20. | $-\frac{31}{6}$ | $\frac{35}{6}$ |
| 21. | $-\frac{13}{2}$ | $-\frac{9}{4}$ |
| 22. | $3$ | $8$ |
| 23. | $\frac{1}{3}$ | $-\frac{1}{12}$ |
| 24. | $\frac{1}{3}$ | $-\frac{3}{4}$ |
| 25. | $\frac{1}{15}$ | $-\frac{1}{300}$ |
| 26. | $-\frac{\sqrt{2}}{2}$ | $-3$ |

27. $-(4 + 7) = -11$ $\qquad$ 28. $-(6 + (-5)) = -1$

    $4(7) = 28 \qquad\qquad\qquad 6(-5) = -30$

    $x^2 - 11x + 28 = 0 \qquad x^2 - x - 30 = 0$

29. $-(1 + (-10)) = 9$ $\qquad$ 30. $-(-2 + (-17)) = 19$

    $1(-10) = -10 \qquad\qquad -2(-17) = 34$

    $x^2 + 9x - 10 = 0 \qquad x^2 + 19x + 34 = 0$

31. $-\left(\frac{5}{2} + 2\right) = -\frac{9}{2}$ $\quad$ 32. $-\left(-\frac{3}{4} + 8\right) = -\frac{29}{4}$

    $\frac{5}{2}(2) = 5 \qquad\qquad\qquad -\frac{3}{4}(8) = -6$

    $x^2 - \frac{9}{2}x + 5 = 0 \qquad x^2 - \frac{29}{4}x - 6 = 0$

    $2x^2 - 9x + 10 = 0 \qquad 4x^2 - 29x - 24 = 0$

33. $-\left(\dfrac{2}{3} + -\dfrac{3}{2}\right) = \dfrac{5}{6}$

$\dfrac{2}{3}\left(-\dfrac{3}{2}\right) = -1$

$x^2 + \dfrac{5}{6}x - 1 = 0$

$6x^2 + 5x - 6 = 0$

34. $-(-1.4 + (-2.2)) = 3.6$

$-1.4(-2.2) = 3.08$

$x^2 + 3.6x + 3.08 = 0$

35. $-(\sqrt{2} + (-\sqrt{2})) = 0$

$\sqrt{2}(-\sqrt{2}) = -2$

$x^2 - 2 = 0$

36. $-(\sqrt{3} + \sqrt{3}) = -2\sqrt{3}$

$\sqrt{3}(\sqrt{3}) = 3$

$x^2 - 2\sqrt{3}x + 3 = 0$

37. $-(2 + \sqrt{3} + 2 - \sqrt{3}) = -4$

$(2 + \sqrt{3})(2 - \sqrt{3}) = 4 - 3 = 1$

$x^2 - 4x + 1 = 0$

38. $-(-4 + \sqrt{10} + (-4) - \sqrt{10}) = 8$

$(-4 + \sqrt{10})(-4 - \sqrt{10}) = 16 - 10 = 6$

$x^2 + 8x + 6 = 0$

39. $-(3 + \sqrt{5} + 5 + \sqrt{3}) = -(8 + \sqrt{5} + \sqrt{3})$

$(3 + \sqrt{5})(5 + \sqrt{3}) = 15 + 3\sqrt{3} + 5\sqrt{5} + \sqrt{15}$

$x^2 - (8 + \sqrt{5} + \sqrt{3})x + (15 + 3\sqrt{3} + 5\sqrt{5} + \sqrt{15}) = 0$

40. $-\left(\dfrac{2 - \sqrt{11}}{3} + \dfrac{2 + \sqrt{11}}{3}\right) = -\dfrac{4}{3}$

$\left(\dfrac{2 - \sqrt{11}}{3}\right)\left(\dfrac{2 + \sqrt{11}}{3}\right) = \dfrac{4}{9} - \dfrac{11}{9} = -\dfrac{7}{9}$

$x^2 - \dfrac{4}{3}x - \dfrac{7}{9} = 0$

$9x^2 - 12x - 7 = 0$

41. $\dfrac{c}{a} = -21$

$3r = -21$

$r = -7$

$-7 + 3 = -\dfrac{b}{a}$

$-4 = -k$

$k = 4$

42. $\dfrac{c}{a} = 5$

$1 \cdot r = 5$

$r = 5$

$5 + 1 = -\dfrac{b}{a}$

$6 = -k$

$k = -6$

43. $-\dfrac{b}{a} = -12$

$-5 + r = -12$

$r = -7$

$-5 \cdot -7 = \dfrac{c}{a}$

$35 = k$

44. $-\dfrac{b}{a} = -6$

$3 + r = -6$

$r = -9$

$3 \cdot -9 = \dfrac{c}{a}$

$-27 = -k$

$k = 27$

45. $-(q + r) = -\dfrac{b}{a}$

$q \cdot r = \dfrac{c}{a}$

Let $a = 1$.

$x^2 - (q + r)x + qr = 0$

46. $\dfrac{-b + \sqrt{b^2 - 4ac}}{2a} + \dfrac{-b - \sqrt{b^2 - 4ac}}{2a} = \dfrac{-2b}{2a} = -\dfrac{b}{a}$

47. $\left(\dfrac{-b + \sqrt{b^2 - 4ac}}{2a}\right)\left(\dfrac{-b - \sqrt{b^2 - 4ac}}{2a}\right)$

$= \dfrac{b^2 - (b^2 - 4ac)}{4a^2} = \dfrac{4ac}{4a^2} = \dfrac{c}{a}$

48. $H = -16t^2 + vt + h$

$122 = -16t^2 + 72t + 50$

$16t^2 - 72t + 72 = 0$

$t = \dfrac{72 \pm \sqrt{(72)^2 - 4(72)(16)}}{2(16)}$

$t = \dfrac{72 \pm \sqrt{576}}{32} = \dfrac{72 \pm 24}{32}$

$t = 3 \qquad t = 1.5$

Initial velocity was $72 \dfrac{\text{ft}}{\text{sec}}$.

49. A ticket price of $8.00 results from four $0.50 price increases ($6.00 + 4 \cdot $0.50 = $8.00). Thus, for the maximum income to occur when the ticket price is $8.00, the vertex of the expression $I = 3000 + 100p - 12.5p^2$ must have an $x$-coordinate of 4.

$b = -\dfrac{b}{2a}$

$= -\left(\dfrac{100}{2(-12.5)}\right)$

$= -\dfrac{100}{-25}$

$= 4$

Thus, the expression is correct.

50. $\left(\dfrac{5}{7}a^2 - \dfrac{3}{4}a + \dfrac{1}{2}\right) - \left(\dfrac{3}{7}a^2 + \dfrac{1}{2}a - \dfrac{1}{2}\right)$

$= \dfrac{2}{7}a^2 - \dfrac{5}{4}a + 1$

51. $\dfrac{n^2 - 4}{n^2 - 4n - 12} \div (n - 2)$

$= \dfrac{n^2 - 4}{n^2 - 4n - 12} \cdot \dfrac{1}{n - 2}$

$= \dfrac{(n - 2)(n + 2)}{(n + 2)(n - 6)} \cdot \dfrac{1}{(n - 2)}$

$= \dfrac{1}{n - 6}$

52.

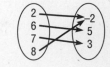

relation: $\{(2, -2), (6, 5), (7, 3), (8, -2)\}$

inverse: $\{(-2, 2), (5, 6), (3, 7), (-2, 8)\}$

53. Let $x$ = rate of canoe in still water.

Let $c$ = rate of current.

Let $t$ = time for log to return to starting point.

$t - 1$ = time canoe traveled downstream

$2 + (x - c)$ = distance canoe traveled downstream

$ct = 2$

$(t - 1)(x + c) = 2 + x - c$

$xt + ct - x - c = 2 + x - c$

$xt + ct - 2x = 2$

$xt + 2 - 2x = 2$

$xt - 2x = 0$

$x(t - 2) = 0$

$x = 0$ or $t - 2 = 0$

$t = 2$

$ct = 2$

$c(2) = 2$    The rate of the

$c = 1$    current was 1 mph.

54. $\sqrt{3x - 5} + x = 11$

$\sqrt{3x - 5} = 11 - x$

$3x - 5 = (11 - x)^2$

$3x - 5 = 121 - 22x + x^2$

$x^2 - 25x + 126 = 0$

$x = \dfrac{25 \pm \sqrt{25^2 - 4(1)(126)}}{2(1)}$

$x = \dfrac{25 \pm \sqrt{121}}{2}$

$x = 7$    $x = 18$

Check: $\sqrt{3(7) - 5} + 7 = \sqrt{16} + 7$

$= 4 + 7 = 11$

$\sqrt{3(18) - 5} + 18 = \sqrt{49} + 18$

$= 7 + 18 = 21$

7 is the correct answer.

55. $h = -5t^2 + 6t + 10$    $h = 0$

$0 = -5t^2 + 6t + 10$

$5t^2 - 6t - 10 = 0$

$t = \dfrac{6 \pm \sqrt{36 - 4(5)(-10)}}{2(5)}$

$t = \dfrac{6 \pm \sqrt{236}}{10}$

$t = 2.14$    $t = -0.94$

2.1 seconds

# Chapter 13    Summary and Review

PAGES 554-556    SKILLS AND CONCEPTS

1. $y = x^2 - 3x - 4$

$x = -\dfrac{b}{2a} = \dfrac{3}{2}$

axis of sym:  $x = \dfrac{3}{2}$

$y = x^2 - 3x - 4$

$y = \left(\dfrac{3}{2}\right)^2 - 3\left(\dfrac{3}{2}\right) - 4$

$y = \dfrac{9}{4} - \dfrac{9}{2} - 4$

$y = -\dfrac{25}{4}$

vertex $\left(\dfrac{3}{2}, -\dfrac{25}{4}\right)$

2. $y = -x^2 + 6x + 16$

$x = -\dfrac{b}{2a} = 3$

axis of sym:  $x = 3$

$y = -x^2 + 6x + 16$

$y = -(3)^2 + 6(3) + 16$

$y = 25$

vertex $(3, 25)$

3. $y = -2x^2 + 9x - 9$

$x = -\dfrac{b}{2a} = \dfrac{9}{4}$

axis of sym:  $x = \dfrac{9}{4}$

$y = -2x^2 + 9x - 9$

$y = -2\left(\dfrac{9}{4}\right)^2 + 9\left(\dfrac{9}{4}\right) - 9$

$y = -\dfrac{81}{8} + \dfrac{81}{4} - 9$

$y = \dfrac{9}{8}$

vertex $\left(\dfrac{9}{4}, \dfrac{9}{8}\right)$

4. $y = 3x^2 + 6x - 17$

$x = -\dfrac{b}{2a} = -1$

axis of sym:  $x = -1$

$y = 3x^2 + 6x - 17$

$y = 3(-1)^2 + 6(-1) - 17$

$y = -20$

vertex $(-1, -20)$

5.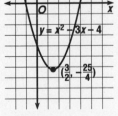

6.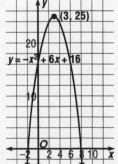

267

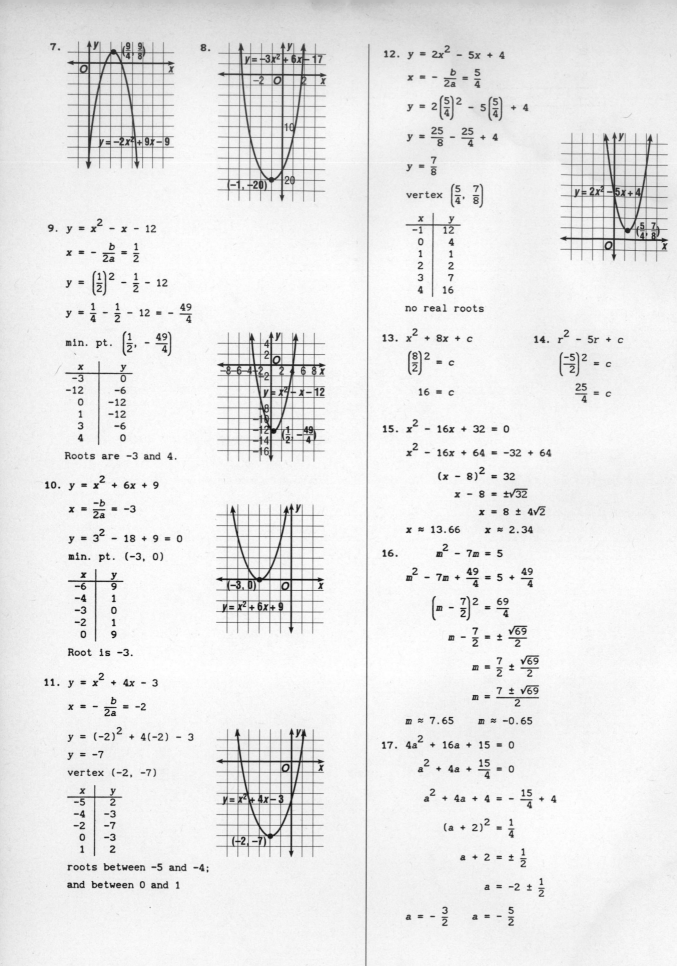

**7.** $y = -2x^2 + 9x - 9$ with vertex $\left(\frac{9}{4}, \frac{9}{8}\right)$

**8.** $y = -3x^2 + 6x - 17$ with vertex $(-1, -20)$

**9.** $y = x^2 - x - 12$

$x = -\frac{b}{2a} = \frac{1}{2}$

$y = \left(\frac{1}{2}\right)^2 - \frac{1}{2} - 12$

$y = \frac{1}{4} - \frac{1}{2} - 12 = -\frac{49}{4}$

min. pt. $\left(\frac{1}{2}, -\frac{49}{4}\right)$

| x | y |
|---|---|
| -3 | 0 |
| -12 | -6 |
| 0 | -12 |
| 1 | -12 |
| 3 | -6 |
| 4 | 0 |

Roots are -3 and 4.

**10.** $y = x^2 + 6x + 9$

$x = \frac{-b}{2a} = -3$

$y = 3^2 - 18 + 9 = 0$

min. pt. $(-3, 0)$

| x | y |
|---|---|
| -6 | 9 |
| -4 | 1 |
| -3 | 0 |
| -2 | 1 |
| 0 | 9 |

Root is -3.

**11.** $y = x^2 + 4x - 3$

$x = -\frac{b}{2a} = -2$

$y = (-2)^2 + 4(-2) - 3$

$y = -7$

vertex $(-2, -7)$

| x | y |
|---|---|
| -5 | 2 |
| -4 | -3 |
| -2 | -7 |
| 0 | -3 |
| 1 | 2 |

roots between -5 and -4;
and between 0 and 1

**12.** $y = 2x^2 - 5x + 4$

$x = -\frac{b}{2a} = \frac{5}{4}$

$y = 2\left(\frac{5}{4}\right)^2 - 5\left(\frac{5}{4}\right) + 4$

$y = \frac{25}{8} - \frac{25}{4} + 4$

$y = \frac{7}{8}$

vertex $\left(\frac{5}{4}, \frac{7}{8}\right)$

| x | y |
|---|---|
| -1 | 12 |
| 0 | 4 |
| 1 | 1 |
| 2 | 2 |
| 3 | 7 |
| 4 | 16 |

no real roots

**13.** $x^2 + 8x + c$

$\left(\frac{8}{2}\right)^2 = c$

$16 = c$

**14.** $r^2 - 5r + c$

$\left(\frac{-5}{2}\right)^2 = c$

$\frac{25}{4} = c$

**15.** $x^2 - 16x + 32 = 0$

$x^2 - 16x + 64 = -32 + 64$

$(x - 8)^2 = 32$

$x - 8 = \pm\sqrt{32}$

$x = 8 \pm 4\sqrt{2}$

$x \approx 13.66 \qquad x \approx 2.34$

**16.** $m^2 - 7m = 5$

$m^2 - 7m + \frac{49}{4} = 5 + \frac{49}{4}$

$\left(m - \frac{7}{2}\right)^2 = \frac{69}{4}$

$m - \frac{7}{2} = \pm\frac{\sqrt{69}}{2}$

$m = \frac{7}{2} \pm \frac{\sqrt{69}}{2}$

$m = \frac{7 \pm \sqrt{69}}{2}$

$m \approx 7.65 \qquad m \approx -0.65$

**17.** $4a^2 + 16a + 15 = 0$

$a^2 + 4a + \frac{15}{4} = 0$

$a^2 + 4a + 4 = -\frac{15}{4} + 4$

$(a + 2)^2 = \frac{1}{4}$

$a + 2 = \pm\frac{1}{2}$

$a = -2 \pm \frac{1}{2}$

$a = -\frac{3}{2} \qquad a = -\frac{5}{2}$

18. $x^2 - 8x = 20$

$x^2 - 8x - 20 = 0$

$x = \dfrac{8 \pm \sqrt{(-8)^2 - 4(1)(-20)}}{2(1)}$

$x = \dfrac{8 \pm \sqrt{144}}{2}$

$x = \dfrac{8 \pm 12}{2}$

$x = 10 \qquad x = -2$

19. $5b^2 + 9b + 3 = 0$

$b = \dfrac{-9 \pm \sqrt{9^2 - 4(5)(3)}}{2(5)}$

$b = \dfrac{-9 \pm \sqrt{21}}{10}$

$b \approx -0.44 \qquad b \approx -1.36$

20. $9k^2 - 1 = 12k$

$9k^2 - 12k - 1 = 0$

$k = \dfrac{12 \pm \sqrt{(-12)^2 - 4(9)(-1)}}{2(9)}$

$k = \dfrac{12 \pm \sqrt{180}}{18}$

$k = \dfrac{2 \pm \sqrt{5}}{3}$

$k \approx 1.41 \qquad k \approx -0.08$

21. $2m^2 = \dfrac{17}{6}m - 1$

$2m^2 - \dfrac{17}{6}m + 1 = 0$

$m = \dfrac{\dfrac{17}{6} \pm \sqrt{\left(\dfrac{17}{6}\right)^2 - 4(2)(1)}}{2(2)}$

$m = \dfrac{\dfrac{17}{6} \pm \sqrt{\dfrac{1}{36}}}{4}$

$m = \dfrac{\dfrac{17}{6} \pm \dfrac{1}{6}}{4}$

$m = \dfrac{3}{4} \qquad m = \dfrac{2}{3}$

22. $3s^2 - 7s - 2 = 0$

$s = \dfrac{7 \pm \sqrt{49 - 4(3)(-2)}}{2(3)}$

$s = \dfrac{7 \pm \sqrt{73}}{6}$

$s \approx 2.59 \qquad s \approx -0.26$

23. $9k^2 - 13k + 4 = 0$

$13^2 - 4(9)(4) = 25$

2 real roots

24. $7x^2 - 6x + 5 = 0$

$(-6)^2 - 4(7)(5) = -104$

no real roots

25. $9a^2 + 25 = 30a$

$9a^2 - 30a + 25 = 0$

$(-30)^2 - 4(9)(25) = 0$

1 real root

26. $4p^2 + 4p = 15$

$4p^2 + 4p - 15 = 0$

$(4)^2 - 4(4)(-15) = 256$

2 real roots

27. Let $x$ = first integer,

$y$ = second integer.

$x + y = 21$

$x = 21 - y$

$xy = 90$

$(21 - y) = 90$

$21y - y^2 = 90$

$y^2 - 21y + 90 = 0$

$(y - 6)(y - 15) = 0$

$y - 6 = 0$ or $y - 15 = 0$

$y = 6 \qquad\qquad y = 15$

28. $(8 + w + 6)(w + 6) - (8 + w)w = 288$

$(w + 14)(w + 6) - (8 + w)w = 288$

$w^2 + 20w + 84 - 8w - w^2 = 288$

$12w + 84 = 288$

$12w = 204$

$w = 17$

$w + 8 = 25$

The dimensions are 17 ft by 25 ft.

29. $y^2 + 8y - 14 = 0$

$-\dfrac{b}{a} = -8$

$\dfrac{c}{a} = -14$

30. $4a^2 - 6a + 11 = 0$

$-\dfrac{b}{a} = -\dfrac{-6}{4} = \dfrac{3}{2}$

$\dfrac{c}{a} = \dfrac{11}{4}$

31. $2x^2 - x = 6$

$2x^2 - x - 6 = 0$

$-\dfrac{b}{a} = -\dfrac{-1}{2} = \dfrac{1}{2}$

$\dfrac{c}{a} = \dfrac{-6}{2} = -3$

32. $-(1 + (-8)) = 7$

$1(-8) = -8$

$x^2 + 7x - 8 = 0$

33. $-\left(\dfrac{3}{2} + (-4)\right) = \dfrac{5}{2}$

$\dfrac{3}{2}(-4) = -6$

$x^2 + \dfrac{5}{2}x - 6 = 0$

$2x^2 + 5x - 12 = 0$

34. $-(3 + \sqrt{5} + 3 - \sqrt{5}) = -6$

$(3 + \sqrt{5})(3 - \sqrt{5}) = 9 - 5 = 4$

$x^2 - 6x + 4 = 0$

35.

| Numbers Between | Number of Palindromes |
|---|---|
| 1000-1999 | 10 |
| 2000-2999 | 10 |
| 3000-3999 | 10 |
| 4000-4999 | 10 |
| 5000-5999 | 10 |
| 6000-6999 | 10 |
| 7000-7999 | 10 |
| 8000-8999 | 10 |
| 9000-10,000 | 10 |

Thus, there are 90 palindromes.

36. Area of square $= \ell^2$

$\ell^2 = \frac{1}{2}(\ell + 2)(\ell + 3)$

$\ell^2 = \frac{1}{2}(\ell^2 + 5\ell + 6)$

$\ell^2 = \frac{1}{2}\ell^2 + \frac{5}{2}\ell + 3$

$\frac{1}{2}\ell^2 - \frac{5}{2}\ell - 3 = 0$

$\ell^2 - 5\ell - 6 = 0$

$(\ell - 6)(\ell + 1) = 0$

$\ell = 6, \quad \ell = -1$

The dimensions of the square is 6 cm by 6 cm.

37. $(500 - 20x)(20 + 1x)$

$10000 + 100x - 20x^2 = 0$

$20x^2 - 100x - 10000 = 0$

$x^2 - 5x - 500 = 0$

$x = -\frac{b}{2a} = \frac{5}{2} = 2.5$

To maximize the income, 2.5 $1 price increases are needed. So $22.50 will maximize the owner's income.

38. $h = 1440t - 16t^2$

a.
$25,000 = 1440t - 16t^2$

$16t^2 - 1440t + 25000 = 0$

$t = \frac{1440 \pm \sqrt{(-1440)^2 - 4(16)(25000)}}{2(16)}$

$t = \frac{1440 \pm \sqrt{473600}}{32}$

$t \approx 66.5 \text{ sec} \qquad t \approx 23.5 \text{ sec}$

b.
$35000 = 1440t - 16t^2$

$16t^2 - 1440t - 35000 = 0$

$t = \frac{1440 \pm \sqrt{(-1440)^2 - 4(16)(35000)}}{2(16)}$

$t = \frac{1440 \pm \sqrt{-166400}}{32}$

The rocket never reaches 35,000 ft.

c. $0 = 1440t - 16t^2$

$0 = t(1440 - 16t)$

$t = 0 \quad$ or $\quad 1440 - 16t = 0$

$t = \frac{-1440}{-16} = 90$

The rocket will hit the ground in 90 sec.

# Chapter 13   Test

1. $y = 4x^2 - 8x - 17$

$x = -\frac{b}{2a} = -\frac{-8}{2(4)} = 1$

axis of sym: $x = 1$

$y = 4x^2 - 8x - 17$

$y = 4(1)^2 - 8(1) - 17$

$y = 4 - 8 - 17$

$y = -21$

vertex $(1, -21)$

2. $y = -3x^2 + 12x + 34$

$x = -\frac{b}{2a} = -\frac{12}{2(-3)} = 2$

axis of sym: $x = 2$

$y = -3x^2 + 12x + 34$

$y = -3(2)^2 + 12(2) + 34$

$y = -12 + 24 + 34$

$y = 46$

vertex $(2, 46)$

3. $y = x^2 + x - 2$

$x = -\frac{1}{2}$

line of sym: $x = -\frac{1}{2}$

$y = \frac{1}{4} - \frac{1}{2} - 2 = -\frac{9}{4}$

min. pt. $\left(-\frac{1}{2}, -\frac{9}{4}\right)$

| x | y |
|---|---|
| -3 | 4 |
| -2 | 0 |
| -1 | -2 |
| 0 | -2 |
| 1 | 0 |
| 2 | 4 |

Roots are -2, and 1.

4. $y = x^2 - 8x + 11$

$x = -\frac{b}{2a} = 4$

axis of sym: 4

$y = 16 - 32 + 11 = -5$

vertex $(4, -5)$

| x | y |
|---|---|
| 1 | 4 |
| 2 | -1 |
| 3 | -4 |
| 4 | -5 |
| 5 | -4 |
| 6 | -1 |
| 7 | 4 |

roots between 1 and 2
and between 6 and 7

5. $m^2 - 8m - 4 = 0$

$m^2 - 8m + \left(\dfrac{8}{2}\right)^2 = 4 + \left(\dfrac{8}{2}\right)^2$

$(m - 4)^2 = 20$

$m - 4 = \pm\sqrt{20}$

$m = 4 \pm 2\sqrt{5}$

$m \approx 8.47 \qquad m \approx -0.47$

6. $2k^2 - 9k + 8 = 0$

$k = \dfrac{9 \pm \sqrt{(-9)^2 - 4(2)(8)}}{2(2)}$

$k = \dfrac{9 \pm \sqrt{17}}{4}$

$k \approx 3.28 \qquad k \approx 1.22$

7. $2x^2 - 5x - 12 = 0$

$x = \dfrac{5 \pm \sqrt{25 - 4(2)(-12)}}{2(2)}$

$x = \dfrac{5 \pm \sqrt{121}}{4}$

$x = \dfrac{5 \pm 11}{4}$

$x \approx 4 \qquad x \approx -\dfrac{3}{2}$

8. $m^2 + 18m + 75 = 0$

$m^2 + 18m + \left(\dfrac{18}{2}\right)^2 = -75 + \left(\dfrac{18}{2}\right)^2$

$(m + 9)^2 = 6$

$m + 9 = \pm\sqrt{6}$

$m = -9 \pm \sqrt{6}$

$m \approx -6.55 \qquad m \approx -11.45$

9. $3y^2 - 2y - 4 = 0$

$y = \dfrac{2 \pm \sqrt{(-2)^2 - 4(3)(-4)}}{2(3)}$

$y = \dfrac{2 \pm \sqrt{52}}{6}$

$y = \dfrac{2 \pm 2\sqrt{13}}{6}$

$y = \dfrac{1 \pm \sqrt{13}}{3}$

$y \approx 1.54 \qquad y \approx -0.87$

10. $3k^2 + 2k = 5$

$3k^2 + 2k - 5 = 0$

$k = \dfrac{-2 \pm \sqrt{(2)^2 - 4(3)(-5)}}{2(3)}$

$k = \dfrac{-2 \pm \sqrt{64}}{6}$

$k = \dfrac{-2 \pm 8}{6}$

$k = 1 \qquad k = -\dfrac{5}{3}$

11. $6n^2 + 7n = 20$

$6n^2 + 7n - 20 = 0$

$n = \dfrac{-7 \pm \sqrt{7^2 - 4(6)(-20)}}{2(6)}$

$n = \dfrac{-7 \pm \sqrt{529}}{12}$

$n = \dfrac{-7 \pm 23}{12}$

$n = \dfrac{4}{3} \qquad n = -\dfrac{5}{2}$

12. $2x^2 - 10 = 3x$

$2x^2 - 3x - 10 = 0$

$x = \dfrac{3 \pm \sqrt{(-3)^2 - 4(2)(-10)}}{2(2)}$

$x = \dfrac{3 \pm \sqrt{89}}{4}$

$x \approx 3.11 \qquad x \approx -1.61$

13. $7a^2 + \dfrac{23}{3}a + 2 = 0$

$21a^2 + 23a + 6 = 0$

$a = \dfrac{-23 \pm \sqrt{(23)^2 - 4(21)(6)}}{2(21)}$

$a = \dfrac{-23 \pm \sqrt{25}}{42}$

$a = \dfrac{-23 \pm 5}{42}$

$a = -\dfrac{3}{7} \qquad a = -\dfrac{2}{3}$

14. $x^2 - 4.4x + 4.2 = 0$

$x^2 - 4.4x + \left(\dfrac{4.4}{2}\right)^2 = -4.2 + \left(\dfrac{4.4}{2}\right)^2$

$(x - 2.2)^2 = 0.64$

$x - 2.2 = \pm 0.8$

$x = 2.2 \pm 0.8$

$x = 1.4 \qquad x = 3$

15. $3y^2 - y - 10 = 0$

$(-1)^2 - 4(3)(-10) = 121$

2 real roots

16. $4b^2 + 12b + 9 = 0$

$(12)^2 - 4(4)(9) = 0$

1 real root

17. $3m^2 - 9m + 7 = 0$

$(-9)^2 - 4(3)(7) = -3$

no real roots

18. $y^2 + y\sqrt{3} - 5 = 0$

$(\sqrt{3})^2 - 4(1)(-5) = 23$

2 real roots

19. $3m^2 - 15m + 41 = 0$

$-\dfrac{b}{a} = -\dfrac{-15}{3} = 5$

$\dfrac{c}{a} = \dfrac{41}{3}$

20. $-\left(-2 + \dfrac{5}{4}\right) = -\dfrac{3}{4} = -\dfrac{b}{a}$

$-2\left(\dfrac{5}{4}\right) = -\dfrac{5}{2} = \dfrac{c}{a}$

Let $a = 1$

$x^2 + \dfrac{3}{4}x - \dfrac{5}{2} = 0$

$4x^2 + 3x - 10 = 0$

21. $-(6 + \sqrt{3} + 6 - \sqrt{3}) = -12 = -\dfrac{b}{a}$

$(6 + \sqrt{3})(6 - \sqrt{3}) = 36 - 3 = 33 = \dfrac{c}{a}$

Let $a = 1$

$x^2 - 12x + 33 = 0$

22. $2w + 2l = 44$

$wl = 105$

$w = \dfrac{105}{l}$

$2\left(\dfrac{105}{l}\right) + 2l = 44$

$210 + 2l^2 = 44l$

$2l^2 - 44l + 210 = 0$

$l^2 - 22l + 105 = 0$

$(l - 7)(l - 15) = 0$

$l = 7$ cm, $w = 15$ cm

23. $x + y = 22 \qquad xy = 125$

$y = \dfrac{125}{x}$

$x + \dfrac{125}{x} = 22$

$x^2 + 125 = 22x$

$x^2 - 22x + 125 = 0$

$x = \dfrac{22 \pm \sqrt{(-22)^2 - 4(1)(125)}}{2}$

$x = \dfrac{22 \pm \sqrt{-16}}{2}$

no number exists

24. $l = 3w$

$(l - 4)(w - 4)(2) = 512$

$(3w - 4)(w - 4)(2) = 512$

$6w^2 - 32w + 32 = 512$

$6w^2 - 32w - 480 = 0$

$w = \dfrac{32 \pm \sqrt{(-32)^2 - 4(6)(-480)}}{2(6)}$

$w = \dfrac{32 \pm \sqrt{12544}}{12}$, $w = 12$ or $-\dfrac{20}{3}$

$w = 12$ cm $\qquad l = 36$ cm

25. $y = -x^2 + 3x + 3$

axis $= -\dfrac{b}{2a} = -\dfrac{3}{-2} = \dfrac{3}{2}$

$y = -\left(\dfrac{3}{2}\right)^2 + 3\left(\dfrac{3}{2}\right) + 3$

$y = 5.25$ m

The maximum height is 5.25 m.

$-x^2 + 3x + 3 = 0$

$x = \dfrac{-3 \pm \sqrt{3^2 - 4(-1)(3)}}{2(-1)}$

$x = \dfrac{-3 \pm \sqrt{21}}{-2}$

$x \approx 3.8 \qquad x \approx -0.8$

He is 3.8 m from the board.

PAGE 557　　　BONUS

$y = ax^2 + bx + c$

axis of sym: $x = -\dfrac{b}{2a}$

$y = a\left(-\dfrac{b}{2a}\right)^2 + b\left(-\dfrac{b}{2a}\right) + c$

$y = \dfrac{b^2}{4a} + \left(-\dfrac{b^2}{2a}\right) + c$

$y = \dfrac{b^2}{4a} - \dfrac{2b^2}{4a} + \dfrac{4ac}{4a}$

$y = \dfrac{4ac - b^2}{4a}$

vertex $\left(-\dfrac{b}{2a}, \dfrac{4ac - b^2}{4a}\right)$

# Chapter 14 Statistics and Probability

| 14-1 | Statistics and Line Plots |
|------|---------------------------|

PAGE 562    CHECKING FOR UNDERDSTANDING

1. The numerical information used in statistics is data.

2. Answers may vary. Sample answer: the information is easier to read and interpret when presented in a table.

3. Answers may vary. Sample answer: taking every 10th student from an alphabetical listing and randomly choosing a student out of each class during the first class of the day.

4. scale from 4 to 10; intervals of 1

5. scale from 10 to 50; intervals of 10

6. scale from 100 to 800; intervals of 100

7. scale from 1000 to 11,000; intervals of 1000

8. a. 56%

   b. 1970

   c. 6 years; 1950, 1955, 1960, 1965, 1980, and 1990

   d. 4 intervals; 1950-1955, 1955-1960, 1965-1970, 1980-1985.

   e. The greatest decrease was 3% from 1970-1975.

   f.

```
                          x
                        x x
   x           x        x x x   x
 <+++++++++++++++++++++++++++++++++++++++>
   55    60    65    70    75    80
```

PAGES  562-564    EXERCISES

9. a. The highest score was 50.

   b. The lowest score was 22.

   c. 30 students took the test since there were 30 "x"'s on the line plot.

   d. 9 students scored in the 40's.

   e. A score of 26 was received by the most students.

10. a.

| High Temp. | Number of Cities | High Temp. | Number of Cities |
|------------|------------------|------------|------------------|
| 82  | 1 | 101 | 1 |
| 83  | 0 | 102 | 2 |
| 84  | 0 | 103 | 3 |
| 85  | 0 | 104 | 1 |
| 86  | 0 | 105 | 0 |
| 87  | 1 | 106 | 1 |
| 88  | 0 | 107 | 1 |
| 89  | 0 | 108 | 1 |
| 90  | 2 | 109 | 0 |
| 91  | 4 | 110 | 1 |
| 92  | 4 | 111 | 0 |
| 93  | 0 | 112 | 0 |
| 94  | 5 | 113 | 0 |
| 95  | 3 | 114 | 0 |
| 96  | 5 | 115 | 0 |
| 97  | 3 | 116 | 0 |
| 98  | 4 | 117 | 0 |
| 99  | 3 | 118 | 1 |
| 100 | 3 |     |   |

   b. 118° was the highest temperature.

   c. 82° was the lowest temperature.

   d. 94° and 96° occurred most frequently.

   e. The temperatures 93°, 105°, and 109° are not in the table.

   f. 3 cities had a high temperature of 100°F.

   g. 15 cities had at least a high temperature of 100°F.

   h. 20 cities had a high temperature of at most 95°F.

11. a.

```
                   x   xx x
                   x  xxxx        x
               x  xxxx xxxx     x   x
   xx   xxxxxx xxxxx xxx xx    xx
 <+++++++++++++++++++++++++++++++++++++++>
   40    45    50    55    60    65    70
```

   b. 42 ages are given.

   c. yes; Ages 54-57 appear clustered.

12. a.

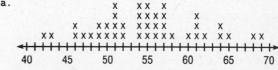

```
                    x  x
            x      xxx x       x
   x       xxx  xxxxxx xx  x   x        xx
 <+++++++++++++++++++++++++++++++++++++++>
   90   100   110   120   130   140   150
```

   b. The greatest number of RBI's is 149.

   c. The least number of RBI's is 91.

   d. The most frequent number of RBI's is 121 and 125.

   e. 13 players

13. a. Ms. Lee's group watched a total of 270 hours of television and Mr. Jebsen's group watched a total of 315 hours of television. Mr. Jebsen's group watched the most television.

b. No, the pattern does not appear to be the same. The number of hours of television watched for Ms. Lee's students is more spread out while the number of hours watched for Mr. Jebsen's students is more clustered between 15 and 30 hours.

14. Mr. Jebsen's group: $\frac{315}{15} = 21$ hours.

Mr. Lee's group : $\frac{270}{15} = 18$ hours.

Answers may vary. Sample answer: Yes, because Mr. Jebsen's group watched more hours of television.

15.

```
                X X
          XX  X  X  X
          XX XXXXXX  X
          XXX XXXXXXX XX
   X    X  XXX XXXXXXXXXXX XXX  X          X
◄─┼┼┼┼┼┼┼┼┼┼┼┼┼┼┼┼┼┼┼┼┼┼┼┼┼┼┼┼┼┼┼┼┼┼┼┼┼┼┼┼─►
  80   85   90   95  100  105  110  115  120
```

The temperatures 91°, 92°, and 98° occurred exactly four times.

16.

| Age on First Inauguration | Number of Times |
|---|---|
| 41–45 | 2 |
| 46–50 | 7 |
| 51–55 | 14 |
| 56–60 | 9 |
| 61–65 | 7 |
| 66–70 | 2 |

The interval of ages 51–55 occurs most often.

17.

```
                    X
         X       X  X
         X XXXXXX X          X
      XX XXXXXXXX XX      X  X  X
   ◄─┼┼┼┼┼┼┼┼┼┼┼┼┼┼┼┼┼┼┼┼┼┼┼┼┼┼─►
      5    10   15   20   25   30
```

15 detergents cost at most 17¢ per cup.

18. Let $t$ = number of hours to 10 A.M.

$d = rt$

$rt = rt$

$36(x + 1) = 54(x - 1)$

$x = 5$

If $x = 5$, then $36(x + 1) = 216$.

$d = rt$

$216 = 5r$

$43.2 = r$

19. $g[f(a)] = 1 - 3(a^2 - 2a)$

$= 1 - 3a^2 + 6a$

$= -3a^2 + 6a + 1$

20. Two points on the line are (1, 450) and (5,3250) where $x$ is the number of months and $y$ is the number of tennis racket covers manufactured. The slope $m = \dfrac{3250 - 450}{5 - 1} = \dfrac{2800}{4} = 700$.

The y-intercept can be found by solving $y = 700x + b$.

$450 = 700(1) + b$

$450 = 700 + b$

$-250 = b$

The equation then becomes $y = 700x - 250$. To find the number of covers manufactured after 12 months, substitute 12 for $x$.

$y = 700(12) - 250$

$= 8400 - 250$

$= 8150$

At the end of the year, 8150 tennis racket covers will be manufactured.

21. geometric mean $= \sqrt{12 \cdot 27}$

$= \sqrt{324}$

$= 18$

22. $x = \dfrac{7}{3}$ and $x = -3$

$x - \dfrac{7}{3} = 0$ and $x + 3 = 0$

$\left(x - \dfrac{7}{3}\right)(x + 3) = 0$

$x^2 + \dfrac{2}{3}x - 7 = 0$

$3x^2 + 2x - 21 = 0$

## 14-2　Stem-and-Leaf Plots

1. Add stem 10 and leaf 0 to its right (10|0) in the plot.

2. Use stem 9 and leaf 9 since the data are truncated in the plot.

3. The plot of 6498 cannot be determined since the example does not show whether the data is being rounded or truncated.

4. in situations where you want to compare two sets of data

5. The stems are 1, 2, 3, 4, and 5.

6. The stems are 0, 1, 2, 3, 4, 5, 6, 7, 8, 9, and 10.

7. The stems are 19, 20, 21, 22, 23, 24, 25, and 26.

8. The stems are 0, 1, 2, 3, 4, 5, 6, and 7.

9. Rounded:　46
   Truncated:　45

10. Rounded:　35
    Truncated:　34

11. Rounded:　43
    Truncated:　43

12. Rounded:　12
    Truncated:　12

13. a. 85°F was the highest temperature recorded.

b. 49°F was the lowest temperature recorded.

c. For 11 days the high temperature was in the 70's.

d. 77°F occurred most frequently.

PAGES 567-569   EXERCISES

14. a. 106 catches

b. 60 catches

c. 31 seasons

d. 71 and 73 catches

e. 9 times

15. a.

| Stem | Leaf |
|---|---|
| 1 | 6 7 7 8 8 8 8 8 9 9 9 9 9 9 9 |
| 2 | 0 0 2 3 4 4 5 5 6 7 7 |
| 3 | 0 2 3 3 5 6 |
| 4 | 5 8    4\|8 = |
| 5 | 5      48 years old |

b. 35 people

c. 55 - 16 = 39 years

d. 19 years old

e. Teens are most widely represented.

f. 12 students

16. a. $740-$749

b. $260-$269

c. 6 occupations

d. 5|1 represents $510-$519.

e. The leaf values have been truncated since 3|8 represents $380-$389.

17. a.

| Stem | Leaf |
|---|---|
| 13 | 9 9 9 |
| 14 | 0 3 3 4 5 7 9 9 |
| 15 | 1 1 3 3 6 7 8 9 9 9 |
| 16 | 1 1 2 2 2 3 4 8 |
| 17 | 1 |
| 18 | 6     15\|1 = 151 mph |

b. Most cars were in the 150-159 mph range.

18. a.

| Stem | Leaf |
|---|---|
| 1 | 3 5 7 |
| 2 | 3 8 9 |
| 3 | 2 3 5 6 |
| 4 | 4 4 7 |
| 5 | 0 2 6 |
| 6 | 4 5 |
| 7 | 3 |
| 8 | 3 3 3 4 6 8 |
| 9 | 2 2 3 |

3|6 = 355-364 shares

b. 930 - 130 = 800 shares     c. 10 times

d. The range of 825-834 shares occurred most often.

19. a.

| Stem | Leaf |     | Stem | Leaf |
|---|---|---|---|---|
| 6 | 5 8 9 |   | 14 | 5 |
| 7 | 3 4 4 6 7 |   | 15 | 7 |
| 8 | 0 2 2 3 5 |   | 17 | 4 |
|   | 5 9 |   | 18 | 2 |
| 9 | 4 8 |   | 21 | 2 |
| 10 | 4 |   | 26 | 2 |
| 11 | 2 |   | 29 | 0 |
| 13 | 6 |   | 9\|4 = $94,000 | |

b. $290,000 - $65,000 = $225,000

c. Most homes are in the $80,000 - $89,000 price range.

20. a.

| Males | Stem | Females |
|---|---|---|
|  | 86 | 3 4 |
|  | 87 | 2 5 7 8 |
|  | 88 | 0 |
| 9 | 91 | |
| 8 4 | 92 | 6 |
| 6 5 4 2 | 93 | 5 |
| 8 | 96 | |
| 7 | 97 | |

92|6 = 926 points

b. Answers may vary. Sample answer: all scores average in the 800 or 900 range.

21. Let each stem represent an interval of 5 inches. Use 6| to represent heights from 60 to 64 inches and use 6 · | to represent heights from 65 to 69 inches.

22. $x$ = Carita's score for the last game

$$\frac{(b + 2) + (b + 3) + (b - 2) + (b - 1) + (x)}{5} = b + 2$$

$b + 2 + b + 3 + b - 2 + b - 1 + x = 5b + 10$

$4b + 2 + x = 5b + 10$

$4b - 4b + 2 + n = 5b + 10 - 4b$

$2 + x = b + 10$

$2 + x - 2 = b + 10 - 2$

$x = b + 8$

Carita's final game score must be $b + 8$.

23. $$\frac{12x^4 + 12x^3 - 9x^2}{12x^3 - 18x^2 - 12x} = \frac{3x^2(4x^2 + 4x - 3)}{6x(2x^2 + 3x - 2)}$$

$$= \frac{x(2x + 3)(2x - 1)}{2(x + 2)(2x - 1)}$$

$$= \frac{x(2x + 3)}{2(x + 2)}$$

**24.** $y$ = distance Mrs. Sumner lives from Fullerton

|  | $r$ | $t$ | $d$ |
|---|---|---|---|
| To Fullerton | 40 | $x$ | $y = 40x$ |
| Return trip | 56 | $x - 2$ | $y = 56(x - 2)$ |

$$y = 40x \qquad \Rightarrow \qquad y = 40x$$
$$y = 56(x - 2) \Rightarrow \quad (-)y = 56x - 112$$
$$\overline{\quad\quad 0 = -16x + 112}$$
$$16x = 112$$
$$x = 7$$

$$y = 40x$$
$$= 40(7)$$
$$= 280$$

Mrs. Sumner lives 280 miles from Fullerton.

**25.** $d = \sqrt{(y_2 - y_1)^2 + (x_2 - x_1)^2}$

$\quad = \sqrt{(-3 - 8)^2 + (2 - 10)^2}$

$\quad = \sqrt{(-11)^2 + (-8)^2}$

$\quad = \sqrt{121 + 64}$

$\quad = \sqrt{185}$

$\quad \approx 13.6$

**26.** $\frac{1}{2}t^2 - 2t - \frac{3}{2} = 0$

$\quad t^2 - 4t - 3 = 0$

$\quad\quad t^2 - 4t = 3$

$\quad t^2 - 46 + 4 = 3 + 4$

$\quad\quad (t - 2)^2 = 7$

$\quad\quad \sqrt{(t - 2)^2} = \sqrt{7}$

$\quad\quad |t - 2| = \sqrt{7}$

$\quad\quad t - 2 = \pm\sqrt{7}$

$\quad\quad t = 2 \pm \sqrt{7}$

**27.**

1 @ 64      2 @ 65      2 @ 66

1 @ 67      3 @ 68

The most common height was 63 inches.

---

## 14-3    Measures of Central Tendency

**PAGE 572**    CHECKING FOR UNDERSTANDING

**1.** Measures of central tendency represent *middle* values of a set of data.

**2.** The *median* is the middle number.

**3.** Extremely high or low values affect the *mean* of a set of data.

---

**4.** The set has no *mode* if all numbers occur the same number of times.

**5.** Mean: $\frac{4 + 6 + 12 + 5 + 8}{5} = \frac{35}{5} = 7$

Median: 4, 5, 6, 8, 12 $\Rightarrow$ 6 since it is in the middle

Mode: There is no mode since all the data occur once.

**6.** Mean: $\frac{9 + 9 + 9 + 9 + 8}{5} = \frac{44}{5} = 8.8$

Median: 8, 9, 9, 9, 9 $\Rightarrow$ 9 since it is in the middle

Mode: 9 since it occurs most often

**7.** Mean: $\frac{7 + 19 + 9 + 4 + 7 + 2}{6} = \frac{48}{6} = 8$

Median: 2, 4, 7, 7, 9, 19 $\Rightarrow \frac{7 + 7}{2} = \frac{14}{2} = 7$ since it is the value halfway between the two middle elements

Mode: 7 since it occurs most often

**8.** Mean: $\frac{300 + 34 + 40 + 50 + 60}{5} = \frac{484}{5} = 96.8$

Median: 34, 40, 50, 60, 300 $\Rightarrow$ 50 since it is in the middle

Mode: There is no mode since all the data occur once.

**9.** Mean: $\frac{23 + 23 + 23 + 12 + 12 + 12 + 17.5}{7} = \frac{122.5}{7}$

$\quad\quad = 17.5$

Median: 12, 12, 12, 17.5, 23, 23, 23 $\Rightarrow$ 17.5 since it is in the middle.

Mode: 12 and 23 since they both occur three times each

**10.** Mean: $\frac{10 + 3 + 17 + 1 + 8 + 6 + 12 + 15}{8} = \frac{72}{8} = 9$

Median: 1, 3, 6, 8, 10, 12, 15, 17 $\Rightarrow$ $\frac{8 + 10}{2} = \frac{18}{2} = 9$ since it is the value halfway between the two middle elements

Mode: There is no mode since each of the data occur once.

---

**PAGES 573-574**     EXERCISES

**11.** Median: 4            **12.** Median: 46

Mode: 2               Mode: 35 and 63

**13.** Median: 94          **14.** Median: 77

Mode: 82             Mode: 77 and 88

**15.** Median: 218

Mode: 219

**16.** Answers may vary. Sample answer: 20, 20, 30, 50, 80, and 100

**17.** Answers may vary. Sample answer: 5, 65, 65, 85, 100, 100

18. $y$ = largest number

$x$ = average of other numbers

$\dfrac{9x}{9} = 4$ $\qquad$ $\dfrac{9x + y}{10} = 5$

$x = 4$ $\qquad\qquad$ $9x + y = 50$

$\qquad\qquad\qquad\quad$ $9(4) + y = 50$

$\qquad\qquad\qquad\quad$ $36 + y = 50$

$\qquad\qquad\qquad\quad$ $y = 14$

19. $\dfrac{137.6(5) + 155}{6} = \dfrac{843}{6} = 140.5$ yards

20. Mean: $\dfrac{499 + 895 + 679 + 1195 + 1400}{5}$

$= \dfrac{4668}{5} = \$933.60$

Median: 499, 679, 895, 1195, 1400 ⇒ $895 since

it is the value in the middle

21. Mean: $\dfrac{12 + 4 + 5 + 3 + 11 + 23 + 4 + 6 + 7 + 8}{10}$

$= \dfrac{83}{10} = 8.3$ points

Median: 3, 4, 4, 5, 6, 7, 8, 11, 12, 23 ⇒

$\dfrac{6 + 7}{2} = \dfrac{13}{2} = 6.5$ points

Mode: 4 since it occurs twice and all other

data occur only once.

22. Mean:

$\dfrac{20 + 21 + 18 + 21 + 22 + 22 + 24 + 21 + 20 + 19 + 23}{11}$

$= \dfrac{231}{11} = 21$

Median: 18, 19, 20, 20, 21, 21, 21, 22, 22,23, 24

⇒ 21 since it is the value in the middle

Mode: 21 since it occurs three times and all

other data occur less than three times

23. Mean: $43.4 + 43.4 + 43.1 + 43.2 + 40.2 + 40.2 +$
$40.1 + 40.3 + 39.44 + 39.17 + 38.03 +$
$\dfrac{38.19 + 36.45 + 37.14}{14}$

$= \dfrac{562.32}{14} = 40.17$

Median: 36.45, 37.14, 38.03, 38.19, 39.17,

39.44, 40.1, 40.2, 40.2, 40.3, 43.1,

43.2, 43.4, 43.4 ⇒ $\dfrac{40.1 + 40.2}{2}$

= 40.15 since it is the value between

the two middle numbers

Mode: 40.2 and 43.4 since they occur two times

and all other data occur once

24. Mean: $31700 + 1697 + 242 + 700 + 22,300 + 451 +$
$374 + 432 + 23,000 + 207 + 1000 + 1361 +$
$315 + 625 + 9,910 + 215 + 458 + 360 +$
$\dfrac{7550 + 435}{20}$

$= \dfrac{103,332}{20} = 5166.6$ square miles

Median: 207, 215, 242, 315, 360, 374, 432, 435,

451, 458, 625, 700, 1000, 1361, 1697,

7550, 9910, 22300, 23000, 31700 ⇒

$\dfrac{458 + 625}{2} = \dfrac{1003}{2} = 541.5$ square miles

Mode: There is no mode since all numbers occur

only once.

25. Mean: $0 + 10 + 8 + 5 + 8 + 9 + 3 + 3 + 2 + 9 + 7$
$0 + 4 + 2 + 4 + 6 + 2 + 9 + 13 + 3 + 1 + 5$
$+ 5 + 7 + 2 + 6 + 5 + 3 + 4 + 7 + 1 + 1 +$
$\dfrac{5 + 3 + 3 + 1 + 4 + 5 + 1 + 2}{40}$

$= \dfrac{178}{40} = 4.45$

Median: 0, 0, 1, 1, 1, 1, 1, 2, 2, 2, 2, 2, 3, 3,

3, 3, 3, 3, 4, 4, 4, 4, 5, 5, 5, 5, 5, 5,

6, 6, 7, 7, 7, 8, 8, 9, 9, 9, 10, 13 ⇒ 4

since it is the value in the middle

Mode: 3 and 5 since they both occur six times

26. The scores of 7.3 and 9.0 are eliminated since

they are the highest and lowest scores. The

mean of the remaining five scores is

$\dfrac{7.7 + 8.2 + 8.2 + 8.3 + 8.6}{5} = \dfrac{41}{5} = 8.2$.

Then $8.2 \times 3.3 = 27.06$, which is her score.

27. Mean: $(16 \cdot 4.75) + (4 \cdot 5.50) + (3 \cdot 6.85) +$
$\dfrac{(6 \cdot 4.85) + (13 \cdot 5.25)}{42}$

$= \dfrac{215.9}{42} = \$5.14$

Median: The middle value occurs as the average

of the 21st and 22nd values when all 42

wages are listed from smallest to

largest. There are sixteen workers who

earn $4.75 and six workers who earn

$4.85 for a total of twenty-two workers.

Therefore the median is $4.85 since it

occurs in the middle.

Mode: $4.75 since most workers make that much

money per hour.

28. Mean: $38500 + 34000 + 27500 + 38500 + 63500 +$
$125000 + 31500 + 30000 + 38500 + 31500 +$
$\dfrac{92500 + 31000}{12}$

$= \dfrac{582000}{12} = \$48,500$

Median: 27500, 30000, 31000, 31500, 31500,

34000, 38500, 38500, 38500, 63500,

92500, 125000 ⇒

$\dfrac{34000 + 38500}{2} = \dfrac{72500}{2} = \$36,250$

Mode: $38,500 since three people make that

money

a. As the personnel director, you should quote

the mean to a job applicant since it is

higher.

b. The employees should quote the median if they

want a pay raise since it is the lowest

measure and half of the employees make less

than this amount.

**29.**
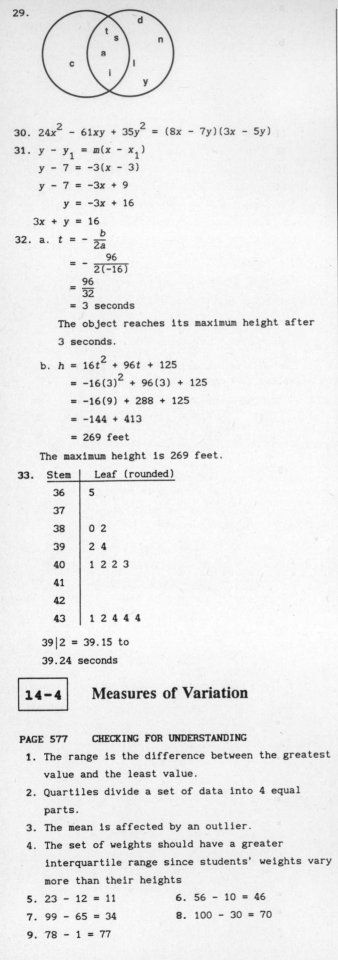

**30.** $24x^2 - 61xy + 35y^2 = (8x - 7y)(3x - 5y)$

**31.** $y - y_1 = m(x - x_1)$

$y - 7 = -3(x - 3)$

$y - 7 = -3x + 9$

$y = -3x + 16$

$3x + y = 16$

**32.** a. $t = -\dfrac{b}{2a}$

$= -\dfrac{96}{2(-16)}$

$= \dfrac{96}{32}$

$= 3$ seconds

The object reaches its maximum height after 3 seconds.

b. $h = 16t^2 + 96t + 125$

$= -16(3)^2 + 96(3) + 125$

$= -16(9) + 288 + 125$

$= -144 + 413$

$= 269$ feet

The maximum height is 269 feet.

**33.**

| Stem | Leaf (rounded) |
|------|----------------|
| 36 | 5 |
| 37 | |
| 38 | 0 2 |
| 39 | 2 4 |
| 40 | 1 2 2 3 |
| 41 | |
| 42 | |
| 43 | 1 2 4 4 4 |

$39|2 = 39.15$ to

$39.24$ seconds

---

**14-4** **Measures of Variation**

**1.** The range is the difference between the greatest value and the least value.

**2.** Quartiles divide a set of data into 4 equal parts.

**3.** The mean is affected by an outlier.

**4.** The set of weights should have a greater interquartile range since students' weights vary more than their heights

**5.** $23 - 12 = 11$
**6.** $56 - 10 = 46$
**7.** $99 - 65 = 34$
**8.** $100 - 30 = 70$
**9.** $78 - 1 = 77$

**10.** 12, 16, 17, 18, 23

Median: 17

Upper Quartile: $\dfrac{23 + 18}{2} = \dfrac{41}{2} = 20.5$

Lower Quartile: $\dfrac{12 + 16}{2} = \dfrac{28}{2} = 14$

**11.** 10, 34, 37, 43, 45, 56

Median: $\dfrac{43 + 37}{2} = \dfrac{80}{2} = 40$

Upper Quartile: 45

Lower Quartile: 34

**12.** 65, 68, 77, 78, 84, 96, 99

Median: 78

Upper Quartile: 96

Lower Quartile: 68

**13.** 30, 40, 50, 60, 70, 80, 90, 100

Median: $\dfrac{60 + 70}{2} = \dfrac{130}{2} = 65$

Upper Quartile: $\dfrac{80 + 90}{2} = \dfrac{170}{2} = 85$

Lower Quartile: $\dfrac{40 + 50}{2} = \dfrac{90}{2} = 45$

**14.** 1, 3, 3.2, 3.4, 4, 5, 5, 5.3, 6, 7, 8, 21, 26, 45, 78

Median: 5.3

Upper Quartile: 21

Lower Quartile: 3.4

**15.** 55, 58, 59, 62, 67, 69, 69, 73, 75, 76, 77, 77, 82, 85, 92

Range: $92 - 55 = 37$

Median: 73

Upper Quartile: 77

Lower Quartile: 62

Interquartile Range: $77 - 62 = 15$

**16.** 835, 975, 1005, 1025, 1050, 1055, 1075, 1075, 1095, 1100, 1125, 1125, 1145, 1175

Range: $1175 - 835 = 340$

Median: $\dfrac{1075 + 1075}{2} = \dfrac{2150}{2} = 1075$

Upper Quartile: 1125

Lower Quartile: 1025

Interquartile Range: $1125 - 1025 = 100$

**17.** 180, 197, 199, 200, 204, 205, 206, 206, 207, 208, 208, 210, 211, 211, 212, 212, 213, 220, 225, 229

Range: $229 - 180 = 49$

Median: $\dfrac{208 + 208}{2} = \dfrac{416}{2} = 208$

Upper Quartile: $\dfrac{212 + 212}{2} = \dfrac{424}{2} = 212$

Lower Quartile: $\dfrac{204 + 205}{2} = \dfrac{409}{2} = 204.5$

Interquartile Range: $212 - 204.5 = 7.5$

18. Range: 48 - 0 = 48

Median: 26

Upper Quartile: 39

Lower Quartile: 17

Interquartile Range: 39 - 17 = 22

19. Range: 11.9 - 7.3 = 4.6

Median: 8.7

Upper Quartile: $\frac{10.0 + 10.1}{2} = \frac{20.1}{2} = 10.05$

Lower Quartile: $\frac{7.8 + 8.0}{2} = \frac{15.8}{2} = 7.9$

Interquartile Range; 10.05 - 7.9 = 2.15

20. Range: 2990 - 2500 = 490

Median: $\frac{2750 + 2760}{2} = \frac{5510}{2} = 2755$

Upper Quartile: $\frac{2830 + 2850}{2} = \frac{5680}{2} = 2840$

Lower Quartile: $\frac{2630 + 2640}{2} = \frac{5270}{2} = 2635$

Interquartile Range: 2840 - 2635 = 205

21. Answers may vary. Sample answer:

20, 20, 45, 40, 43, 50, 55, 56, 60, 79, 80

$20 - (1.5)(15) = 70 - 22.5$

$\qquad\qquad\qquad = -2.5$

$80 + (1.5)(15) = 80 + 22.5$

$\qquad\qquad\qquad = 102.5$

No, this set does not have an outlier.

22. Art: 54, 65, 66, 68, 73, 75, 75, 78, 82, 82, 87, 97

Gina: 57, 65, 69, 70, 71, 73, 74, 76, 77, 80, 91, 100

a. Art; Range 97 - 54 = 43

Interquartile Range: $\frac{66 + 68}{2} = \frac{134}{2} = 67$

$\qquad\qquad\qquad\quad \frac{82 + 82}{2} = \frac{164}{2} = 82$

$\qquad\qquad\qquad\quad 82 - 67 = 15$

Gina: Range : 100 - 57 = 43

Interquartile Range: $\frac{69 + 70}{2} = \frac{139}{2} = 69.5$

$\qquad\qquad\qquad\quad \frac{77 + 80}{2} = \frac{157}{2} = 78.5$

$\qquad\qquad\qquad\quad 78.5 - 69.5 = 9.0$

b. $82 + (1.5)(15) = 82 + 22.5$

$\qquad\qquad\qquad = 104.5$

$67 - (1.5)(15) = 67 - 22.5$

$\qquad\qquad\qquad = 44.5$

Art had no outliers.

$78.5 + (1.5)(9) = 78.5 + 13.5$

$\qquad\qquad\qquad = 92.0$

$69.5 - (1.5)(9) = 69.5 - 13.5$

$\qquad\qquad\qquad = 56.0$

Gina's score of 100 is an outlier.

c. Gina had more consistent scores since she had the smaller interquartile range.

23. a. Range: $0.32 - 0.06 = $0.26

Interquartile Range: $0.18 - 0.09 = $0.09

b. $0.18 + (1.5)(0.09) = 0.18 + 0.135$

$\qquad\qquad\qquad\qquad = 0.315$

$0.09 - (1.5)(0.09) = 0.09 - 0.135$

$\qquad\qquad\qquad\qquad = -0.045$

$0.32 is an outlier

24. (In millions of dollars)

86.3, 86.8, 89.0, 94.4, 96.3, 98.2, 105.5,

108.0, 109.0, 112.0, 115.5, 115.6, 129.5, 132.7,

140.6, 141.6, 150.5, 168.0, 193.5, 228.6

a. Range: $228.6 - 86.3 = $142.3 million

Lower Quartile:

$\frac{96.3 + 98.2}{2} = \frac{194.5}{2} = $97.25 million

Median:

$\frac{112.0 + 115.5}{2} + \frac{227.5}{2} = $113.75 million

Upper Quartile:

$\frac{140.6 + 141.6}{2} = \frac{282.2}{2} = $141.1 million

Interquartile Range:

$141.1 - 97.25 = $43.85 million

b. $141.1 + (1.5)(43.85) = $141.1 + 65.775

$\qquad\qquad\qquad\qquad = $206.875 million

$97.25 - (1.5)(43.85) = $97.25 - 65.775

$\qquad\qquad\qquad\qquad = $31.475 million

E.T. at $228.6 million is an outlier.

25. $-5 < 4 - 3x < 13$

$\quad -5 < 4 - 3x \qquad\qquad 4 - 3x < 13$

$-5 - 4 < 4 - 3x - 4 \quad 4 - 4 - 3x < 13 - 4$

$\quad -9 < -3x \qquad\qquad\qquad -3x < 9$

$\qquad 3 > x \qquad\qquad\qquad\qquad x > -3$

$\qquad\qquad\qquad -3 < x < 3$

26. {(3, -3), (-2, 2), (1, -1), (0, 0), (1, 1)}

27. $r = \frac{1}{2} \sqrt{\frac{s}{\pi}}$

$= \frac{1}{2} \sqrt{\frac{400 \text{ in.}^2}{\frac{22}{7}}}$

$= \frac{1}{2} \sqrt{(440 \text{ in.}^2)\left(\frac{7}{20}\right)}$

$= \frac{1}{2} \sqrt{(20 \text{ in.}^2)(7)}$

$= \frac{1}{2} \sqrt{140 \text{ in.}^2}$

$= \frac{1}{2} \sqrt{(4 \cdot 35) \text{ in.}^2}$

$= \frac{1}{2} \cdot 2 \sqrt{35} \text{ in.}^2$

$= \sqrt{35}$ in.

$\approx 5.92$ in.

**28.** $35x^2 - 11x - 6 = 0$

$$x = \frac{-b \pm \sqrt{b^2 - 4ac}}{2a}$$

$$= \frac{-(-11) \pm \sqrt{(-11)^2 - 4(35)(-6)}}{2(35)}$$

$$= \frac{11 \pm \sqrt{121 + 840}}{70}$$

$$= \frac{11 \pm \sqrt{961}}{70}$$

$$= \frac{11 \pm 31}{70}$$

$$x = \frac{11 + 31}{70} = \frac{40}{70} = \frac{3}{5} \qquad x = \frac{11 - 31}{70} = \frac{-20}{70} = -\frac{2}{7}$$

The solution are $\frac{3}{5}$ and $-\frac{2}{7}$.

**29.** Mean: $\dfrac{299 + 369 + 525 + 359 + 228 + 398}{6}$

$$= \frac{2178}{6} = \$363$$

Median: $228, 299, 359, 369, 398, 525 \Rightarrow$

$$\frac{359 + 369}{2} = \frac{728}{2} = \$364$$

---

## 14-5   Box-and-Whisker Plots

1. The scale must be large enough to include the greatest and least values.

2. One whisker connects the least value with the lower quartile value and the other whisker connects the greatest value with the upper quartile value.

3. 50% of the data is included in the box.

4. Answers may vary. Sample answers: quartile values, interquartile range, and outliers

5. 25% since this is a whisker

6. 95 is the median.      7. 85 is the least value.

8. between 90 and 120

9. 90 is the upper quartile.

10. 90 is the greatest number.

11. 75% of the data is between 50 and 90.

12. The upper quartile and the greatest value are the same.

13. $x$ has the lesser median of 40.

14. $y$ has the greater range of 50.

15. $y$ has the lesser interquartile range of 20.

---

**16.** 81.8, 82.5, 83.1, 83.2, 83.8, 84.9, 86.8, 88.2, 89.3, 90.8, 93.5, 95.0

Median: $\dfrac{84.9 + 86.8}{2} = \dfrac{171.7}{2} = 85.85$

UQ: $\dfrac{89.3 + 90.8}{2} = \dfrac{180.1}{2} = 90.05$

LQ: $\dfrac{83.1 + 83.2}{2} = \dfrac{166.3}{2} = 83.15$

Outliers: $90.05 - 83.15 = 6.90$

$90.05 + (1.5)(6.9) = 90.05 + 10.35$
$= 100.4$

$83.15 - (1.5)(6.9) = 83.15 - 10.35$
$= 72.8$

There are no outliers.

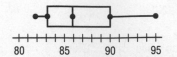

**17.** $0°, 2°, 4°, 5°, 5°, 5°, 6°, 7°, 12°, 16°, 16°, 17°, 20°, 30°$

Median: $\dfrac{7 + 6}{2} = \dfrac{13}{2} = 6.5°$

UQ: $16°$

LQ: $5°$

Outliers: $16° - 5° = 11°$

$16 + (1.5)(11) = 16 + 16.5$
$= 32.5$

$5 - (1.5)(11) = 5 - 16.5$
$= -11.5$

The are no outliers.

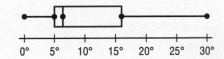

**18.** 31.2, 31.7, 32.3, 32.5, 32.9, 33.1, 33.5, 33.6, 34.0, 34.5, 34.7, 34.8, 35.0, 35.6, 36.5, 37.1, 37.9, 38.4, 44.8, 50.4

Median: $\dfrac{34.5 + 34.7}{2} = \dfrac{69.2}{2} = 34.6$

UQ: $\dfrac{36.5 + 37.1}{2} = \dfrac{73.6}{2} = 36.8$

LQ: $\dfrac{32.9 + 33.1}{2} = \dfrac{66.0}{2} = 33.0$

Outliers: $36.8 - 33.0 = 3.8$

$36.8 + (1.5)(3.8) = 36.8 + 5.7$
$= 42.5$

$33 - (1.5)(3.8) = 33 - 5.7$
$= 27.3$

There are two outliers; 44.8 and 50.4.

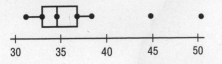

**19.** Median: $\dfrac{24 + 27}{2} = \dfrac{53}{2} = 26.5$

UQ: $\dfrac{32 + 33}{2} = \dfrac{65}{2} = 32.5$

LQ: $\dfrac{24 + 24}{2} = \dfrac{48}{2} = 24$

Outliers: $32.5 - 24 = 8.5$

$34 + (1.5)(8.5) = 34 + 12.75$
$= 46.75$

$24 - (1.5)(8.5) = 24 - 12.75$
$= 11.25$

There are no outliers.

**20.** A: 290, 300, 360, 370, 395, 450, 497, 500, 520, 740

B: 350, 375, 400, 405, 410, 450, 460, 485, 495, 520

Median: A: $\dfrac{395 + 450}{2} = \dfrac{845}{2} = 422.5$

B: $\dfrac{410 + 450}{2} = \dfrac{860}{2} = 430$

UQ: A: 500

B: 485

LQ: A: 360

B: 400

Outliers: A: $500 - 360 = 140$

$500 + (1.5)(140) = 500 + 210$
$= 710$

$360 - (1.5)(140) = 360 - 210$
$= 150$

A has an outlier of 740.

B: $485 - 400 = 85$

$485 + (1.5)(85) = 485 + 127.5$
$= 612.5$

$400 - (1.5)(85) = 400 - 127.5$
$= 272.5$

B has no outliers.

a.

b. Buy from Manufacturer B because of the more consistent performance of its light bulbs.

**21.** Median: Men: 66.8
Women: 73.7

UQ: Men: 70.0
Women: 77.5

LQ Men: 60.8
Women: 65.2

Outliers:

Men: $70 - 60.8 = 9.2$

$70 + (1.5)(9.2) = 70 + 13.8$
$= 83.8$

$60.8 - (1.5)(9.2) = 60.8 - 13.8$
$= 47.0$

There are no outliers for the men's ages.

Women: $77.5 - 65.2 = 12.3$

$77.5 + (1.5)(12.3) = 77.5 + 18.45$
$= 95.95$

$65.2 - (1.5)(12.3) = 65.2 - 18.45$
$= 46.75$

The life expectancy of a woman is consistently greater than that of a man.

**22.** Answers may vary. Sample answer:
10, 10, 10, 20, 25, 25, 30, 40, 40, 40

**23.**
$$29 - 3a = 2(3a - 4) + 3$$
$$29 - 3a = 6a - 8 + 3$$
$$29 - 3a = 6a - 5$$
$$29 - 3a + 3a = 6a - 5 + 3a$$
$$5 + 29 = 9a - 5 + 5$$
$$34 = 9a$$
$$\dfrac{34}{9} = \dfrac{9a}{9}$$
$$\dfrac{34}{9} = a$$

**24.** $2x - y = 6$
$-y = 6 - 2x$
$y = 2x - 6$

**25.** $x + y = 4 \qquad 3x - 5y = 60 \qquad y = 4 - x$
$\quad\quad y = 4 - x \quad 3x - 5(4 - x) = 60 \quad\quad = 4 - 10$
$\quad\quad\quad\quad\quad\quad 3x - 20 + 5x = 60 \quad\quad = -6$
$\quad\quad\quad\quad\quad\quad\quad\quad 8x - 20 = 60$
$\quad\quad\quad\quad\quad\quad\quad\quad\quad\quad 8x = 80$
$\quad\quad\quad\quad\quad\quad\quad\quad\quad\quad\quad x = 10$

The solution is $(10, -6)$.

**26.** $\dfrac{1}{7 - \sqrt{3}} \cdot \dfrac{7 + \sqrt{3}}{7 + \sqrt{3}} = \dfrac{7 + \sqrt{3}}{(7 - \sqrt{3})(7 + \sqrt{3})}$

$\qquad\qquad\qquad = \dfrac{7 + \sqrt{3}}{49 - 3}$

$\qquad\qquad\qquad = \dfrac{7 + \sqrt{3}}{46}$

**27.** $3n^2 = n - 5 = 0$

$\qquad b^2 - 4ac = (-1)^2 - 4(3)(-5)$

$\qquad\qquad\qquad = 1 - (-60)$

$\qquad\qquad\qquad = 1 + 60$

$\qquad\qquad\qquad = 61$

Since $b^2 - 4ac > 0$, there are two real distinct roots.

**28.** 31.2, 31.7, 32.3, 32.5, 32.9, 33.1, 33.5, 33.6, 34.0, 34.5, 34.7, 34.8, 35.0, 35.6, 36.5, 37.1, 37.9, 38.4, 44.8, 50.4

Range: $50.4 - 31.2 = 19.2$

UQ: $\dfrac{36.5 + 37.1}{2} = \dfrac{73.6}{2} = 36.8$

Median: $\dfrac{34.5 + 34.7}{2} = \dfrac{69.2}{2} = 34.6$

LQ: $\dfrac{32.9 + 33.1}{2} = \dfrac{66.0}{2} = 33.0$

Outliers: $36.8 - 33.0 = 3.8$

$\qquad 36.8 + (1.5)(3.8) = 36.8 + 5.7$

$\qquad\qquad\qquad\qquad = 42.5$

$\qquad 33 - (1.5)(3.8) = 33 - 5.7$

$\qquad\qquad\qquad\qquad = 27.3$

44.8 and 50.4 are outliers.

---

## 14-6   Scatter Plots

1. Mark the horizontal axis of the graph to represent one of the sets of data and mark the vertical axis to represent the other set of data. Then plot corresponding elements in the set as ordered pairs.

2. If the distribution of points resembles a line, then there may be an association between the two sets of data plotted.

3. False, the two sets of data may show no association.

4. This would indicate that Mike's quiz scores were improving with time.

5. positive association    6. positive association

7. negative or positive association

8. negative association    9. no association

10. positive association

11. positive association

12. There is an association but you cannot tell.

13. no association

14. Answers may vary. See student's work.

15. a.

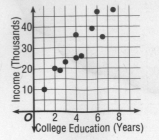

b. From the data, the greater the number of years of college, the greater the income.

16. a.

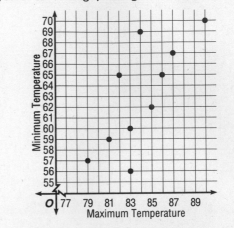

b. Norfolk, VA has the highest maximum and minimum temperatures.

c. Portland, ME has the lowest maximuim and minimum temperatures.

d. Yes, there is a cluster due to the geographical location of the cities.

17. a.

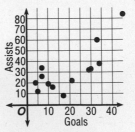

b. The scatter plot shows a positive association.

c. Yes, you could estimate the number of assists by using the points in the scatter plot.

d. Yes, some players have more opportunity to score points because of the position they play for the team.

e. Yes, since more playing time provides a player with more opportunities to score points.

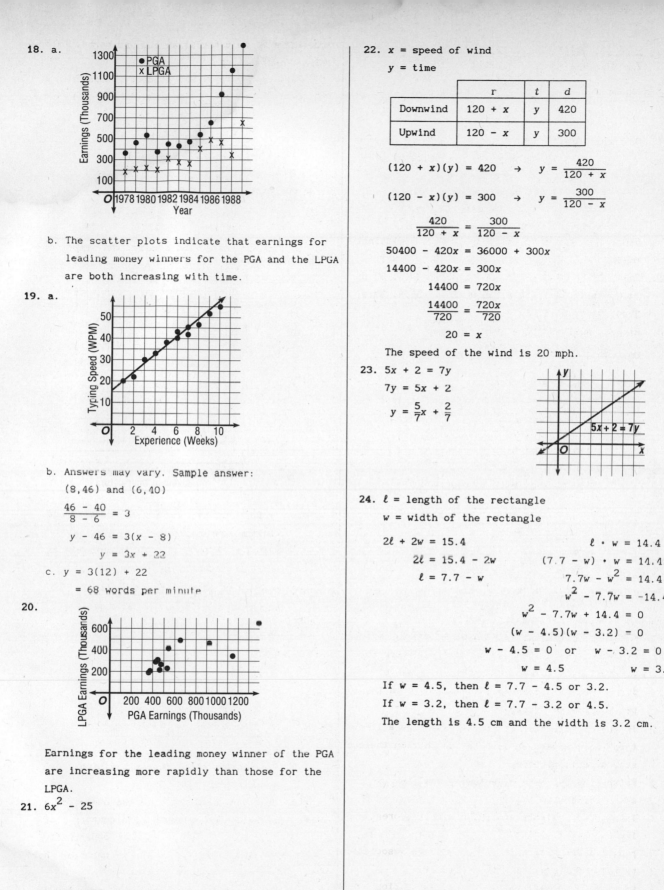

**18. a.**

**b.** The scatter plots indicate that earnings for leading money winners for the PGA and the LPGA are both increasing with time.

**19. a.**

**b.** Answers may vary. Sample answer:

(8, 46) and (6, 40)

$$\frac{46 - 40}{8 - 6} = 3$$

$$y - 46 = 3(x - 8)$$

$$y = 3x + 22$$

**c.** $y = 3(12) + 22$

$= 68$ words per minute

**20.**

Earnings for the leading money winner of the PGA are increasing more rapidly than those for the LPGA.

**21.** $6x^2 - 25$

**22.** $x$ = speed of wind

$y$ = time

|  | $r$ | $t$ | $d$ |
|---|---|---|---|
| Downwind | $120 + x$ | $y$ | 420 |
| Upwind | $120 - x$ | $y$ | 300 |

$$(120 + x)(y) = 420 \quad \rightarrow \quad y = \frac{420}{120 + x}$$

$$(120 - x)(y) = 300 \quad \rightarrow \quad y = \frac{300}{120 - x}$$

$$\frac{420}{120 + x} = \frac{300}{120 - x}$$

$$50400 - 420x = 36000 + 300x$$

$$14400 - 420x = 300x$$

$$14400 = 720x$$

$$\frac{14400}{720} = \frac{720x}{720}$$

$$20 = x$$

The speed of the wind is 20 mph.

**23.** $5x + 2 = 7y$

$7y = 5x + 2$

$y = \frac{5}{7}x + \frac{2}{7}$

**24.** $\ell$ = length of the rectangle

$w$ = width of the rectangle

$2\ell + 2w = 15.4$         $\ell \cdot w = 14.4$

$\quad 2\ell = 15.4 - 2w$     $(7.7 - w) \cdot w = 14.4$

$\quad \ell = 7.7 - w$        $7.7w - w^2 = 14.4$

$\qquad\qquad\qquad\qquad w^2 - 7.7w = -14.4$

$\qquad\qquad\qquad w^2 - 7.7w + 14.4 = 0$

$\qquad\qquad\qquad (w - 4.5)(w - 3.2) = 0$

$\qquad\qquad w - 4.5 = 0 \quad$ or $\quad w - 3.2 = 0$

$\qquad\qquad\qquad w = 4.5 \qquad\qquad w = 3.2$

If $w = 4.5$, then $\ell = 7.7 - 4.5$ or 3.2.

If $w = 3.2$, then $\ell = 7.7 - 3.2$ or 4.5.

The length is 4.5 cm and the width is 3.2 cm.

**25.** 362, 376, 427, 446, 463, 476, 531, 542, 653, 926, 1148, 1395

Median: $\dfrac{476 + 531}{2} = \dfrac{1007}{2} = 503.5$

UQ: $\dfrac{653 + 926}{2} = \dfrac{1579}{2} = 789.5$

LQ: $\dfrac{427 + 446}{2} = \dfrac{873}{2} = 436.5$

Outliers: $789.5 - 436.5 = 353$

$789.5 + (1.5)(353) = 789.5 + 529.5$
$= 1319$

$436.5 - (1.5)(353) = 436.5 - 529.5$
$= -93$

1395 is an outlier.

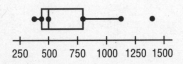

## PAGE 587   MID-CHAPTER REVIEW

**1.** The greatest seasonal precipitation is 18.6 inches in the summer in New Orleans. The least seasonal precipitation is 0.3 inches in the summer in San Francisco.

**2.**

```
        X X  X  X     X  X  X     X
   <+++++++++++++++++++++++++++++++++>
    0        5       10       15
```

**3.**

| Stem | Leaf |
|------|------|
| 1 | 8 |
| 2 | 6 |
| 3 |  |
| 4 | 8 |
| 5 |  |
| 6 | 5 |
| 7 | 1 |
| 8 |  |
| 9 |  |
| 10 | 8 |
| 11 |  |
| 12 | 1  5 |

7|1 represents precipitation of 7.1 inches.

**4.** Mean: $\dfrac{1.4 + 10.1 + 11.0 + 5.9 + 12.9 + 10.2 + 14.2 + 1.9}{8}$

$= \dfrac{67.6}{8} = 8.45$ in.

Median: 1.4, 1.9, 5.9, 10.1, 10.2, 11.0, 12.9, 14.2
$\dfrac{10.1 + 10.2}{2} = \dfrac{20.3}{2} = 10.15$ in.

Mode: There is no mode since all cities have different precipitation measurements for spring.

**5.** 0.3, 3.7, 4.6, 9.8, 10.0, 10.5, 11.9, 18.6
Range: 18.6 − 0.3 = 18.3 in.

UQ: $\dfrac{3.7 + 4.6}{2} = \dfrac{8.3}{2} = 4.15$ in.

Median: $\dfrac{9.8 + 10.0}{2} = \dfrac{19.8}{2} = 9.9$ in.

UQ: $\dfrac{10.5 + 11.9}{2} = \dfrac{22.4}{2} = 11.2$ in.

Interquartile Range: 11.2 − 4.15 = 7.05 in.
Outliers: 11.2 (1.5)(7.05) = 11.2 + 10.575
$= 21.775$

$4.15 - (1.5)(7.05) = 4.15 - 10.575$
$= -6.425$

There are no outliers.

**6.** 8.2, 15.5, 19.8, 29.1, 33.5, 44.2, 44.8, 59.8
Median: $\dfrac{29.1 + 33.5}{2} = \dfrac{62.6}{2} = 31.3$ in.

UQ: $\dfrac{44.2 + 44.8}{2} = \dfrac{89.0}{2} = 44.5$ in.

LQ: $\dfrac{15.5 + 19.8}{2} = \dfrac{35.3}{2} = 17.65$ in.

Outliers: 44.5 − 17.65 = 26.85
$44.5 + (1.5)(26.85) = 44.5 + 40.275$
$= 84.775$

$17.65 - (1.5)(26.85) = 17.65 - 40.295$
$= -22.625$

There are no outliers.

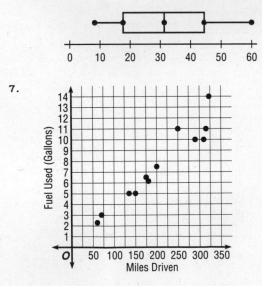

**7.**

# Technology:   Regression Lines

## PAGE 588   EXERCISES

**1.**

284

2.

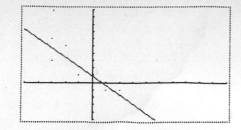

## 14-7    Probability and Odds

1. Answers may vary. Sample answers: rolling a dice, tossing a coin, and choosing a marble at random from a bag.

2. Answers may vary. Sample answer: an impossible event is getting a 7 and a certain event is getting an integer between 1 and 6.

3. Since the odds that the event will occur are (successes):(failures), you need to reverse the successes and failures to find the odds that the event will not occur, or 5:3.

4. They are both correct since the probability is $\frac{7}{2}$ and the odds are 1:1.

5. Answers may vary.      6. Answers may vary.

7. 1          8. $\frac{\text{favorable outcomes}}{\text{possible outcomes}} = \frac{1}{2}$

9. $\frac{\text{favorable outcomes}}{\text{possible outcomes}} = \frac{1}{7}$    10. Answers may vary.

11. Yes, because getting a head or tail is equally likely.

12. No, because each student has different abilities and puts forth different effort.

13. No, because each player has different ability.

14. Yes, because each face of the dice is equally likely to come up.

15. Yes, because each ticket has just as much of a chance to win as another.

16. Yes, because pressing any button is equally likely.

17. $\frac{\text{favorable outcomes}}{\text{possible outcomes}} = \frac{1}{6}$

18. $\frac{\text{favorable outcomes}}{\text{possible outcomes}} = 0$

19. $\frac{\text{favorable outcomes}}{\text{possible outcomes}} = \frac{3}{6} = \frac{1}{2}$

20. $\frac{\text{favorable outcomes}}{\text{possible outcomes}} = \frac{5}{6}$

21. successes:failures = 2:4 = 1:2

22. successes:failures = 3:3 = 1:1

23. successes:failures = 5:1

24. successes:failures = 4:2 = 2:1

25. $\frac{\text{number of black cards}}{\text{total number or cards}} = \frac{26}{52} = \frac{1}{2}$

26. $\frac{\text{number of kings}}{\text{total number of cards}} = \frac{4}{52} = \frac{1}{13}$

27. selecting a club:selecting a heart, spade, or diamond = 13:39 = 1:3

28. not red 7's:red 7's = 50:2 = 25:1

29. $\frac{\text{number of clubs and aces}}{\text{total number of cards}} = \frac{16}{52} = \frac{4}{13}$

30. If the probability is $\frac{2}{3}$, the number of successes is 2 and the number of failures is 3 - 2 or 1. The odds that the event will occur is successes:failures or 2:1.

31. If the probability is $\frac{3}{7}$, the number of successes is 3 and the number of failures is 7 - 3 or 4. The odds that the event will not occur means a failure is a success and a success is a failure. The odds are then 4:3.

32. If the odds are 8:5, then the number of successes is 8 and the number of failures is 5. The total number of outcomes is 8 + 5 or 13. The probability is then $\frac{8}{13}$.

33. If the odds that an event does not occur is 9.14, the number of successes is 9 and the number of failures is 14. To find the probability that the event does occur, reverse the successes and failures. The successes are then 14 and the total number of outcomes is 9 + 14 or 23. The probability is that the event does occur is then $\frac{14}{23}$.

34. a. $\frac{\text{number of females}}{\text{number of students}} = \frac{535}{1035} = \frac{107}{207}$

   b. $\frac{\text{number of 9th grade males}}{\text{number of students}} = \frac{130}{1035} = \frac{26}{207}$

   c. 10th grade students:9th, 11th, and 12th grade students = 250:785 = 50:157

   d. $\frac{\text{number of 11th grade females}}{\text{number of students}} = \frac{110}{1035} = \frac{22}{207}$

     $\frac{\text{number of 11th grade males}}{\text{number of students}} = \frac{100}{1035} = \frac{20}{207}$

   Since the probability that an 11th grade female is selected is greater than the probability that an 11th grade male is selected, it is more likely that the student selected is female.

35. $2x + 3 < 17$
$$2x < 14$$
$$x < 7$$
$\frac{\text{numbers} < 7}{\text{total numbers}} = \frac{7}{10} = 0.7$

36. Since 2, 3, 5, and 7 are the prime numbers from 0 through 9, any three-digit number with a combination of those four numbers is a success. All others are failures. There is a total of 900 three-digit numbers. The number of successes is 64, so the number of failures is 900 − 64 or 832. Therefore the odds are 64:832 or 16:209.

37. $\dfrac{\text{number of moves to the red square}}{\text{number of possible moves to another square}}$
   $= \dfrac{2}{8} = \dfrac{1}{4}$

38. We are looking for the probability that it will rain and that the tent does not arrive. There are 4 possible outcomes: it rains and the tent arrives, it rains and the tent does not arrive, it does not rain and the tent arrives, or it does not rain and the tent does not arrive. The probability is then $\dfrac{1}{4}$ of 0.25.

39. 4% of the 100 clocks is 4 clocks. A success is buying a damaged clock and a failure is not buying a damaged clock. There are 4 successes and 100 − 4 or 96 failures. The odds are 4:96 or 1:24.

40. Since the odds of 1:5 represent successes:failures, there are a total of 1 + 5 or 6 outcomes. Since they plan to sell 180 tickets, they will need $\dfrac{180}{6}$ or 30 prizes.

41. $x \cdot 4 = 340$
    $4x = 340$
    $x = 85$
   Dolores earns \$85/day of $\dfrac{935}{85}$ = 11 days.

42. $|x - 1| < y$

   $x - 1 < y \qquad x - 1 > -y$
   $\quad y > x - 1 \qquad -y < x - 1$
   $\qquad\qquad\qquad y > -x + 1$

43.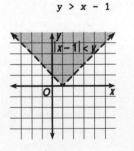

   $a^2 + b^2 = c^2$
   $(70)^2 + b^2 = (250)^2$
   $4900 + b^2 = 62500$
   $b^2 = 57600$
   $b = \sqrt{57600}$
   $b = 240 \text{ ft}$

44. From the graph, there are no real roots.

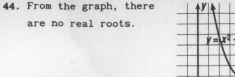

45. a.

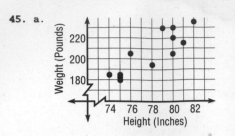

   b. The taller the player, the greater the weight.

**Empirical Probability**

PAGES 595–596   CHECKING FOR UNDERSTANDING

1. Empirical probability is probability calculated by making observations or performing experiments.

2. No, because the empirical probability is only an approximation of the probability that is expected.

3. No, it is possible to get a 6 each time in ten rolls of a fair die. More trials are needed to determine whether or not this die is fair.

4. a. Student   1: P(heads) = $\dfrac{21}{30} = \dfrac{7}{10}$ or 0.7

   2: P(heads) = $\dfrac{22}{30} = \dfrac{11}{15}$ or $0.7\overline{3}$

   3: P(heads) = $\dfrac{18}{30} = \dfrac{3}{5}$ or 0.6

   4: P(heads) = $\dfrac{20}{30} = \dfrac{2}{3}$ or $0.6\overline{7}$

   5: P(heads) = $\dfrac{21}{30} = \dfrac{7}{10}$ or 0.7

   6: P(heads) = $\dfrac{21}{30} = \dfrac{7}{10}$ or 0.7

   7: P(heads) = $\dfrac{19}{30}$ or $0.6\overline{3}$

   8: P(heads) = $\dfrac{22}{30} = \dfrac{11}{15}$ or $0.7\overline{3}$

   9: P(heads) = $\dfrac{18}{30} = \dfrac{3}{5}$ or 0.6

   10: P(heads) = $\dfrac{19}{30}$ or $0.6\overline{3}$

   b. No, the coin does not appear to be fair.

   c. Answers will vary. Sample answer: Using the mean, an estimate is 20.1.

   d. To get a better estimate, do more trials.

5. Answers may vary. Sample answers are given.

a.

| Sums of Faces | | Times Occurred |
|---|---|---|
| 2 | || | 2 |
| 3 | 卌 | 5 |
| 4 | 卌 |||| | 9 |
| 5 | 卌 卌 | 10 |
| 6 | 卌 卌 卌 | | 16 |
| 7 | 卌 卌 卌 | | 16 |
| 8 | 卌 卌 ||| | 13 |
| 9 | 卌 卌 |||| | 14 |
| 10 | 卌 || | 7 |
| 11 | 卌 | | 6 |
| 12 | || | 2 |

b. $P(3) = \dfrac{\text{number of 3's rolled}}{\text{total times rolled}} = \dfrac{5}{100} = 0.05$

c. $P(7) = \dfrac{\text{number of 7's rolled}}{\text{total times rolled}} = \dfrac{16}{100} = 0.16$

d. P(a sum less than 5)

$= \dfrac{\text{all 2's, 3's, and 4's rolled}}{\text{total times rolled}}$

$= \dfrac{3 + 5 + 9}{100} = \dfrac{17}{100} = 0.17$

e. P(a sum greater than 6)

$= \dfrac{\text{all 7's, 8's, 9's, 10's, 11's, and 12's rolled}}{\text{total times rolled}}$

$= \dfrac{16 + 13 + 14 + 7 + 6 + 2}{100} = \dfrac{58}{100} = 0.58$

f. The sum of 6 and 7 occurred most often. This is what was expected since there are six number combinations that add up to 7 on the dice while the other numbers have five or less number combinations that will result in that number when added together.

g. The sums of 2 and 12 occurred least often. This is what was expected since there is only one number combination that will add to 2 and 12, namely 1 + 1 and 6 + 6.

6. Answers may vary. Sample answers are given.

a. Three pennies were used.

| Combinations | | Times Occurred |
|---|---|---|
| 3 heads | 卌 卌 卌 | | 16 |
| 2 heads, 1 tail | 卌 卌 卌 <br> 卌 卌 卌 <br> |||| | 34 |
| 1 head, 2 tails | 卌 卌 卌 <br> 卌 卌 卌 <br> ||| | 33 |
| 3 tails | 卌 卌 卌 || | 17 |

b. $P(\text{3 heads tossed}) = \dfrac{\text{times 3 heads were tossed}}{\text{total number of tosses}}$

$= \dfrac{16}{100} = \dfrac{4}{25} = 0.16$

c. P(tossing exactly one tail)

$= \dfrac{\text{times 1 tail was tossed}}{\text{total number of tosses}} = \dfrac{34}{100} = \dfrac{17}{50}$

$= 0.34$

d. P(tossing at least 2 tails)

$= \dfrac{\text{times 2 or 3 tails were tossed}}{\text{total number of tosses}}$

$= \dfrac{33 + 17}{100} = \dfrac{50}{100} = \dfrac{1}{2} = 0.50$

e. P(tossing at most 2 heads)

$= \dfrac{\text{times 0, 1, or 2 heads were tossed}}{\text{total number of tosses}}$

$= \dfrac{17 + 33 + 34}{100} = \dfrac{84}{100} = 0.84$

f. The results of 2 heads and 1 tail occur most often. This is what was expected since three out of the eight combinations of tosses (H-H-T, H-T-H, and T-H-H) result in 2 heads and one tail. Also, the results of 1 head and 2 tails being so close behind is expected since three of the eight combinations of tosses (T-T-H, T-H-T, and H-T-T) result in 1 head and 2 tails.

g. The result of three heads being tossed occurred least often. This is what was expected since there is only one combination of tosses (H-H-H) that will result in three heads. The combination of three tails being so close is also expected since there is only one combination of tosses (T-T-T) that will result in three tails.

7. a. P(getting the same card twice in a row)

$= \dfrac{\text{number of ways to get same card two times}}{\text{total combinations of cards}}$

$= \dfrac{42}{42 \cdot 42} = \dfrac{1}{42} \approx 0.02$

b. P(getting the same card three times in a row)

$= \dfrac{\text{number of ways to get same card two times}}{\text{total combinations of cards}}$

$= \dfrac{42}{42 \cdot 42 \cdot 42} = \dfrac{1}{42^2} = \dfrac{1}{1764} \approx 0.0006$

c. P(getting an ace, then a two, then a three, etc. up to ten)

$= \dfrac{\text{number of ways to get ace, 2, 3, 4, ... 10}}{\text{total combinations of cards}}$

$= \dfrac{60,000}{42 \cdot 41 \cdot 40 \cdot 39 \cdot 38 \cdot 37 \cdot 36 \cdot 35 \cdot 34 \cdot 33}$

$\approx 1.1 \times 10^{-11}$

8. Since the 124 people who liked both flavors must also like one of the flavors, we need to subtract them from the total number of people who like blueberry or chocolate swirl.

$$415 + 269 = 684$$
$$684 - 124 = 560$$

So 560 people like a flavor of yogurt. Then 700 - 560 = 140 people do not like yogurt. The probability that a person dislikes both flavors is then

$$\frac{\text{number who dislike yogurt}}{\text{total number interviewed}} = \frac{140}{700} = 0.2$$

9. The odds are successes:failures. We are only concerned with the 16 stadiums with natural grass. Therefore, the odds that the stadium belongs to an American League team is 10:6 or 5:3.

10. P(student who works after school is a senior)

$$= \frac{\text{number of seniors who work after school}}{\text{total number of students who work after school}}$$

$$= \frac{72}{236} = \frac{18}{59} \approx 0.31$$

P(a senior works after school)

$$= \frac{\text{number of seniors who work after school}}{\text{total number of seniors}}$$

$$= \frac{72}{100} = 0.72$$

The probabilities are not necessarily the same since you are looking at the total population of students for the first probability and you are only looking at seniors for the second probability.

11. a. Since there are two possible outcomes, namely, heads and tails, when tossing a coin, input 2 for $N$ (line 10) and 400 for $K$ (line 20).

    b. Since there are six possible outcomes, namely 1 through 6, when rolling a die, input 6 for $N$ (line 10) and 500 for $K$ (line 20.)

12.
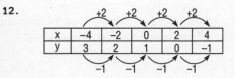

The y-values are $-\frac{1}{2}$ times the x-values. So check $y = -\frac{1}{2}x$. Using $(-4, 3)$ in the equation, we see that we must add 1 to $-\frac{1}{2}x$ to obtain a value of 3. This suggests the equation is
$$y = -\frac{1}{2}x + 1 \quad \text{or} \quad y = 1 - \frac{1}{2}x.$$

13.
$$m = \frac{y_2 - y_1}{x_2 - x_1}$$
$$-\frac{5}{3} = \frac{r - 1}{2 - 5}$$
$$\frac{-5}{3} = \frac{r - 1}{-3}$$

$$(-5)(-3) = 3(r - 1)$$
$$15 = 3r - 3$$
$$18 = 3r$$
$$6 = r$$

14. Let $u$ = units digit
    Let $t$ = tens digit
    $$10u + t = 2(10t + u) - 6$$
    $$10u + t = 20t + 2u - 6$$
    $$8u - 19t = -6$$
    If $u = 1$, $t = \frac{14}{19}$.
    If $u = 2$, $t = \frac{24}{19}$.
    If $u = 3$, $t = \frac{30}{19}$.
    If $u = 4$, $t = \frac{38}{19} = 2$.
    If $u = 5$, $t = \frac{46}{19}$.
    If $u = 6$, $t = \frac{54}{19}$.
    If $u = 7$, $t = \frac{62}{19}$.
    If $u = 8$, $t = \frac{70}{19}$.
    If $u = 9$, $t = \frac{78}{19}$.

    The integer is 24.

15. $8\sqrt{50} + 5\sqrt{72} - 2\sqrt{98}$
    $$= 8\sqrt{2 \cdot 5 \cdot 5} + 5\sqrt{2 \cdot 2 \cdot 3 \cdot 3} - 2\sqrt{2 \cdot 7 \cdot 7}$$
    $$= 8 \cdot 5\sqrt{2} + 5 \cdot 6\sqrt{2} - 2 \cdot 7\sqrt{2}$$
    $$= 40\sqrt{2} + 30\sqrt{2} - 14\sqrt{2}$$
    $$= 56\sqrt{2}$$
    $$\approx 79.20$$

16. There are 12 face cards, so 40 are not face cards. The odds are then 40:12 or 10:3.

### 14-9  Problem-Solving Strategy: Solve a Simpler Problem

PAGE 599   CHECKING FOR UNDERSTANDING

1. You can solve a simpler problem and use those methods for solving the original problem.

2. You can also use the strategy of looking for a pattern.

3. The numbers 1-9 have one digit. This uses 9 digits and leaves 2992. The numbers 10-99 each have two digits, so they use $2 \cdot 90 = 180$ digits. This leaves 2812 digits. The numbers 100-999 have three digits each, so they use $3 \cdot 900 = 2700$ digits. This leaves $2812 - 2700 = 112$ digits. Since the next numbers use four digits each, $112 + 4 = 28$ more pages were printed. Therefore, $999 + 28 = 1027$ pages were printed.

**4.** Look at line segments with fewer points.

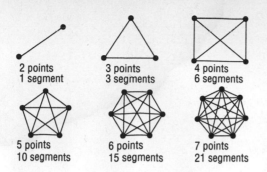

2 points
1 segment

3 points
3 segments

4 points
6 segments

5 points
10 segments

6 points
15 segments

7 points
21 segments

The pattern developing is as follows:

1 point  -  0 segments
2 points -  1 segment
3 points -  1 + 2 = 3 segments
4 points -  1 + 2 + 3 = 6 segments
5 points -  1 + 2 + 3 + 4 = 10 segments
6 points -  1 + 2 + 3 + 4 + 5 = 15 segments
7 points -  1 + 2 + 3 + 4 + 5 + 6 = 21 segments

So to find the number of line segments needed to connect 1001 points, we need to find the sum of 1 to 1000. From the example, this is 500,500 line segments.

### PAGE 599    EXERCISES

**5.** Yes, he can take the cat across first. Then go back, pick up either the dog or the bird and take it across the bridge. Now go back with the cat, leave it, pick up the remaining animal and take it across. Finally, go back, pick up the cat again and take it across.

**6.** One way to find the number is to square the cube and cube the square. In other words, $(x^3)^2 = (x^2)^3$. Now find an $x$ that when raised to the 6th power is a three digit number. Start with z. $2^6 = 64$ so it does not work. Try 3. $3^6 = 729$. The number is therefore 729 since $(3 \cdot 3 \cdot 3)^2 = 27^2 = 729$ and $(3 \cdot 3)^3 = 9^3 = 729$.

**7.** Answers may vary. Sample answer.

$x$ = cost of a pear
$x + 0.03$ = cost of a peach
$x + (x + 0.03) = \dfrac{3.78}{6}$
$2x + 0.03 = 0.63$
$2x = 0.6$
$x = 0.3$

The cost of a pear is 30¢. The cost of a peach is 33¢. If she buys half of each, it should cost $3.78.

$0.03(6) + 0.33(6) = 1.80 + 1.98$
$= \$3.78$

**8.** Looking at the sequence, we notice that
$0 + 1 + 1 = 2$, $1 + 1 + 2 = 4$, $1 + 2 + 4 = 7$, $2 + 4 + 7 = 13$, $4 + 7 + 13 = 24$. From this, the next numbers are

$7 + 13 + 24 = 44$,
$13 + 24 + 44 = 81$

and $24 + 44 + 81 = 149$.
This follows since $44 + 81 + 149 = 274$ and $81 + 149 + 274 = 504$.

**9.** If a hen and a half can lay an egg and a half in a day and a half, one hen can lay one egg in one day. Therefore, 12 hens are need to lay 12 eggs in one day.

### PAGE 599    COOPERATIVE LEARNING ACTIVITY

Since there are 36 possible combinations, each sum must have a probability of $\dfrac{3}{36} = \dfrac{1}{12}$. Also, since the sum of 1 must be possible, one die must have three 0's since the only way to add to 1 is 0 + 1. If one die has three zeros and the other die is regular, then the probabilities of getting the sums of 1-6 are all the same. Now we need to create probabilities for the sums of 7 - 12. Since one die is regular, there needs to be three 6's on the other die to get the sum of 7 three times. Therefore one die has sides 1, 2, 3, 4, 5, 6, and the other die has sides 0, 0, 0, 6, 6, 6.

## 14-10    Compound Events

### PAGE 602    CHECKING FOR UNDERSTANDING

**1. a.** If she buys a beige skirt we add four more possible combinations of skirt and blouse, namely beige-yellow, beige-white, beige-striped, and beige-tan. So now there are 12 + 4 = 16 outfits.

   **b.** If she buys a beige blouse we add three more possible combinations of skirt and blouse, namely blue-beige, yellow-beige, and red-beige. So now there are 12 + 3 = 15 outfits.

   **c.** If she buys both a beige skirt and a beige blouse, we add eight more possible combinations of skirt and blouse, namely blue-beige, yellow-beige, red-beige, beige-yellow, beige-white, beige-striped, beige-tan, and beige-beige for a total of 20 combinations.

**2.** A compound event consists of two or more simple events. Tossing a coin is a simple event while tossing two coins is a compound event.

3. a. 4 cars will have a manual transmission, so the probability $\frac{4}{8} = \frac{1}{4} = 0.5$.

   b. 2 cars will be blue with manual transmission, so the probability is $\frac{2}{8} = \frac{1}{4} = 0.25$.

   c. 2 cars will have a 4-cylinder engine with a manual transmission, so the probability is $\frac{2}{8} = \frac{1}{4} = 0.25$.

   d. only 1 car will be blue with a 6-cylinder engine and an automatic transmission. The probability is $\frac{1}{8} = 0.125$.

## PAGES 602-603    EXERCISES

4.

| First Child | Second Child | Third Child | Fourth Child | Outcomes |
|---|---|---|---|---|

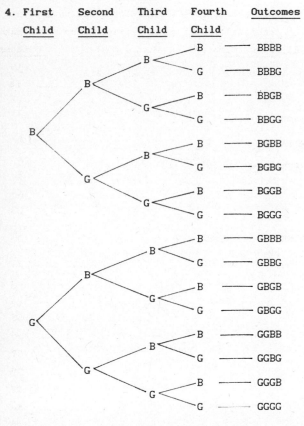

a. P(exactly 4 girls) = $\frac{1}{16}$ = 0.0625

b. P(2 boys and 2 girls) = $\frac{6}{16}$ = $\frac{3}{8}$ = 0.375

5.

| Coin 1 | Coin 2 | Coin 3 | Coin 4 | Outcomes |
|---|---|---|---|---|

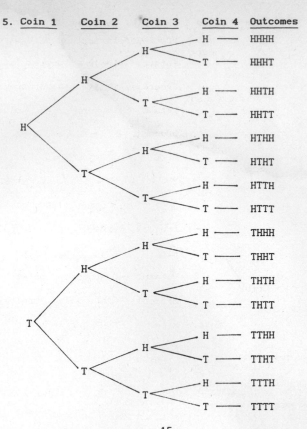

p(at least one tail) = $\frac{15}{16}$ = 0.9375

6. Answers may vary. Sample answer: The trees appear to be the same since both compound events are composed of four simple events. One difference is that boys and girls are used instead of heads and tails.

7.

| Box A | Box B | Box C | Outcomes |
|---|---|---|---|

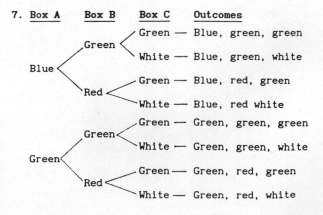

a. P(all marbles are green) = $\frac{1}{8}$ = 0.125

b. P(exactly two marbles are green) = $\frac{3}{8}$ = 0.375

c. P(at least one marble is not green) = $\frac{7}{8}$ = 0.875

8.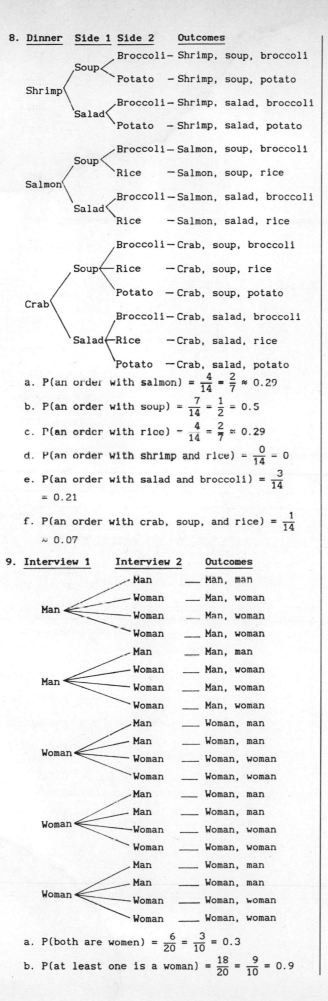

Dinner  Side 1  Side 2  Outcomes

Shrimp
Soup
Broccoli – Shrimp, soup, broccoli
Potato – Shrimp, soup, potato
Salad
Broccoli – Shrimp, salad, broccoli
Potato – Shrimp, salad, potato

Salmon
Soup
Broccoli – Salmon, soup, broccoli
Rice – Salmon, soup, rice
Salad
Broccoli – Salmon, salad, broccoli
Rice – Salmon, salad, rice

Crab
Soup
Broccoli – Crab, soup, broccoli
Rice – Crab, soup, rice
Potato – Crab, soup, potato
Salad
Broccoli – Crab, salad, broccoli
Rice – Crab, salad, rice
Potato – Crab, salad, potato

a. P(an order with salmon) = $\frac{4}{14} = \frac{2}{7} \approx 0.29$

b. P(an order with soup) = $\frac{7}{14} = \frac{1}{2} = 0.5$

c. P(an order with rice) = $\frac{4}{14} = \frac{2}{7} \approx 0.29$

d. P(an order with shrimp and rice) = $\frac{0}{14} = 0$

e. P(an order with salad and broccoli) = $\frac{3}{14}$
= 0.21

f. P(an order with crab, soup, and rice) = $\frac{1}{14}$
$\approx 0.07$

9. Interview 1   Interview 2   Outcomes

Man
Man — Man, man
Woman — Man, woman
Woman — Man, woman
Woman — Man, woman

Man
Man — Man, man
Woman — Man, woman
Woman — Man, woman
Woman — Man, woman

Woman
Man — Woman, man
Man — Woman, man
Woman — Woman, woman
Woman — Woman, woman

Woman
Man — Woman, man
Man — Woman, man
Woman — Woman, woman
Woman — Woman, woman

Woman
Man — Woman, man
Man — Woman, man
Woman — Woman, woman
Woman — Woman, woman

a. P(both are women) = $\frac{6}{20} = \frac{3}{10} = 0.3$

b. P(at least one is a woman) = $\frac{18}{20} = \frac{9}{10} = 0.9$

c. P(one is a woman and the other is a man)

= $\frac{12}{20} = \frac{3}{5} = 0.6$

P(both people are either men or women)

= $\frac{8}{20} = \frac{2}{5} = 0.4$

The probability that one person is a woman and the other is a man is more likely.

10. Since we are looking for the probability that Kelly will go to a friend's house, she must have gone to pick up a pizza after the game. She is among 80% of the students. Since 40% of that 80% go home after pizza, 60% of the 80% go to a friend's house. To find 60% of 80%, find 0.6 × 0.8 = 0.48 or 48%. Therefore, the probability that Kelly will go to a friend's house is 48%.

11. First Number   Second Number   Outcomes

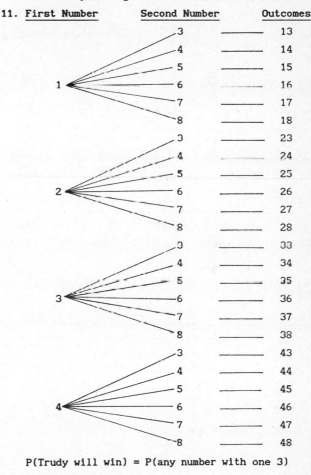

1
3 ——— 13
4 ——— 14
5 ——— 15
6 ——— 16
7 ——— 17
8 ——— 18

2
3 ——— 23
4 ——— 24
5 ——— 25
6 ——— 26
7 ——— 27
8 ——— 28

3
3 ——— 33
4 ——— 34
5 ——— 35
6 ——— 36
7 ——— 37
8 ——— 38

4
3 ——— 43
4 ——— 44
5 ——— 45
6 ——— 46
7 ——— 47
8 ——— 48

P(Trudy will win) = P(any number with one 3)

= $\frac{8}{24} = \frac{1}{3} = 0.\overline{3}$

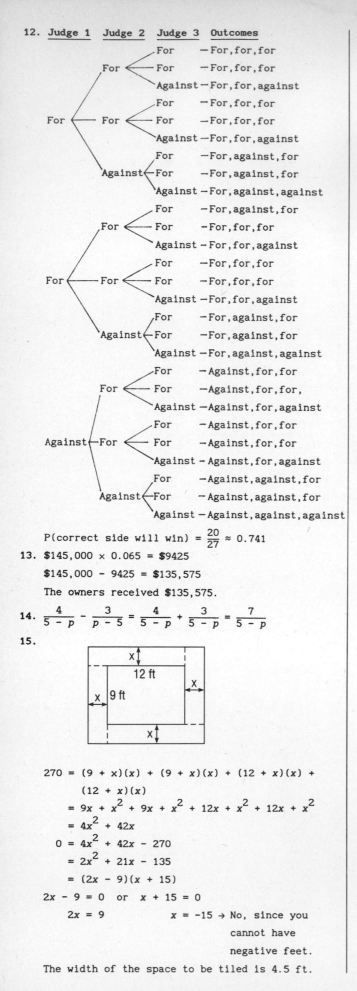

12.

| Judge 1 | Judge 2 | Judge 3 | Outcomes |
|---------|---------|---------|----------|

For — For — For — For,for,for
For — For — For — For,for,for
For — For — Against — For,for,against
For — For — For — For,for,for
For — For — For — For,for,for
For — For — Against — For,for,against
For — Against — For — For,against,for
For — Against — For — For,against,for
For — Against — Against — For,against,against
For — For — For — For,against,for
For — For — For — For,for,for
For — For — Against — For,for,against
For — For — For — For,for,for
For — For — For — For,for,for
For — For — Against — For,for,against
For — Against — For — For,against,for
For — Against — For — For,against,for
For — Against — Against — For,against,against
Against — For — For — Against,for,for
Against — For — For — Against,for,for,
Against — For — Against — Against,for,against
Against — For — For — Against,for,for
Against — For — For — Against,for,for
Against — For — Against — Against,for,against
Against — For — For — Against,against,for
Against — For — For — Against,against,for
Against — Against — Against — Against,against,against

$P(\text{correct side will win}) = \frac{20}{27} \approx 0.741$

13. $\$145,000 \times 0.065 = \$9425$

$\$145,000 - 9425 = \$135,575$

The owners received $\$135,575$.

14. $\frac{4}{5 - p} - \frac{3}{p - 5} = \frac{4}{5 - p} + \frac{3}{5 - p} = \frac{7}{5 - p}$

15.

$270 = (9 + x)(x) + (9 + x)(x) + (12 + x)(x) +$
$\quad (12 + x)(x)$

$\quad = 9x + x^2 + 9x + x^2 + 12x + x^2 + 12x + x^2$

$\quad = 4x^2 + 42x$

$0 = 4x^2 + 42x - 270$

$\quad = 2x^2 + 21x - 135$

$\quad = (2x - 9)(x + 15)$

$2x - 9 = 0 \quad \text{or} \quad x + 15 = 0$

$2x = 9 \qquad\qquad x = -15 \rightarrow$ No, since you cannot have negative feet.

$x =$

The width of the space to be tiled is 4.5 ft.

16. Answers may vary. Sample answer:

My coin landed on heads 23 times and on tails 27 times.

$P(\text{heads}) = \frac{23}{50} = 0.46$

The results are close to what I expected. They should be approximately $\frac{1}{2}$ or 0.50. If not, the results do not necessarily imply that the coin is not fair because of the low number of trials. More trials must be done in order to determine whether or not the coin is fair.

17. Using Exercise 4 and the example from Lesson 14-9, we need to find the sum of the digits of 1 to 99. This is

$$1 + 99 = 100$$
$$2 + 98 = 100$$
$$3 + 97 = 100$$
$$\vdots$$
$$49 + 51 = 100$$
$$50$$

$49(100) + 50 = 4900 + 50 = 4950$ diagonals

## Chapter 14   Summary and Review

**PAGES 604–606   SKILLS AND CONCEPTS**

1. Philip Morris had the least sales.

2. Mobil had the least income.

3. Exxon: $\frac{3.5}{89} = 0.040 = 4.0\%$

   Ford Motor: $\frac{3.8}{97} = 0.039 = 3.9\%$

   General Electric: $\frac{3.9}{55} = 0.071 = 7.1\%$

   General Motors: $\frac{4.2}{127} = 0.033 = 3.3\%$

   IBM: $\frac{3.8}{63} = 0.060 = 6.0\%$

   Mobil: $\frac{1.8}{60} = 0.03 = 3.0\%$

   Philip Morris: $\frac{2.9}{39} = 0.074 = 7.4\%$

   Philip Morris had the greatest income as a percent of sales.

   No, it was not the company with the greatest income.

4.

5.

6.

| Stem | Leaf |
|------|------|
| 4 | 0 1 2 2 4 |
| 5 | 0 5 6 |
| 6 | 2 5 6 9 |
| 7 | 6 8 |
| 8 | 3          6|2 = $62 |

6 prices are between $40 and $50.

7.

| Rounded | Stem | Truncated |
|---------|------|-----------|
| 8 6 5 1 | 3 | 1 4 6 8 |
| 4 3 | 4 | 2 4 9 |
| 8 7 6 0 | 5 | 6 6 8 |
| 8 | 6 | 7 |

rounded data: 3|1 = 3050 - 3249

truncated data: 3|1 = 3100 - 3199

8. Mean: 6.8 + 8.4 + 6.2 + 5.7 + 5.6 + 7.1 + 9.9 +

$$\frac{1.5 + 7.1 + 5.4 + 3.4}{11}$$

$$= \frac{67.1}{11} = 6.1$$

1.5, 3.4, 5.4, 5.6, 5.7, 6.2, 6.8, 7.1, 7.1, 8.4, 9.9

Median: 6.2 since it is the sixth value

Mode: 7.1 since it occurs twice and all others occur only once.

9. Mean: 3 + 6 + 7 + 7 + 7 + 7 + 9 + 10 + 10 + 10 +

10 + 10 + 10 + 13 + 14 + 14 + 16 + 16 + 17

$$\frac{+ 17 + 19 + 19 + 20 + 21 + 31}{25}$$

$$= \frac{323}{25}$$

$$= 12.92$$

Median: 10 is the median since it is the twelfth value.

Mode: 10 is the mode since it occurs six times and all others occur less than six times.

10. Range: 31 - 3 = 28

LQ: $\frac{7 + 9}{2} = \frac{16}{2} = 8$

Median: 10

UQ: $\frac{17 + 17}{2} = \frac{34}{2} = 17$

Interquartile Range: 17 - 8 = 9

11. 59.8, 63.8, 64.3, 68.6, 70.7, 77.1, 82.3, 88.9, 91.7, 110.5, 111.5, 254.8

LQ: $\frac{64.3 + 68.6}{2} = \frac{132.9}{2} = 66.45$

UQ: $\frac{91.7 + 110.5}{2} = \frac{202.2}{2} = 101.1$

Interquartile range: 101.1 - 66.45 = 34.65

Outliers:

101.1 + (1.5)(34.65) = 101.1 + 51.975

= 153.075

66.45 - (1.5)(34.65) = 66.45 - 51.975

= 14.475

254.8 in. is an outlier.

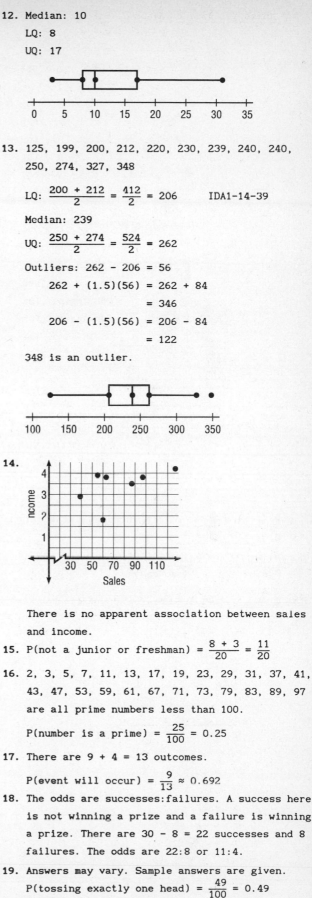

12. Median: 10

LQ: 8

UQ: 17

13. 125, 199, 200, 212, 220, 230, 239, 240, 240, 250, 274, 327, 348

LQ: $\frac{200 + 212}{2} = \frac{412}{2} = 206$     IDA1-14-39

Median: 239

UQ: $\frac{250 + 274}{2} = \frac{524}{2} = 262$

Outliers: 262 - 206 = 56

262 + (1.5)(56) = 262 + 84

= 346

206 - (1.5)(56) = 206 - 84

= 122

348 is an outlier.

14.

There is no apparent association between sales and income.

15. P(not a junior or freshman) = $\frac{8 + 3}{20} = \frac{11}{20}$

16. 2, 3, 5, 7, 11, 13, 17, 19, 23, 29, 31, 37, 41, 43, 47, 53, 59, 61, 67, 71, 73, 79, 83, 89, 97 are all prime numbers less than 100.

P(number is a prime) = $\frac{25}{100} = 0.25$

17. There are 9 + 4 = 13 outcomes.

P(event will occur) = $\frac{9}{13} \approx 0.692$

18. The odds are successes:failures. A success here is not winning a prize and a failure is winning a prize. There are 30 - 8 = 22 successes and 8 failures. The odds are 22:8 or 11:4.

19. Answers may vary. Sample answers are given.

P(tossing exactly one head) = $\frac{49}{100} = 0.49$

20. Answers may vary. Sample answers are given.

P(tossing at least one head) = $\frac{77}{100} = 0.77$

**21.**

| 1st Sock | 2nd Sock | Outcomes |
|---|---|---|

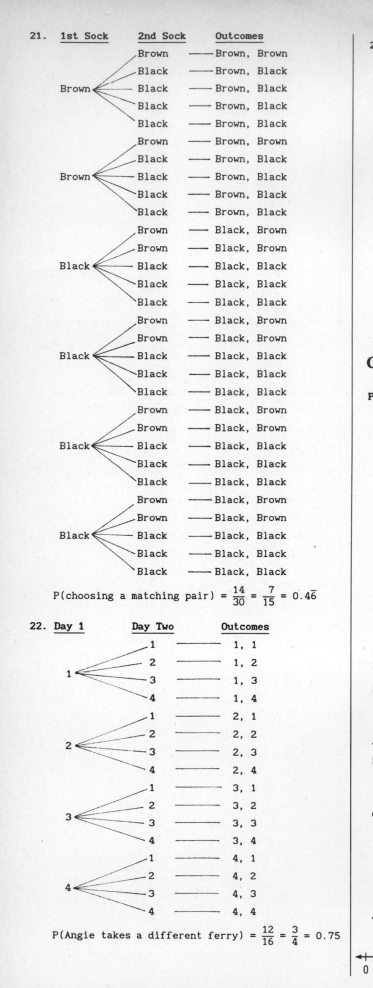

$$P(\text{choosing a matching pair}) = \frac{14}{30} = \frac{7}{15} = 0.4\overline{6}$$

**22.**

| Day 1 | Day Two | Outcomes |
|---|---|---|
| | 1 | 1, 1 |
| | 2 | 1, 2 |
| 1 | 3 | 1, 3 |
| | 4 | 1, 4 |
| | 1 | 2, 1 |
| | 2 | 2, 2 |
| 2 | 3 | 2, 3 |
| | 4 | 2, 4 |
| | 1 | 3, 1 |
| | 2 | 3, 2 |
| 3 | 3 | 3, 3 |
| | 4 | 3, 4 |
| | 1 | 4, 1 |
| | 2 | 4, 2 |
| 4 | 3 | 4, 3 |
| | 4 | 4, 4 |

$$P(\text{Angie takes a different ferry}) = \frac{12}{16} = \frac{3}{4} = 0.75$$

**23.** 1st Round: $\frac{208}{2}$ = 104 games

2nd Round: $\frac{104}{2}$ = 52 games

3rd Round: $\frac{52}{2}$ = 26 games

4th Round: $\frac{26}{2}$ = 13 games

5th Round: $\frac{12}{2}$ = 6 games

6th Round: $\frac{6}{2}$ = 3 games

7th Round: $\frac{4}{2}$ = 2 games

8th Round: $\frac{2}{2}$ = <u>1</u> game

207 games

Another way to solve this is to reason that every game must have a loser and only one team will win all their games. Therefore, there were 208 − 1 = 207 losses or 207 games.

# Chapter 14  Test

PAGE 607    CHAPTER 14 TEST

**1.**

| Stem | Leaf |
|---|---|
| 13 | 1 3 6 6 7 |
| 14 | 6 6 6 9 |
| 15 | 0 1 2 4 4 7 8 8 9 9 |
| 16 | 0 1 2 4 5 8 |
| 17 | 0 0 1 1 2 5 6 8 8 8 |
| 18 | 2 2 4 4 5 5 7 |
| 19 | 3 8 |
| 20 | 3 4 6 |
| 21 | 1 |
| 22 | 7 |
| 23 | |
| 24 | 5 |

13|1 represents 13.1 students per teacher

**2.** There were 10 ratios in the 17's.

**3.** Median: $\frac{16.8 + 17.0}{2}$ = 16.9

Mode: There are two modes; 14.6 and 17.8. They both occur three times.

**4.** The range is 24.5 − 13.1 = 11.4.

**5.** UQ: 18.4

LQ: 15.4

Interquartile Range: 18.4 − 15.4 = 3.0

**6.** Outliers:

18.4 + (1.5)(3) = 18.4 + 4.5
= 22.9

15.4 − (1.5)(3) = 15.4 − 4.5
= 10.9

24.5 is an outlier

**7.**

```
 x     xx x    x x        x    x              x              x
<--+----+----+----+----+----+----+----+----+-->
   0   10   20   30   40   50   60   70   80
```

8. The greatest number of shots made is 36. The least number of shots made is 1.

9. Mean of shots attempted:

$$\frac{60 + 25 + 35 + 12 + 80 + 4 + 15 + 42 + 11 + 22}{10}$$

$$= \frac{306}{10} = 30.6$$

Mean of shots made:

$$\frac{25 + 10 + 15 + 4 + 36 + 1 + 6 + 16 + 4 + 8}{10}$$

$$= \frac{125}{10} = 12.5$$

10. 4, 11, 12, 15, 22, 25, 35, 42, 60, 80

LQ: 12

Median: $\frac{22 + 25}{2} = \frac{47}{2} = 23.5$

UQ: 42

Interquartile Range: 42 − 12 = 30

11.

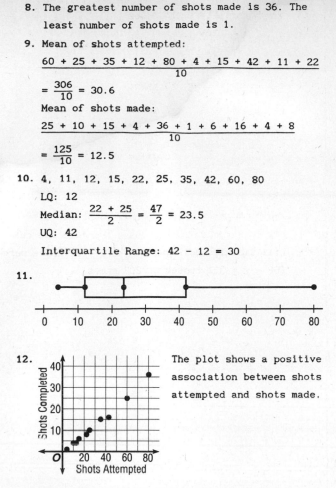

12.

The plot shows a positive association between shots attempted and shots made.

13. P(hard rock song is playing) $= \frac{7}{20} = 0.35$

14. The odds are successes:failures. There are 5 successes and 8 + 7 = 15 failures. The odds are 5:15 or 1:3.

15. 185 + 200 = 385

165 + 140 + 185 + 205 + 105 + 200 = 1000

P(person did not vote) $= \frac{385}{1000} = 0.385$

16. A success is a yes vote. A failure is a no vote. The odds are 165:140 or 33:28.

17. P(person who voted no is a woman) $= \frac{105}{245} = \frac{3}{9} \approx 0.43$

18. There are 3 + 7 = 10 outcomes and the number of successes is 3. So P(rain) $= \frac{3}{10} = 0.3$.

19. P(rain) $= 0.45 = \frac{45}{100}$ means that there are 45 rainy days and 100 total days. There are 100 − 45 = 55 days that are not rainy. Here a day without rain is a success and a rainy day is a failure. The odds are successes:failures, or $\frac{55}{100} : \frac{45}{100} = 0.55:0.45$ or 0.11:0.9.

**PAGE 607    BONUS**

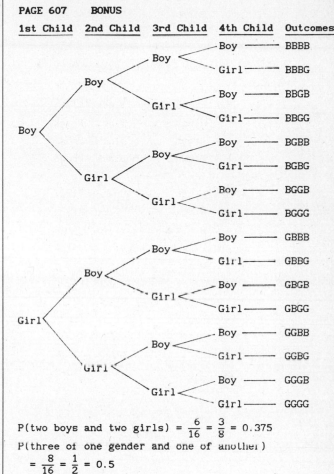

P(two boys and two girls) $= \frac{6}{16} = \frac{3}{8} = 0.375$

P(three of one gender and one of another)

$= \frac{8}{16} = \frac{1}{2} = 0.5$

A couple is more likely to have three of one gender and one of another.

# Chapter 15   Trigonometry

**PAGE 612    CHECKING FOR UNDERSTANDING**

1. A compliment is an expression of praise. A complement is something that completes or fills. The word complement has mathematical meaning.

2. left:acute; center:obtuse; right:right

3. No; the sum of the measures of the angles of a triangle is $180°$. Since the measure of each angle is greater than $0°$, having two $90°$ angles would result in a sum that is greater than $180°$.

4. $90° - 42° = 48°$

5. $90° - 13° = 77°$

6. $90° - 45° = 45°$

7. $90° - 24° = 66°$

8. $90° - 11° = 79°$

9. $90° - 76° = 14°$

10. $90° - 3x°$
$= (90 - 3x)°$

11. $90° - (2x + 40)°$
$= (50 - 2x)°$

12. $90° - (x - 7)°$
$= (97 - x)°$

13. $180° - 130° = 50°$

14. $180° - 65° = 115°$

15. $180° - 87° = 93°$

16. $180° - 90° = 90°$

17. $180° - 32° = 148°$

18. $180° - 156° = 24°$

19. $180° - y°$
$= (180 - y)°$

20. $(180 - 6m)°$

21. $180° - (x - 20)°$
$= (200 - x)°$

**PAGES 613-614    EXERCISES**

22. $90° - 42° = 48°$
$180° - 42° = 138°$

23. $90° - 87° = 3°$
$180° - 87° = 93°$

24. none
$180° - 125° = 55°$

25. none
$180° - 160° = 20°$

26. $90° - 90° = 0°$
$180° - 90° = 90°$

27. $90° - 68° = 22°$
$180° - 68° = 112°$

28. $90° - 21° = 69°$
$180° - 21° = 159°$

29. none
$180° - 174° = 6°$

30. none
$180° - 99° = 81°$

31. $(90 - a)°$
$(180 - a)°$

32. $(90 - 3y)°$
$(180 - 3y)°$

33. $90° - (x + 30)° = (60 - x)°$
$180° - (x + 30)° = (150 - x)°$

34. $90° - (x - 38)° = (128 - x)°$
$180° - (x - 38)° = (218 - x)°$

35. $90° - 5x° = (90 - 5x)°$
$180° - 5x° = (180 - 5x)°$

36. $90° - (90 - x)° = x°$
$180° - (90 - x)° = (90 + x)°$

37. $90° - (180 - y)° = (y - 90)°$
$180° - (180 - y)° = y°$

38. $180° - 16° - 42° = 122°$

39. $180° - 40° - 70° = 70°$

40. $180° - 50° - 45° = 85°$

41. $180° - 90° - 30° = 60°$

42. $180° - 89° - 90° = 1°$

43. $180° - 63° - 12° = 105°$

44. $180° - 43° - 118° = 19°$

45. $180° - 4° - 38° = 138°$

46. $180° - x° - y° = (180 - x - y)°$

47. $180° - x° - (x + 20)° = (160 - 2x)°$

48. $180° - y° - (y - 10)° = (190 - 2y)°$

49. $180° - m° - (2m + 1)° = (179 - 3m)°$

50. $37°$
and $180° - 37° - 37° = 106°$

51. $x° + (x + 2)° + (x + 4)° = 180°$
$\qquad (3x + 6)° = 180°$
$\qquad 3x° = 174°$
$\qquad x° = 58°$
$\qquad (x + 2)° = 60°$
$\qquad (x + 4)° = 62°$
$58°, 60°, 62°$

52. $x° + (x - 38)° = 90°$
$\qquad (2x - 38)° = 90°$
$\qquad 2x° = 128°$
$\qquad x° = 64°$
$\qquad (x - 38)° = 64° - 38° = 26°$
$26°, 64°$

53. $180° - 53° - 37° = 90°$

54. $x° + (x + 10)° + 2[x + (x + 10)]° = 180°$
$\qquad [2x + 10 + 2x + 2(x + 10)]° = 180°$
$\qquad [2x + 10 + 2x + 2x + 20] = 180°$
$\qquad (6x + 30)° = 180°$
$\qquad 6x° = 150°$
$\qquad x° = 25°$
$25°, 35°, 120°$

55. $(3x + 30)° + x° = 90°$
$\qquad (4x + 30)° = 90°$
$\qquad 4x° = 60°$
$\qquad x° = 15°$
$15°, 75°$

56. $x° + (x + 10)° = 90°$
$\qquad (2x + 10)° = 90°$
$\qquad 2x° = 80°$
$\qquad x° = 40°$
$\qquad (x + 10)° = 50°$

57. $x° + (x - 30)° = 180°$
$\qquad (2x - 30)° = 180°$
$\qquad 2x° = 210°$
$\qquad x° = 105°$
$\qquad (x - 30)° = 105° - 30° = 75°$

58. $x° + \frac{1}{2}x° = 90°$

$\qquad \frac{3}{2}x° = 90°$

$\qquad x° = 90 \cdot \frac{2°}{3}$

$\qquad x° = 60°$

$\qquad \frac{1}{2}x° = \frac{1}{2} \cdot 60° = 30°$

59. $x° + \frac{1}{2}x° = 180°$

$\qquad \frac{3}{2}x° = 180°$

$\qquad x° = 180 \cdot \frac{2°}{3}$

$\qquad x° = 120°$

$\qquad \frac{1}{2}x° = \frac{1}{2} \cdot 120° = 60°$

60. $x° + 2x° + 3x° = 180°$

$\qquad 6x° = 180°$

$\qquad x° = 30°$

$\qquad 30°, 60°, 90°$

61. $x° + (x + 5)° + (2x + 3)° = 180°$

$\qquad (4x + 8)° = 180°$

$\qquad 4x° = 172°$

$\qquad x° = 43°$

$\qquad (x + 5)° = 43° + 5° = 48°$

$\qquad (2x + 3)° = (2 \cdot 43 + 3)° = 89°$

$\qquad 43°, 48°, 89°$

62. $6x° + (x - 3)° + (3x + 7)° = 180°$

$\qquad (10x + 4)° = 180°$

$\qquad 10x° = 176°$

$\qquad x° = 17.6°$

$\qquad 6x° = 6(17.6°) = 105.6°$

$\qquad (x - 3)° = 17.6° - 3° = 14.6°$

$\qquad (3x + 7)° = 3(17.6°) + 7° = 59.8°$

$\qquad 105.6°, 14.6°, 59.8°$

63. An octagon can be divided into six triangles by drawing the five diagonals from a single vertex of the octagon. The sum of the measures of the angles of these triangles, which is $6 \cdot 180°$ or $1080°$, is equal to the sum of the measures of the interior angles of the octagon.

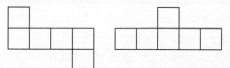

64. $90° - 40° = 50°$       65. $180° - 30° - 30° = 120°$

66. $90° - 50° = 40°$       67. $R = am - z$

68. $-35a^5b^2c$          69. $x \leq 2, y \geq 2$

70. $d = \sqrt{(7 - 5)^2 + (2 - (-3))^2}$

$\qquad = \sqrt{2^2 + 5^2}$

$\qquad = \sqrt{4 + 25}$

$\qquad = \sqrt{29} \approx 5.385$

71. $x = \frac{-b}{2a} = \frac{-15}{2(-5)} = \frac{-15}{-10} = \frac{3}{2}$

$\qquad y = -5\left(\frac{3}{2}\right)^2 + 15\left(\frac{3}{2}\right) + 23$

$\qquad y = -5\left(\frac{9}{4}\right) + \frac{45}{2} + 23$

$\qquad y = \frac{-45}{4} + \frac{90}{4} + \frac{92}{4}$

$\qquad y = \frac{137}{4}$

$\qquad \left(\frac{3}{2}, \frac{137}{4}\right)$

72. $(b + 14)(b - 2) = 0$

$\qquad b = -14, \quad b = 2$

$\qquad -14 + 2 = -12$

$\qquad -14 \cdot 2 = -28$

73. $\frac{1}{3} = 0.\overline{3}$

15-2 **Problem-Solving Strategy: Make a Model**

PAGES 615-616    CHECKING FOR UNDERSTANDING

1. Sketches of the six squares or cardboard squares from some board game. Answers will vary.

2. Answers may vary; two typical answers are shown below.

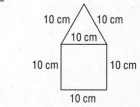

3. Pieces of paper or cardboard that represent pieces of furniture can be moved around on a scale drawing of the room. Answers may vary.

4. Perimeter = $5 \cdot 10$ cm
   $\qquad = 50$ cm

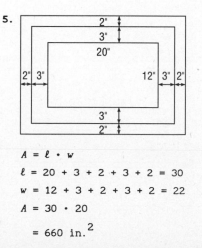

5.

$A = \ell \cdot w$

$\ell = 20 + 3 + 2 + 3 + 2 = 30$

$w = 12 + 3 + 2 + 3 + 2 = 22$

$A = 30 \cdot 20$

$\qquad = 660 \text{ in.}^2$

297

**6.**

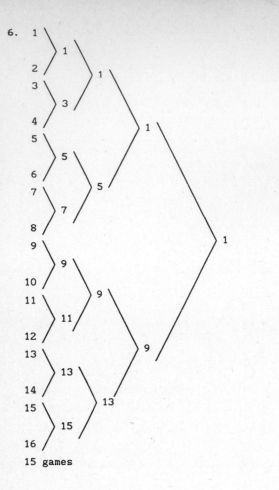

15 games

PAGE 616    EXERCISES

**7.** Let $h$ = number of Hong's marbles.

Let $d$ = number of Dora's marbles.

$$\left.\begin{array}{l} h - 1 = d + 1 \\ h + 1 = 2(d - 1) \end{array}\right\}$$

$$\left.\begin{array}{l} h - d = 2 \\ h + 1 = 2d - 2 \end{array}\right\}$$

$$\left.\begin{array}{l} h - d = 2 \\ h - 2d = -3 \end{array}\right\}$$

$$\left.\begin{array}{l} -h + d = -2 \\ h - 2d = -3 \end{array}\right\}$$

$$-d = -5$$
$$d = 5$$

$$h = d + 2 = 5 + 2 = 7$$

Hong: 7, Dora: 5

**8. a.** 8 cubes

   **b.** 24 cubes

   **c.** 24 cubes

   **d.** 64 - 8 - 24 - 24 = 8 cubes

**9.** Work backwards.

Store 5

| | | |
|---|---|---|
| undo - $1 | | $1 |
| undo $\frac{1}{2}$ | | 2 · 1 = $2 |

Store 4

| | | |
|---|---|---|
| undo - $1 | | 2 + 1 = $3 |
| undo $\frac{1}{2}$ | | 2 · 3 = $6 |

Store 3

| | | |
|---|---|---|
| undo - $1 | | 6 + 1 = $7 |
| undo $\frac{1}{2}$ | | 2 · 7 = $14 |

Store 2

| | | |
|---|---|---|
| undo - $1 | | 14 + 1 = $15 |
| undo $\frac{1}{2}$ | | 2 · 15 = $30 |

Store 1

| | | |
|---|---|---|
| undo - $1 | | 30 + 1 = $31 |
| undo $\frac{1}{2}$ | | 2 · 31 = $62 |

Mr. Zerman started with $62.

PAGE 616    COOPERATIVE LEARNING ACTIVITY
Place 3 boxes on each side of the scale. If both sides weigh the same, weigh the remaining 2 boxes to determine which contains the ring. If one side weighs more, keep those 3 boxes and set the others aside. Place one box on each side of the scale. If one box weighs more, then it contains the ring. Otherwise, the box not weighed contains the ring.

## 15-3    30° - 60° Right Triangles

PAGE 619    CHECKING FOR UNDERSTANDING

**1.** Yes; the simplest form of the ratio will always be $1 : \sqrt{3} : 2$.

**2.** $2x$ cm

**3.** 2 · $2x$ cm
   = $4x$ cm

**4.** 4 m

**5.** 8 cm

**6.** 6.5 mm

**7.** 4.5 mi

**8.** $2\frac{1}{4}$ in.

**9.** $1\frac{11}{16}$ in.

**10.** 8.18 m

**11.** 2.315 cm

**12.** 4 ft, 8 ft

**13.** 2 cm, 4 cm

**14.** 8 m, 16 m

**15.** 1 mi, 2 mi

PAGES 619-621    EXERCISES

**16.** 14 m

**17.** 12.4 cm

**18.** 8.7 mm

**19.** 9 mi

**20.** $12\frac{3}{4}$ in.

**21.** 26 m

**22.** 7.72 cm

**23.** $15\frac{1}{2}$ in.

**24.** $4\sqrt{3}$ cm
   ≈ 6.928 cm

25. $5\sqrt{3}$ ft     26. 7 units     27. 10 units
    $\approx 8.660$ ft

28. $\frac{1}{2}$ m       29. $2.5\sqrt{3}$ or $\approx 4.330$ yd

| | Hypotenuse | Side Opposite 30° Angle | Side Opposite 60° Angle |
|---|---|---|---|
| 30. | 6 m | 3 m | $3\sqrt{3}$ m |
| 31. | 4.75 mm | 2.375 mm | $2.375\sqrt{3}$ mm |
| 32. | $3\frac{1}{2}$ in. | $1\frac{3}{4}$ in. | $\frac{7}{4}\sqrt{3}$ in. |
| 33. | 16 cm | 8 cm | $8\sqrt{3}$ cm |
| 34. | 13 m | 6.5 m | $6.5\sqrt{3}$ m |
| 35. | $6\frac{1}{2}$ in. | $3\frac{1}{4}$ in. | $\frac{13}{4}\sqrt{3}$ in. |
| 36. | 4 m | 2 m | $2\sqrt{3}$ m |
| 37. | 7 cm | 3.5 cm | $3.5\sqrt{3}$ cm |

38. Let $x$ = distance from $A$ to right triangle.

$$5^2 + x^2 = 10^2$$
$$25 + x^2 = 100$$
$$x^2 = 75$$
$$x = \sqrt{75}$$
$$x = \sqrt{3} \cdot \sqrt{25}$$
$$x = 5\sqrt{3}$$
$$x - \overline{AB} = 5\sqrt{3} - 3\sqrt{3}$$
$$= 2\sqrt{3}$$
$$(\overline{BC})^2 = 5^2 + (2\sqrt{3})^2$$
$$(\overline{BC})^2 = 25 + 4 \cdot 3$$
$$(\overline{BC})^2 = 25 + 12$$
$$(\overline{BC})^2 = 37$$
$$\overline{BC} = \sqrt{37} \text{ or } \approx 6.08 \text{ m}$$

39. $\overline{PR}$ is $2 \cdot 8\sqrt{3} = 16\sqrt{3}$ yd

$\overline{PQ}$ is 16 yd

$\overline{RQ}$ is $2 \cdot 16 = 32$ yd

$P = 16\sqrt{3} + 16 + 32$

   $= 48 + 16\sqrt{3}$ yd

   $\approx 75.71$ yd

40. $\overline{AB} = \overline{CD} = 4\sqrt{3}$ in.

$\overline{AD} = \overline{BC} = 6$ in.

$P = 2 \cdot 4\sqrt{3} + 2 \cdot 6$

   $= 8\sqrt{3} + 12$ in.

   $\approx 25.86$ in.

41. $\overline{JK} = \overline{ML} = 10$m

$\overline{KL} = \overline{JM} = \frac{10}{\sqrt{3}}$ m

$P = 2 \cdot 10 + \frac{2 \cdot 10}{\sqrt{3}}$

   $= 20 + \frac{20}{\sqrt{3}} \cdot \frac{\sqrt{3}}{\sqrt{3}}$

   $= 20 + \frac{20\sqrt{3}}{3}$

   $= \frac{60 + 20\sqrt{3}}{3}$ m $\approx 31.547$ m

42.

height = $15\sqrt{3}$ ft

    $\approx 25.98$ ft

43.

4 ft

44. $-7.54$

45. $(3y - 1)(y + 2)$

46.     $2x = 3y - y$

      $x = \frac{3y - y}{2}$

      $x = \frac{2y}{2}$

      $x = y$

$2x - y = 3x$

$2x - x = 3x$

    $x = 3x$

The only time this is true is when $x = 0$.

$2(0) - y = 3y$

      $y = 3y$

The only time this is true is when $y = 0$.
The solution is $(0, 0)$.

47. $\frac{-\sqrt{289}}{\sqrt{100}} = -\frac{17}{10}$

48. $2t^2 - t - 4 = 0$

$$t = \frac{1 \pm \sqrt{(-1)^2 - 4 \cdot 2 \cdot (-4)}}{2 \cdot 2}$$

$$= \frac{1 \pm \sqrt{1 + 32}}{4}$$

$$= \frac{1 \pm \sqrt{33}}{4}$$

49. 34       50. $90° - 17° = 73°$

## PAGE 621    MID-CHAPTER REVIEW

1. $90° - 85° = 5°$     2. none
   $180° - 85° = 95°$       $180° - 127° = 53°$

3. $90° - 65° = 25°$     4. none
   $180° - 65° = 115°$       $180° - 108° = 72°$

5. $90° - x° = (90 - x)°$
   $180° - x° = (180 - x)°$

6. $90° - (3x + 5)° = (85 - 3x)°$
   $180° - (3x + 5)° = (175 - 3x)°$

7. 3 m, 6 m      8. 7 yd, 14 yd

9. 9 mm, 18 mm    10. $\frac{1}{3}$ in., $\frac{2}{3}$ in.

11. The figure below shows the view from directly above the pins. Move the three pins as indicated in this figure.

---

## 15-4    Similar Triangles

### PAGE 624    CHECKING FOR UNDERSTANDING

1. $\angle M$ and $\angle W$, $\angle T$ and $\angle Q$, $\angle Y$ and $\angle V$

2. The measures of their corresponding sides are proportional, and the measures of their corresponding angles are equal.

3. $\angle B$ and $\angle R$, $\angle I$ and $\angle E$, $\angle G$ and $\angle D$

4. $\overline{BI}$ and $\overline{RE}$, $\overline{IG}$ and $\overline{ED}$, $\overline{BG}$ and $\overline{RD}$

5. $\frac{BI}{RE} = \frac{IG}{ED}$, $\frac{BI}{RE} = \frac{BG}{RD}$, $\frac{IG}{ED} = \frac{BG}{RD}$

6. $\triangle DFE$      7. $\triangle WQC$      8. $\triangle WNC$

### PAGES 624-625    EXERCISES

9. yes      10. no

11. $\frac{b}{e} = \frac{a}{d}$      $\frac{c}{f} = \frac{a}{d}$

$\frac{b}{5} = \frac{5}{7}$      $\frac{c}{6} = \frac{5}{7}$

$b = \frac{25}{7}$      $c = \frac{30}{7}$

12. $\frac{a}{d} = \frac{c}{f}$      $\frac{b}{e} = \frac{c}{f}$

$\frac{a}{5} = \frac{11}{6}$      $\frac{b}{4} = \frac{11}{6}$

$a = \frac{55}{6}$      $b = \frac{44}{6} = \frac{22}{3}$

13. $\frac{a}{d} = \frac{b}{e}$      $\frac{c}{f} = \frac{b}{e}$

$\frac{a}{2.1} = \frac{4.5}{3.4}$      $\frac{c}{3.2} = \frac{4.5}{3.4}$

$a \approx 2.78$      $c \approx 4.24$

14. $\frac{d}{a} = \frac{e}{b}$      $\frac{f}{c} = \frac{e}{b}$

$\frac{d}{16} = \frac{7}{13}$      $\frac{f}{12} = \frac{7}{13}$

$d = \frac{112}{13}$      $f = \frac{84}{13}$

15. $\frac{d}{a} = \frac{f}{c}$      $\frac{e}{b} = \frac{f}{c}$

$\frac{d}{17} = \frac{6}{10}$      $\frac{e}{15} = \frac{6}{10}$

$d = \frac{102}{10} = \frac{51}{5}$      $e = \frac{90}{10} = 9$

16. $\frac{a}{d} = \frac{c}{f}$      $\frac{b}{e} = \frac{c}{f}$

$\frac{a}{18} = \frac{18}{12}$      $\frac{b}{16} = \frac{18}{12}$

$a = \frac{324}{12} = 27$      $b = \frac{288}{12} = 24$

17. $\frac{c}{f} = \frac{b}{e}$      $\frac{d}{a} = \frac{e}{b}$

$\frac{c}{1\frac{3}{4}} = \frac{5\frac{1}{2}}{2\frac{3}{4}}$      $\frac{d}{4\frac{1}{4}} = \frac{2\frac{3}{4}}{5\frac{1}{2}}$

$\frac{c}{\frac{7}{4}} = \frac{\frac{11}{2}}{\frac{11}{4}}$      $\frac{d}{\frac{17}{4}} = \frac{\frac{11}{4}}{\frac{11}{2}}$

$c = \frac{7}{4} \cdot \frac{11}{2} \cdot \frac{4}{11}$      $d = \frac{17}{4} \cdot \frac{11}{4} \cdot \frac{2}{11}$

$c = \frac{7}{2}$      $d = \frac{34}{16} = \frac{17}{8}$

18. $\frac{d}{a} = \frac{f}{c}$      $\frac{e}{b} = \frac{f}{c}$

$\frac{d}{10\frac{1}{2}} = \frac{5}{7\frac{1}{2}}$      $\frac{e}{15} = \frac{5}{7\frac{1}{2}}$

$\frac{d}{\frac{21}{2}} = \frac{5}{\frac{15}{2}}$      $\frac{e}{15} = \frac{5}{\frac{15}{2}}$

$d = \frac{21}{2} \cdot 5 \cdot \frac{2}{15}$      $e = 15 \cdot 5 \cdot \frac{2}{15}$

$d = 7$      $e = 10$

19. $\frac{b}{e} = \frac{c}{f}$      $\frac{d}{a} = \frac{f}{c}$

$\frac{b}{8.1} = \frac{5}{2.5}$      $\frac{d}{12.6} = \frac{2.5}{5}$

$b = 16.2$      $d = 6.3$

20. $\frac{6}{10} = \frac{x}{x + 5}$

$6(x + 5) = 10x$

$6x + 30 = 10x$

$4x = 30$

$x = \frac{30}{4} = \frac{15}{2} = 7\frac{1}{2}$

21. $A = \frac{1}{2}b \cdot h$

$\frac{\frac{1}{2} \cdot 2b \cdot 2h}{\frac{1}{2} \cdot 3b \cdot 3h} = \frac{4bh}{9bh}$      4:9

22. $\frac{x}{5} = \frac{25}{9}$      23. $\frac{x}{70} = \frac{120}{80}$

$x = \frac{125}{9}$ ft      $x = \frac{8400}{80}$ m

$\approx 13$ ft 11 in.      $= 105$ m

24. $\frac{7}{0.435} = \frac{90}{x}$

$7x = 0.435(90)$

$7x = 39.15$

$x \approx 5.6$ in.

25. $13x = 11$

$x = \frac{11}{13}$

26. $\frac{6}{(a-b)^2} - \frac{6}{a-b} = \frac{6}{(a-b)^2} - \frac{6(a-b)}{(a-b)^2}$

$= \frac{6 - 6a + 6b}{a^2 - 2ab + b^2}$

27. $\left.\begin{array}{r} 2x + y = 8 \\ x - y = 3 \end{array}\right\}$

$3x \quad\;\; = 11$

$x = \frac{11}{3}$

$y = 8 - 2x$

$y = 8 - 2\left(\frac{11}{3}\right)$

$y = \frac{24}{3} - \frac{22}{3}$

$y = \frac{2}{3}$

$\left(\frac{11}{3}, \frac{2}{3}\right)$

28. $\sqrt{3} \cdot \sqrt{16} - \sqrt{3} \cdot \sqrt{4} + \sqrt{3} \cdot \sqrt{100}$

$= 4\sqrt{3} - 2\sqrt{3} + 10\sqrt{3}$

$= (4 - 2 + 10)\sqrt{3}$

$= 12\sqrt{3}$

29. $x^2 - 4x + 4 = -1 + 4$

$(x - 2)^2 = 3$

$x - 2 = \pm\sqrt{3}$

$x = 2 \pm \sqrt{3}$

30. mean =

$\frac{26.89 + 26.27 + 25.18 + 25.63 + 27.16 + 27.18}{6}$

$= 26.385$ sec

median $= \frac{26.89 + 26.27}{2}$

$= 26.58$ sec

31. 5, 10

## 15-5 Trigonometric Ratios

1. 8    2. 3    3. sine and cosine    4. tangent

5. $\frac{9}{41}$    6. $\frac{40}{41}$    7. $\frac{40}{41}$    8. $\frac{9}{41}$    9. $\frac{9}{40}$    10. $\frac{40}{9}$

11. yes    12. They are equal.    13. 0.9063

14. 0.6009    15. 0.9455    16. 0.4384    17. 0.1584

18. 0.0349

19. $\sin N = \frac{16}{65} \approx 0.246$

$\cos N = \frac{63}{65} \approx 0.969$

$\tan N = \frac{16}{63} \approx 0.254$

20. $\sin N = \frac{35}{37} \approx 0.946$

$\cos N = \frac{12}{37} \approx 0.324$

$\tan N = \frac{35}{12} \approx 2.917$

21. $\sin N = \frac{6}{10} = 0.600$

$\cos N = \frac{8}{10} = 0.800$

$\tan N = \frac{6}{8} = 0.750$

22. $8^2 + 15^2 = c^2$

$64 + 225 = c^2$

$c^2 = 289$

$c = \sqrt{289}$

$c = 17$

$\sin N = \frac{8}{17} \approx 0.471$

$\cos N = \frac{15}{17} \approx 0.882$

$\tan N = \frac{8}{15} \approx 0.533$

23. $a^2 + 21^2 = 29^2$

$a^2 + 441 = 841$

$a^2 = 400$

$a = \sqrt{400}$

$a = 20$

$\sin N = \frac{21}{29} \approx 0.724$

$\cos N = \frac{20}{29} \approx 0.690$

$\tan N = \frac{21}{20} \approx 1.050$

24. $48^2 + b^2 = 73^2$

$2304 + b^2 = 5329$

$b^2 = 3025$

$b = \sqrt{3025}$

$b = 55$

$\sin N = \frac{55}{73} \approx 0.753$

$\cos N = \frac{48}{73} \approx 0.658$

$\tan N = \frac{55}{48} \approx 1.146$

25. $16°$    26. $32°$    27. $75°$

28. $38°$    29. $44°$    30. $83°$

31. $\tan N = \frac{9}{2} = 4.5$

$N \approx 77°$

32. $\sin N = \frac{2}{11} \approx 0.182$

$N \approx 10°$

33. $\cos N = \frac{17}{21} \approx 0.810$

$N \approx 36°$

34. $9^2 + b^2 = 15^2$

$81 + b^2 = 225$

$b^2 = 144$

$b = \sqrt{144} = 12$

$\cos N = \frac{12}{20} = 0.600$

$N \approx 53°$

35. $a^2 + 5^2 = 13^2$

$a^2 + 25 = 169$

$a^2 = 144$

$a = \sqrt{144}$

$a = 12$

$\sin N = \frac{12}{16} = 0.750$

$N \approx 49°$

**36.** $\sin P = \dfrac{12}{37} \approx 0.324$

$\quad P \approx 19°$

$\quad \cos Q = \dfrac{12}{20} = 0.600$

$\quad\quad Q \approx 53°$

$\quad 90° + 19° + 53° + N = 180°$

$\quad\quad\quad N = 18°$

**37.** $A = \dfrac{1}{2}(16)(9)\sin 36°$

$\quad\quad \approx 72(0.588)$

$\quad\quad \approx 42.3 \text{ cm}^2$

**38.** a. true $\quad \sin Z = \dfrac{z}{x}$

$\quad\quad\quad\quad\quad \cos Y = \dfrac{z}{x}$

b. false

c. false

d. true $\quad \tan Z = \dfrac{z}{y}$

$\quad\quad\quad \dfrac{\sin Z}{\cos Z} = \dfrac{\frac{z}{x}}{\frac{y}{x}} = \dfrac{z}{y}$

e. true $\quad \sin Y = \dfrac{y}{x}$

$\quad\quad\quad (\tan Y)(\cos Y) = \dfrac{y}{z} \cdot \dfrac{z}{x} = \dfrac{y}{x}$

**39.** $R = \dfrac{40^2}{32} \cdot \sin(2 \cdot 35)°$

$\quad R = 50 \sin 70°$

$\quad R \approx 50(0.940) = 47 \text{ ft}$

**40.** $t = 25.5 \sin\left[\dfrac{360}{365}(274 - 106)\right]° + 50$

$\quad t \approx 25.5 \sin(165.670) + 50$

$\quad t \approx 56°F$

**41.** $\dfrac{\sin y°}{\sin 40°} = 0.752$

$\quad\quad\quad y \approx 29°$

$\quad \dfrac{\sin 29°}{\sin 40°} = \dfrac{\text{speed of light in water}}{3 \times 10^8}$

speed of light in water $\approx 2.3 \times 10^8$ m/s

**42.** a. 5; 36.9°, 53.1°; $\sin A1 = 0.600$,

$\quad \sin A2 = 0.800$; $\cos A1 = 0.800$,

$\quad \cos A2 = 0.600$; $\tan A1 = 0.750$,

$\quad \tan A2 = 1.333$

b. 13; 22.6°, 67.4°; $\sin A1 = 0.385$,

$\quad \sin A2 = 0.923$; $\cos A1 = 0.923$,

$\quad \cos A2 = 0.385$; $\tan A1 = 0.417$,

$\quad \tan A2 = 2.400$

c. 44.7; 26.6°, 63.4°; $\sin A1 = 0.447$,

$\quad \sin A2 = 0.894$; $\cos A1 = 0.894$,

$\quad \cos A2 = 0.447$; $\tan A1 = 0.500$,

$\quad \tan A2 = 2.000$

d. 160.1; 51.3°, 38.7°; $\sin A1 = 0.781$,

$\quad \sin A2 = 0.625$; $\cos A1 = 0.625$,

$\quad \cos A2 = 0.781$; $\tan A1 = 1.250$,

$\quad \tan A2 = 0.800$

**43.** $76x = 19$ $\quad\quad\quad$ **44.** $\{1, 2, -2, 3\}$

$\quad x = \dfrac{19}{76}$ $\quad\quad\quad\quad\quad \{1, 4, 9\}$

$\quad x = 0.25$

25%

**45.** $(2, -2)$

**46.** $\sqrt{2} \cdot \sqrt{2} \cdot \sqrt{30} \cdot \sqrt{a^2} \cdot \sqrt{a} \cdot \sqrt{b} = 2|a|\sqrt{30ab}$

**47.** upper quartile = 31

$\quad$ lower quartile = 6

$\quad$ interquartile range = 31 − 6 = 25

## 15-6 Solving Right Triangles

**PAGE 634** $\quad$ **CHECKING FOR UNDERSTANDING**

**1.** Use the Pythagorean Theorem.

**2.** If you were given two acute angle measures only, you could not solve the triangle.

**3.** $\angle FED$, $\angle EDG$ $\quad$ **4.** $\angle JKL$, $\angle MJK$ $\quad$ **5.** $\angle QRP$, $\angle SPR$

**6.** tangent $\quad\quad$ **7.** sine $\quad\quad\quad$ **8.** cosine

**9.** $\quad \tan 39° = \dfrac{x}{12}$ $\quad$ **10.** $\cos X = \dfrac{12}{13}$

$\quad 12 \tan 39° = x$ $\quad\quad\quad \cos X \approx 0.9231$

$\quad\quad\quad x = 9.7$ $\quad\quad\quad\quad\quad X = 23°$

**PAGES 634-636** $\quad$ **EXERCISES**

**11.** $\angle B = 180° - 90° - 21°$ $\quad$ **12.** $6^2 + 8^2 = \overline{AB}^2$

$\quad\quad = 69°$ $\quad\quad\quad\quad\quad\quad\quad \overline{AB}^2 = 64 + 36$

$\quad \cos 21° = \dfrac{13}{\overline{AB}}$ $\quad\quad\quad\quad \overline{AB}^2 = 100$

$\quad \overline{AB} = \dfrac{13}{\cos 21°}$ $\quad\quad\quad \overline{AB} = \sqrt{100}$

$\quad \overline{AB} \approx 13.9 \text{ in.}$ $\quad\quad\quad \overline{AB} = 10 \text{ ft}$

$\quad \sin 21° = \dfrac{\overline{BC}}{13.9}$ $\quad\quad\quad \sin A = \dfrac{8}{10}$

$\quad \overline{BC} = 13.9 \sin 21°$ $\quad\quad\quad \angle A \approx 53°$

$\quad \overline{BC} \approx 5.0 \text{ in.}$ $\quad\quad\quad \sin B = \dfrac{6}{10}$

$\quad\quad\quad\quad\quad\quad\quad\quad\quad\quad \angle B \approx 37°$

In the diagram near problem 36: labels Q, N, 12, 20, 37, P

In problem 45 diagram: $3x - 2y = 10$ and $x + y = 0$

13. $\angle B = 180° - 90° - 70°$

$\angle B = 20°$

$\tan 70° = \dfrac{9}{\overline{AC}}$

$\overline{AC} = \dfrac{9}{\tan 70°}$

$\overline{AC} \approx 3.3$ cm

$\cos 20° = \dfrac{9}{\overline{AB}}$

$\overline{AB} = \dfrac{1}{\cos 20°}$

$\overline{AB} \approx 9.6$ cm

14. $\angle A = 180° - 90° - 60°$

$\angle A = 30°$

$\sin 30° = \dfrac{\overline{BC}}{16}$

$\overline{BC} = 16 \sin 30°$

$\overline{BC} = 8$ m

$\cos 30° = \dfrac{\overline{AC}}{16}$

$\overline{AC} = 16 \cos 30°$

$\overline{AC} \approx 13.9$ m

15. $\angle B = 180° - 90° - 40°$

$\angle D = 50°$

$\sin 40° = \dfrac{\overline{BC}}{16}$

$\overline{BC} = 16 \sin 40°$

$\overline{BC} \approx 10.3$ m

$\sin 50° = \dfrac{\overline{AC}}{16}$

$\overline{AC} = 16 \sin 50°$

$\overline{AC} \approx 12.3$ m

16. $\angle B = 180° - 90° - 35°$

$\angle B = 55°$

$\tan 55° = \dfrac{\overline{AC}}{7}$

$\overline{AC} = 7 \tan 55°$

$\overline{AC} \approx 10.0$ km

$\sin 35° = \dfrac{7}{\overline{AB}}$

$\overline{AB} = \dfrac{7}{\sin 35°}$

$\overline{AB} \approx 12.2$ km

17. $\tan 62° = \dfrac{x}{200}$

$x = 200 \tan 62°$

$x \approx 376$ ft

$\cos 62° = \dfrac{200}{y}$

$y = \dfrac{200}{\cos 62°}$

$y \approx 426$ ft

18. $\cos 52° = \dfrac{40}{x}$

$x = \dfrac{40}{\cos 52°}$

$x \approx 65$ ft

19. $\tan 41° = \dfrac{x}{75}$

$x = 75 \tan 41°$

$x \approx 65$ ft

20. $\sin A = \dfrac{20}{130}$

$A \approx 9°$

21. $\tan 25° = \dfrac{40}{x}$

$x = \dfrac{40}{\tan 25°}$

$x \approx 85.8$ cm

$A = \dfrac{1}{2}(40)(85.8)$

$= 1716$ cm$^2$

22. $\tan 65° = \dfrac{x}{70}$

$x = 70 \tan 65°$

$x \approx 150.1$ m

$\tan 18° = \dfrac{y}{150.1}$

$y = 150.1 \tan 18°$

$y \approx 48.8$ m

height of plane = 70 m + 48.8 m

$= 118.8$ m

23. $\tan 60° = \dfrac{x}{100}$

$x = 100 \tan 60°$

$x \approx 173.2$ m

24.

$\sin A = \dfrac{15}{250}$

$A \approx 3.4°$

25. $\tan 29° = \dfrac{y}{1}$

$y = \tan 29°$

$y \approx 0.5543$

$y = 0.5543x + 5$

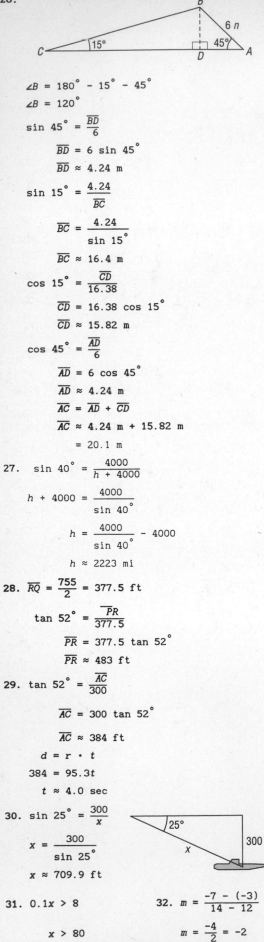

**26.**

$\angle B = 180° - 15° - 45°$

$\angle B = 120°$

$\sin 45° = \dfrac{\overline{BD}}{6}$

$\overline{BD} = 6 \sin 45°$

$\overline{BD} \approx 4.24$ m

$\sin 15° = \dfrac{4.24}{\overline{BC}}$

$\overline{BC} = \dfrac{4.24}{\sin 15°}$

$\overline{BC} \approx 16.4$ m

$\cos 15° = \dfrac{\overline{CD}}{16.38}$

$\overline{CD} = 16.38 \cos 15°$

$\overline{CD} \approx 15.82$ m

$\cos 45° = \dfrac{\overline{AD}}{6}$

$\overline{AD} = 6 \cos 45°$

$\overline{AD} \approx 4.24$ m

$\overline{AC} = \overline{AD} + \overline{CD}$

$\overline{AC} \approx 4.24$ m $+ 15.82$ m

$= 20.1$ m

**27.** $\sin 40° = \dfrac{4000}{h + 4000}$

$h + 4000 = \dfrac{4000}{\sin 40°}$

$h = \dfrac{4000}{\sin 40°} - 4000$

$h \approx 2223$ mi

**28.** $\overline{RQ} = \dfrac{755}{2} = 377.5$ ft

$\tan 52° = \dfrac{\overline{PR}}{377.5}$

$\overline{PR} = 377.5 \tan 52°$

$\overline{PR} \approx 483$ ft

**29.** $\tan 52° = \dfrac{\overline{AC}}{300}$

$\overline{AC} = 300 \tan 52°$

$\overline{AC} \approx 384$ ft

$d = r \cdot t$

$384 = 95.3t$

$t \approx 4.0$ sec

**30.** $\sin 25° = \dfrac{300}{x}$

$x = \dfrac{300}{\sin 25°}$

$x \approx 709.9$ ft

**31.** $0.1x > 8$

$x > 80$

**32.** $m = \dfrac{-7 - (-3)}{14 - 12}$

$m = \dfrac{-4}{2} = -2$

**33.** $\left.\begin{array}{l} 2x + y = 3x - 15 \\ -x - 4y = \phantom{3x} -5 \end{array}\right\}$

$\left.\begin{array}{l} -x + y = -15 \\ \phantom{-}x + 4y = \phantom{-}5 \end{array}\right\}$

$5y = -10$

$y = -2$

$x = 5 - 4y$

$= 5 - 4(-2) = 5 + 8 = 13$

**34.** $(\sqrt{2x + 7})^2 = 5^2$

$2x + 7 = 25$

$2x = 18$

$x = 9$

**35.** $b^2 - 4ac$

$= (-1)^2 - 4(2)(-3)$

$= 1 + 24$

$= 25$

$25 > 0$

2 real roots

**36.** $\dfrac{1}{6}$

**37.** $45°$

## Technology: Trigonometric Functions

**PAGE 637    EXERCISES**

1. Change the following two lines in the program:
   10 PRINT "ANGLE", "COSINE"
   40 LET R1 = INT(COS(R)*1000 + .5)/1000
2. positive    **3.** negative    **4.** negative
5. positive    **6.** $\cos 30°$    **7.** $\sin 90°$    **8.** $0°$, $360°$
9. $90°$    **10.** $0°$, $180°$, $360°$    **11.** $180°$

## Chapter 15    Summary and Review

**PAGES 638-640    SKILLS AND CONCEPTS**

1. $90° - 66° = 24°$          **2.** $90° - 62° = 28°$
   $180° - 66° = 114°$          $180° - 62° = 118°$
3. no complement          **4.** $90° - y° = (90 - y)°$
   $180° - 148° = 32°$          $180° - y° = (180 - y)°$
5. $180° - 16° - 72° = 92°$
6. $180° - 41° - 121° = 18°$
7. $180° - 37° - 90° = 53°$
8. $180° - x° - y° = (180 - x - y)°$

|  | Hypotenuse | Side Opposite 30° Angle | Side Opposite 60° Angle |
|---|---|---|---|
| **9.** | 8 cm | 4 cm | $4\sqrt{3}$ cm |
| **10.** | 4.25 cm | 2.125 cm | $2.125\sqrt{3}$ cm |
| **11.** | 6 in. | 3 in. | $3\sqrt{3}$ in. |
| **12.** | 4 in. | 2 in. | $2\sqrt{3}$ in. |

13. $\dfrac{b}{e} = \dfrac{a}{d}$

$\dfrac{b}{14} = \dfrac{5}{11}$

$b = \dfrac{70}{11}$

$\dfrac{c}{f} = \dfrac{a}{d}$

$\dfrac{c}{6} = \dfrac{5}{11}$

$c = \dfrac{30}{11}$

14. $\dfrac{d}{a} = \dfrac{f}{c}$

$\dfrac{d}{10} = \dfrac{9}{16}$

$d = \dfrac{90}{16} = \dfrac{45}{8}$

$\dfrac{e}{b} = \dfrac{f}{c}$

$\dfrac{e}{12} = \dfrac{9}{16}$

$e = \dfrac{108}{16} = \dfrac{27}{4}$

15. $\dfrac{d}{a} = \dfrac{f}{c}$

$\dfrac{d}{8} = \dfrac{12}{10}$

$d = \dfrac{96}{10} = \dfrac{48}{5}$

$\dfrac{e}{b} = \dfrac{f}{c}$

$\dfrac{e}{6} = \dfrac{12}{10}$

$e = \dfrac{72}{10} = \dfrac{36}{5}$

16. $\dfrac{b}{e} = \dfrac{c}{f}$

$\dfrac{b}{11} = \dfrac{12}{9}$

$b = \dfrac{132}{9} = \dfrac{44}{3}$

$\dfrac{d}{a} = \dfrac{f}{c}$

$\dfrac{d}{8} = \dfrac{9}{12}$

$d = \dfrac{72}{12} = 6$

17. $\dfrac{28}{53}$   18. $\dfrac{28}{53}$   19. $\dfrac{45}{53}$   20. $\dfrac{45}{53}$   21. $\dfrac{28}{45}$

22. $\dfrac{45}{28}$   23. $39^\circ$   24. $7^\circ$   25. $80^\circ$   26. $42^\circ$

27. $\angle B = 180^\circ - 90^\circ - 62^\circ = 28^\circ$

$\tan 28^\circ = \dfrac{\overline{AC}}{7}$

$\overline{AC} = 7 \tan 28^\circ$

$\overline{AC} \approx 3.7$ m

$\sin 62^\circ = \dfrac{7}{\overline{AB}}$

$\overline{AB} = \dfrac{7}{\sin 62^\circ}$

$\overline{AB} \approx 7.9$ m

28. $\cos A = \dfrac{9}{13}$

$\angle A \approx 46^\circ$

$\sin B = \dfrac{9}{13}$

$\angle B \approx 44^\circ$

$\tan 46^\circ = \dfrac{\overline{BC}}{9}$

$\overline{BC} = 9 \tan 46^\circ$

$\overline{BC} \approx 9.4$ in.

APPLICATIONS AND CONNECTIONS

29.

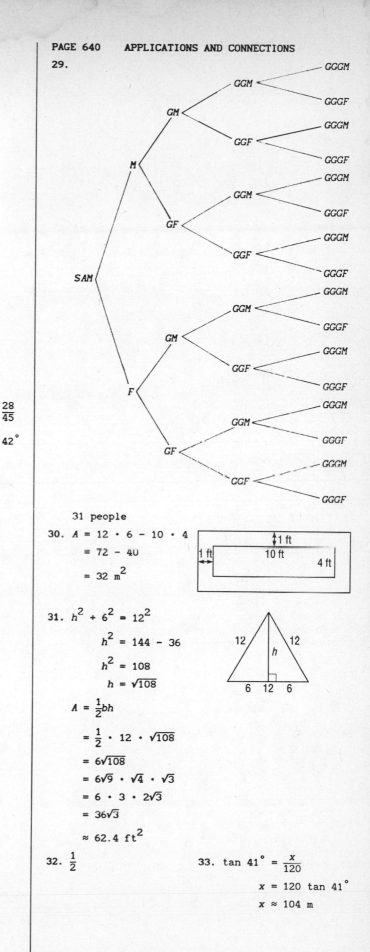

31 people

30. $A = 12 \cdot 6 - 10 \cdot 4$

$= 72 - 40$

$= 32$ m$^2$

31. $h^2 + 6^2 = 12^2$

$h^2 = 144 - 36$

$h^2 = 108$

$h = \sqrt{108}$

$A = \dfrac{1}{2}bh$

$= \dfrac{1}{2} \cdot 12 \cdot \sqrt{108}$

$= 6\sqrt{108}$

$= 6\sqrt{9} \cdot \sqrt{4} \cdot \sqrt{3}$

$= 6 \cdot 3 \cdot 2\sqrt{3}$

$= 36\sqrt{3}$

$\approx 62.4$ ft$^2$

32. $\dfrac{1}{2}$

33. $\tan 41^\circ = \dfrac{x}{120}$

$x = 120 \tan 41^\circ$

$x \approx 104$ m

305

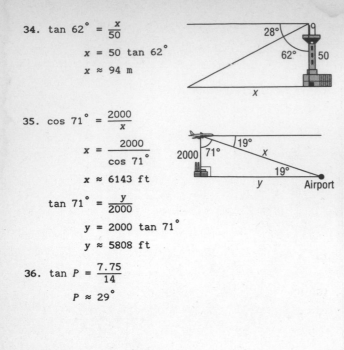

34. $\tan 62° = \dfrac{x}{50}$

$x = 50 \tan 62°$

$x \approx 94 \text{ m}$

35. $\cos 71° = \dfrac{2000}{x}$

$x = \dfrac{2000}{\cos 71°}$

$x \approx 6143 \text{ ft}$

$\tan 71° = \dfrac{y}{2000}$

$y = 2000 \tan 71°$

$y \approx 5808 \text{ ft}$

36. $\tan P = \dfrac{7.75}{14}$

$P \approx 29°$

# Chapter 15    Test

1. $90° - 28° = 62°$     2. $90° - 69° = 21°$

$180° - 28° = 152°$      $180° - 69° = 111°$

3. $90° - (y + 20)° = (70 - y)°$

$180° - (y + 20)° = (160 - y)°$

4. $180° - 16° - 47° = 117°$

5. $180° - 89° - 66° = 25°$

6. $180° - 45° - 120° = 15°$

|  | Hypotenuse | Side Opposite 30° Angle | Side Opposite 60° Angle |
|---|---|---|---|
| 7. | 17 in. | 8.5 in. | $8.5\sqrt{3}$ in. $\approx 14.722$ in. |
| 8. | 16 ft | 8 ft | $8\sqrt{3}$ ft $\approx 13.856$ ft |
| 9. | 18 m | 9 m | $9\sqrt{3}$ m $\approx 15.588$ m |

10. $\dfrac{a}{j} = \dfrac{c}{h}$

$\dfrac{a}{12} = \dfrac{20}{15}$

$a = \dfrac{240}{15} = 16$

$\dfrac{b}{k} = \dfrac{c}{h}$

$\dfrac{b}{16} = \dfrac{20}{15}$

$b = \dfrac{320}{15} = \dfrac{64}{3}$

11. $\dfrac{j}{a} = \dfrac{h}{c}$

$\dfrac{j}{6} = \dfrac{10}{12}$

$j = \dfrac{60}{12} = 5$

$\dfrac{k}{b} = \dfrac{h}{c}$

$\dfrac{k}{13} = \dfrac{10}{12}$

$k = \dfrac{130}{12} = \dfrac{65}{6}$

12. $\dfrac{j}{a} = \dfrac{k}{b}$

$\dfrac{j}{4.5} = \dfrac{5}{7.5}$

$j = \dfrac{22.5}{7.5} = 3$

$\dfrac{h}{c} = \dfrac{k}{b}$

$\dfrac{h}{6.5} = \dfrac{5}{7.5}$

$h = \dfrac{32.5}{7.5} = \dfrac{13}{3}$

13. $\dfrac{j}{a} = \dfrac{h}{c}$

$\dfrac{j}{3} = \dfrac{1\frac{1}{2}}{4\frac{1}{2}}$

$j = \dfrac{4\frac{1}{2}}{4\frac{1}{2}} = 1$

$\dfrac{b}{k} = \dfrac{c}{h}$

$\dfrac{b}{2\frac{1}{4}} = \dfrac{4\frac{1}{2}}{1\frac{1}{2}}$

$b = \dfrac{\frac{9}{4} \cdot \frac{9}{2}}{\frac{3}{2}}$

$= \dfrac{9}{4} \cdot \dfrac{9}{2} \cdot \dfrac{2}{3}$

$= \dfrac{27}{4}$

14. $\angle B = 180° - 90° - 56°$

$= 34°$

$\tan 56° = \dfrac{17}{b}$

$b = \dfrac{17}{\tan 56°}$

$b \approx 11.5$

$\sin 56° = \dfrac{17}{c}$

$c = \dfrac{17}{\sin 56°}$

$c \approx 20.5$

15. $\tan B = \dfrac{16}{12}$

$\angle B \approx 53°$

$\tan A = \dfrac{12}{16}$

$\angle A \approx 37°$

$\sin 37° = \dfrac{12}{c}$

$c = \dfrac{12}{\sin 37°}$

$c \approx 20 \text{ mm}$

16. $\angle A = 180° - 42° - 90°$

$\angle A = 48°$

$\cos 42° = \dfrac{a}{10}$

$a = 10 \cos 42°$

$a \approx 7.4 \text{ cm}$

$\sin 42° = \dfrac{b}{10}$

$b = 10 \sin 42°$

$b \approx 6.7 \text{ cm}$

17. $\cos A = \dfrac{21}{29}$

$\angle A \approx 44°$

$\sin B = \dfrac{21}{29}$

$\angle B \approx 46°$

$\sin 44° = \dfrac{a}{29}$

$a = 29 \sin 44°$

$a \approx 20$

18. $\sin 58° = \dfrac{h}{300}$

$h = 300 \sin 58°$

$h \approx 254.4 \text{ ft}$

19. $\cos 70° = \dfrac{1000}{x}$

$x = \dfrac{1000}{\cos 70°}$

$x \approx 2923.8 \text{ ft}$

20. $\frac{6}{4} = \frac{x}{50}$

$x = \frac{300}{4}$

$x = 75 \text{ ft}$

**PAGE 641    BONUS**

$\tan 50° = \frac{60}{x}$

$x = \frac{60}{\tan 50°}$

$x \approx 50.35 \text{ ft}$

$\tan 40° = \frac{y}{50.35}$

$y = 50.35 \tan 40°$

$y \approx 42 \text{ ft}$

height of second building = 60 ft + 42 ft = 102 ft

# Chapter 15    College Entrance Exam Preview

**PAGES 642-643**

1. C

$\frac{70 - c + 70 + 2c + 45 - c}{3} = \frac{185}{3}$

$= 61\frac{2}{3}$

2. A

$2 \cdot (-3) = -6$

3. D

$ab - 5abc = -6$

$b(a - 5ac) = -6$

$b = \frac{-6}{a - 5ac}$

$= \frac{6}{5ac - a}$

4. C

$1518 + 23x = 2300$

$23x = 782$

$x = 34$

5. A

$3y + 2 + 2$

$= 3y + 4$

6. B

$\frac{3(-0.8) - (-0.8)}{2}$

$= -0.8$

7. C

$\frac{x}{8} = -2$

$\frac{x}{8} \cdot 4 = -2 \cdot 4$

$\frac{x}{2} = -8$

8. C

$n = 2m - 8 \qquad m = 14 - p$

$n = 2(14 - p) - 8$

$n = 28 - 2p - 8$

$n = 20 - 2p$

9. A

$-3a + 3b$

$= 3(b - a)$

10. A

$\frac{(1)^2 \cdot (-2)}{(1 - 2)^2}$

$= \frac{-2}{1}$

$= -2$

11. C

$\frac{c}{12} = \frac{11}{4} - 1$

$\frac{c}{12} = \frac{7}{4}$

$c = \frac{84}{4}$

$c = 21$

12. B

$x + \frac{x}{3} = 40$

$\frac{4}{3}x = 40$

$x = 40 \cdot \frac{3}{4}$

$x = 30$

13. A

14. A

$1 \cdot 2 \cdot 1 = 2$

15. D

$B + 4 = 2P$

$E = 3B$

$24 = 3B$

$B = 8$

$8 + 4 = 2P$

$12 = 2P$

$P = 6$

16. D

$\frac{20x}{\frac{x}{5}} = \frac{400}{y}$

$20x \cdot \frac{5}{x} = \frac{400}{y}$

$100 = \frac{400}{y}$

$y = 4$

17. D

18. A

$4(b - d) = 1$

$4b - 4d = 1$

$-4d = 1 - 4b$

$d = \frac{1 - 4b}{-4}$

$d = b - \frac{1}{4}$

19. D

$\frac{2a}{5b} - 1$

$= 6 - 1 = 5$

20. B

$\frac{3\frac{1}{5}}{2\frac{1}{2}} = \frac{\frac{16}{5}}{\frac{5}{2}} = \frac{32}{25}$

21. A

$\frac{b + 2 + b + 3 + b - 2 + b - 1 + x}{5} = b + 2$

$\frac{4b + 2 + x}{5} = b + 2$

$4b + 2 + x = 5(b + 2)$

$4b + 2 + x = 5b + 10$

$x = b + 8$

22. C

$a \cdot c \cdot c = 4$

$a = \frac{4}{c^2}$

23. D

sum = 6x, average = x

24. D

25. B